# SCIENCE FOR ALL CHILDREN

## Elementary School Methods

**ANTHONY D. FREDERICKS**
YORK COLLEGE

**DEAN L. CHEESEBROUGH**
YORK COLLEGE

WAVELAND
PRESS, INC.
Prospect Heights, Illinois

To all my former teachers at the Orme School in Mayer, Arizona, who influenced the dreams of a student and inspired the possibilities of an educator.

—A. D. F.

To Jan, who is always there with support, humor, enthusiasm, insight, confidence, and inspiration.

—D. L. C.

For information about this book, write or call:
    Waveland Press, Inc.
    P.O. Box 400
    Prospect Heights, Illinois 60070
    (847) 634-0081

For permission to use copyrighted material, grateful acknowledgement is made to the copyright holders on pp. 410–411, which are hereby made part of this copyright page.

# CONTENTS

# PREFACE

One of our favorite "Far Side" cartoons by Gary Larson shows a group of dinosaurs standing outside a cave. The dinosaurs are lighting up some cigarettes and furtively glancing in several directions. The caption reads: "The real reason dinosaurs became extinct." We like that cartoon for several reasons, but primarily because it illustrates the fun that can be had with science. Although Larson gives science and scientists a gentle jab now and again, he also demonstrates how science is a part of everyday life.

We also think science can be fun. We believe that science can be one of the most exciting subjects of the elementary curriculum. Children are naturally curious about the world around them ("Why is the sky blue?" "Why do geese fly south?" "Where do babies come from?"), and the investigation of that world can be made a stimulating and meaningful part of their lives—particularly when presented by teachers who can transmit the fun and excitement of science every day.

We think it important that you understand how this book came to be and what propelled us as we prepared the manuscript. Basically, we were driven by two distinct yet highly related concepts. First, in our conversations with educators around the country, work with our own student teachers, observations of elementary classrooms, and some exhaustive research, we became convinced that science is the area of the elementary curriculum teachers fear most. We were aware that whatever information or methods that were to be presented to teachers (both current and future) would have to be in a form that would help them feel secure in their teaching competence.

We wanted to dispel the notion that a teacher of science has to be a repository of vast sums of statistical data, factual information, and chemical equations in order to be effective. Our emphasis is on "teacher as learner"; that is, the most successful teachers of science are those who are willing to learn along with their students, who provide the processes and a supportive arena in which students can begin making their own discoveries and pursue self-initiated investigations. This text, then, is inquiry-based or process-oriented. It is designed to focus on the *doing* parts of science more than the *facts* part of science.

Our writing was also guided by the fact that most college students find textbooks to be lifeless, dull, and dry. We believe that if science is to be exciting, dynamic, and energetic, these attributes should be woven throughout all dimensions of a methods text. We have worked to ensure that our ideas, principles, and strategies are couched in an interesting format and in a familiar language (in other words, we made an honest effort to stay away from an excessive amount of "professor-ese"). Of course, we welcome your insights and perceptions on this course of action.

## Note to Instructors

We believe that helping pre-service teachers become successful teachers of science means instilling in *them* the sense of wonder, mystery, and creative spirit young children are noted for. Teachers need to know that science is a "touchable," "smellable," "tasteable," "hearable," and "seeable" discipline; that it is not book-bound or confined to a teacher's manual or curriculum guide. Rather, it is a participatory subject that offers opportunities to "get down and dirty" with the world and all the inhabitants therein. In essence, effective science teaching is a constant process of involvement—on the part of both students and teachers.

Given the fact that many teachers are uneasy with science and with the teaching of science, we tried to create a text that is both "comfortable" and useful. This text is designed not only as an instructional tool for future educators, but also as a reference for teachers once they enter classrooms. Obviously, we tried to emphasize practicality and utility.

In our attempt to make this a purposeful text we have included several features throughout the book. These include:

- *Process/discovery approach:* We believe that science is best learned and best taught when it involves students completely in all its dynamics. This text is designed to help teachers take a participatory approach to science. A host of engaging activities and strategies have been provided throughout the text for students to use in understanding important concepts.
- *Teacher as learner:* After more than 55 years of combined teaching experience, we still believe that we have much to discover about how kids learn and how teachers teach. We also believe that good teachers should be continual learners—looking for new ideas, new possibilities, and new horizons to explore. One of the major threads woven throughout this text is that *teaching is a constant process of learning.*
- *Integrative approach:* One of the major trends in science education is the integration of science throughout the entire elementary curriculum. We have tried to present science not as an isolated subject area, but rather as part of a process of investigation that can span all subjects and all aspects of any child's life.
- *"To Investigate":* Included within each chapter are suggestions for designs and practices that teachers can look for when they observe elementary classrooms in their local area. These observations (which may be assigned as part of the methods course or as an element of the pre–student teaching experience) allow education students to see how chapter concepts are (or are not) being utilized in real-life classrooms. Those observations can form the focus for later discussions in the methods class.
- *Children's literature:* Another growing trend in education is the inclusion of trade books throughout the elementary curriculum (e.g., the "literature-based reading program"). This is particularly true in science, and, given the significant number of quality science books published each year, this represents a major element in the design of meaningful science curricula. References to some of the best works in science literature are included throughout the text.
- *"Points of Discussion":* At the end of each chapter is a list of questions and projects that extend chapter concepts and give readers opportunities to try out the information in a variety of contexts (both in and outside the methods classroom).

## Note to the Student

It's probably safe to say that you find many college textbooks less than exciting. Filled with obscure facts, incomprehensible figures, and easily forgotten data, they are hardly the type of book you would want to take with you on spring break. Nevertheless, we know that you need a text with purpose and meaning that will serve as a functional guide throughout the length of this course. We also like to think that this textbook will be a resource for you during your first few years of teaching. We hope it will be a book you will want to consult in designing dynamic and engaging science lessons for many years.

To assist you in learning how to become an effective and successful teacher of science, we have included several items we feel will be useful in your methods course:

- *Anticipatory web:* At the beginning of each chapter is an anticipatory web that lists the concepts and principles discussed within the chapter. Feel free to record your background knowledge about those ideas as well as any questions you may have directly on the web. You will discover that the web serves as a meaningful study guide in preparation for quizzes and exams.
- *Classroom vignettes:* We have included stories of typical elementary classrooms and some of the exciting events that take place in schools around the country. These serve to illustrate some of the concepts discussed within the chapter and help personalize the principles and ideas.
- *"Idea Boxes":* Each chapter contains one or more "Idea Boxes." These offer you an exciting strategy or technique to *energize* the teaching and learning of science. Each "Idea Box" is keyed to the topic of the chapter and helps you understand the practical application of a specific idea.
- *"Did you Know?":* Sprinkled throughout each chapter are interesting facts from the world of science. These items demonstrate some of the amazing events that take place around us every day. They also underscore the wonder that should be a part of your classroom. Along with each fact is a classroom activity that provides an opportunity for elementary students to engage in an application related to the designated fact.
- *"Teacher to Teacher":* We wrote to some of the most successful science teachers in the country and asked them to share their ideas and techniques for making science exciting. Some of their thoughts and anecdotes are included in each chapter, offering you a refreshing perspective into what happens in elementary classrooms every day.

We would like to emphasize that this text is designed for anyone wishing to actively engage children in all the dynamics and possibilities of science. Both preservice and in-service teachers will discover a wealth of opportunities for their classrooms. But we would be remiss if we did not also state that this text should be but one resource in your professional library. Consider this book as a single element of a very exciting subject, one that encompasses a variety of resources and techniques and one that helps elementary students of all ages, grades, and ability levels participate actively in the wide-ranging dimensions of science. We hope that this text (along with the other resources listed in the appendices) will encourage everyone to become an active participant in science—learning, growing, and developing in much of the same manner as young children.

A good teacher tells
A superior teacher shows
A great teacher involves
A successful teacher learns

## Acknowledgments

No book of this scope could have been prepared without the capable support and assistance of many people. This three-year project was made possible through the efforts of several groups and individuals, without whom we would have been "up the creek without a paddle."

To all our students at York College we owe an incredible debt of gratitude. They served as "guinea pigs" for many of the processes and activities described within these pages. They also shared with us their incredible talent and creativity in the design of exciting and dynamic science-oriented classrooms.

Our associates and colleagues at York College who supported and encouraged us throughout the writing of this text deserve special mention—in particular, Cheryl Smith, who was able to transform reams of scribbles, notes, and doodles into a comprehensible manuscript; and Bill Kreiger, who not only kept us in good humor, but also checked and double-checked our data for accuracy. They surely merit a standing ovation.

We are equally indebted to the teachers and classrooms we visited around the country. Many nameless teachers (we are truly "absent-minded professors") contributed to the ideas presented in these pages. We are particularly appreciative of the many teachers who contributed their thoughts and anecdotes for inclusion in the "Teacher to Teacher" sections of this book. We believe their insights and experiences are positive markers for the future of science education in this country. Noteworthy, too, are our friends and former colleagues at Sheckler Elementary School in Catasauqua, Pennsylvania, who, under the capable guidance of principal Ed Bruchak, have created one of the most dynamic elementary science curricula around.

Our friend and confidant, Chris Jennison, deserves the "Nobel prize for editorship." His support and guidance has made this project an exciting one, and it would not have been possible without his leadership. So, too, does Shadla Grooms deserve a medal of valor for making sure deadlines were met and chapters were in sequence, and for providing constant good cheer throughtout all facets of the writing. Sarah Troutt and Sheryl Lilke of Publication Services merit special recognition for their masterful direction in ushering the manuscript though the labyrinths of copy editing, art production, and galleys.

We are forever indebted to the reviewers, whose insights and perceptions helped us fashion a book much better than we would have been able to do alone. Their notes, suggestions, and ideas gave strength to the entire project. A round of applause goes to Raymond E. Myers of Seattle Pacific University, Michael E. Leyden of Eastern Illinois University, Mark R. Malone of the University of Colorado, and Dana L. Zeidler of the University of Massachusetts at Lowell.

Tony gives special recognition to the life-long inspiration and influence of two former high school teachers: Sid Thomas, who opened the door to the magic and marvels of science; and Buck Hart, who demonstrated the beauty, power, and friendship of words. Dean gives special recognition to a mentor, life-long friend, and confidant: Donald L. Edwards. He opened new vistas, demonstrated the finest qualities of a teacher and scholar, and presented a challenge that had to be met.

Finally, but certainly most importantly, to our wives Phyllis and Jan go incalculable honors, kudos, and accolades. For three years they suffered through forgotten weekends, missed appointments, early-morning typing, late-night editing, and "the attic that never got cleaned." They provided the love, emotional sustenance, and constant encouragement that made the writing of this book possible and our lives complete.

—Anthony D. Fredericks
—Dean L. Cheesebrough

# PROLOGUE: AN OPEN LETTER TO STUDENTS

Dear Student:

If you are like most prospective teachers, you're probably somewhat fearful about teaching science. Perhaps your experiences as a student of science were not all that pleasurable. Perhaps your science teachers were not as encouraging or stimulating as you would have liked them to be. Perhaps you never found science to be as exciting as other subjects. And yet you will be expected to share with your future students the joys and magic of science. You want to be an excellent teacher in every subject, but you're still a little scared.

We experienced those same fears and trepidations when we began our careers. It seemed like there was so much to know, so many responsibilities to take care of, and so many different people to deal with every day. Yet we also discovered that teaching was much more than writing behavioral objectives, memorizing lists of facts and figures, and taking a teacher exam. We found out, as you will, that teaching is as much an art as it is a science, and that how we perceived teaching was as important as what we did in our teaching.

With that in mind, we'd like to tell you about a friend of ours—Cathy Swanson. Cathy was an elementary education major at Kutztown University in Kutztown, Pennsylvania. Bright, energetic, and creative, she entered the teaching profession because she wanted to stimulate the natural curiosity of children and utilize her innate talents to promote learning as an active and engaging process. During her student-teaching semester and shortly before she began sending out applications to various school districts, Cathy sat down to write out her educational philosophy. Writing a philosophy allowed her to assess her personal strengths as a teacher and provided her with a direction for the future. It also allowed Cathy to key into the personal attributes and attitudes she wanted to share with children. In short, she gave herself a direction and a goal for those first critical years of her teaching career.

We sincerely believe that Cathy's philosophical statement not only says a lot about her, but also reveals a lot about how future teachers should approach teaching—more specifically, the teaching of science. We would like to share Cathy's statement with you, and we ask that you keep it in mind as you read the chapters of this book. Think about how your philosophy of teaching, particularly your philosophy of teaching science, compares with Cathy's philosophy. In other words, what will you bring to your classroom that will ensure your success as a teacher of science and your students' success as learners of science?

## Philosophy of Education

Lao-Tse once described an effective leader as one who imparts to his charges the feeling, "We did it ourselves!" So it is in the realm of teaching and learning.

An effective educator does not simply disseminate facts and figures, but acts as a catalyst, teaching (by example) a love for learning. By providing provocative questions rather than patent answers, children are led to discover knowledge; thus they become active participants in the learning process rather than passive receptors.

To be a successful "catalyst" requires a great deal. As a doctor selects the appropriate tool to execute a surgical procedure or an artist the correct brush to express a desired gesture, a teacher must have the knowledge and creativity to utilize a plethora of tools.

In order to meet the individual needs of students, an educator must skillfully incorporate visual, aural, and tactile activities via a variety of teacher strategies. However, even the wisest tactical decisions are rendered ineffective unless a climate of love, excitement, humor, and mutual respect is engendered.

To provide an environment that fosters both intellectual and emotional growth is a responsibility of the greatest magnitude. The reward, however, is of equal proportion if one is truly committed to leading children to love learning, live, and to say, "We did it ourselves!"

Cathy Swanson
Lower Salford Elementary School
Souderton, Pennsylvania

Cathy is now a very successful elementary teacher. Her classroom is filled with the love, excitement, humor, and mutual respect she subscribes to in her educational philosophy. She is enthusiastic about teaching, and her students are enthusiastic about learning!

But more important is the fact that Cathy is as much a learner as she is a teacher. Not only does she serve as a positive role model for her students; she constantly seeks new ideas and strategies for inclusion in her daily plans. We believe that it is teachers like Cathy who set the standard for what education should be—more specifically, for what science education can become.

We hope that when you finish this course you will be able to prepare a statement on your philosophy of education that reflects all the dynamism that outstanding teachers have and that any science program should promote. We invite you to reread Cathy's philosophy at the conclusion of this course and compare it with your own philosophy on the teaching of elementary science. We sincerely hope that this book and this course will help you become that successful teacher of science as well as an equally successful learner!

Anthony D. Fredericks
Dean L. Cheesebrough

CHAPTER

# 1

# CHILDREN, TEACHERS, AND SCIENCE EDUCATION

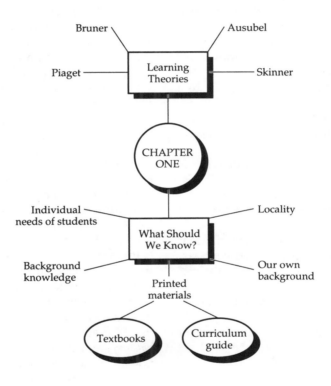

## Chapter Objectives

After reading this chapter you should be able to:

1. Define science literacy and its implications for the classroom and society at large.

2. Describe the four key elements of any elementary science program.

3. Cite the importance of students' background knowledge to their mastery of science principles.

4. Explain the role of textbooks and curriculum guides in the study of science.

5. Explain the significance of teacher background and locality on the design of science programs.

6. Describe various learning theories, identify their proponents, and explain their relevance to science education.

# BELIEFS ABOUT SCIENCE EDUCATION

Read the following statements. Indicate whether you generally agree (A) or disagree (D) with each. Circle the ones about which you hold particularly strong opinions. (Note: Record your responses on a separate sheet of paper. You will be asked to do this survey again at the end of the course.)

1. _____ Every teacher should be a teacher of science.
2. _____ Not all learning is meaningful.
3. _____ What students already know about a topic will determine what they can learn about it.
4. _____ One way to have students understand science concepts is to have them read about those concepts in their textbooks.
5. _____ Most problems in teaching science are due to a lack of quality materials.
6. _____ Students who have difficulties in reading the textbook will have difficulties learning necessary science information.
7. _____ Interest in the topic is an important determiner of understanding.
8. _____ All children are capable of learning science.
9. _____ A good science teacher is one who knows a lot about science.
10. _____ One of the best ways to teach children science is to have them do lots of science experiments.
11. _____ Science is the most important subject in the elementary curriculum.
12. _____ Teachers must be interested in a topic in order to teach it well.
13. _____ Students must be interested in a topic in order to learn it well.
14. _____ Science is very difficult to teach.

15. _____ The goal of science education is to create more scientists.

Consider the following facts:

• One study of more than 130 elementary teachers revealed that only about 15 percent of them taught science on a daily basis.
• A nationwide test administered in 1989 indicated that U.S. students ranked near the bottom of all industrialized countries in terms of science knowledge.
• Noted scientist Carl Sagan found that less than half of all Americans know that the Earth moves around the sun and that it takes a year to do so—a fact established a few centuries ago.
• Another leading scientist postulates that fully 94% of all Americans are scientifically illiterate.

These are staggering statistics to be sure—statistics that may indicate that current practices in elementary science education are not producing a level of science competence or interest commensurate with our rapidly increasing technology and knowledge base.

Although it's easy to condemn both the messengers and the message, what emerges from these facts is the need to rethink science education in this country. How can elementary teachers be better prepared for teaching the next generation of students? The answer is not publishing more materials, but rather providing teachers with the processes and principles of science—that is, underscoring science as a venture of *discovering*, *valuing*, and *exploring*. (The use of gerunds is intentional, for science should be a *verb* and not the subject of a verb!) Children need to know that science is an ongoing, multifaceted exploration of the world they live in as well as worlds around them. In short, science should be promoted as a lifelong investigation driven by a sense of wonder, amazement, and the natural curiosity of children.

Science is the subject many elementary teachers fear most. This may be due to any of a number of factors, including their own dismal experiences with science when they were students, the view that they should be repositories of scientific facts and figures, a feeling that science is complex and far removed from everyday experiences, and the belief that there is not sufficient time to teach science during the normal school day. There is a need to make prospective teachers (that means you!) *comfortable* in teaching science and to ensure that students find science (and "sciencing") to be an enjoyable and rewarding part of every school day. This means that you will need to under-

stand science concepts and processes, not simply science facts. It means that you must be able to stimulate the inherent scientist in every child and capitalize on the natural enthusiasm and interest of children. It also means that you must weave management techniques, questioning strategies, thinking skills, and down-to-earth activities into a program that extends science throughout the curriculum and throughout the school day. In short, you must be able to demystify science, maximize its impact throughout the elementary curriculum, and ensure the scientific competence of each student. That sounds like a tall order—but it is far from impossible!

## SCIENCE LITERACY

One of the "buzz" phrases you will hear throughout your teaching career is *science literacy* (see the appendix) or its opposite, "scientific illiteracy." This term has become synonymous with the way science is taught (or not taught) in this country. It implies that there is a basic set of concepts, facts, or principles that must be known by all students and that ignorance of those ideas results in a corps of pupils with little or no knowledge of basic scientific precepts or practices.

Actually, science literacy is more generic and more general. It is more than the memorization of science facts (e.g., the nearest planet to the sun is Mercury) or science principles (e.g., a body in motion tends to remain in motion unless acted upon by an outside force). Rather, science literacy should be defined as a *process* of posing questions and proposing answers. In essence, science is simply a way of looking at the world—nothing more, nothing less.

You should infer from this definition that science is much, much more than a series of dry, lifeless facts waiting to be committed to memory. Rather, it is an attempt to take advantage of the natural queries—questions beginning with the words *how* and *why*—that children ask unceasingly (just ask the parents of any four-year-old). Science literacy is the practice of providing youngsters not only opportunities to ask those questions, but opportunities to pursue the answers. Thus, the inclination to seek out answers, rather than the answers themselves, is at the very heart of science literacy.

What does that mean for your future classroom? A great deal. For example, take a look at the recommen-

dations of the American Association for the Advancement of Science (1989) in their description of the basic dimensions of scientific literacy. The AAAS states that students should:

- Be familiar with the natural world and recognize both its diversity and its unity.
- Understand key concepts and principles of science.
- Be aware of some of the important ways in which science, mathematics, and technology depend on one another.
- Know that science, mathematics, and technology are human enterprises and know what that implies about their strengths and limitations.
- Have a capacity for scientific ways of thinking.
- Use scientific knowledge and ways of thinking for individual and social purposes.

You will notice as you scan this list that there is a broad variety of topics, that there are no distinct boundaries established between subject categories (e.g., biology, geology, botany), and that thinking is emphasized more than memorization. This means that you do not need to rely on the traditional methods of teaching science—lecture, textbooks, and rote memorization—to create an atmosphere of science literacy in your classroom and promote science awareness and appreciation in your students. Your approach to science literacy should emphasize the *processes* of science, not the *products*. In short, science literacy is students doing and thinking science—not memorizing and regurgitating science.

## WHAT SHOULD WE KNOW?

The second-grade recess was shortened by a sudden and unexpected April shower. As the students filed back into their classrooms, many of them were upset because planned ball games and other activities were interrupted. "Why does it have to rain, Mrs. Frasca?" was a question asked by more than one student.

This is only one example of the hundreds of decisions teachers like Mrs. Frasca are required to make

every day. In this particular case, Mrs. Frasca must decide: Is there really an indication of interest in precipitation, or was the question merely rhetorical? Was the question an indication of an interest of a few children? Should weather be included in the second-grade curriculum? How much time should be devoted to the question—a few minutes, a class period, or a unit of study lasting several weeks? A greater question all elementary teachers must address is "What is my science curriculum?" The answer may not be easy or readily apparent. A teacher must consider all of the components in making a decision. Your decision should be based on four key elements—the students, con-

tent, teaching strategies, and your concept of learning theories—as well as on the assessment of the program (Figure 1.1).

An initial responsibility of all elementary teachers is to make students cognizant of the scientific world in which they live and their numerous daily encounters with science. Too often, students come to school with the belief that "science" is a topic that is taught and learned in the classroom. Many children do not realize that science is concerned with how we perceive and experience the world around us. Science becomes a subject only when it is relegated to a specific time slot in the school day. As mentioned previously, science should be viewed more as an experience than as a topic.

**IDEA BOX**

Engage students in a brief discussion during the first week of school, and ask them to think of all of the experiences with science they have had during the preceding day. Children in grades three through six could work in groups of three to five to develop a list of the ways they or their families utilized science during the previous 24 hours. These lists could be discussed to help the class to become more aware of science in their lives; to help them become cognizant of how much they know about science; and to help the teacher gain insight in the gaps, strengths, and weaknesses in the depth and breadth of the science knowledge of students. In kindergarten through third grade, you may do this orally with the class and record students' responses.

The preceding exercise serves several purposes: (1) You will give an indication that your science program will be action-oriented and that you will not be overly reliant on the textbook, (2) It will provide considerable insight into the depth of students' knowledge of the involvement of science in their lives, (3) It will serve as an example of social interaction and a reminder that students can learn from one another as well as from you, (4) It will be a valuable aid in developing the science program for the year, (5) The exercise could be expanded into a lesson that stimulates the students' language skills as they write the results for their groups.

## Background Knowledge of Students

The effective science curriculum must place the student at its center. This means that you must look at the children in your class (regardless of the number of children and how they were selected for the classroom) as a number of individuals with a wide variety of intellectual abilities, experiential backgrounds, interest levels, learning styles, and motivations.

Why is there such variety within a group of children who are approximately the same chronological

**FIGURE 1.1** The assessment umbrella

age? Certainly, one must consider their backgrounds. For some, parents and other significant adults have discussed and demonstrated many phenomena in the child's environment. The child's observational skills and vocabularies were developed as he or she was directed to notice different shapes and different kinds of flowers, animals, homes, vehicles, and other elements in the immediate environment. Such children were encouraged to ask questions and participate in discussions related to their world. The opposite end of the continuum is represented by students who were rarely exposed to anything stimulating. Their environment is sterile and they are given little opportunity to verbally participate with others in their world.

### DID YOU KNOW? _____

The oyster is one of the few animals in the world that is ambisexual. This means that it begins its life as a male and later changes to a female, then back again to a male, and so on throughout its entire life.

**Classroom Activity** Ask students to imagine the consequences if all animals (including humans) were ambisexual. What problems would occur? How could those problems be worked out? How would the sexes be differentiated? What are some of the possible long-term effects? Would there be any advantages? Although there are no right answers to any of these questions, a variety of opinions, ideas, and possibilities will be stimulated. Students may wish to record their thoughts in individual journals or on a special bulletin board display. ■

How does one determine the backgrounds of students? Sylvia Ashton Warner suggests that we give children an opportunity to share their knowledge with teachers (Ashton-Warner, 1971). She stresses that educators should not look upon their students as empty vessels waiting to be filled; rather, pupils are individuals who already possess knowledge. Some have limited

knowledge; others possess a great deal of information. Teachers must develop a classroom ambience in which students freely share concepts and misconceptions with their instructors and peers.

It is very important that you take time to sufficiently determine the level and degree of background knowledge your students have about science topics and procedures. This information is critical to the design of effective lesson plans and to student mastery of scientific concepts. Holmes and Roser (1987) have suggested several ways to assess the amount and quality of students' prior knowledge about a topic. Their list has been modified and expanded here to apply to the elementary science program. Table 1.1 lists some of the assessment methods that can be used to determine your students' background knowledge in science.

## Sources of Content

One of the most important aspects of teaching any subject is to ascertain the content you want the students to acquire. Content includes factual information, concepts, skills, and generalizations. The following discussion will provide insight into the variety of sources at your disposal.

### Textbooks

Textbooks are traditionally the primary source of content for elementary science programs. They are usually well organized, are perceived as the appropriate source for most children and teachers, and have a controlled vocabulary. Most texts are supplemented by a teacher's manual with a prescriptive approach to teaching from the book. Included in the manual is a wide assortment of questions, key concepts, audiovisual aids, and supporting activities. These are some of the more appeal-

TABLE 1.1

........................................................................................

## METHODS OF ASSESSING BACKGROUND KNOWLEDGE

........................................................................................

| Method | Procedure | Advantages |
|---|---|---|
| Questions | Ask students a series of open-ended questions about the topic. | Students have an opportunity to share data in a relaxed atmosphere. |
| Free recall | Ask students to record everything they know about a specific topic. | There are no limits on the type or quantity of data students record. |
| Brainstorming | Give the class a topic and ask students to think of everything they know about the topic. Data is recorded on the chalkboard. | Allows for a free flow of ideas. Students have an opportunity to "piggyback" on the ideas of their classmates. |
| Word association | Say a word and ask students to write or say any other word that comes to mind. | This yields a lot of information in a relatively easy format. |
| Pictures | Post several pictures or illustrations of a topic at the front of the room. Students can describe each picture in writing or orally. | Some students will find it easier to respond to pictures than to words. |
| Discussion | Students are asked to describe any experiences they have had with the topic. | All ideas and thoughts are valid and acceptable. |

ing aspects of the textbook; however, it should not be perceived as a cookbook where, if a few ingredients are modified, deleted, or added, the end product will be ruined.

In addition, texts are usually built around a scope and sequence that enables teachers to build on concepts taught previously. However, a note of caution is in order here. Texts are designed for a wide population and directed toward the average student in an average class. The authors have no way of knowing the backgrounds and interests of children in individual classrooms or the interest, abilities, and knowledge of their teachers. Thus, teachers have two alternatives in the use of textbooks. One is an active role in which the text is used to help the teacher in the educational process. The second is a passive position in which the individual is a conduit for the decisions made by others (i.e., the textbook authors). A teacher who elects the latter position is a consumer of a textbook and uses content that has been selected and organized by others. The teacher has "surrendered to the textbook the responsibility to define, analyze, and develop the curriculum" (Pasch, 1990, p. 1). The other option enables the teacher to assume a greater responsibility in the educational process of the class. The individual teacher makes decisions in all aspects of teaching: the content, sequence, scope, depth, and complexity. In this role the teacher is an able professional who helps develop district- or grade-level goals, creates units of study, writes instructional objectives, and makes decisions about instructional materials (Pasch, 1990).

## TEACHER TO TEACHER

One very enjoyable aspect of being an elementary teacher in a small town is the opportunity for longitudinal observation. Visits by former students, all grown-up and sophisticated, are always gratifying. I have noticed over the years, however, that few of these visitors mention specific content we covered in their days in my class. For instance, no one ever comes and asks, "Do you still teach that great unit on mitosis?" or "Do you remember what fun we had with the Periodic Table?" Inevitably, these visitors will recall events which may have seemed insignificant to me at the time. "Got any good snakes this year?" "Do you still have that salt water aquarium?" "Does your class still go out behind the school and collect insects in the spring?" These are the things they remember from our time together. Experience has taught me that while specific content may be quite important, it is equally important to provide students with many interesting and stimulating experiences. After all, is it not our personal collection of experiences which determines our attitudes, and to a large degree, our identities?

Robert B. McDonald
Blaschke Intermediate School
Ingleside, TX

## Curriculum Guides

Curriculum guides may be designed by groups at the state level, in local school districts, or at an individual school. You should become aware of the guides available in your school to ensure that the required material is being presented in the designated courses or grade level. You should also realize the significance of these guides, which provide you with the content, concepts, and skills to be presented at the respective grade levels and thus give you an awareness of the continuity of the science program. This does not imply that you can assume that all of the children in your class will have the background suggested; however, it does enable you to design an outline for your science curriculum for the year that reinforces and carries out the school's program. Modifications will have to be made to meet the needs of your class and individuals within the class because of the uniqueness of the students' abilities, backgrounds, and interests.

## Background of Teachers

If teaching science is to be interesting, challenging, and rewarding, the individuality of the teacher must be considered as a significant source of science content. All teachers have some knowledge and skill in science; however, these traits vary from one individual to another. Although there may be a curriculum guide to follow, there is considerable allowance for the individuality of the teacher to be utilized. A few elementary teachers have depth in all science areas, some in several areas, and many in at least one. For example, you may feel insecure in earth science but be very astute in sound because of a background in music. This background can be utilized effectively in a science unit covering sound energy. Other teachers may have a keen interest in weather forecasting and still others in flying, tropical fish, or growing exotic plants. All of these interests are science-related, and scientific concepts can be enhanced by in-depth study of any of these top-

TABLE **1.2**

................................................................................................

## CHARACTERISTICS OF A GOOD SCIENCE PROGRAM

................................................................................................

The following items identify *some* of the features of a good classroom science program. This check sheet can be used to evaluate your own classroom or that of another teacher. Place a check mark in front of those items that are present in the classroom or that are done on a regular basis. Those items without check marks may indicate areas of improvement.

_____ 1. Is there a curriculum guide or a scope and sequence chart?

_____ 2. Is the curriculum guide followed in the classroom?

_____ 3. Has regular time for the teaching of science been scheduled for every school day?

_____ 4. Is the time allotted for teaching science consistent with the emphases stated in the curriculum guide?

_____ 5. Is there a match between the curriculum guide and the sequence of topics in the science textbook?

_____ 6. Does the teacher move beyond the curriculum guide and take advantage of "teachable moments" or students' interests?

_____ 7. Is the teacher involved in determining the procedures and process to be used in teaching relevant concepts?

_____ 8. Do students have an active role in the science curriculum?

_____ 9. Does the teacher involve parents and other community members regularly in various aspects of the science program?

_____ 10. Does the teacher work in concert with other teachers to promote science in the school?

_____ 11. Does the teacher have input as to the goals and objectives of the science program?

_____ 12. Is there a balanced approach to the life, physical, and earth and space sciences?

_____ 13. Are the students engaged in a "hands-on, minds-on" approach to science?

_____ 14. Is the science program built on a process approach to learning science?

_____ 15. Are the students actively engaged in problem solving and critical thinking activities?

_____ 16. Are the materials and supplies appropriate for the developmental levels of students?

_____ 17. Are students provided opportunities to apply their science knowledge in real-life situations?

_____ 18. Is the science curriculum divergent and open-ended?

_____ 19. Is science integrated with other subject areas?

_____ 20. Is there a sufficient quantity of science materials and supplies?

_____ 21. Do the students enjoy science?

ics. In addition to the factual knowledge acquired and shared, attitudes and interests can be enhanced as students observe the teacher in the role of a scientist who is actively participating in the development of a scientific phenomenon.

It is not essential for a teacher to be versed in all aspects of the science curriculum. Although this principle may seem anathema to the intent of your methods course, it is a significant element in the success of a science program. In other words, a curriculum that is student-driven (where students seek out answers to self-initiated questions) as opposed to teacher-driven (where teachers march through the textbook dispensing facts and figures according to a pre-determined plan) is more dynamic, engaging, and productive. When teachers and students work together as "learners," the science program becomes exciting and successful.

Table 1.2 lists some of the features of a successful science program.

## Locality

Each area of the globe is unique and holds a personal interest for those living in the locality. The uniqueness may relate to the weather or climate, terrain features, flora and fauna, elevation, or the influence of human beings on the area. All of these, and many more, unique features are science-related.

Max Kline, a teacher in the Pittsburgh area, related the major industry in the area (steel making) to science. This topic was selected because of its relevance to the lives of many of the pupils. A number of scientific principles were developed during the unit through pictures, models, diagrams, and demonstrations. The students were taught physics through the simple machines utilized by the workers in their jobs, such as the inclined plane, wheel and axle, and the lever. The chemistry

of mixing various ingredients (e.g., limestone, magnesium, and iron ore) to produce a specific type of steel demonstrated the practical application of science in the industrial world. The impact of the pollutant by-products on the environment helped students comprehend acid rain, lifeless rivers, and the contents of smog. The lumber industry, dairy farming, glass making, and textile manufacturing are examples that could be utilized in the Far West, Midwest, South, and Northeast, respectively, to help develop scientific principles and their application.

### TO INVESTIGATE

Survey the local community (within a five-mile radius) of your college town. Try to list five resources for life science (e.g., a natural history museum), five resources for physical science (e.g., a generating station), and five resources for earth and space science (e.g., a recycling center). Observe a science class in a local elementary school for several days, and note how many times the teacher utilizes one or more local resources. You may wish to ask the teacher how often he or she uses community resources to extend science concepts. What are the implications of your findings for your classroom? ■

## LEARNING THEORIES

After the teacher has considered the students and source of content, the next major consideration is how to teach the material. "The act of teaching includes listening, talking, thinking, watching, reading, writing, moving and shaping in order to: observe, monitor, consider, confirm; plan, prepare, provide, organize; demonstrate, present, explain, discuss, encourage; question, challenge, extend; guide, direct, intervene; acknowledge, respond, compliment, praise; check, test, observe" (Mooney, 1990, p. 54).

The teacher's responsibility in any subject area is to ascertain the most appropriate aspect of teaching for a unique group of children or an individual. Most teachers can follow a manual or a detailed curriculum guide. A professional, however, is one with a thorough knowledge of child development, the structure of the academic discipline, and a theory of learning to match the science content to the learning style of the student. One of the difficulties confronting teachers is the lack of agreement on how individuals learn and, thus, on the best method or strategy to follow when teaching. The contributions of Skinner, Piaget, Bruner, and Ausubel are well documented in educational psychology textbooks, and their applications for the classroom are widely espoused. We will explore their theories briefly and suggest some applications to the science program.

## Jean Piaget

One individual who has had a significant impact on teaching science in the elementary school during the past 35 years was Jean Piaget (1963, 1970). This Swiss psychologist believed that individuals move through different stages of mental development and that these stages determine how one approaches and solves problems in his or her environment. He stressed that all individuals inherited two basic tendencies: the tendency to organize and the tendency to adapt to objects, events, and situations in the environment. People organize their thinking processes into schemes or psychological structures that help them understand and interact with their world. These schemes may be simple or complex systems—as simple as drinking from a cup to something as complex as understanding Einstein's theory of relativity.

Piaget suggests that the ability of individuals to adapt to their environment is accomplished through two basic processes called *assimilation* and *accommodation*. Through assimilation, one understands something new by fitting it into what he or she already knows. For example, we need not learn all the components of an automobile every time we see a new model or a unique vehicle. Once we know that a car is moved by some type of energy, that it is mobile, that it is a means of transportation, and so forth, we are able to assimilate a "new" car into our scheme of an automobile.

In accommodation, an individual changes his or her psychological structure to respond to a new species, object, or event. For example, children may understand and have a schema for a permanent magnet and its features; however, when children begin to learn how electricity interacts with a magnet to produce an electromagnet, they may have to modify their existing scheme of a magnet.

**DID YOU KNOW?** _____

When most of us think of coral, we think of the tropical regions of the world. However, some of the world's oldest coral reefs are in Lake Champlain near its border with Vermont.

**Classroom Activity** The preceding data was probably something you had to *accommodate* into your understanding of coral; in other words, your existing psychological structure had to be modified. Children do this all the time. Have several children obtain a copy of *Bet You Can't: Science Impossibilities to Fool You* by Vicky Cobb (New York: Lothrop, Lee & Shepard, 1980) or *Elephants Can't Jump and Other Freaky Facts about Animals* by Barbara Seuling (New York: Lodestar, 1984). Ask several students to share one or more pieces of information from those books with other members of the class. Have the children discuss their reactions to that new information. How did their perceptions change? How was their understanding altered? If they don't believe the data, why is that so? These discussions will help children appreciate the reasons why some science knowledge is assimilated and some accommodated. ■

The actual changes in one's thinking occur through a process Piaget calls *equilibration*. If an individual applies his or her schema to a particular object, event, situation, or problem and it is satisfactory for understanding, equilibrium exists. If it is not adequate, disequilibrium exists. The latter state, Piaget stressed, motivates one to keep searching for a solution through the processes of assimilation and accommodation (Woolfolk, 1990).

Another important aspect of Piaget's theory is that all human beings move through four stages of mental development. Although individuals pass through these stages in the same sequence, they do not reach a particular stage at the same chronological age, nor do they abandon the previous stage completely upon arriving at the next level. The ages assigned by Piaget are approximate, and individuals do not always function at the highest developmental level because of the complexity of the situation and the experiential background brought to the material being considered. These developmental levels and the approximate ages for each stage are:

| | |
|---|---|
| Sensorimotor | Birth to age 2 |
| Preoperational | Ages 2 to 7 |
| Concrete operational | Ages 7 to 11 |
| Formal operational | Age 11 and up |

Most children in elementary school function at either the preoperational or the concrete operational stage. Many cognitive psychologists suggest that teachers working with students in the preoperational stage (grades K–2) should use concrete materials and visual aids frequently. When students are studying seeds for example, teachers should have an assortment of seeds available for students to manipulate, look at under a hand lens, and discuss with other students, and perhaps a book with drawings or pictures to compare. For studying plants, the instructor should provide a variety of live plants in the classroom, diagrams of plants and their parts, and live models of roots, stems, leaves, flower, and seeds.

Teachers working with pupils at the concrete operational stage (grades 2–6) should provide opportunities for students to manipulate and test material. These pupils are capable of making discoveries and testing the results of their findings. A unit on electricity can serve this objective well if the teacher provides batteries, wires, bulbs, and switches to the class. Students are encouraged to manipulate and experiment with the materials as they discover parallel and series circuits, closed and open circuits, the function of a switch, and other aspects of current electricity. Also at this level, models can be used effectively to help students learn about the solar system and the relationship of the sun, moon, and earth; volcanoes; the human body and its various systems (e.g., circulatory, digestive, and nervous); and a host of other phenomena (Woolfolk, 1990, p. 47).

A few pupils in the upper intermediate grades will have reached the formal operational stage in some activities. These pupils should continue to use manipulative materials; however, they should be given the opportunity to explore abstract ideas and hypothetical situations. A few examples of questions to challenge them are: What will the world be like in 100 years if we continue to pollute our air with carbon monoxide? What would our sunsets look like if the colors had different wavelengths? What would happen to the earth if ice were heavier than water? At this stage stu-

dents can begin to use some of the elements of scientific experimentation by developing a problem, stating a hypothesis, and controlling variables as they seek to understand the processes of science.

Although all psychologists do not agree with Piaget's theories, especially his assignment of the stages of mental development, Piaget has taught us something about how children think and the significance of teachers listening to them and observing the way they solve their problems. By trying to understand what is occurring within the child, we may be able to match our teaching to the child's ability.

## Jerome Bruner

Jerome Bruner has had a strong influence on the teaching of science in elementary schools during the second half of the twentieth century. His emphasis is on discovery learning. He is an adamant proponent of presenting children with problems and situations, with no preselected or prearranged materials, and then having the pupils seek solutions, either individually or as a group (Bruner, 1962, 1966). Like Piaget, he believes that individuals perceive the world differently according to their level of mental development. He, too, identified stages through which individuals progress. His initial stage is the *enactive mode*. This occurs at the preschool age when children are very active and deal with the

world primarily through the actions they perform on it. The next stage is the *iconic mode*, where children rely heavily on pictures, images, diagrams, and other concrete embodiments to help them understand the myriad of ideas, facts, and generalizations they encounter in the learning process. The third and final stage is the *symbolic mode*. Children at the end of the elementary school experience and during early adolescence function in this mode. They are capable of thinking with verbal and written presentations, mathematical formulas, and other abstract configurations. Although older children are capable of performing at this level, Bruner believes they may still call upon the enactive and iconic modes to assist them in their learning (Bruner, 1962).

A major responsibility of the teacher, according to Bruner, is to help the student understand the structure of the subject. This involves learning the fundamental ideas of a subject and how they relate to each other. The statement that is perhaps most frequently identified with Bruner is that "any subject can be taught to any child in some honest form" (Bruner, 1971, p. 71). He would employ the spiral curriculum to accomplish this goal. In this curriculum, material is initially presented at the child's level of thinking in a simplified, interesting manner. As the individual moves through the educational process, the same ideas are presented in more complex ways. Children at the kindergarten or first-grade level may be introduced to the magnet by allowing them to manipulate several magnets. As they handle these objects, they realize that magnets can either push or pull one another. They also become aware that magnets will stick to some things, such as the refrigerator, but not to others, such as a wooden door. At a later grade children will learn that a bar magnet will point to the North and South poles of the earth when suspended on a string. At the upper elementary school level, children begin to understand the relationship of electricity and magnetism, for example how magnetism is involved in generating electricity, ringing a door bell, and moving huge objects.

Although Bruner has many supporters, he is not without critics. Some believe that the discovery approach takes too much time and prevents the teacher from covering an adequate amount of material. Another criticism is that students become frustrated because their primary source of information and direction—the teacher—does not provide the support they need. A third concern is that the bright students frequently dominate the program (Biehler, 1990).

## David Ausubel

An approach to directing the learning activities of students that is in many ways the opposite of Bruner's discovery approach is advocated by David Ausubel

(Ausubel, 1977). He is a proponent of expository teaching, in which the teacher presents the material in its final form. The teacher decides upon the material, the facts, generalizations, concepts, and skills to be learned, and organizes the lesson in such a way that it can be easily related to the students' existing schemes.

Ausubel places considerable stress on meaningful learning, which involves relating the content of the lesson to the student's knowledge base, experiential background, and capacity to learn. He believes that "the most important single factor influencing learning is what the learner already knows. Ascertain this and teach him accordingly" (Ausubel, Novak, & Hunesian, 1978, flyleaf).

**DID YOU KNOW?** _____

Although the human brain constitutes only about 2 percent of the total body weight of a human, it uses approximately 25 percent of the body's oxygen intake.

**Classroom Activity**  Students can make some rough calculations as to how much oxygen their brain uses each day. Provide each student with a fully stretched balloon. Ask the students to take deep breaths and blow as much air as possible into the balloon. Each balloon can be weighed using a balance scale. Each student then calculates how many breaths he or she takes each day by measuring the number of breaths taken in five minutes and multiplying that by 288 (the number of five-minute segments in 24 hours). That figure can be multiplied by the weight of the balloon to determine an approximate amount of air taken into the lungs each day. Multiply that by 0.16 (the amount of oxygen in the air) and then divide that subtotal by 4 (or multiply by 0.25). The result will be a rough approximation of the amount of oxygen the person's brain uses during a normal day.  ■

Teachers, Ausubel believes, should use advance organizers to help students engage in meaningful learning. These are introductory materials that assist the student in relating the new information to their existing knowledge base (see Chapter 7). These organizers should be more general and abstract than the information or material that the students are expected to learn (Ausubel, 1977). An advance organizer for students studying circuits may be a diagram of series and parallel circuits that will be more completely explained and illustrated in the lesson. A major criticism of Ausubel's theory is that students may have acquired a superficial understanding of a subject and believe that this acquisition constitutes in-depth knowledge.

## B. F. Skinner

A theory that has had a significant influence on American education during the past four decades is B. F. Skinner's concept of operant conditioning. The basic

Just as other theorists have their critics, Skinner is not without his. Perhaps the major criticism is that "reinforcing a student for accomplishments may put too much emphasis on the system for receiving rewards and undermine the student's natural interest in learning for its own sake" (Woolfolk, 1990, p. 223).

**DID YOU KNOW?** _____

You can determine the approximate weight of your skin if you divide your body weight by 16.

**Classroom Activity** Involve students in the weighing and measuring of various body parts. What similarities are there, for example, among all the hands in the room? All the feet? How will students be able to weigh body parts? Determine the approximate percentage of a body part in relation to the rest of the body and calculate accordingly? Provide students with an opportunity to chart the dimensions and weights of several body parts of other students. What similarities do they notice? What differences? How would that data reflect the general population? How would it be useful? ∎

idea behind operant conditioning is that "all behaviors are accompanied by certain consequences, and these consequences strongly influence whether or not these behaviors are repeated and at what level of intensity" (Biehler, 1990, p. 322). When a teacher wishes a behavior to be repeated, she or he encourages the behavior with positive reinforcement. An example of a positive reinforcement is candy, a smiley face, a star, a smile, or other positive feedback. Negative reinforcement is used to remove an unwanted behavior and replace it with the desired behavior. Students may modify their behavior of not turning in homework, not participating in science experiments or demonstrations, or not cleaning up after science activities to escape the nagging, negative comments from the teacher and peer group.

Skinner applied his theories of operant conditioning to education in his book *Walden Two,* where he points out that people do not develop positive or negative characteristics because of inherited attributes; they become leaders, productive citizens, and creative individuals because they receive the appropriate reinforcements throughout their formative years. He suggests that teachers consider four factors when designing material for their students. They should be clear about what is to be taught, teach first things first, allow students to learn at their own rates, and program the subject matter (Skinner, 1948). The recommendations of Skinner led to the development of programmed instruction material and to computer-assisted instruction. These programs have been found to be effective supplements to regular classroom instruction, especially for low achievers (Biehler, 1990).

As one reviews learning theories and their proponents, it becomes clear that most individuals recognize the importance of providing students with a knowledge of the basic subjects and the basic skills of reading, writing, and computing, and of enhancing their ability to develop problem-solving skills and the opportunity to be creative. None of the learning theorists suggests that student's material interest should be stymied. Most of them recognize the importance of a predetermined body of knowledge and the need to memorize some material. However, "what differences exist among theorists are in emphases" (Biehler, 1990, p. 424).[1]

The methodology for teaching science is the primary responsibility of the individual teacher. You are the one who knows the students in your classroom and the material, techniques, and approaches that are most appropriate for learning. You will find that your students represent a divergent group with widely varying backgrounds of experience, knowledge, and ability. As you attempt to fill the educational needs of your students, you must keep in mind that the source of material may be textbooks, trade books, and other printed materials; the students; yourself; and materials provided by the state and school district in the form of curriculum guides. Curriculum guides and textbooks are to be used at your discretion; they are not to be followed as one follows a prescription. It is important for

[1] A number of other individuals have presented excellent theories for teachers to ponder as they assume their positions in education. These include Albert Bandura's contributions on observational learning theory (Bandura, 1986) and Robert Gagnè's approach to problem solving (Gagnè, 1977). Consult any of the excellent texts suggested at the end of this chapter for additional information on learning theories.

you to develop a style of teaching that reflects your understanding of how children learn. The level of the material, the manner in which the material is presented, and the expectations of the lesson will reflect that understanding.

## TEACHER TO TEACHER _____

Remember that you are the face of science in your students' minds. If you create a pleasant science class, they will think "science is fun!" They are so excited to bring you a fossil, a bug, a book with great pictures, rattlesnake rattles, moldy bread, and pond water. Act like it is the greatest fossil, the prettiest bug, and the best mold you have ever seen. Use the object and the student's name in your lessons. If it is so interesting to one student, it will probably also interest the others.

Elaine Hampton
Zia Middle School
Las Cruces, NM

## A SCIENCE SELF-ASSESSMENT

You have undoubtedly brought a host of experiences to this science class. Many of those events will determine your approach to science teaching and your success in helping children make science a rewarding part of their lives. The following survey is designed to allow you to articulate your background and experiences with science. There are no right or wrong answers. Just complete each section as fully as you feel is necessary. Later, you may want to share your data with others in the class in an open discussion.

What are some of your most memorable experiences in elementary school science?

What would you like to forget about elementary school science?

Who, if anyone, was most influential in shaping your attitudes toward science?

Specifically, what did that individual do?

What does the study of science involve?

Complete the following statements.
Scientists are:

Science is:

Science education should be . . .

Science teachers . . .

## POINTS OF DISCUSSION

1. Obtain copies of two or more curriculum guides from different school districts. What similarities do you note? What differences?
2. Interview several teachers concerning their philosophies of teaching science. Which of the theorists mentioned in this chapter would each teacher embrace?
3. Identify four students in a second-grade class. What Piagetian stage is each one in? How do you know?
4. Write a paragraph on your philosophy of teaching science. With which of the theories mentioned in this chapter do you agree with most? With which do you differ most?

5. Interview a first-grade student and a sixth-grade student. How do they enjoy science? What do they do in science class? How does their enjoyment of science relate to how their science classes are conducted? What are some implications for your future classroom?

6. Make a list of your personal attributes that will contribute to your success as a science teacher. How do they compare with those of your classmates?

7. Describe your own learning style. What accommodations will you have to make to effectively teach students who have learning styles different from yours?

## REFERENCES AND SUGGESTED READINGS

American Association for the Advancement of Science. (1989). *Science for all Americans: Summary*. Washington, DC: Author.

Ashton-Warner, Sylvia. (1971). *Teacher*. New York: Bantam.

Ausubel, D.P. (1977). "The facilitation of meaningful verbal meaning in the classroom." *Educational Psychologist, 12,* 162–178.

Ausubel, David P., Novak, J. D., Hunesian, H. (1978). *Educational psychology: A cognitive view*. (2nd ed.). New York: Holt, Rinehart & Winston.

Bandura, Albert. (1986). *Social foundations of thought and action: A social cognitive theory*. Englewood Cliffs, NJ: Prentice-Hall.

Biehler, Robert F., & Snowman, Jack. (1990). *Psychology applied to teaching*. (6th ed.). Boston: Houghton Mifflin.

Bruner, J. S. (1962). *The process of education*. Cambridge, MA: Harvard University Press.

Bruner, J. S. (1966). *Toward a theory of instruction*. New York: Norton.

Bruner, J. S. (1971). *The relevance of education*. New York: Norton.

Gagné , R. M. (1977). *The conditions of learning* (3rd ed.). New York: Holt, Rinehart & Winston.

Glasgow, D. R. (1983). Identifying the "real" elementary science curriculum. *Science and Children, 20,* 56–59.

Holmes, B., & Roser, N. (1987). "Five ways to assess readers' prior knowledge." *The Reading Teacher, 40,* 646–649.

Mooney, Margaret. (1990). What do you do when you teach? *Teaching Pre K–8,* August/September, *21*(1), 54–55.

Pasch, Marvin, Sparks-Langer, Georgea, Gardner, Trevor, Starko, Alane, & Moody, Christella. (1990). *Teaching as decision making. Instructional practices for the successful teacher*. White Plains, NY: Longman.

Piaget, J. (1963). *Origins of intelligence in children*. New York: Norton.

Piaget, J. (1970). *The science of education and the psychology of the child*. New York: Orion Press.

Skinner, B. F. (1948). *Walden two*. New York: Macmillan.

Woolfolk, Anita E. (1990). *Educational psychology*. (4th ed.). Englewood Cliffs, NJ: Prentice-Hall.

# 2

# THE GOALS AND PROCESSES OF SCIENCE

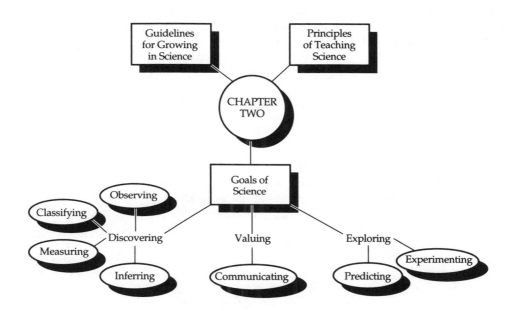

## Chapter Objectives

After reading this chapter you should be able to:

1. Delineate the principles of teaching science to elementary youngsters.

2. Describe the three major goals of instruction for an effective science curriculum.

3. Enumerate the seven key processes that should drive the elementary science program.

4. Provide examples of enabling questions and their utility in science lessons.

5. Illustrate introductory activities and strategies that extend the processes of science instruction.

Science is fun! Science is an exploration of the unknown. Science is filling in gaps in our knowledge base, changing old ideas, modifying concepts, and discovering that we don't necessarily have all the answers just because we know a bunch of facts. In some ways, science is a testament to our innate ignorance—an ignorance stimulating a desire to know more about ourselves and our world, not one signifying a complete dearth of knowledge.

For students, science should be a dynamic and interactive discipline. It should allow students to examine new ideas, play around with concepts and precepts, and discover that knowledge is not finite. What does this mean for the teacher of elementary science? It means that children must be given a multitude of opportunities to probe, poke, and peek into the mysteries of the universe—whether that universe is the child's own back yard or a galaxy far away.

Science should also give children a host of opportunities to think rather than just memorize. Knowing the parts of a frog or the number of planets in the solar system means very little unless youngsters are provided with opportunities to use that information in some useful way. Asking children to store that data in their minds is not teaching science but rather is asking them to parrot science. Little appreciation of the wonders of the scientific community grows from this procedure, and little application of the facts and figures of science comes about through this "traditional" way of teaching science. Indeed, science is more than numbers, charts, and graphs; it is a venture and an adventure of the mind, the constant learning and relearning of new data and new ideas. Providing youngsters with opportunities to inquire about their world, question basic assumptions, and actively seek solutions to various mysteries places a value on the power of the human mind—particularly the minds of students.

## GUIDELINES FOR GROWING IN SCIENCE

Children need many opportunities to make sense of their world and to lay a foundation for future discoveries. The following guidelines should be considered basic principles on which elementary science programs can be built.

1. Students need to be provided with a basic body of knowledge, skills, and attitudes that will form the foundation for future discoveries. Being able to identify certain types of leaves may be important in helping students gain an appreciation for conservation measures. Knowing the different types of simple machines provides a basis for students to comprehend the working of more complex machinery. Yet meaningful science programs must move beyond these facts. Contrary to the arguments of some, an accumulation of facts is no more science than a collection of bricks is a house.

2. Students need to develop positive attitudes toward the entire world of science. Learning how to use and deal with scientific data in a way that will benefit all living things is an important part of the science curriculum. Not only should students understand how things work or behave, they must also realize the interdependencies and interrelationships among all elements of the world around them.

3. Students need to use science information in a practical and personal way. Possessing the skills of science is one thing; being able to use those skills in some meaningful way is quite another. Elementary science instruction should be geared toward offering youngsters a myriad of opportunities to put their knowledge into practice—not only to refine their individual knowledge bases, but also to increase their appreciation of adding information to their respective knowledge bases.

4. Learning is a process of physical maturation. New possibilities for the cognitive system are presented to children as they grow and mature. As children develop physically, new vistas open up for the assimilation or accommodation of data.

5. Children love to experiment with their environment. Typically, these experiments are of three types: (1) intellectual exercises, activities by which children ponder and pursue unfamiliar elements of their world; (2) physical experiences, activities that emphasize the attributes of an object or event; and (3) logicomathematical experiences, situations where children reflect on their own actions or the actions of objects rather than of the objects themselves.

6. Children are also influenced by social experiences. The interaction with the cultural or educational environment allows children to benefit from the experiences of others. These experiences may be conveyed through books, TV, or other familiar transmitters of knowledge.

7. The child's cognitive system is in a state of flux; it changes and adjusts. What this means for the teacher of science is that students are receptive to learning new information when that information challenges or modifies previously learned concepts. In other words, children want a rational perspective of the world and how it operates, not a "bag" of facts that must be memorized. To achieve this, they must *be active participants* in their own learning.

The implications of these guidelines for teachers of science are that: (1) students need and want constant intellectual stimulation; (2) integrating physical, emotional, and cognitive needs produces not only a well-rounded science program, but well-rounded student scientists, too; and (3) science means an active and energetic processing of data, not a spoon-feeding of insipid facts. Again, science should be fun—and can be when it is linked with children's intuitive search for meaning and their meaningful search for truth.

# PRINCIPLES OF TEACHING SCIENCE

The study of science should be dynamic. That is, children's daily contacts with the scientific world should involve constant interaction between the known and the unknown. Children need to discover and play with new ideas, and to modify, strengthen, or reject the rest. What helps children develop a scientific outlook are the principles that drive the classroom program.

## Principles of Science Education

1.  Children must bear the responsibility for their own learning. Children must be allowed to make choices or select learning opportunities based on their goals and interests. Students who are given the chance to do so begin to assume greater control over their personal learning options and are more willing to pursue learning for its own sake.

2.  Children bring a wealth of experiences and backgrounds to the science curriculum. When teachers provide children opportunities to use their experience in tandem with the procedures and processes of science, knowledge mushrooms accordingly.

3.  Children are naturally curious. Their innate curiosity about the world around them can be used as a powerful motivator throughout the science curriculum. This curiosity is often dulled when children are faced with workbooks and senseless drills that inhibit expression and creativity rather than enhance it.

**DID YOU KNOW?**

The average adult elephant has approximately one ton of skin covering its body.

**Classroom Activity** All children are fascinated by elephants. Encourage them to investigate the life habits of elephants, including what they eat, where they live, their gestation period, and how they move around. Also address some of the environmental concerns involving elephants, including the poaching of elephants in Africa. Students may wish to write to Defenders of Wildlife (1244 19th Street, NW, Washington, DC 20036), Friends of the Earth (530 7th Street, SE, Washington, DC 20003), or the Fund for Animals (200 West 57th Street, New York, NY 10019) for additional information on elephants. ∎

4.  Each child brings a special set of skills and attributes to the classroom. Capitalizing on the diversity of skills in the classroom is one of the most exciting opportunities you will have as a teacher.

5.  Children are naturally active. Few children enjoy sitting in a classroom desk all day, manipulating workbooks or circling items on a skill sheet. The very nature of science implies an *action-oriented* and *process-oriented* approach to learning. This means that children need to "get their hands dirty" in science; they need to manipulate objects, try out different approaches, spill things, break an occasional dish or test tube, handle substances and animals, look around them, taste various objects, and so on.

**TO INVESTIGATE** ⎯⎯⎯⎯⎯⎯⎯⎯⎯⎯

Observe several classrooms in a local school. Are students actively engaged? Are they provided with a diversity of hands-on experiences and opportunities to become personally involved in making discoveries and drawing their own conclusions? Based on your observations, is there a relationship between students' level of involvement and their interest in science? Do students who participate in a host of hands-on activities have positive attitudes toward science? Is the students' interest in science in any way related to the amount of time they are given to experiment and explore on their own? What are the implications of your observations for your future classroom? ∎

6. Science is a subject for all! Unfortunately, too many youngsters feel that science is a male-oriented subject, that only boys can get interested in what happens throughout the natural world. The wonders of science are available to all.

7. Children want to make sense of their world. Students are bombarded with a host of stimuli every day—from news stories on TV, to discussions of current events in the daily newspaper, to the big news items happening in the local community. Children sometimes have a difficult time sorting through this mass of information. Through an integrated and purposeful science program, teachers can offer students some rationale and precepts on which to base meaningful decisions.

8. Children need to be stimulated in diverse ways. Tasting, hearing, seeing, feeling, and smelling are the avenues by which children learn about their immediate environment as well as environments outside the home. These senses can be made an integral part of the science curriculum, too, signifying to students that the skills they have always relied on can be used continuously to foster a better understanding about new areas of discovery and exploration.

9. Children need to be engaged in intellectually stimulating encounters with their environment. Science provides children with a host of opportunities to

question and think about their world. Portraying science as a stagnant subject doesn't do justice to the natural curiosity of children. Students must be provided with critical thinking opportunities and challenging situations that allow them to set their own learning goals and satisfy them through self-discovery.

These principles suggest that science education, to be productive, requires a partnership among the science curriculum, the joy of teaching, and children's developing curiosity about their environment. Helping students appreciate their potential for contributing not only to their personal knowledge base, but to their world can be the cornerstone of a purposeful science program.

## THE GOALS OF SCIENCE

Many books portray science as a collection of facts or a body of "knowledge" to be learned. Unfortunately, the impression this may leave with children is that science is nothing more than memorizing facts and mastering theories. As you may have gathered by now, there is much room in science for intuitive, hypothetical, playful, and imaginative forms of learning.

Chapter 1 presented the concept of science as a *verb*. This implies that science is active, interactive, and reactive. Science involves a host of activities and learning experiences that are not restricted to any single corner of the curriculum. Science as a verb underscores it as a "doing" activity, one in which the focus is on students' personal engagement in the dynamics of learning and the excitement of self-discovery.

Wasserman and Ivany (1988) believe that the term should be changed to a gerund—"sciencing." In a way, *sciencing* is a combination of *science* and *thinking*, a term that implies active student control over the material learned as well as the utilization of that material. It also implies an interaction of students and concepts as opposed to a memorization of facts and information.

"Sciencing" also means that students are handling science; they are manipulating it, working it into new shapes and formats, integrating it into every corner of their world, and playing with it in heretofore unknown ways. "Sciencing" suggests that children are in control of an important part of the personal curriculum: They can adapt ideas to meet their needs or to increase their understanding. As children learn to think through the designs and developments of science, they also learn a sense of self-responsibility that transcends all subject areas.

"Sciencing" means playing with concepts and concerns that confront humans every day. It means that children can and do learn through experience. Their minds and hands work together to create knowledge and enhance their appreciation for the laws and principles that guide our existence.

Science is driven by basic goals. These goals are not independent but are intertwined and multidisciplinary, providing youngsters with a multitude of opportunities to become involved in science. Each goal involves one or more processes that need to be considered in the development of an effective science curriculum. The three goals and their attendant processes are:

| Goals | Processes |
|---|---|
| Discovering | Observing |
|  | Classifying |
|  | Measuring |
|  | Inferring |
| Valuing | Communicating |
| Exploring | Predicting |
|  | Experimenting |

Science teachers must incorporate a healthy dose of each of the three goals into every corner of the curriculum. To do that, attention must be given to the processes behind the goals. Those processes (since, they too, are given as gerunds) ensure that any science lesson or unit is predicated on the curiosity of children as well as the needs of the curriculum. A process approach to science (also known as discovery learning) means that science is not confined to a period of the day or a chapter in a textbook.

A process approach to science stimulates divergent thinking and provides a means for children to investigate their world based on what they know as well as on what they wish to discover. It is the teacher's responsibility to generate situations and opportunities that will enable scientific investigations to occur both in and out of the classroom. Few educators would argue with the statement that one of the basic objectives of any lesson in any discipline is to have learners gain knowledge. Yet, as Piaget has demonstrated, knowledge is a *process* rather than a state. Knowledge is an event or a relationship between the knower and the known. In short, a person constructs knowledge rather than accumulates knowledge. Knowledge built on a model of self–discovery is intrinsically more valuable than knowledge force-fed to an individual by others.

The three goals and seven processes adapted from (Fredericks, Cressman, & Hassler, 1987) pertain to every science curriculum in the elementary grades. They make science relevant and practical for all students. These goals and processes should be introduced to students during the first few weeks of the school year and periodically reviewed throughout the year. Teachers should plan class discussions that will cover each goal and process in addition to engaging in some introductory activities. Students should be encouraged to suggest other appropriate activities for each process, and these can be recorded in a class notebook. The enabling questions for each process provide possibilities for extended class discussions related to all aspects of the science curriculum. Teachers should include examples of all goals and processes throughout the entire science curriculum.

## Discovering

Discovering involves much of what we typically associate with elementary science programs. It puts value on students' contacts with the world around them and how they interact with it. It relies on students' sensory awareness as well as their ability to make sense or order of the things they touch, taste, or smell. It implies first-hand contacts with the world and manipulation of those contacts into recognizable patterns and structures for interpreting new information.

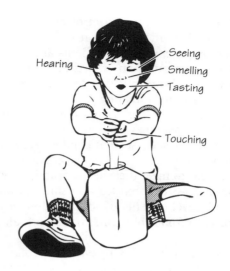

Hearing
Seeing
Smelling
Tasting
Touching

## DID YOU KNOW?

The sex of a crocodile is determined by the temperature of the air, not by the parents. If the air surrounding crocodile eggs is warm, more males will hatch; if the air is cool, more females will hatch. Crocodiles are the only vertebrates whose sex is not decided at the moment of conception.

**Classroom Activity**   Ask students to create two collages—one on crocodiles and one on alligators. Students can cut out pictures from several old nature magazines and paste illustrations of crocodiles and alligators on sheets of construction paper. Have students list different facts about alligators and crocodiles on each collage, and have them investigate some of the similarities as well as some of the differences between these two animals. Where do they live? What do they eat? How long do they live? What differences are there in their reproductive habits? Have students record this information on the appropriate collages.   ■

Discovering is based on children's natural curiosity about the world they live in. Children are known to ask questions such as "Why is the sky blue?" "Where do babies come from?" "What's the biggest mountain or dog or person in the world?" Children have a natural need to know about how things operate, survive, or are distinctive. This natural base for the elementary science curriculum can be an important component in any child's appreciation of the scientific world.

## Observing

Observing involves all the primary senses: seeing, hearing, smelling, tasting, and touching. It is an immediate reaction to one's environment and is the source of knowledge that humans employ most. Children sometimes overrely on their observational powers or do not use them in tandem with other investigative abilities. When students are provided with opportunities to evaluate and question their observational skills, they gain a sense of the importance of this process. Scientific skills are enhanced when pupils use observation in combination with other processes, such as predicting and experimenting.

## TEACHER TO TEACHER

At the beginning of the year I use a game to sharpen students' observation skills and help them realize how valuable writing can be in the scientific process. I choose seven children to stand in front of the class and instruct the other students to observe the seven carefully. Then I ask those seven students to step into the hall, where I quietly tell them to change several different things about their appearance, such as untying a shoe, rolling down a sock, or switching a bracelet from one arm to another.

The students return to the classroom, and the remaining students must figure out what changes were made. As the process is repeated with other children, the students become very proficient at observing and pointing out the changes.

At this point I change the rules. In the hall I tell the next seven children to make no changes, but simply return to the classroom and stand before the class in a different order. Just as before, the other students eagerly look for changes in appearance, but this time I ask them to physically rearrange the seven students until they are standing in their original positions. This sequencing causes considerable difficulty. Even when the exercise is repeated and students know the order will be changed, they still have problems arranging the seven in the proper order.

Eventually students ask if they can write down the order, pointing out that it will make it much easier for them to play the game. This conclusion, arrived at on their own, helps to motivate them to write down their scientific observations. The students realize that entering accurate observations in a journal or notebook isn't simply boring busywork. It's record-keeping that is essential to success.

Wanda J. Gray
Richland Elementary School
Memphis, TN

## INTRODUCTORY ACTIVITIES

**1.** Direct small groups of children to look out a window for one minute. Afterward, ask them to record everything they saw. Ask the groups to compare their lists.

**2.** Ask one child to come into the classroom and perform a series of four or five actions (sit on a chair, tie shoes, point with a pencil, etc.). Ask students to record the actions and compare their lists.

3. Have students listen to the radio for 30 or 60 seconds and then discuss all the sounds they heard.
4. Fill several paper bags with objects that vary in texture (wool, sandpaper, leather, etc.). Direct students to reach into the bags and describe the objects they feel.
5. Blindfold a student and ask him or her to taste bits of onion, celery, lettuce, and potato and describe the differences in taste. Repeat with other students.

## DID YOU KNOW?

Despite their reputation, pigs cannot overeat. Pigs have a natural hormone (known as cholecystokinin) that acts as a messenger from the brain to the stomach "telling" the pig when it's time to stop eating. This appetite suppressant is being researched as an aid for human dieters. In a few years, "eating like a pig" will be a compliment rather than a put-down.

**Classroom Activity** Digesting food is something most kids take for granted. You can help them appreciate this powerful process with the following activity. Provide students with four plastic containers (with lids). Into one place a piece of raw meat, into another a piece of bread, into another a piece of banana, and into the fourth a piece of chocolate. Have one student cover each piece with some saliva and close the lids. Instruct the students to check the samples at one-day intervals and note what happens. Afterward, have them cover the samples with some vinegar (an acid) and note the results. Then have the students cover some samples with a mixture of vinegar and baking soda (a base) and note any results. ∎

6. Copy the chart in Table 2.1. Ask children to select one of the blocks and discuss what it means to them. (*Note:* This activity will stretch their perceptions of the world around them.) Ask them about any difficulties they experience in describing the identified senses. Encourage children to create their own charts similar to this one.

## Enabling Questions

1. How do your observations differ from Mary's?
2. Can you offer an explanation for your observations?
3. Have you ever seen or heard anything similar to this?
4. Would your observations be identical if you were to do the same things again?

## TEACHER TO TEACHER

Be prepared for all sorts of results when teaching observation skills to primary age children. They need to practice looking beyond a single surface quality and identifying as many characteristics as possible. During a group discussion about observations one student, who usually sat silently, raised his hand. Thinking I'd finally hit upon a topic of interest to him I immediately called on him. I was surprised when he asked me how old I was. My response was to question why he asked. Not missing a beat he answered, "Well, your face is kind of old *but* your legs look young...so just how old are you?" He was using more complete observation skills and evaluating his findings to reach a conclusion. What more could a science teacher ask?

Bernice Stephenson
Mason Heights Elementary School
Mason, OH

TABLE **2.1**

### MIXED SENSE CHART

|  | Sight | Taste | Smell | Touch | Hearing |
|---|---|---|---|---|---|
| **Sight** |  | What does red taste like? | What does the sky smell like? | What do mountains feel like? | What does blue sound like? |
| **Taste** | How does sour look? |  | What does sweet smell like? | How does bitter feel? | What does ice cream sound like? |
| **Smell** | What does the smell of rain look like? | How does perfume taste? |  | What do the smells of dinner cooking feel like? | What does the smell of soap sound like? |
| **Touch** | How does soft look? | What does rough rock taste like? | How does silky smell? |  | What does fur sound like? |
| **Hearing** | How does a whisper look? | What does laughing taste like? | What does barking smell like? | How does a siren feel? |  |

*Source:* Joe Abruscato and Jack Hassard. *Loving and Beyond.* Glenview, IL: Scott, Foresman, 1976. Used by permission.

## Classifying

Classifying is the process of assigning basic elements to specific groups. All the items within a particular group share a basic relationship that may or may not be reflected in other groups. As new ideas are encountered, they are added to previously formulated groups on the basis of similar elements. Classifying enhances scientific comprehension because it provides students with the opportunity to relate prior knowledge to new concepts.

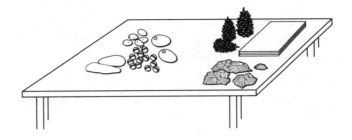

### INTRODUCTORY ACTIVITIES

1. Have students cut out magazine pictures that depict a particular class of animals (e.g., mammals, birds). These pictures may be collected in a class scrapbook.
2. Ask students to create mobiles or murals illustrating a particular class of words (e.g., nouns, adjectives).
3. Ask students to bring in different types of collections (rocks, butterflies, bottle caps, etc.) to share with the class.
4. Pupils may wish to start specimen boxes of various artifacts (animal bones, arrowheads, leaves, etc.).

### Enabling Questions

1. How are these items related?
2. How many different ways can you think of in which these items could be grouped?
3. Are there any similarities between these items and something else you may have seen at home or in your neighborhood?
4. Are there other categories in which some of these items could be placed?

## Measuring

Scientists are constantly measuring. Measuring provides the hard data necessary to confirm hypotheses and make predictions. It yields the first-hand information necessary for all other stages of the scientific investigation. Measuring includes gathering data on size, weight, and quantity. For obvious reasons, it is important that this information be accurate and specific. Measuring is also a valid means of making comparisons using very definite terms rather than vague language such as large, small, huge, heavy, or light.

### DID YOU KNOW?

Salmonella bacteria, a common source of food poisoning and diarrhea, causes 500 deaths in the United States each year. In addition, it is responsible for over $50 billion in health care costs annually.

**Classroom Activity** Direct students to create a chart of some of the more common diseases (e.g., common cold, measles, flu, malaria). Have them investigate the costs, the number of people affected each year, and the prevention techniques for those diseases and add that information to their chart. Invite the school nurse, a doctor, or a laboratory specialist into your classroom to discuss the causes and prevention of the diseases. Students may wish to write to the Centers for Disease Control in Atlanta, Georgia, for additional information. You may wish to obtain a copy of *Disease Detectives* by Melvin Berger (New York: Crowell, 1978) to share with students. ■

### INTRODUCTORY ACTIVITIES

1. Direct small groups of students to measure the heights, widths, and lengths of specific items in the room. Record this information on the chalkboard and question students on any discrepancies.
2. Bring in several boxes, jars, or bottles of commercial food items. Ask students to measure the contents of each to see whether they match the listed proportions and quantities on the package labels. Try to determine the reasons for any differences.
3. Direct students to make charts of items in the room whose measurements change over time (e.g., kids, plants) and those that remain constant (e.g., desks, rugs). What characteristics are similar? What characteristics are different?
4. Ask students to look through various books (other than science books) and collect examples of words that deal with measurement. Have them organize these examples into a class notebook.

5. Play a measuring game with students. Ask one student to lie down on a sheet of butcher paper. Have another student draw an outline of the first individual on the paper. Now challenge members of the class to devise different ways of measuring the first individual. Many students will say that the individual could be measured in inches or feet, let your students invent some new ways of measuring, too. Have them complete the following chart.

> How long is (name of student) in:
>   Inches?
>   Feet?
>   Paper clips?
>   Tennis shoes?
>   Thumbs?
>   Pencils?
>   Floor tiles?
>   Paper cups?
>   Shoelaces?
>   Science textbooks?
>   Chalkboard erasers?

After students have determined each measurement, have each student select one item from the chart and measure a selected area of the outline. Following are some possibilities:

> How many paper clips wide is the head?
> What is the distance in pencils between the fingers on one hand and the fingers on the other?
> How many thumbs are necessary to measure from the waist to the end of the left foot?
> How many tennis shoes (e.g., size 6) does it take to go around the entire body?

> How many paper cups will fill in the space between the neck and the waist?
> Allow students to create other measuring possibilities.

6. Ask students how large "large" is, how heavy is "heavy," how huge is "huge," and so on.

**DID YOU KNOW?** _____

If everyone in the world joined together to count the number of atoms in less than one-tenth of an ounce of matter, with each person counting one atom per second and working 48 hours a week, the chore would take more than 3 billion years.

**Classroom Activity** Children are always fascinated with large numbers. Ask your students to estimate how long it would take them to collect one thousand units of a particular item (e.g., bottle caps, paper clips, staples). Ask them to estimate how long it would take to collect a million of those items. Then tell them to begin collecting. They will be amazed at the length of time needed. Be sure to share with them David Schwartz's book *How Much Is a Million?* (New York: Lothrop, 1985). Ask them to determine advanced methods scientists use for counting large numbers of items. Ask them about shortcuts to counting large numbers of objects.    ■

**Enabling Questions**

1. Why do you think these two measurements differed?
2. Do you feel we need more data before we go on?
3. Do you think we should measure again to see whether we are truly accurate?
4. If the size (weight) of this object were larger (smaller), how do you think it would affect our experiment?

---

## Inferring

Students often need to make conjectures and suppositions on the basis of a minimum of data. Inferring is of two types: deductive (going from the general to the specific) and inductive (going from the specific to the general). Making inferences requires that students have a sufficient background of personal experiences as well as opportunities and encouragement to draw tentative conclusions or explanations.

INTRODUCTORY ACTIVITIES

1. Have students look at a collection of photographs. Ask them to describe the emotions that various people show.
2. Show a foreign film to the class and ask students to speculate on what the characters are saying.
3. Read an exciting story to the class, but stop at a climactic point. Have students speculate on what may happen next.
4. Show various street signs to the class and ask students to guess the meaning of each one.

5. Place three small plants on the window sill of your classroom. Plant 1 will get both sunlight and water. Plant 2 will get sunlight, but no water. Plant 3 will get no sunlight (cover with a box), but will get water. Ask students to observe the plants for a week and record their observations. Ask them to infer answers to the following questions:

- Where did the water go that we gave to plants 1 and 3?

|  | Number of Responses |
|---|---|
| "Into the air" | _____ |
| "Into the plant" | _____ |
| "It evaporates" | _____ |
| "Nowhere" | _____ |

- What did the sunlight do to plants 1 and 2?

|  | Number of Responses |
|---|---|
| "Helped it grow" | _____ |
| "Evaporated the water" | _____ |
| "Nothing" | _____ |
| "Turned the water into nutrients" | _____ |

- What happend to plants 2 and 3?

|  | Number of Responses |
|---|---|
| "They didn't get what they needed" | _____ |
| "They got too much of a one thing" | _____ |
| "They weren't strong enough" | _____ |
| "I don't know" | _____ |

**Enabling Questions**

1. Why do you believe that?
2. Do you have any reason for saying that?
3. Can you think of any other possibilities?
4. Why didn't this come out the way we wanted it to?

## Valuing

Valuing emphasizes children's feelings, emotions, and attitudes as they learn science. It places a premium on the fact that a student's affective development is just as important as his or her cognitive development. We have learned from decades of research that a student's success in a curricular area is often determined by how well his or her personal needs are being met in that area.

In helping students appreciate science, it is important that the teacher act as a facilitator, guiding individuals to reach their own decisions and investigate their self-initiated discoveries. When students are provided with sufficient opportunities to direct some of their own learning in a subject, attitudes related to that subject multiply enormously.

The significance of a value-based curriculum is that it decreases the distance between teacher and student as well as the distance between student and subject matter. Incorporating valuing activities throughout the science curriculum makes learning a genuine process, one that recognizes the unique personality of each child, the contributions each child can make to the common good, and the personality dynamics that add a luster to each and every classroom project.

## Communicating

Communication is the means by which information is disseminated. It involves not only interacting with others but organizing data so that it can be effectively passed on to others. Communicating takes many forms, including gestures, verbal and written responses, reading, listening, showing, and questioning. The effective communicator is one who is able to organize ideas in such a way that they will be immediately comprehended by others.

### INTRODUCTORY ACTIVITIES

1. Direct a group of students to create their own form of sign language and to present a short demonstration of the language to the rest of the class. You may want to show them a book on sign language to give them some ideas.
2. Have some students study pictographs or hieroglyphics and make a report to the rest of the class.
3. Ask some pupils to choose several sentences from a specific chapter of the science book and to rewrite the sentences in random order. Give them to other students to write in the correct order.
4. Ask a student to describe an object in the classroom without using words. What methods of communication are most easily understood?
5. Direct students to select one of the following questions. Have them record their thoughts in a logbook. Then have them ask the same question of a peer and an adult. What differences or similarities

are there between the three responses to the question?

  **a.** If you could be a flower or vegetable, what would you be and why? What qualities should the perfect flower or vegetable have?

  **b.** Go outside and locate a living thing that you hate. Why do you hate it? Locate a living thing that you love. Why do you love it?

  **c.** What are some living things that people try to get rid of (e.g., weeds, moles)? Develop an argument for preserving those living things.

  **d.** If you were asked to design a work of art for an important building using only living things, which ones and how many would you choose?

  **e.** If you were asked to write a commercial for the planet Earth, what would you include in your advertisement?

  **f.** What is something about the world outside your classroom that makes you feel comfortable? What is something that makes you feel uncomfortable? What would you need to do to change something from "uncomfortable" to "comfortable"?

### Enabling Questions

**1.** Why is this easy (hard) to understand?

**2.** Can you show us another way to communicate this information?

**3.** What other information do we need to pass on to others about this project?

**4.** Why is it important for us to write (read, tell) this information?

## Exploring

An unfortunate design of several science programs is that teachers tend to *give* students information rather than allow students to reach their own conclusions and decisions. In an effort to "cover the curriculum," teachers may feel the need to get through a set number of pages in the textbook or a previously designated number of chapters in the teacher's manual. What is unfortunate about this practice is that the science curriculum is based not necessarily on what students want to learn, but rather on what someone in the central office or at the state level dictates must be covered.

Exploring implies that children should be provided with a multitude of opportunities to reach out into their world and direct some of their own learning. It means that children not only have the capacity for learning through self-initiated processes, but must be given opportunities to do so. As a teacher it will be important for you to establish the *conditions* under which your students can learn, but not necessarily the *results* of their learning. Pupils must be allowed to inspect a slice of their world and formulate their own conclusions about how that slice relates to knowledge previously discovered.

## Predicting

Scientific investigation is a constant process of making predictions. Predicting is the process of extrapolating information based on a minimum of data or on information already known. The scientist tries to confirm or refute the prediction based on the gathering of new data. Predictions provide scientists with a road map by which to conduct their experiments. They provide goals—albeit tentative ones. The data-gathering process provides scientists with the evidence they need to verify their original predictions.

### INTRODUCTORY ACTIVITIES

**1.** Ask students to make predictions about the next day's weather. List the predictions on the chalkboard. On the next day, share the weather report from the newspaper to determine the accuracy of the predictions.

**2.** Ask some students to predict the heights or weights of their classmates. Question them on how they could prove the accuracy of their predictions. Is any information needed to assist in making such predictions?

**3.** Ask students to list the preliminary information they would need to make predictions concerning:

- The height of a building
- The length of a pencil
- The age of an adult
- The time necessary to cook a food item

**4.** Ask students to look through the newspaper to locate predictions on subjects other than the weather (horoscopes, sports scores, etc.). Lead a discussion on how these predictions are made.

**5.** Direct each student to create a package in which a raw egg will be placed and which will then dropped from the top of a one-story building. The package must be constructed so that the egg does not break. Before initiating the construction process have students predict which of the following materials, alone or in combination, will provide the best protection for the egg.

|  | **Definitely** | **Maybe** | **No Way!** |
|---|---|---|---|
| Water |  |  |  |
| Styrofoam |  |  |  |
| Cardboard |  |  |  |
| Foam |  |  |  |
| Newspaper strips |  |  |  |
| Cloth |  |  |  |
| Many boxes |  |  |  |
| Grass clippings |  |  |  |
| Other: _____ |  |  |  |

Of course, students will want to test their predictions!

### Enabling Questions

1. How did you arrive at your prediction?
2. What makes you feel that your prediction is accurate?
3. What evidence do you think we need to confirm or reject that prediction?
4. Do you have a reason for saying that?

### TEACHER TO TEACHER

The classroom pond study area is a 45 gallon aquarium. It is inhabited by the creatures contributed each year by the students. We have crayfish, various species of fish, and an occasional frog who lives on the "frog log" that floats on the pond's surface.

One year we had a bass and frog of equal size. The day inevitably came when the food chain lesson was reenacted for us. The bass attempted to swallow the frog. After the feeling of horror passed, scientific thinking entered the struggle we observed.

We timed the length of the bass's attempt to swallow the frog.

We each predicted how long the swallowing process would take. We recorded our predictions in our science journals. The outcome of the impromptu science lesson was after 45 minutes the bass spit the grateful frog out.

Our conclusion was, 'The bass had eyes bigger than its stomach" and "he bit off more than he could chew."

Barbara Clark
Checotah Elementary School
Checotak, OK

### Experimenting

By definition, a true scientist is one who is constantly experimenting. Through experimenting, ideas are proved or disproved and hypotheses confirmed or denied. Experimentation involves the identification and control of variables in order to arrive at a cause-effect conclusion. Experimenting also involves manipulating data and assessing the results. Students need to understand that they conduct experiments every day, from watching ice cream melt to deciding on what clothes to wear outside. Scientific experimentation, however, involves a more formalized process, albeit one that touches our everyday activities.

### DID YOU KNOW?

Scientists at the National Autonomous University in Mexico City have "invented" a cow that stands just two feet tall and produces about a gallon of milk a day.

**Classroom Activity**   Have students create a scrapbook of animal "world records." Direct them to investigate a number of library resources on the biggest mammal, longest reptile, heaviest bird, or smallest fish, for example. This can be an ongoing project throughout the year, with students adding new information as it is learned or collected. You may wish to divide the class into several groups (the "mammal" group, the "amphibian" group, etc.), with each group responsible for collecting data related to their designated group of animals. *Joan Emberly's Collection of Amazing Animal Facts* (New York: Delacorte Press, 1983) would be a good book to share with students.   ■

### INTRODUCTORY ACTIVITIES

1. Direct groups of students to invent a "chalkboard washer" that improves the way the chalkboard looks in addition to saving time and labor.
2. Provide students with several thermometers, glass jars, magnifying glasses, and lights. Challenge them to create a situation that raises the temperature of the air in each glass. Ask them to explain their procedures.
3. Ask students to create a musical scale using soda bottles or jars and measured quantities of water.
4. Have a group of students design an experiment for younger pupils that demonstrates the processes of condensation and evaporation.
5. Invite students to each create an original design for a paper airplane. They may use any materials at their disposal, in addition to one or more sheets

of paper. After the airplanes have been constructed and flown several times in the classroom, ask students to determine the characteristics that make paper airplanes fly the furthest. Ask them to complete the following chart:

| | Major Factor | Minor Factor | No Factor |
|---|---|---|---|
| Wingspan | _____ | _____ | _____ |
| Wing length | _____ | _____ | _____ |
| Length of plane | _____ | _____ | _____ |
| Weight of plane | _____ | _____ | _____ |
| Balance | _____ | _____ | _____ |
| Initial thrust | _____ | _____ | _____ |
| Height thrown from | _____ | _____ | _____ |
| Variety of materials | _____ | _____ | _____ |
| Width of body | _____ | _____ | _____ |
| Tail section | _____ | _____ | _____ |
| Weight in nose section | _____ | _____ | _____ |
| Weight in tail section | _____ | _____ | _____ |
| Other:_____ | _____ | _____ | _____ |

### Enabling Questions

1. What else could we have done in this experiment to arrive at this conclusion?
2. Is there another experiment we might do to arrive at the same conclusion?
3. Do we need any more evidence before we can say that?
4. Why do you think we did this experiment?

## TO INVESTIGATE

Make arrangements to observe a science lesson conducted by a teacher in a nearby school. Prior to your visit construct an informal observation sheet listing each of the seven processes of science down the left side. During your observation of the lesson keep a tally of how many times the teacher uses each of the seven processes, particularly in the types of questions he or she asks (you may want to ask permission to taperecord the lesson for playback at a later time). After you have tallied the entire lesson, compare your list with those of your classmates. What similarities or differences do you notice? Do teachers tend to ask one type of question to the exclusion of others? Do teachers use all seven processes in their teaching of science? What ramifications are there in these observations for your future classroom? (*Note:* You will want to keep the name of the teacher anonymous if you share your list with others in the class.) ∎

It's an unfortunate fact of life that some elementary teachers feel inadequately prepared to teach science. This may be because teachers assume that they must be fonts of all the knowledge available in the universe or that they must be practicing scientists themselves. This belief predominates in many classrooms; as a result, science is relegated to the last 30 minutes of the school day or to an infrequent slot in one's lesson plans. However, the effective teacher of science does not have to be a never-ending dispenser of science knowledge, but rather one who is a facilitator of learning, one who responds to children's behavior, and one who desires to learn more about science. This method of teaching, traditionally referred to as inquiry teaching, assumes that children have the capacity to make their own educational decisions and chart their own courses through the curriculum. It is not necessary for you to perform in front of a group of students, sharing your vast storehouse of knowledge or conducting elaborate experiments in which the answers have all been predetermined. The science curriculum becomes vital and vibrant when teachers assume a secondary role, moving out of the way so that children can initiate and pursue their own learning.

Anyone who has witnessed a typical elementary classroom for an entire day knows the exhaustion that sets in shortly after lunch and the relief that comes when the final bell rings and children are scooted out the door to waiting parents. In many cases this is the result of the teacher doing too much work, most of the talking, nearly all of the thinking, all the questioning, and in many cases most of the answering. No wonder many teachers suffer from premature burnout! Yet when those responsibilities are turned over to students, then students and teachers enter into a compact that places the bulk of learning responsibility on the shoulders of each pupil. This suggests that teachers must be willing to give up some of their autonomy in the classroom and help students become responsible learners—learners who chart their own courses of discovery and investigation, which are facilitated (not directed) by the classroom teacher. In short, students should become active participants in the learning process, not empty sponges waiting to soak up everything the teacher dispenses. Teachers are also recharged as they learn along with their students.

If science is in fact one of the most dynamic subjects youngsters will encounter in their lifetimes, it stands to reason that it must be joyous, exciting, and purposeful to them while they are in school. Helping students achieve a measure of self-initiated direction throughout the science curriculum remains a challenge for teachers.

To a great extent, children can teach themselves. We can serve a tremendous function by being catalysts—as facilitators to children in their learning processes. However, we cannot make a child learn. The processes we employ determine whether or not children learn. The climate in the classroom, the opportunities to learn, the model we exemplify, and the emphasis we place on learning versus teaching all determine how much the child will learn. If true learning is to take place, it must take place in the hearts and minds of children, not in the manuals and guides of teachers.

## TEACHER TO TEACHER

Science is the one area of the curriculum where being wrong can be all right. Using the scientific process of thinking to reject the hypothesis is acceptable and will lead students to a new level of critical thinking. What went wrong? What would I do differently?

Unfortunately, too many areas of learning are boxed into right and wrong answers, but science is excluded from this category. When children are taught science using the scientific process of forming hypotheses, testing, gathering data, organizing data, and drawing conclusions, right answers are not important, the *process* is. The beauty of this approach is twofold. First, children become thinkers. This is a very hard concept to teach, but science does it quite naturally. Second, the children who may suffer academically because of reading problems usually are very good in science when taught this way. Due to academic failure these children have learned to look at things in many different ways and are not afraid to try new and creative ways to solve problems, especially when it brings success.

To teach the scientific process to children takes time, but the benefits are long-lasting. Take that time with your students to make learning active and applicable.

Marjorie A. Setser
Mount Royal School
Mount Royal, NJ

# USING SCIENCE PROCESSES IN A TEXTBOOK LESSON

It may not be possible to use all the processes in every science lesson you teach; that's not the intent. Rather, it is important that you give some consideration as to how you can incorporate several processes in every lesson. By doing so, you will provide your students with some rewarding opportunities to actively experience all the nuances of a specific topic.

Let's take a look at how several processes can be made part of a typical science lesson. The lesson in Figure 2.1, reprinted, from a third-grade science text, focuses on plant growth—specifically, on how roots, stems, and leaves are important to a plant. Observe how the teacher's manual is set up, and then we will see how some processes can be easily incorporated into this lesson to enhance it.

## Observing

1. Bring three different types of plants (e.g. dandelion, carrot, marigold) into the classroom. Ask students to observe these plants and to make a chart of all the similarities and differences between the plants.
2. Ask students to discuss the similarities in root structure of the three plants. Similarities in stems and leaves can be recorded as well.
3. Students can discuss the differences in root structure as well as differences in the leaves and stems of the three plants.
4. What similarities or differences do these plants have with other plants students collect from their homes.

## Classifying

1. Ask students to cut out pictures of many different plants from old magazines. What characteristics do some of the plants share?
2. Ask each student to bring in one house plant from home. Direct class members to classify the plants according to similar leaf structures or similar stem structures.
3. Have students create a specimen box with several compartments. Pupils can place examples of similar roots (collected from plants at home) in each compartment of the box.

## Measuring

1. Have students measure the different lengths of roots from several plants. Which plants have the longest roots? Why is that?
2. Provide students with three glasses of water, each with a different quantity of sugar mixed in (1 tablespoon, 3 tablespoons, 5 tablespoons). Mix some food coloring in the water and place a celery stalk in each glass. Have students measure the amount of time it takes for the colored water to rise three inches in the celery stalk. Does the amount of sugar in the water affect the rate at which the water rises?
3. Put three bean plants on the windowsill of your classroom. Cover one with light cellophane and one with dark cellophane. Provide the plants with equal amounts of water. Ask students to note any differ-

## TEACHING PLAN

### Lesson Objectives

- *Describe* plant roots, and *identify* roots as plant parts that anchor plants and absorb and conduct water and minerals from the ground.
- *Explain* how stems support plants, and transport water and minerals.
- *Explain* the process by which green leaves make the food a plant needs.

### Lesson Vocabulary

carbon dioxide, mineral, oxygen

### *1. Motivate*

#### Demonstration Activity ◆

Draw an "anyplant" on the chalkboard. Include a root, stem, leaf, seed, and fruit. Obtain a carrot root, an asparagus stem, lettuce leaf, rice grains, and an apple. Have the students try to match each food item with the appropriate part of the plant.

#### Discussion

Write the following words on a chalkboard: *root, leaf, stem, fruit,* and *seed.* Ask students to name other foods from plant parts (examples: beet—root; spinach—leaf; broccoli—stem; orange—fruit; peanut—seed)

## Teaching Options

### *Science Background*

Roots anchor plants in the soil and help hold soil around plants. Root hairs grow from the outside layer of a plant's root. The root hairs help the root take in water and minerals. Xylem and phloem make up the tubelike structures that go through the roots, stems, and leaves of vascular plants. Xylem tissues carry water and minerals through a plant. Phloem cells carry food from the leaves through the plant. In leaves, green plants make food through photosynthesis. Chlorophyll and other pigments in leaves absorb light energy from the sun, and change light into chemical energy. The plant uses the stored chemical energy to change carbon dioxide and water into glucose (a sugar) and oxygen.

**10**    Unit 1   Chapter 1   Lesson 1    ◆ *Suitable as a language development activity*

---

### LESSON GOALS

You will learn
- how plant roots help plants live and grow.
- how plant stems are important to plants.
- how green leaves make food for plants.

**mineral** (min′ər əl), a material that was never alive and that can be found in soil.

## 1 How Are Roots, Stems, and Leaves Important?

Your body has many parts. Each part of your body helps you in a different way. Plants also have many parts. Each part of a plant helps the plant in a different way.

### How Roots Are Important

Imagine trying to pull a weed like this one out of the ground. You might find that the weed does not come out easily. Compare the pictures of plant roots. Notice that the weed has a long, thick root that grows deep into the soil. The grass plant has thin roots that spread out under the plant. Both kinds of roots hold plants tightly in soil.

Roots take in water and **minerals**—materials in the soil that were never alive. Plants need water and minerals to live.

### Reading Strategies ◆

**1.** Guide students' pre-reading by asking: Which parts of the lesson are known to you and which parts are new?
**2.** Assign these strategies: Visualizing Information and Writing a Memory Sentence. (See pages T26–T29.)
**3.** Pair students to share what information is clear and unclear and initiate discussion using students' unanswered questions.

---

FIGURE **2.1**    Teacher's plan for a lesson on plant growth.

### How Stems Are Important

The stems of most plants hold up the leaves and other plant parts that grow above the ground. Look at the different kinds of stems in the picture. Find the plants with thin stems growing along the ground. Which plant has thick, woody stems that hold up many leaves?[1]

Stems have tiny tubes. These tubes carry water and minerals from the roots to the other parts of a plant. The tubes also carry food from the leaves to the roots.

[1] the bush

11

**Teaching Tips**

● Help students learn about how plants adapt to different climates. Describe an arid climate where ground water lies several meters below the surface. Questions: **How might the roots of a plant look in an arid climate?** (They might be very long and extend deep into the ground.) Next, describe a moderate climate where water is near the ground's surface. Have students *infer* the possible differences in root structure between the two environments. **What might the roots look like where water is close to the surface?** (Roots might be shallower and spread out more.)

● **Possible Misconception:** Some students might think that a plant absorbs water and minerals separately. Explain that minerals must be dissolved in water before a plant can absorb them.

---

**Workbook    page 1 \***

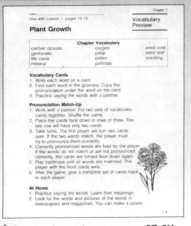

**Science and Social Studies**

Encourage students to find out which plants are considered "cash crops" in your state. You might want to discuss what types of plants can be grown in the different geographic regions of the country.

**Special Education**

Have students with learning disabilities draw pictures of plants and label the roots, stems, and leaves. Display the pictures and discuss the function of each of the plant parts labeled. You might want to bring examples of different types of plant roots to show the students.

**\* Answers to masters on pages 8E–8H**

Unit 1   Chapter 1   Lesson 1   **11**

FIGURE 2.1 (*Continued*)   Teacher's plan for a lesson on plant growth.

# ▶ TEACHING PLAN

### Teaching Tips

● Refer students to the *DISCOVER* on page 9 in which they made rubbings of leaves. Have students examine their rubbings and *observe* the lines left by veins. Question: **What is the purpose of the lines in leaves?** (Lines represent veins, which are tubes that carry sugar and water between the leaves and the other parts of the plant.)

● Have students *compare* and *contrast* the patterns of the vein lines in different leaves. In some leaves, veins are parallel. In others, veins form a netted pattern. Question: **Do the lines in leaves form special patterns?** (Yes, each plant has a characteristic vein pattern.)

**carbon dioxide** (kär′bən dī ok′sīd), a gas in the air that plants use to make food.

**oxygen** (ok′sə jən), a gas in the air that living things need to stay alive.

**Green Plants Make Food**

## How Leaves Are Important

Think about different kinds of leaves you have seen. The leaves of green plants make most of the food a plant needs. This food is sugar.

Look at the picture as you read about the way a plant makes sugar. Find the arrow that goes from the soil to the leaves. This arrow shows that water goes from the soil through the roots and stems to the leaves. Now find the arrows that point to the leaf. A gas from the air, called **carbon dioxide,** goes into the plant through tiny openings in the leaves. Green leaves use sunlight to change water and carbon dioxide to sugar and **oxygen.** Oxygen is a gas in the air that living things need to stay alive. The oxygen from the plant goes into the air. Plants use the sugar to live and grow.

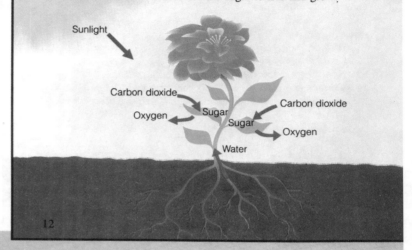

Sunlight
Carbon dioxide
Oxygen
Sugar
Sugar
Carbon dioxide
Oxygen
Water

12

# ▶ Teaching Options

### *Science Anecdote*

**A** winter rye plant can produce 611 km (380 miles) of roots in .05 m³ (1.8 ft³) of soil.

### Reinforcement

Explain that roots have hairs that help take water and minerals into the plant. If possible, bring in an entire root system of a dandelion plant or a grass plant. Carefully wash the soil from the root and let students examine the root hairs with a hand lens. *CAUTION:* Instruct students not to use lenses to concentrate the sun's rays onto skin or paper. Have students wash their hands thoroughly after this activity.

### Enrichment

Measure the rate of imbibition (rise of fluids in a plant) in paper plants. Cut paper "plants" from blotter paper. Place the paper plants in colored water and measure (in cm per minute) the rate at which the paper plant imbibes the water. *CAUTION:* Immediately wipe up any water that spills on the floor. Try the experiment again using a different type of paper. Have the students compare the results. Question: **Do you think that all plants take in water at the same rate?** (no)

**12**   Unit 1   Chapter 1   Lesson 1          ◆ *Suitable as a language development activity*

**FIGURE 2.1 (** *Continued* **)**    Teacher's plan for a lesson on plant growth.

Spring

Summer

Autumn

Winter

Most plants store some of the sugar they make in their stems and roots. Plants use stored food when the leaves cannot make enough food for the plant.

Notice how this tree changes from season to season. How do leaves help the tree in the summer?[1] What happens to the leaves in the autumn?[2] You can see that the tree has no leaves in the winter. Then the tree uses stored food. The tree also uses stored food to make new leaves in the spring.

### Lesson Review
1. How do roots help plants?
2. How are stems important to plants?
3. How do green leaves make food for plants?
4. **Challenge!** What makes this tree need more water in the summer than in the winter?

Study on your own, pages 316–317.

Look in a book about plants to find out what chemical makes some plants green. Write a few sentences explaining how this chemical helps plants make food.

PHYSICAL SCIENCE
FIND OUT
ON YOUR OWN
CONNECTION

*SCIENCE IN YOUR LIFE*

People eat some plant roots and stems that store food. You eat roots when you eat carrots, radishes, or beets. You eat stems when you eat potatoes or asparagus.

[1] they make food
[2] they fall off

13

## 3. Assess

### Lesson Review
1. Roots hold plants in the ground and carry in water and minerals.
2. Stems hold up leaves and other plant parts. They carry water and minerals from roots, and food from leaves.
3. Green plants use sunlight to change carbon dioxide and water into sugar and oxygen.
4. **Challenge!** The plant needs more water in summer to help make food. **Thinking Skill:** *Inferring*

### Find Out On Your Own
Green indicates the presence of chlorophyll. Chlorophyll captures energy from the sun. The leaf uses this energy to change water and carbon dioxide to sugar and oxygen. **Thinking Skill:** *Restating or explaining Ideas*

---

**Workbook    page 2 ***

Name:                              Chapter 1
Use with Lesson 1 pages 10-13
**A Plant That Eats Insects**        Science and Reading

Read the story. Then answer the questions.

Most plants get all the minerals they need from the soil. But the Venus's-flytrap grows in soil that does not have enough minerals. Where does the Venus's-flytrap get the minerals it needs? It "traps flies" and "eats" them. It gets its minerals from the insects it catches.

Each leaf of the flytrap has six hairs. When an insect touches these hairs, the sides of the leaf close. The insect gets caught in the leaf. The insect cannot escape.

The Venus's-flytrap has special juices that break down the insect so that the minerals in the insect can be used by the plant. The plant uses the minerals from the insect to help the plant grow. It takes the plant 5 to 10 days to use up the insect. Then the leaf opens up and is ready to catch another insect.

The Venus's-flytrap grows only in one small part of the United States. This part is a strip of wet, swampy ground in North Carolina. This area is only about 1,000 square kilometers.

Circle the best answer.
1. The Venus's-flytrap is unusual because it
   a. grows in soil.
   b. catches insects.
   c. does not need water.
2. The Venus's-flytrap needs insects
   a. for minerals.
   b. for water.
   c. to move.
3. The Venus's-flytrap catches insects with
   a. its flowers.
   b. its leaves.
   c. its stem.
4. The Venus's-flytrap grows in
   a. dry, sandy deserts.
   b. snowy mountains.
   c. wet, swampy ground.

***Answers to masters on pages 8E–8H**

**Game Suggestion ◆**

Make up a Bingo-like game board for each student. Label the rows with the letters P L A N T. At random, write the names or draw pictures of plant parts (roots, stems, leaves, and so on) in the squares on the boards. Then, hold up large cards with the names or pictures of plant parts. Direct students to cover the appropriate squares on their boards until someone has a *plant bingo*.

**Reteaching Suggestion ◆**

Bring to class several roots, stems, and leaves. Provide hand lenses and allow students to *observe* and *compare* varieties of each plant part. *CAUTION:* Direct students not to use lenses to concentrate the sun's rays onto skin or paper. Questions: **Are the roots thick or thin, long or short? Are the stems thin and flexible or thick and woody? What are the patterns, edges, and textures of the leaves?** Discuss how each plant part contributes to a plant's growth.

Unit 1   Chapter 1   Lesson 1   **13**

FIGURE 2.1 (*Continued*)   Teacher's plan for a lesson on plant growth.

ences in growing rate among the three plants. Did the color of the light getting to the plant affect its rate of growth?

## Inferring

1. Show students photos or slides of various plants with different root structures—for example, plants with broad, expansive root structures; plants with short, stubby root structures; and plants with massive, deeply penetrating root structures. What can students infer about the condition of the soil or the amount of rainfall in the area where each plant lives?
2. Provide students with three small flowers in pots. Ask them to cut the flower off one plant, and the flower and stem off another plant. Ask them to infer what will happen to each plant.
3. Before beginning the lesson, have students speculate on some of the following questions:

   • Why do some trees lose their leaves in the fall?
   • How do green plants make their food?
   • Why is the stem important to a plant?
   • How are leaves important to a plant?

## Communicating

1. Have students create a make-believe dialogue between the leaves of a plants and its roots. What would these two plant parts say to each other if they could communicate?
2. Have two students describe a plant without using any descriptive words (adjectives). What difficulties do they encounter?
3. Have students write a catalog description of a particular plant. Provide them with some seed catalogs for illustrative purposes.
4. Have students read one of the following books and then tell what they learned or what else they would have liked to learn as a result of reading that book.

   Bruce Macmillan, *Apples: How They Grow* (Boston: Houghton Mifflin, 1979).
   Richard Mabey, *Oak and Co.* (New York: Greenwillow, 1983)
   James R. Newton, *A Forest is Reborn* (New York: Crowell, 1982)
   Cynthia Overbeck, *Sunflowers* (Minneapolis: Lerner, 1981)
   Millicent Selsam, *Tree Flowers* (New York: Morrow, 1984)

## Predicting

1. Ask students to predict what might happen if plants were grown in an area without air. Construct an experiment to validate their predictions.

2. Have students predict the types of plants that might live in a desert region or in a tropical region. What characteristics would those plants have that would help them survive in the designated area?
3. Direct students to predict the role of sunlight on the growth of plants. Is the heat important, or is the light from the sun important?

## Experimenting

1. Have students conduct all of the experiments just listed and record their results in lab notebooks.
2. Direct students to develop an experiment that would test the ability of different root systems to absorb water. Which type of root system takes in the most water? Do the roots determine how much water is taken in, or do the nutrients in the water determine the rate of osmosis?
3. Have students create a classroom garden. Several different sites can be constructed, such as in milk cartons, in a plot of land on the school playground, or in the classroom. Have students grow several plants using various soil types, light factors, and nutrients. What effects do these factors have on the condition of the leaves, roots, and stems?

## General Enabling Questions

1. What reasons can you offer for these results?
2. What else have you observed that is similar to this?
3. What do you suspect might happen if this were done to an identical plant?
4. What other kinds of conditions might affect the way this looks or feels?
5. How is this related to something you do at home?
6. What other kinds of conditions would cause this to happen?
7. What other type of information do you need before you can conclude this project?

**General Enabling Questions**

1. What reasons can you offer for these results?
2. What else have you observed that is similar to this?
3. What do you suspect might happen if this were done to an identical plant?
4. What other kinds of conditions might affect the way this looks or feels?
5. How is this related to something you do at home?
6. What other kinds of conditions would cause this to happen?
7. What other type of information do you need before you can conclude this project?
8. Do you believe your measurements are accurate? What would you need to do to make those measurements more accurate?
9. Are there other types of measurements that could be taken?
10. Why are you making that type of conclusion?
11. Did this come out the way you thought it would?
12. Was this easy or difficult for you to understand?
13. What else do you think we still need to learn?
14. What makes you feel that your information or conclusion is appropriate?
15. Why are you saying that?
16. Why did we do this?

What should be evident is the fact that a basic lesson on plants has been elaborated and expanded beyond the structure provided in the teacher's manual. By doing so, you offer your students a wealth of opportunities for **discovering, valuing,** and **exploring** the world of science. Students begin to appreciate the limitless possibilities of a "scientific mind," one that knows no limits. In other words, your science lessons should be constructed to give students rewarding ventures into science.

## POINTS OF DISCUSSION

1. If possible, obtain copies of several teacher's manuals for different science series. Try to determine the philosophy behind each series, and compare and contrast those philosophies.
2. Talk to several elementary teachers about their goals for the year in science. Are those goals realistic? Are they activity-based or knowledge-based? Are they exciting?
3. Discovery opportunities vary with the location of the school; however, all schools have indoor and outdoor possibilities for children to explore and discover science. Discuss how the kitchen, furnace room, playground, and other areas can be used as examples of science in action.
4. Interview several children about their perceptions of science. How should science be taught? How should science be learned? What differences do you note between young students (grades K–3) and older students (grades 4–6)?
5. What is your concept of a successful science teacher? What attributes should an elementary teacher have to effectively teach science?
6. Interview a parent, a child, and a teacher about how science should be taught. Compare and contrast what the three tell you about the principles and practices that should be included in any science program.
7. List two goals for your class after you have completed your first three months of teaching. Explain why you have selected those goals.
8. What will your science classroom look like five years from now? Draw an illustration and describe the placement of furniture and the materials you will use.

## REFERENCES AND SUGGESTED READINGS

Abruscato, J., & Hassard, J. (1976). *Loving and beyond.* Glenview, IL: Scott, Foresman.

Fredericks, A. (1990). *Science brainstretchers.* Glenview, IL: Scott, Foresman.

Fredericks, A., Cressman, B., & Hassler, R. (1987). *The science discovery book.* Glenview, IL: Scott, Foresman.

Pennsylvania Department of Education. (no date). *Science unlimited.* Harrisburg: Author.

Wasserman, S., & Ivany, J. (1988). *Teaching elementary science: Who's afraid of spiders?* New York: Harper & Row.

# 3

# QUESTIONING STRATEGIES

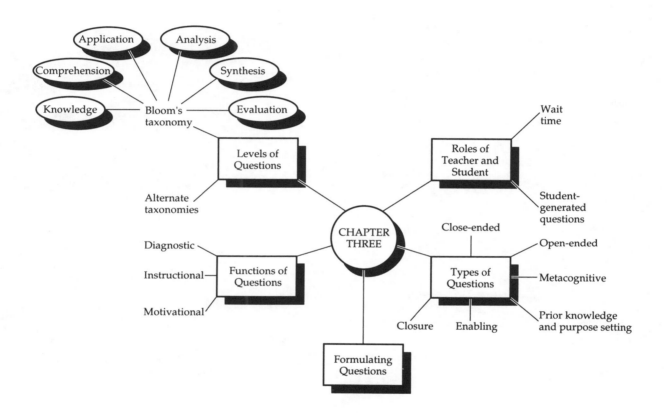

## Chapter Objectives

After reading this chapter you should be able to:

1. Clarify the three basic functions of questions.

2. Describe and create open-ended, closed-ended, and metacognitive questions.

3. Explain the roles of teacher and students in the questioning process.

4. Define and provide examples of the different levels of Bloom's taxonomy.

5. Elaborate on the conditions necessary for effective questioning.

It was a hot October afternoon when Mr. Spanos began the science lesson. For the previous week, students in his third-grade class had been studying rocks, including the three different types of rocks, how they are created, and where they are found. Students had begun a rock collection of samples from the local area and were about to set up a learning center in the back of the classroom.

"Who can tell us what a rock is?" Mr. Spanos asked the class.

No response.

"Doesn't anybody remember what we talked about two days ago?" he inquired.

Still no response.

"Once again, what is a rock?" he asked.

By this time boredom was beginning to set in, even though the lesson was just beginning.

"O.K., Jeremy, can you give me an example of an igneous rock?"

"I dunno," Jeremy replied.

"Melissa, what about you?"

"I can't remember," Melissa answered.

"Julio, can you tell us one rock that might be classified as igneous?" Mr. Spanos asked.

The question caught Julio unawares, as he was doodling in the margin of his science book. "I don't know," he replied.

"Karen, what about you?"

"Limestone," she guessed.

"No, that's not the correct answer."

Finally, Mr. Spanos, frustrated at the lack of answers from his students, told them that granite is an example of an igneous rock. Some of the students dutifully wrote the word in their notebooks, while others forced themselves to stay alert for the next round of questions from the teacher's manual Mr. Spanos always kept at his side.

The preceding scenario may be more prevalent than we like to admit. It depicts a teacher asking inane questions, students with little or no involvement in the lesson, and a kind of mental ping-pong in which the teacher keeps asking low-level questions of various students until one student gets the right answer or until the teacher is forced to give the answer to a class of uninterested and uninvolved students. As you might imagine, no instruction has taken place; the only objective is to obtain an answer to a predetermined question. It's a guessing game between students and the teacher in which students try to guess the answers imbedded in the teacher's head. If they "get it," the game moves on to the next question; if they don't, the teacher keeps asking until someone does get it or until the teacher supplies the correct answer to the class. Durkin (1978–79) has demonstrated that most of the questions teachers ask are relatively low-level, literally based questions in search of single correct answers.

There is little attempt to engage students in critical thinking or problem-solving strategies; the goal seems to be to move students through the text as rapidly as possible using questions that are quickly asked (and, presumably, quickly answered) or by giving out the answers when students can't answer queries from the teacher or the text.

One of the most used (and most abused) teaching tools is questioning. This teaching method undoubtedly extends as far back as the concept of having one individual help another learn a skill or concept. A study reported by Kauchak and Eggen (1989) indicated that questions occupy approximately 80 percent of classroom time and that teachers at high schools ask over 390 questions a day. A recent study reported by the same authors revealed that, at the elementary school level, it is not unusual for teachers to ask more than 50 questions in an average 30-minute class (Kauchak, 1989). DeVito and Krockover (1976) report that the average teacher's questioning rate is about 3 ½ questions per minute. This works out to about 27 teacher questions asked for every student question. Unfortunately, most of this questioning is trivial, with the emphasis on memory and information giving. Seldom are students given any opportunity to think about what they are reading or doing, and rarely are they invited to generate their own questions for discovery. The usual result is students who are "turned off" by science because they perceive it as nothing more than meaningless questions that have single right answers. They think science is simply the memorization of facts and figures.

## TO INVESTIGATE

Visit a local elementary classroom. Observe a science lesson and note the kinds of questions the teacher asks the students. On a sheet of paper, record questions according to whether they are straight from the textbook or whether they are posed by the teacher. Determine whether the questions could be considered as having single right answers or whether the bulk of the questions could have many possible answers. You may wish to use a chart similar to the following one to record your observations.

|  | **From the Textbook** | **From the Teacher** |
|---|---|---|
| Only one right answer |  |  |
| Many possible answers |  |  |

You may also want to record the level of student interest in the lesson. Were they excited? Stimulated? Enthusiastic? Were they bored? Disinterested? Uninvolved?

Based on your observations, what conclusions can you draw for your own classroom? How might the types of questions the teacher asks affect student participation? How will you use questioning in your classroom? ■

# FUNCTIONS OF QUESTIONS

Although questions are widely used and serve many functions, teachers frequently rely heavily on factual questions that do not challenge the learning abilities of students. If, as some researchers have pointed out, teachers ask upwards of 400 questions every school day, and if the majority of those questions are memorization or factual questions, this suggests that little creative thinking is taking place in the classroom.

One all-important distinguishing factor keys the successful science program.

---

Students' level of thinking is based on the types of questions they anticipate receiving from the teacher.

---

This means that if students are constantly bombarded with questions that require only low levels of involvement (or no involvement whatsoever), they will tend to think accordingly. Conversely, students who are given questions based on higher levels of cognition will tend to think more creatively and divergently. In other words, if you wish your students to engage in high levels of problem solving and creative thought, you need to ask them questions that utilize problem solving, are divergent in nature, and promote a multiplicity of responses.

The initial step in becoming proficient in asking questions is for the novice to be cognizant that "questions have different characteristics, serve various functions, and create different levels of thinking" (Cooper, 1990, p. 115). Questions have been identified as serving three major functions: diagnostic, instructional, and motivational (Kauchak & Eggen, 1989). These functions correspond roughly to Costa's (1985) categories of input, processing, and output question (Table 3.1).

## Diagnostic Questions

Teachers at all levels and in all areas of the curriculum must direct their objectives to the needs of the students. By effectively using questions, you can determine what students know or don't know, how they think in arriving at an answer, or how they draw a conclusion about a concept or topic. Several examples of diagnostic questions are:

What are two types of electricity?
What causes an eclipse of the moon?
What causes water to form on the inside of a classroom or kitchen window on a cold day?

Once you have identified the needs of your students, you can begin your preparation for instruction.

TABLE **3.1**

### QUESTION CLASSIFICATION

Although there are several ways of identifying questions, Costa (1985) has established a classification system based on how questions are used by students. In this system, questions are divided into three groups: *input* (a recalling of information or pertinent data), *processing* (understanding the relationships between items), and *output* (the ability to use information in new and creative ways). The following examples illustrate how selected questions from a science text might be classified into these categories.

| | |
|---|---|
| **Input** | Identify three characteristics of birds. |
| | What is sedimentary rock? |
| | How many moons does Saturn have? |
| | What are the six types of simple machines? |
| | List the major oceans of the world. |
| **Processing** | How could you group these plants together? |
| | Organize these rocks from softest to hardest. |
| | How are reptiles similar to amphibians? |
| | What do you think caused the river to change course? |
| | Why are so many volcanoes located along the "Ring of Fire"? |
| **Output** | What do you think would happen if we added more water? |
| | Design a space colony for living on the moon. |
| | What would be another way we could test our idea? |
| | Use what you know about gears to design a new machine. |
| | Make a rule for why birds are able to fly. |

## TO INVESTIGATE

The questions typically found in science textbooks are of the low-level cognitive variety (input questions). These questions can be turned into processing and output questions through a procedure known as the *textbook scan* (Abell, Pizzini, & Shepardson, 1989). Take any science text and open it to any chapter. Write down all of the questions (to be asked by the teacher) on a separate piece of paper. Classify each as either input, processing, or output. (You will probably discover that most are of the input variety.) Afterward, take several of the designated input questions and turn them into processing and output questions. For example:

| | |
|---|---|
| Input | "What is an example of an igneous rock?" |
| Processing | "How are igneous rocks similar to metamorphic rocks?" |
| Output | "What if igneous rocks were no longer available?"  ∎ |

## Instructional

Although there are a number of instructional techniques (e.g., lecture, discussion, and demonstration), teachers frequently use questions to ascertain if skills have been developed, if information has been acquired, and if directions have been followed. Questions can serve six purposes during a lesson. They can effectively be used to:

1. Preassess students' knowledge.
2. Evaluate during the lesson.
3. Evaluate at the end of the lesson.
4. Determine if students follow directions.
5. *Get students involved in the lesson.* (Emphasis added.)
6. Challenge the thinking of the students to a higher level. (Montague, Huntsberger, & Hoffman, 1989.)

Students can be made aware that the material that has been presented is a cohesive body of knowledge, the means to development of a skill, or a foundation for additional information. This is frequently accomplished by a series of questions intended to review the material in a succinct fashion, to review the steps in the skill process, or to establish basics. For example, at the conclusion of a lesson on clouds in which a filmstrip was used to illustrate the types of clouds, the following questions may be asked: What were the four types of clouds we saw? Which type of cloud indicates that a storm is about to erupt? How are clouds formed?

Instructional questions are those that help students process data into a comprehensible and cohesive format (see Table 3.2). They are not designed to test students' knowledge but rather to coalesce that knowledge into a meaningful whole. They are posed to assist students in making their own decisions and arriving at their own solutions to problems. This is most easily ac-

TABLE  **3.2**

## PROCESS QUESTIONS

| | |
|---|---|
| **Observing** | What have you noticed about this animal? |
| | How are your observations similar to Bill's? |
| | What else have you observed? |
| | How would you explain what you saw? |
| **Classifying** | What similarities do you note in these items? |
| | How many different categories can we put these in? |
| | What is the fewest number of groups you see? |
| | Could an item belong in more than one group? |
| **Inferring** | How did you arrive at that idea? |
| | What leads you to believe that? |
| | Can you give an explanation for your choice? |
| | What is your reasoning? |
| **Communicating** | How can we share the results with others? |
| | What data do we need to record? |
| | What would be an easy way to explain this? |
| | How could we make sure others could do this, too? |
| **Measuring** | What would be the best way to measure our results? |
| | What factors would change our measurements? |
| | Is there more than one way to measure this? |
| | Do we have a sufficient amount of information? |
| **Predicting** | How do you think this will turn out? |
| | Can you make some guesses? |
| | What evidence do you need to make a decision? |
| | Why are you saying that? |
| **Experimenting** | How can we solve this problem? |
| | Is there an experiment we can do to solve this problem? |
| | Is there another way of looking at this? |
| | Are you satisfied with your results? |

complished when teachers embrace a process approach to science (see Chapter 2). When the responsibility for learning is kept with the student and facilitated by the teacher, higher levels of involvement, appreciation, and understanding will result.

## Motivational

One of the most difficult aspects of teaching is to motivate students to an appropriate thinking level. The initial phase of teaching involves getting to know the backgrounds of the students. Questions can be presented in written or oral form to determine the informational backgrounds of the students, their interests, their abilities in science, and their levels of thinking. After this data has been acquired, you can use it to motivate students to seek more knowledge about a science topic. They may know that puddles dry up because of the evaporation process, but what is the role of wind in the process? Many students have a keen interest in rocks. How can this interest be extended? One way is by asking students to think not only about the shape, color, weight or type of a rock but also about how we use rocks. Answers will vary depending on the student's background. There are few wrong answers. You can readily accept the responses fuel, building, and jewelry and then challenge the student to research other uses, such as holding back water (dams), studying our past, backing up a monetary system (gold), and health-related uses. Questions can also be used to challenge student answers. When students are asked to give an example of a simple machine and they reply "the inclined plane," challenge them by asking, "What is gained and what is sacrificed by using the inclined plane?"

One very effective motivational strategy is to engage students in a process known as "what-iffing," which is designed to stimulate creative thought and involve students in a variety of thinking possibilities. Very simply, it involves asking students a series of questions that begin with the two words "what if." "What if" questions also provide you and your students with numerous avenues for exploration throughout a lesson as well as at the end of a lesson.

Creating "what if" questions simply means changing or rearranging some pertinent facts and then tagging on the words "what if." Fredericks (1991) has outlined several effective procedures you can use to design your own "what if" questions:

*Creating new combinations:* What if all rocks were made of the same material?

*Altering the way things happen:* What if there were more earthquakes on the eastern seaboard than the western seaboard of the United States?

*Changing the course of nature:* What if mammals had evolved before other forms of life?

*Applying a particular characteristic to every member of a group:* What if all animals were covered with feathers?

*Magnifying or miniaturizing events or details:* What if the earth were the same size as the sun? What if the sun were the same size as the moon?

Table 3.3 lists additional examples of "what if" questions. Using "what if" questions will enable students to generate an abundance of potential responses. It's important that youngsters be given opportunities to elaborate on each of those responses. Follow up each response with a series of probing or extending questions, such as: "What other possibilities are there?" "Can you elaborate on your response?" "Can you add some additional details?"

## TEACHER TO TEACHER

One way in which I begin a couple of my science units is to ask my students to write down as many questions as they can think of about the topic. I have done this most often with third and fifth graders at the start of units on burning candles and the moon. This process is valuable for several reasons. First, it emphasizes that science means questioning and being curious. There are usually one or two students who say, "I can't think of any questions." But after about five minutes of thinking and perhaps some help from me everyone comes up with at least a few. I model the activity by sitting and writing my own questions, stressing that not even I, the teacher, can answer all the questions. Secondly, the questions give me important insights about where my students are coming from

TABLE   **3.3**

## WHAT IS vs. WHAT IF

| What Is | What If |
|---|---|
| Nine planets orbit the sun. | What if all the planets orbited the earth? |
| Human beings are the most intelligent of all animals. | What if your cat were smarter than you? |
| Water freezes at 32 degrees (F). | What if water froze at 50 degrees (F)? |
| Mercury is the only metal that normally occurs in a liquid state. | What if gold or silver normally occurred in a liquid state? |
| Light travels more quickly than sound. | What if sound traveled faster than light? |
| Wind and water are primary forms of erosion. | What if all houses were built of sandstone? |
| Paper is a primary product of trees. | What if paper could be created from a source other than trees? |

as individuals and what their preconceptions about the topic are. Questions such as, "Why is there water at the bottom of the wick?" or, "Why does the moon stay up in the sky?"

help me know where to begin and what needs emphasis in subsequent classes. Thirdly, when I type up all the students' questions and we begin to discuss and look for the answers, the students have a wonderful sense of "ownership" of the lesson. Their interest is usually high, and they feel that their questions have value, which helps build their confidence that they can "do science."

Gwyn Loud
Tenacre Country Day School
Wellesley, MA

## TO INVESTIGATE

The next time you are observing an elementary classroom, count the number of questions asked by the teacher. Before going into the class prepare a grid with the following headings: "Diagnostic questions," "Informational questions," and "Motivational questions." Analyze the questions as soon as possible after the class. Were they effective? Would you have asked them differently? Would you have used more or fewer questions? Where was the teacher when the questions were asked? Could all of the students hear the questions? The answers? Were the questions effective and successful? ■

## FORMULATING QUESTIONS

Formulating questions is a skill. The development of any skill requires an awareness of the effects of poor habits, a general concept of what is required of the skill, and practice to finely hone it. You must not become discouraged as difficulties occur; failing is part of the developing and learning process.

Not all questions are formulated well. It is rather easy to fall into the habit of asking questions that provide all of the information you desire through a simple yes or no answer (Montague et al., 1989). "Is granite an example of a sedimentary rock?" "Does one use a third-class lever when sweeping with a broom?" These are examples of questions requiring a yes/no answer. A teacher may assume that the correct answer indicates an understanding of the concept, but the student responding has only two possible answers and a 50 percent chance of being correct even if he or she is guessing. You should refrain from using questions beginning with *Do, Could, Is, Are, Have, Can, Should,* or *Was.* Such questions tend to emphasize single right an-

swers and yes/no responses. The following section lists various types of questions that you should practice.

### DID YOU KNOW?

The Tonle Sap River in Cambodia flows north for half the year and south for the other half of the year.

**Classroom Activity**  Involve students in creating a scrapbook on the rivers of the world. You may wish to divide students into several groups, each reporting on the major rivers of a continent or hemisphere. Students may wish to select certain rivers and report on their history and influence on selected countries. What characteristics do all rivers share? What factors make some rivers large and other rivers small? Why are major cities located near the mouths of some rivers? Why are some rivers important in history? Students may also wish to create three-dimensional models of selected rivers. Their scrapbooks and models can be set up as a permanent classroom display. You will discover that the information collected on rivers can be used in many different science areas (e.g., erosion, ecology, wildlife studies, forces, and plant life). ■

## TYPES OF QUESTIONS

Just as you will discover that there are many kinds of students in your classroom, so too will you discover that there are many types of questions you can use with those students. There is no such thing as a per-

fect question; rather, there are varieties of questions that are appropriate for discussion and investigation throughout any science lesson. You should select questions that allow your students to take an active role in the science lesson rather than asking questions for the sake of getting correct answers or, worse yet, using up classroom time.

The following types of questions are categorized according to structure and purpose. Any or all of them can be successfully incorporated into a science lesson to promote discussion, ensure mastery of important concepts, invite further investigation, or stimulate creative exploration.

1. Prior knowledge and purpose setting
2. Open-ended and closed-ended
3. Metacognitive
4. Enabling
5. Closure

## Prior Knowledge and Purpose-Setting Questions

Before using any questioning strategy—or, for that matter, any teaching strategy—it is vital that you know the type and level of background information your students are bringing to the lesson. Questioning, when it is planned and sequential, can yield valuable information on what your students know about a topic. Although many teachers will be tempted to use closed-ended questions, you should consider a series of open-ended questions at the beginning of a lesson. These questions are less threatening and may yield more useful data about your students' background information than convergent questions. For example, if you were to begin a unit on the uses of plants, these are some opening questions you might pose:

> "What are some of the uses of plants in every-day life?"
> "Why do you think plants are useful to humans?"
> "How have you used plants in the last 24 hours?"
> "What would our lives be like if we had no plants?"

These questions are nonthreatening but can provide important data with which to structure an effective lesson.

Purpose-setting questions, on the other hand, allow students to focus on the objectives of the lesson. It is important that students understand the direction a lesson is to take so that they can become active participants. Purpose-setting questions allow students to define the limits of a lesson, making it specific and purposeful. For example, instead of saying, "Today's lesson will be on plant life" (which is about as general

as you can get), you can help students focus by asking questions such as: "What can you tell us about how plants are used as a food source?" "Does anyone know just how many plants they ate in the last 24 hours?" Questions such as these alert students to the fact that the upcoming lesson will deal with plants as a food source for humans. As you have probably noticed from the two examples, purpose-setting questions can also be used as prior knowledge questions. Not only do you notify students as to the direction of the lesson, you allow them to share their background information on the subject—information necessary to your lesson-planning process.

## Open-Ended Questions

Open-ended or process-oriented questions (Table 3.4) are useful when you are attempting to create a responsive atmosphere. Students can respond with reasonable confidence that their answers will not be wrong. This type of question serves as an excellent motivator as it encourages students to use their individual backgrounds to think about a global type of situation. When teachers use open-ended questions, they are not asking for something that requires memorization or a one-to-one association. Frequently, students at the elementary school level have difficulty giving a definition of a word or a process and seem more comfortable responding with a "like a" answer. Open-ended questions can usually be answered with a descriptive response. An example of this type of question is, "What are some examples of static electricity?" Students may respond with answers such as "It's like

---

TABLE **3.4**

......................................................

### EXAMPLES OF OPEN-ENDED QUESTIONS

......................................................

What do you see?
What explanation can you offer for these events?
Can you make a prediction?
Can you suggest a way to group these together?
What might be another way of doing this?
When would you observe these again?
How are these similar?
Are there other ways of looking at this?
How would you explain this to a friend?
When would you use this?
What do you think will happen to these next time?
What if we reversed the order of events?
What advantages are there when we do it this way?
Why is this important to know?

---

combing your hair in the winter." "The way clothes cling to one another when you take them out of the dryer." "The spark that happens when I walk across the room and touch the doorknob."

Open-ended questions need not be of the descriptive variety. They can be used to compare and contrast processes involving a scientific principle, which requires students to use a higher-level thought process because they are dealing with two or more concepts in arriving at a conclusion or an answer to a question. For example, you may ask your class to compare and contrast different ways of transferring heat. Students may compare conduction and convection. One student may reply that heat can be transferred from the stove burner to the base of the pan and then to the handle. Another may reply that heat is transferred from an electric heater against one wall to the opposite side of the room by convection. You might then ask the class to compare and contrast the two ways of heat transfer and discuss the advantages and disadvantages of each.

One distinctive advantage of open-ended questions is that they invite other types of questions. By using *probing questions* you open up new and exciting dimensions for students to explore. Borich (1988) identifies three purposes for probing questions: (1) to elicit clarification of a student's answer ("Is there another way you could describe the formation of thunderstorms?"), (2) to solicit new information to extend or build upon a student's response ("Now that you've discussed the characteristics of the inclined plane, how can you use that information to design playground equipment?"), and (3) to refocus or restructure a student's response in a more productive direction ("That might be one way of looking at it, but how would that apply to a large group of animals?"). Probing questions send a powerful signal to students that question asking is more than the teacher asking one question and expecting one response. The message is that questioning should be an interactive exchange of information and investigation.

Kauchak and Eggen (1989) suggest that "the single most powerful questioning skill a teacher can possess is the ability to effectively prompt students" (p. 122). To use this technique successfully, you must keep the ultimate objective for the lesson in mind, and you must possess the ability to "think on your feet" when students are not headed in the proper direction. This requires you to be aware of the feedback students provide verbally and nonverbally. When asked "What is the cause of the moisture on the outside of a glass pitcher filled with ice water?" a student may reply "condensation." The answer is correct, but it indicates only the ability to apply a term to a phenomenon. A follow-up prompting question must be pursued. Asking "What factors might cause the condensation to form?" would be an appropriate next step in determining if the stu-

dents truly understand condensation. The reply "water vapor in the air condenses" is closer, but one needs to pursue it further until the class demonstrates the understanding that cold air cannot hold as much water vapor as warm air, and when it reaches the dew point moisture forms.

## Closed-Ended Questions

Of the various types of questions, the one that is probably most used (and most overused) is the closed or convergent type. When teachers use this type of question, they usually have one answer in mind. The answers must converge on a fact, idea, example, or principle. These questions are effective when the teacher is reviewing a particular set of facts, directions for using specific instruments, procedures to follow in an experiment or demonstration, or relationships among various elements. Examples of this type of question are:

1. When a string of lights is connected in such a manner that if one light goes out in the circuit they all go out we have what type of an electrical circuit?
2. What directions must we follow when using a first-class lever?
3. What procedures are necessary for testing the contents of a glass of water for pH analysis?
4. Explain the relationship between the sun and the earth in the solar system and how the sun influences the earth's orbit.

Convergent questions can be used to ensure that there is specific understanding of the various elements of the lesson or as a "pretest" to determine what the students know about the material the teacher will be presenting (Montague et al., 1989). You must be aware, however, that students frequently refrain from answering closed questions for fear of being wrong and embarrassed. You have the responsibility for creating a classroom atmosphere where giving wrong answers is not criticized but considered an important part of any learning process. This is not an easy task, and your nonverbal message must convey the same signal as the verbal encouragement to participate. If students are reluctant to participate in class discussions and fail to respond to convergent questions, you should consider more utilization of open-ended questions until students' confidence is raised and they feel comfortable responding even though their answers may be incorrect.

However, a word of caution is in order here. Too many teachers rely on closed-ended questions to drive their science lessons. This may be due to uncomfortableness with the material, an adherence to the teacher's manual, or a lack of sufficient background knowledge. Whatever the reason, it is important that students understand that scientific investigation requires the use of few closed-ended questions and many open-ended questions. Too many closed-ended questions tend to restrict student thinking, inhibit classroom discussion, and limit students' decision-making skills.

## IDEA BOX

You serve as an important role model for your students. How you approach science will be a major determinant of how your students will approach science. There is a tendency for teachers, particularly novices, to believe that they must possess a considerable amount of scientific knowledge to be good teachers of science. However, it is much more important that you keep your mind open to discovery and investigation. You should occasionally respond to students' comments with remarks such as the following:

> "I'm not sure. Why don't we find out together?"
> "I don't know, but let's try an experiment to find out."
> "Maybe you're right and I'm wrong."
> "That certainly sounds like a better idea than mine."

Use of such comments does not diminish your role as a teacher. Rather, it enhances your role as a scientist, one who constantly seeks answers to inspiring questions.

## Metacognitive Questions

Simply stated, metacognition is thinking about one's thinking. In other words, when students are given opportunities to think about their own thought processes, they are provided with wonderful insights into how scientists approach their tasks as well as how they might arrive at their own conclusions or solutions. Students

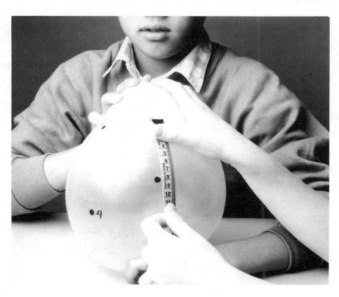

who are aware of their thinking will understand more of what is taking place in the science classroom.

You can enhance the metacognitive process by posing questions that help students "look inside their heads." In so doing, you will be giving them a valuable skill—not just for the area of science, but for their other subjects as well. Metacognitive questions can be used at any time during a lesson to help students achieve a certain focus and to promote concept formation.

## Enabling Questions

Teachers can help students explore new concepts through a questioning process that stimulates thinking and encourages scientific discovery as a natural part of all lessons (see Chapter 3). In this way the study of science becomes open-ended, encouraging creativity and divergence.

Creating an environment that fosters an appreciation for the goals and processes of science can be accomplished through a careful integration of *enabling questions*—questions that, instead of demanding finite answers, stimulate discovery and further exploration. Enabling questions provide an opportunity for students to arrive at their own answers, which are not dependent on the teacher or text.

The following examples illustrate the utility of enabling questions in enhancing the goals and processes of science. (Pennsylvania Department of Education, n.d.) These classroom vignettes demonstrate the value of science as an interactive exchange and refinement of knowledge in which students are provided with opportunities to discover answers on their own.

| Enabling | Inhibiting |
|---|---|
| Tom, what did you do that was different from what Jean did? | Tom, you probably didn't leave the thermometer in the water long enough. |
| Why don't you both do it again to find out what caused your different observations? | Jimmie got the right answer. Andy, you must have done something wrong. |
| When you turn the big wheel once, what does the little wheel do? | Can you see how the big wheel is used to increase speed? |
| What might you do with your mystery box to try to find out how many objects are in it? | How many objects do you think the box contains? |
| Ginny, you said the salt feels like sand. Could your hand lens help you find out more about the shape of salt and sand grains? | That's right, they both have sharp corners. |

The following classroom exchange was conducted during a lesson on ice and water. Notice how the teacher constantly encourages students to arrive at their own conclusions.

| Event | Questions/Statements |
|-------|---------------------|
| Several ice cubes are placed in a glass of water. | "What do you observe when the ice is placed in water?" "What things do you notice about the ice? About the water level?" |
| More ice cubes are placed in the glass of water. | "How do you explain this change?" "How do you explain the change in water level?" |
| Time passes. | "Why do you think it is a good idea to keep a record of our observations during this investigation?" "How might the observations recorded now help us later in our investigation?" |
| Ice is pushed down with a fork. | "What do you notice when the ice is pushed under the water?" "Tell us what you see happening to the water." |

Investigation-type science learning can be divergent since it focuses on what children find meaningful and what they ask about their investigations. Some of the questions that arise can be directly answered by further investigation. However, we should not let children feel that they can find or understand the answers to all their questions. They can't.

### TO INVESTIGATE _____

Observe two different classroom science lessons. Record the types of questions the two teachers ask of their classes on the following chart. ■

| Enabling | Inhibiting |
|----------|-----------|
|          |           |

Did either teacher ask more enabling questions than inhibiting questions? If so, what were the resultant attitudes of students? In other words, does the type of question a teacher asks affect student attitudes toward the topic? Does your observation provide you with any strategies for your future classroom?

## Closure Questions

Many good lessons lose their effectiveness because of an abrupt ending. The students may have participated during the lesson, were highly motivated, and asked relevant questions. You sensed that all of the material was covered adequately, and you must now end the lesson. How do you bring it to an effective closing? Techniques that can be employed are (1) to ask the students to summarize, in two or three statements, what was covered in the lesson; (2) to ask the class to assist in listing the major topics covered; and (3) to raise questions about the items covered. The questions raised can reinforce the students' conclusions, generalizations, and solutions for the issues, concepts, and problems addressed during the lesson (Esler & Sciortino, 1988). To close a lesson, you may also want to direct the students' attention to the next one. You can challenge the students by asking: "As a result of today's lesson, we recognize the need to get more information. Where can we get it?" "What are some additional things we want to know about mold?"

### DID YOU KNOW? _____

There is a star named R-136A that puts out more energy in one second than our sun does in five years.

**Classroom Activity** Provide your students with an opportunity to read one or more of the following books: *The Sun* by Alice Fields (New York: Watts, 1980), *Sun Up, Sun Down* by Gail Gibbons (San Diego: Harcourt Brace Jovanovich, 1983), *Exploring the Sun* by William Jabber (New York: Messner, 1980), and *Sunpower Experiments: Solar Energy Explained* by Maggie Spooner (New York: Sterling, 1980). Direct small groups of students to each construct a lesson on the sun to be presented to other groups or to another class. Be sure to instruct them on the kinds of questions they should include in their lessons to help other students enjoy the information. If possible, you may wish to videotape selected lessons. By adding several videotaped lessons each year, you can build a library to use throughout your science program. ■

### IDEA BOX _____

An exciting way to close your lesson is to offer students several "answers" or important pieces of information from the lesson and ask them to develop their own questions. In other words, they have the answers and must design appropriate questions. Although this can certainly be done in an oral format, what follows illustrates this procedure in a written format. A portion of a science lesson has been rewritten so that students can supply questions to designated answers.

When people build houses, roads, or factories, they change the habitats of many organisms. An organism gets everything it needs from its habitat, such as food, water, and shelter. If the habitat changes, the organism might not be able to live there anymore.

Question:   What are some things organisms
                   get from their habitats?

Answer:    Food, water, and shelter

Question: _____
Answer:    It would be difficult to live there.

Sometimes, people change habitats by adding harmful things to them. *Pollution* is anything harmful added to the air, water, or land. Pollution can kill organisms and can destroy their habitats.

Question: _____
Answer:    Usually, people are responsible.

Question: _____
Answer:    Organisms may lose their food source and die out.

## ROLES OF THE TEACHER AND STUDENTS IN QUESTIONING SITUATIONS

Teachers frequently have difficulty with classroom silence after a question has been asked. Extensive research has demonstrated that teachers typically wait less than one second for students to respond to a question. Teachers often conclude that students do not know the answer to a question if they do not respond quickly. Also, when students do respond, they usually use literal-or knowledge-level responses (to be discussed).

Rowe (1974, 1987) found that teachers who increase their *wait time* (the time between the asking of a question and the solicitation of a response) to three seconds or more obtain greater speculation, conversation, and argument from students. She discovered that three seconds of wait time yields the following results:

1. The length of student response increases 400–800 percent.
2. The number of unsolicited but appropriate responses increases.
3. Failure to respond decreases.
4. Confidence of children increases.
5. The number of questions asked by students increases.
6. Slow students contribute more. The increase is from 1.5 to 37 percent.
7. The variety of responses increases. There is more reacting to each other, structuring of procedures, and soliciting.
8. Speculative thinking increases as much as 700 percent.
9. Discipline problems decrease.
10. Achievement improves in cognitively complex tasks on written tests. (Rowe, 1987)

Rowe also discovered that teacher behaviors change as a result of using increased wait time in their questioning procedures. Such teachers tend to:

1. Exhibit more flexible types of responses.
2. Change the number and kinds of teacher questions.
3. Modify their expectations for student performance. Teachers were less likely to expect only the brighter students to reply and viewed their class as having fewer academically slower students.

### TO INVESTIGATE

Observe an elementary teacher for a 15-minute period. Record the amount of time the teacher allows between the asking of a question and the solicitation of a response. (*Note:* You will probably find this to be a relatively short period of time, so you may want to count the space between the question and the response solicitation as "one Mississippi, two Mississippi," etc.) Record the number of questions asked in the 15-minute period and the average length of wait time. What do you think would be the implications for the lesson were the teacher to use a three-second wait time? Based on Rowe's research, how would the use of longer wait time have resulted in a significantly better lesson for the students? How do your results compare with the results of your classmates?   ∎

Questions for your science lessons must be thought through carefully. The formulation process involves consideration of the level of difficulty of the questions, how the questions relate to the material being presented, the backgrounds and abilities of the students, and the purpose of each question. Asking questions is a skill, and it is important that you think them out in advance of the presentation and not rely on spontaneously coming up with an appropriate question.

Another consideration is what to do with the answer once a student has responded. Many teachers develop good questions and give serious consideration to those of whom the questions are asked, but they respond to the answers with little if any positive feedback. You must be prepared for the student who replies, "I don't know" or the one who is silent and does not respond. Is the response, or the lack of one, an indication that the student is fearful that his or her answer will cause embarrassment? Is the student being defiant? Or does he or she truly not know the answer? These questions require you to reflect on the responses you get during the day and to try to solve some of the riddles encountered.

## DID YOU KNOW?

Spiders have sensors near their leg joints that enable them to remember every twist and turn they take. As a result, they can retrace their path through a maze with absolute precision.

**Classroom Activity** Ask students to locate and capture several spiders from the local area. Construct a simple maze with pieces of cardboard glued inside a shoebox. Have students release a spider in the maze and track its movements using a sheet of graph paper. Direct students to repeat the activity several times with a single spider to determine if it is able to retrace its steps identically in each trial. What did students observe? If there are deviations, what are some possible explanations? (*Note:* Be sure to release the spiders back to their original habitat when this activity is completed.) ■

Considerable attention has been given to the process involved in the teacher's formulation of questions, but asking questions is an equally important skill for students to develop. This skill is frequently overlooked, but it should be an important element in the science program. Students must not only know the answers to questions raised by the teacher, but they must also learn what to question and how to verbalize their concerns and their pursuit of the unknown.

The opportunity for students to ask questions is at the very heart of an effective science program. Offering your students support and encouragement to ask their own questions is one of the most important gifts they will get in your classroom. Too many questions in the typical elementary classroom are teacher-directed. When students are offered genuine, stimulating invitations to participate actively in question asking, they assume a higher level of independence and motivation throughout the entire science curriculum.

Getting students to generate their own questions, however, is not as easy as it sounds. Far too many students have been part of classes where the teacher was the predominant question asker, and they have grown overly dependent on the teacher to pose all of the questions. Students rarely have opportunities to generate questions other than the most rudimentary ("May I go to the bathroom?" "When will we have recess?" "What's for lunch today?").

Encouraging student queries can be one of the most productive processes for the science classroom. It puts students in the role of scientists—those who are always asking questions and trying to discover the answers to those questions. You serve as a powerful role model for students in terms of the kinds of questions you ask, the frequency of questioning in the classroom, the difficulty of the questions, and the purposes for which questions are asked. It is valuable, therefore, that you become a competent question asker so that students will emulate your questioning behavior.

Chapter 8 outlines other processes for helping students ask their own questions about textual material. Following is a series of additional activities you can incorporate into your classroom proceedings to facilitate question asking on the part of your students.

## IDEA BOX

1. Have one student take on the role of scientist. Direct other students to question that student about actions, events, or discoveries relevant to the topic under discussion.
2. Divide the class into two groups. Have each group develop a list of 10 questions (on a reading selection, class experiment, demonstration, or field trip) to be answered by the other group.
3. Ask students a question about a recently read chapter or an experiment conducted in class. The students correctly answering the question get to ask you a question in return (about the chapter or experiment).
4. Display an illustration or photograph related to a concept discussed in the text. Direct students to write as many questions as possible about the picture. Then ask them to write a short paragraph that contains answers to all of their questions. This activity can be done prior to or immediately after discussion of a specific topic.
5. Have students generate a series of sentence stems, which can be recorded on index cards and kept in a box ("Why did this experiment...?" "Do you believe this process...?" "Are these results similar...?"). After students have completed an assignment, cards can be randomly drawn from the box and each student can create a question relevant to the lesson. Have students exchange cards and respond accordingly.

## TEACHER TO TEACHER

Questioning is one of the very important science skills, and research has shown that the teacher who knows all the answers to the student's questions actually discourages the students. Your students can generate a continual stream of good questions if you develop an atmosphere that encourages and rewards it. The most effective way I have found is a big question mark attached to the wall. The students are given credit for writing science questions on the question mark. When a question arises in class, I try to withhold my answer and encourage the student to write it on the question mark. As other students enter the room, they read the questions and answer any they know. They are also motivated to look up the answers, ask others who might know, or experiment to find out. Correct answers also give credit and the student's name in print on the answer board. After a few weeks, we share the questions and correct answers with all the students. We have a research day to go to the library to find more answers. Some questions lead to science experiments and science fair ideas. And, of course, some questions remain unanswered—seeds in the students' minds for interest and research in the years to come.

Elaine Hampton
Zia Middle School
Las Cruces, NM

## LEVELS OF QUESTIONS: A CLASSIFICATION SYSTEM

One criticism of teacher questions is that they emphasize facts, whereas research indicates that an emphasis on higher cognitive powers is more effective (Gall, 1989). An alternative approach to fact questions is to consider higher-level questioning techniques based on Bloom's taxonomy. This classification system was developed by Benjamin Bloom and his associates (Bloom et al., 1956) and is used extensively for developing educational objectives, test questions, and classroom questions. The system contains six levels arranged in hierarchical form, from the least complex to the most complex. Individuals move through the hierarchy, using the skills, behaviors, and knowledge gained at the lower levels to help them function at the succeeding levels. The six levels, from the simplest to the most complex, are:

1. Knowledge
2. Comprehension
3. Application
4. Analysis
5. Synthesis
6. Evaluation

### Knowledge

Questions used to determine if students possess knowledge usually require the students to recall or identify information in basically the same form in which it was presented. Questions at this level ask students to remember facts dealing with specifics. Students are frequently asked to demonstrate their knowledge of conventions, trends and sequences, classifications, principles, and generalizations.

### Key Verbs Used in Knowledge Questions

| | | |
|---|---|---|
| Know | Define | Memorize |
| Repeat | Record | List |
| Recall | Name | Relate |
| Arrange | Find | Identify |
| Match | Point to | Select |
| State | Tell | Show |

### Generic Knowledge Question Stems

"Who...?"
"What...?"
"When...?"
"Where...?"
"Describe...."
"Define...."
"What is the one best...?"
"Which one...?"
"How much...?"

## Specific Knowledge Questions

1. What is the formula for finding out how much energy is required to move an object 4 feet?
2. List the three main parts of an insect.
3. What is the name of the rotating part of a motor?
4. How would you describe a parallel circuit?
5. What steps would you follow in trying to determine the classification of _____?

**DID YOU KNOW?** _____ _____

A Giant Sequoia tree does not begin to flower until it is at least 175 to 200 years old.

**Classroom Activity**  Obtain one or more of the following books for your students: *Oak and Co.* by Richard Mabey (New York: Greenwillow, 1983); *A Forest is Reborn* by James Newton (New York: Crowell, 1982); and *Tree Flowers* by Millicent Selsam (New York: Morrow, 1984). Share the books with students and ask each student to compose a list of literal (knowledge) questions, each written on a separate index card. Have students exchange their cards and create appropriate responses to the questions (a student may want to read the book or ask the previous reader of the book for appropriate answers). Take time afterward to discuss how answers were located and how this activity can relate to other science areas. ∎

## Comprehension

Comprehension encompasses "probably the largest general class of intellectual abilities and skills emphasized in schools" (Bloom et al., 1956, p. 89). At this level, one must consider three types of behavior: translation, interpretation, and extrapolation. Translating means that the student must be capable of placing the information into other terms or another form of communication. An example of this is the ability to translate information from a graph, diagram, or formula or to define or explain a scientific term. Interpretation requires the student to be able to explain why a scientific phenomenon occurs. Extrapolation is the ability to estimate or predict on the basis of one's understanding of the conditions or tendencies of the data or observations made.

### Key Verbs Used in Comprehension Questions

| | | |
|---|---|---|
| Restate | Discuss | Describe |
| Recognize | Explain | Express |
| Identify | Locate | Report |
| Review | Tell | Convert |
| Expand | Account for | Demonstrate |
| Outline | Calculate | Propose |

## Generic Comprehension Question Stems

"What does this mean...?"
"In your own words,...?"
"What exceptions are there...?"
"What seems to be...?"
"What seems likely...?"
"Is this the same as...?"
"What would happen if...?"
"Explain what is happening...."
"Explain what is meant...."
"Is it true that...?"

## Specific Comprehension Questions

*Translation:*

1. How would you explain what occurs when rust forms on a metal?
2. How would you illustrate the water cycle?

*Interpretation:*

1. What steps are required to change water from a gas to a liquid?
2. Explain what would happen in a permanent magnet if the magnet were dropped and the molecules were rearranged.

*Extrapolation:*

1. Predict what will happen when a cold air mass rides over a warm air mass.
2. What will happen when we move the mold from a warm, damp environment to a cold, dry area?

## Application

At the application level, students are asked to take information they already know and apply it to a new situation.

### Key Verbs Used in Application Questions

| | | |
|---|---|---|
| Translate | Interpret | Apply |
| Employ | Demonstrate | Use |
| Dramatize | Practice | Sketch |
| Illustrate | Construct | Employ |
| Make use of | Manipulate | Relate |
| Put to use | Classify | Utilize |

### Generic Application Question Stems

"Can you predict what would happen if...?"
"Can you calculate the effects of...?"

"Tell what would happen...."
"What would result...?"
"Are you able to tell how much change there
   would be...?"
"When would this...?"
"Will you use this...?"

### Specific Application Questions

1. You have learned that a fire needs three ingredients
   to burn: oxygen, combustible material, and attainment of its kindling point. Why is water applied to
   a fire to put it out? What are some other ways a fire
   can be extinguished?
2. Demonstrate why the climate of England is affected
   by the Gulf of Mexico.
3. If you had to lift a 200-pound object to a platform 10 feet above the road, demonstrate how you
   would get the object on the platform even though
   you could not lift that much weight at one time.
4. If you had 8 inches of water in your basement and
   a hose, explain how you would use the hose to get
   the water out.

## Analysis

Analysis is a critical area in science, as it "requires solutions of problems in the light of conscious knowledge of
the parts and processes of reasoning" (Sanders, 1966,
p. 98). The student must be able to identify the elements making up the whole, see the relationships of
the parts, and break down the whole into its related
parts.

### Key Verbs Used in Analysis Questions

| | | |
|---|---|---|
| Distinguish | Analyze | Differentiate |
| Appraise | Calculate | Experiment |
| Compare | Criticize | Debate |
| Relate | Solve | Diagram |
| Infer | Simplify | Survey |
| Screen | Take apart | Test for |

### Generic Analysis Question Stems

"What assumptions...?"
"Can you make a distinction...?"
"What ideas apply...?"
"What is the function of...?"
"What ideas justify...?"
"What is the relationship between...?"
"What are the elements of...?"
"Which parts are...?"

### Specific Analysis Questions

1. When you use scissors or a broom to do work, you
   are using a lever. Compare the two examples and
   explain the difference between the two levers.
2. What causes the lights connected in a series to glow
   more dimly as additional lights are added to the
   circuit? Compare this with a parallel circuit. Are the
   results the same?
3. What are the major differences between pumice and
   obsidian rocks? What is the reason for the differences?
4. Compare the sounds of two rubber bands, one
   thick and one thin. Which sound has the higher
   pitch? Why? Can you make the pitch lower in one?
   Higher? How?

## Synthesis

Synthesis questions challenge children's imagination
and encourage them to engage in creative and original thinking. This is not to suggest that the results of
their thinking is new to others, but that it is new to
them. This level is important because it helps motivate
and encourage the child who has a questioning mind
and enjoys the challenge of a problem. The teacher
who wishes to utilize this level must try to create a
classroom atmosphere that elicits and rewards originality. Students at this level need freedom to explore
and need to be assured of the acceptability of many
possible answers or solutions.

### Key Verbs Used in Synthesis Questions

| | | |
|---|---|---|
| Compose | Plan | Propose |
| Design | Formulate | Arrange |
| Assemble | Construct | Create |
| Set up | Organize | Prepare |
| Blend | Combine | Generate |
| Produce | Revise | Plan |

### Generic Synthesis Question Stems

"How would you test...?"
"How else would you...?"
"Can you formulate a theory...?"
"What is an alternative...?"
"How might you organize...?"
"When would you arrange...?"
"How would you assemble...?"
"Where would you produce...?"

### Specific Synthesis Questions

1. What do you think would happen if we combined
   a series circuit with a parallel one?

2. What would happen if we were to place a piece of anthracite coal under a lot of pressure and heat?
3. One of the problems in America today is that we are running out of places to get rid of our trash. What alternatives can we use other than burying it or burning it?
4. We are trying to demonstrate that cold air moves in to replace warm air. Can you design an example or a demonstration that will prove this for us?

### DID YOU KNOW?

Because fleas are the primary carriers of plague, they have caused more deaths throughout the world than all the wars ever fought.

**Classroom Activity**   Ask students to create a large classroom chart of the various diseases transmitted by animals. Which diseases are carried by insects (e.g., mosquitoes—malaria), which are transmitted by mammals (e.g., bats—rabies), and which are carried by fish (e.g., tuna—mercury poisoning)? Students may wish to synthesize their information in the form of a brochure or booklet that describes various diseases or illnesses, how animals are involved in carrying those diseases, and prevention techniques.   ■

## Evaluation

Evaluation requires an individual to make a judgment about something. We are asked to judge the value of an idea, a candidate, a work of art, a solution to a problem, or some other item. "Evaluation is placed at this point in the taxonomy because it is regarded as being at a relatively late stage in a complex process which involves some combination of all the other behaviors of Knowledge, Comprehension, Application, Analysis, and Synthesis" (Bloom et al., 1956, p. 185). Students engaged in decision making and problem solving should be thinking at this level. However, evaluation may be used as "prelude to the acquisition of new knowledge, a new attempt at comprehension or application, or a new analysis and synthesis" (Bloom et al., 1956, p. 185).

### Key Verbs Used in Evaluation Questions

| | | |
|---|---|---|
| Judge | Appraise | Evaluate |
| Rate | Compare | Value |
| Revise | Assess | Estimate |
| Criticize | Decide | Interpret |
| Prioritize | Rank | Rule on |

### Generic Evaluation Question Stems

"Which is more important...?"
"How would you compare...?"
"What would be an appropriate...?"
"Is it logical to...?"
"What is the best...?"
"How would you rank...?"
"What do you think about...?"

### Specific Evaluation Questions

1. What is your opinion of using more nuclear power to generate electricity in America?
2. There is a big debate on whether or not the habitat of the spotted owl should be preserved at the expense of abandoning the practice of cutting down trees for lumber. Which side would you defend? Why?
3. What is your position on not allowing smoking on any airline flights originating and terminating in America?
4. If you could select any place in the world as your home, where would you live? Why?

Let's combine all six question types in terms of a specific science concept.

1. What is it? (knowledge)
2. Can you state in your own words what it does? (comprehension)
3. How does one use this? (application)
4. How does it work? (analysis)
5. Can you create an entirely new use for this? (synthesis)
6. On a scale of 1 to 10, how would you rate this as a useful medical tool? (evaluation)

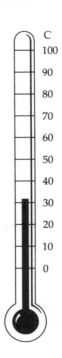

At this point it will be helpful to restate an idea presented earlier in this chapter:

---

Students' level of thinking is based on the types of questions they anticipate receiving from the teacher.

---

That is, students will tend to approach science as a knowledge-based subject if they are presented with an overabundance of knowledge-level questions. On the other hand, students will tend to approach science as a subject based on application, analysis, synthesis, and evaluation if they are presented with an abundance of questions at these levels of cognition. You can influence, to a considerable degree, your students' awareness and appreciation of science by the types of questions you pose throughout your science curriculum.

Although Bloom's taxonomy is the most prevalent hierarchy of question types in use, there are other arrangments used to provide students with a multiplicity of question types throughout the science program. One method of categorizing questions is described in Table 3.5. You will note obvious similarities between this and Bloom's question types. What is important is that you become sensitive to the variety of questions you can ask your students—questions that will help them become active pursuers of information.

**IDEA BOX** _____

Sprinkle some of the following types of questions in your science lessons. Not only will they add some variety and creativity to your discussions of concepts and principles, they will stimulate some new perspectives and observations.

### Fluency Questions

List all the words you can think of to describe _____.

What are all the possible solutions for _____?

How many ways can you come up with _____?

### Flexibility Questions

How is _____ like _____?

What ideas from _____ are like _____?

What _____ is most like a _____?

### Reorganization Questions

What would happen if there were more _____?

Suppose _____ happened. What would be the results?

What would happen if _____ were true?

### Viewpoint Questions

How would _____ view this?

How would a _____ describe _____?

How would this look to a _____?

---

### TABLE 3.5

..............................................................

## CREATIVE QUESTIONING
..............................................................

C  Combine: Blend two or more details together.
   "What would be the consequences if all reptiles could breathe underwater and on land?"

R  Rearrange: Change the order of events.
   "What would change if January were a summer month (in the Northern Hemisphere) and July were a winter month?"

E  Eliminate: Remove one or more details.
   "How would the monkey's life be different if it didn't have a tail?"

A  Adapt: Use data from another source.
   "What would change if all precipitation were in the form of rain?"

T  Take advantage of: Use textual details in a different way.
   "What would have happened if all the planets had a circular orbit?"

I  Insert something else: Substitute new ideas.
   "What would happen if diamonds could be created in the same way as sedimentary rocks?"

V  Vary: Make changes in factual information.
   "What would be the consequences if all spiders were poisonous?"

E  Exaggerate: Magnify events or details.
   "What would be the effects if all insects were 100 times their current size?"

**TEACHER TO TEACHER** _____

Many teachers are only comfortable with science when they know where to look up the answers because they view science as do many students as a body of facts. Yet, there are still many unanswered questions. Not every specie has been well observed and documented. When another teacher had some caterpillars that were eating the leaves of a tree in her yard I took this opportunity for my class studying insects to make observations. Neither of us had any idea what kind they were other than they were not tent caterpillars because the web was different. My students continued to feed the caterpillars the same kind of leaves. Shortly they made cocoons. In a couple of weeks they emerged as white moths. Throughout this time the children asked numerous questions such as how big will they get as caterpillars, will they make cocoons or chrysalis, or when will they emerge—to which I had no answers. I was able to find webworm moths in an insect book with the children, but it certainly did not answer our many questions. Most of our questions had to be answered by observation, making measurements, and recording data. This opportunity certainly reinforced the idea of science as "doing" for all of us, including the teacher.

Elaine S. Heine
Ocean Breeze Elementary School
Indian Harbour Beach, FL

To assist you in designing your own science-related questions, the following guidelines are offered. You may wish to use these as a set of markers with which to evaluate your question-asking competency, or you may wish to have a colleague evaluate your question asking within the context of a lesson. Whichever way you decide to use this chart, you will find that the skill of questioning can always be improved, not just for your benefit but for the ultimate benefit of your students.

### Questioning Guidelines

_____ I provide students with a host of divergent, rather than simply convergent, questions.

_____ I use questions to determine students' background knowledge for the purpose of structuring my lessons.

_____ I stimulate students to look for more than single right answers.

_____ I encourage the development of student-generated questions.

_____ I help students think about their mental processes by asking metacognitive questions during a lesson.

_____ I utilize wait time whenever I ask a question.

_____ I ask a multitude of higher-level questions to all my students.

_____ I stimulate independent questioning strategies through appropriate modeling behaviors.

_____ I follow up students responses with appropriate probing questions that encourage higher levels of thinking as well as support for initial responses.

_____ I ask students questions that encourage them to elaborate previous responses.

_____ I steer away from simple yes/no questions, focusing instead on questions that demand elongated responses.

_____ I monitor my questioning during class discussions and know the approximate proportion of "higher-level" questions I ask (Klein, 1989).

_____ I am aware that my students' thinking will be affected by the kinds of questions I ask them.

In conclusion, be aware that good questioning helps students focus on the *processes* of science more than on the *products*. The questioning strategy you use in your classroom will determine, in large measure, how your students perceive science and how they will react to science. Helping students become active thinkers and doers is what effective questioning is all about.

## POINTS OF DISCUSSION

1. Obtain a teacher's manual for a science series. Record the questions listed for one of the lessons and arrange them according to Bloom's taxonomy. What do you notice?

2. Choose one of your college classes and make notations on the questioning strategy of the professor. Does he or she use wait time at all? If not, how active are students in volunteering information? If so, how would you gauge the level of participation? Are there any implications for your future classroom?

3. Design a series of questions for this chapter. What kinds of questions do you think should be included in a chapter on questioning? Where and when

would you place those questions? How many questions would be appropriate?

4. Interview an elementary teacher and a secondary teacher on how they each design and write classroom questions. Are there any similarities? Are there any major differences?

5. Interview a novice teacher (less than two years of experience) and an experienced teacher (more than fifteen years of experience). What has each noticed about the effects of good questioning on their students? How would they like to improve their questioning skills?

6. What kinds of questions do you enjoy answering? Are they high-level or low-level questions? Which

kinds of questions are most stimulating? Most creative? Most challenging? Will the kinds of questions you enjoy answering in a classroom determine the kinds of questions you will ask in your own classroom? Please explain.

**7.** Define a good question.

## REFERENCES AND SUGGESTED READINGS

Abell, S. K., Pizzini, E. L., & Shepardson, D. P. (1989). "The textbook scan." *Science and Children, 27*(2), 36–37.

Anderson, R. C., & Faust, G. W. (1973). *Educational psychology: The science of instruction and learning.* New York: Dodd, Mead.

Bloom, Benjamin J., et al. (1956). *Taxonomy of educational objectives handbook I: Cognitive domain.* New York: David McKay.

Borich, G. D. (1988). *Effective teaching methods.* Columbus, OH: Merrill.

Cooper, James M. (Ed.). (1990). *Classroom teaching skills* (4th ed.) Lexington, MA: D. C. Heath.

Costa, A. L. (1985). "Teacher behaviors that enable student thinking." In A. L. Costa (Ed.), *Developing minds: A resource for teaching thinking.* Alexandria, VA: Association for Supervision and Curriculum Development.

Couch, Lezlie L. (1989, December). "Questioning our way to wisdom, wonder, and serendipitous knowledge." *English Education, 21,* 230–238.

DeVito, A., & Krockover, G. (1976). *Creative sciencing: A practical approach.* Boston: Little, Brown.

Dillon, J. T. (1989). *Questioning and teaching: A manual of practice.* New York: Teachers' College Press.

Durkin, D. (1978–79). "What classroom observations reveal about reading comprehension instruction." *Reading Research Quarterly, 14*(4), 481–533.

Esler, William, & Sciortino, Phil. (1988). *Strategies for teaching.* Raleigh, NC: Contemporary.

Fredericks, A. D. (1991). "Using 'what if' questions across the curriculum." *Learning, 19*(5), 50–53.

Gall, Meredith. (1989, November). "Synthesis of research on teachers' questioning." *Educational Leadership,* 40–47.

Gore, Delores, & Roumagoux, Daniel. (1983). "Wait time as a variable in sex related differences during fourth-grade mathematics instruction." *Journal of Educational Research, 76,* 273–275.

Kauchak, Donald, & Eggen, Paul. (1989). *Learning and teaching research-based methods.* Boston: Allyn & Bacon.

Klein, M. L. (1989). *Developing thinking and comprehension through effective questioning* Western Washington University, Bellingham. Unpublished manuscript.

Montague, Earl J., Huntsberger, John, & Hoffman, James. (1989). *Fundamentals of elementary and middle school classroom instruction.* Columbus, OH: Merrill.

Nordstrom, Brian. (1991, May). "Advice from a collegiate colleague." *Science and Children, 28,* 16–19.

Pennsylvania Department of Education. (n.d.). *Science unlimited.* Harrisburg: Author.

Rowe, M. B. (1974). "Pausing phenomena: Influences on the quality of instruction." *Journal of Psycholinguistics Research, 3,* 203–233.

Rowe, M. B. (1987). "Wait-time: Slowing down may be a way of speeding up." *American Educator, 11*(1), 38–47.

Sanders, Norris M. (1966). *Classroom questions: What kinds.* New York: Harper & Row.

Watson, Edward D. (1988, September). "How to ask better questions." *Learning,* 94.

# 4

# PROBLEM SOLVING, CRITICAL THINKING, AND CREATIVE THINKING

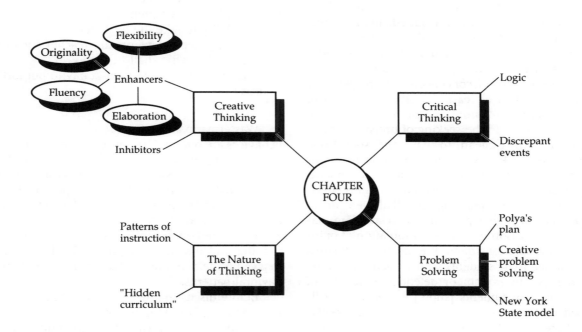

## Chapter Objectives

After reading this chapter you should be able to:

1.  Identify the classroom constraints on productive thinking.

2.  Outline the value of problem solving in the elementary science program.

3.  Elaborate three models for using problem solving.

4.  Explain the need for and the implementation of critical thinking skills in elementary science.

5.  Understand the inhibitors and enhancers of creative thinking throughout the science program.

It should be evident from the previous chapters that science is much more than an accumulation of facts, figures, and principles committed to memory. It is a constant process of learning and doing; scientific knowledge is never stagnant but is in a continual state of flux. To be scientifically literate does not mean that one has ingested large amounts of scientific data but rather that one is open to new possibilities and discoveries because a foundation of concepts and principles has been built through interactive processes and questioning strategies.

Adding to the foundation of science education outlined in Chapters 2 and 3, this chapter considers the role of thinking in the effective classroom program. Although there may be several definitions of thinking, for the purposes of this book thinking is a mental activity by which knowledge is acquired, manipulated, evaluated, or created (Pasch, Sparks-Langer, Gardner, Starko, & Moody, 1991). Not only does it involve a search for answers, meanings, or solutions but it entails the development of concepts and principles, the use of logical chains of reasoning, the evaluation of sources, the solving of problems, the examination of multiple solutions, and the seeking of unusual ideas.

What does this mean to you, the soon-to-be teacher of science? Plenty! John Goodlad in his seminal study (1984) documented the fact that students seldom engage in setting goals and making decisions about their own learning. Goodlad went on to illustrate that less than 1 percent of all classroom dialogue involves "reasoning" or the formulation of opinions. The National Assessment of Educational Progress (1981) reported that "students seem . . . genuinely puzzled at requests to explain or defend their points of view and that few students [show] evidence of well-developed problem-solving or critical thinking skills" (p. 25). Barell (1991) further illustrates this concern when he points out that "[students have a] tendency to give short, one-word answers that avoid the more difficult challenge of thinking about concepts and issues in greater depth" (p. 5).

Rath, Wassermann, Jonas, and Rothstein (1986) documented that children who have had limited opportunities to exercise their thinking skills in higher mental operations show certain observable behavioral patterns such as:

- Extreme impulsiveness (moving into action before thinking about what is to be done)
- Dogmatic behavior (insisting one's idea is right even in the presence of contradictory evidence)
- Rigidity in their ideas (the inability to move from the more comfortable systems into new frameworks)
- An inability to connect means with ends
- An inability to comprehend ("I don't get it")
- An inability to take the next step
- Remaining dependent on the teacher for direction ("I'm stuck—what shall I do now?")
- A lack of confidence in their ability to put forth new ideas

Wassermann and Ivany (1988) point out that these behaviors are often the result of insufficient opportunities to think. In other words, these children have had too much practice with the lower-order mental tasks of remembering and recalling (see Chapter 3), tasks that require single "right" answers and depend on the storage and retrieval of information. The theory of Rath et al. (1986) goes on to explain how students who receive training and practice in higher-order functions learn to give up their counterproductive thinking-related behavioral patterns.

Before discussing ideas on how you can promote and encourage thinking in your science program, let's take a look at some classroom conditions that may hamper problem solving, critical thinking, and creative thinking.

## ALTERING THE STATUS QUO

What do you remember about learning science in the first grade? How about the third grade? The fifth grade? If you're like most people, it is very difficult to separate your experiences in one grade from those in another. In other words, most of your elementary science experiences (as a student) meld into a formless mass that remains fairly constant through the grades. Stated another way, many of us have gone through several regular and predictable patterns of instruction during our elementary careers.

When the patterns of instruction and learning remain constant, the mind is not challenged to face problems, creativity is diminished, and critical thinking skills are not reinforced. If teachers present the same type of material in the same manner throughout the grades, students tend to fall into regular cycles that do not stimulate thinking but rather reinforce the blandness and predictability of learning year after year.

Barell (1991) outlined a series of expectations students have about how classrooms are run and what they will do in those classrooms. As you read this list, think back to your own elementary school experiences and note how many of these statements were true:

The teacher "teaches" and the students "sit and listen" or "learn" passively.

There is one "right answer" to any question, and it is in the book to be read.

The answers to most questions can be given in one or two words, and no one will challenge you to go much deeper.

Books and teachers are always "right," and we learn only from them, not from any other resource in the room, such as our friends.

If we wait long enough, a teacher will answer her own question, and we won't have to do much work. The teacher is the only one worth listening to.

If we ask enough questions about a difficult assignment, we can get the teacher to make it a lot easier and less demanding.

"Thinking" is not something we talk about.

If I memorize enough stuff, I can get a good grade.

Most tasks and tests will demand recall of isolated pieces of information, and I will not have to show how concepts and ideas are related or how facts illustrate underlying principles.

Barell refers to these conditions as the "hidden curriculum," that set of assumptions and conditions students have come to expect from their teachers. Perhaps you even have a hidden curriculum in your approach to your college courses (test yourself and see how many of the statements you would mark "true" for your college courses in general). In other words, after so many years in school, students have come to expect certain things from their teachers, about how they will be taught, and about how they will learn. This may be a major reason why, when we look back on our elementary school experiences (particularly those in science), everything tends to blend together into a mass of "sameness."

## TO INVESTIGATE

Take the preceding statements (Barrell, 1991) and turn them into a simple checklist (yes vs. no). Visit several elementary classrooms and observe how science is taught. Record responses to the statements for each of the different classrooms. Compare your observations with the observations of your classmates. What regularities do you notice? Are the patterns taking place in the classrooms you observe similar to the patterns you experienced as an elementary student? How do you account for those patterns? Afterward you and your classmates may wish to discuss your reactions to the question "Do teachers tend to teach as they were taught?" ■

Science education holds the potential for restructuring students' complacency with regard to their thinking skills. This task will not necessarily be an easy one; rather view it as a challenge that can have a significant impact on your ability to transmit the excitement of science to your students. In addition, it will have an impact on your students' competence in and attitude toward science long after they leave your classroom. It will undoubtedly become exciting for you as you too change your ideas, feelings, and beliefs about science.

Table 4.1 lists several strategies you can use to help students "rethink" their thinking, particularly in regard to the "hidden curriculum" they may bring to your classroom science program. This is only a partial list, with room for you and your classmates to contribute additional ideas from your individual or collective experiences. Keep in mind that this is intended as a constantly evolving list, one that should be added to throughout the remainder of your college career, during your student teaching experiences, and certainly throughout your professional career as a teacher. Remember, learning is an active and ongoing process for you also.

## DID YOU KNOW?

On the average, during a 24-hour period a typical human produces approximately 1 quart of saliva and excretes about 2 ½ quarts of perspiration.

**Classroom Activity**  One of the things we don't often think about is the amazing machine we call the human body. Students are frequently surprised when they discover the daily events taking place in and on their own bodies. You may wish to challenge them by asking them to research or experiment on the daily "activities" of their bodies. For example, students can calculate the amount of blood pumped through the body each day, how long their fingernails grow in one day, the weight of the food and liquid digested in a day, or the number of times their knee flexes in a 24-hour period. Have students conduct their own experiments, talk with medical experts, or do some library research. The information can be charted on an oversized poster of the human body.    ■

It should be evident that thinking is as much a part of the science curriculum as test tubes and microscopes. Long after students have left your classroom (and left

TABLE 4.1

..................................................................................

## FOSTERING A THINKING CURRICULUM

..................................................................................

1. Provide opportunities for students to ask their own questions and to seek answers to those questions through self-initiated explorations (in text, through experiments, by interacting with peers and adult experts, etc.).

2. Permit students to respond only in complete sentences. After a response, ask a student to justify his or her answer ("How did you come up with that answer?" "Why do you believe that to be so?").

3. Give students an opportunity to build an emotional "bridge" to what you are teaching by asking them how they feel about a particular topic.

4. Ask students what they expect from an assignment or experiment. Provide opportunities for students to generate predictions and expectations throughout a body of work.

5. Model your own thinking throughout a learning experience. "Talk out loud" about what is going on in your head as an experience is taking place.

6. Provide opportunities for students to become teacher and for you to become a student. Have students present a lesson or concept and generate appropriate questions for you to respond to.

7. Don't be satisfied with a single answer to any question. Encourage students to provide many responses to a query. Or, better yet, be sure to ask questions that stimulate the production of more than one answer (see Chapter 3).

8. Periodically ask students questions such as "What are you thinking about at this point?"

9. Give students opportunities to relate what they are learning to information gathered from their experiences or previously learned data. Allow students to demonstrate the relationships (verbally or in writing) that exist between facts and concepts.

10. _____

   _____

11. _____

   _____

12. _____

   _____

13. _____

   _____

14. _____

   _____

15. _____

   _____

their test tubes and microscopes behind), they will rely on the thinking strategies and skills you have promoted and encouraged. In short, how we think and what we think about should be long-lasting components of any science program.

Now that we have examined some of the research on and the reasons for thinking in the elementary science program, let's look at the three major dimensions of thinking: problem solving, critical thinking, and creative thinking.

# PROBLEM SOLVING

**Recipe for a Hippopotamus Sandwich**

A hippo sandwich is easy to make.
All you do is simply take
One slice of bread,
One slice of cake,
Some mayonnaise,
One onion ring,
One hippopotamus,
One piece of string,
A dash of pepper—
That ought to do it.
And now comes the problem...
Biting into it!

*Shel Silverstein*

The difficulty of the narrator in this poem underscores problem solving as a frequent (and sometimes humorous) human activity. It is important for students to understand that problems can be of any size or shape from the mundane ("How can I grow tomatoes?") to the perplexing ("How can we reduce our dependence on fossil fuels?"). By its very definition, problem solving is a process—an ongoing activity in which we use what we know to discover what we don't know.

> *Effective problem solving* is the ability to identify and solve science-related problems by applying appropriate skills systematically in ways that demonstrate positive science attitudes and an accurate understanding of science principles.
>
> *New York State Education Department*
> *Elementary Science Syllabus (1985)*

The National Science Teachers Association has posited some recommendations regarding students' participation in a problem-solving curriculum (Pratt, 1981). The NSTA states that science curricula should have these characteristics:

1. Genuine alternatives should exist so that real decisions can be made, real problems solved, and the consequences known or experienced.
2. The problems presented to students should be definable and possible to accomplish and should grow out of first-hand experience.
3. Students should be actively involved in gathering data.
4. Information that is presented should be clearly articulated through alternative modes (e.g., books, films, "hands-on" experiences).
5. Information transmitted should be as appropriate as possible for the age level of the student and should reflect how it is developed.

6. Science programs should be interdisciplinary in nature (involving areas other than science). (See Chapter 8.)

What is evident from these recommendations is that problem solving is a very real part of the elementary science program. Problem solving presupposes that youngsters can take on some of the responsibility for their own learning and can take personal action to resolve conflicts, explore alternatives, and focus on thinking as a vital element of the curriculum.

There are three basic functions to problem solving (Schuncke, 1988):

1. Information seeking
2. Generating new knowledge
3. Decision making

It is clear that problem solving can serve as the crux for an effective science curriculum. In fact, the state of New York has made it the focal point for its elementary science syllabus as illustrated in the following diagram:

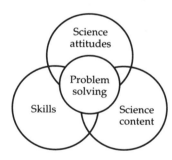

Following are several problem solving models for you to consider. These are *suggested* models, not required ones. Feel free to adopt and adapt portions of these models for use in your own classroom. Don't blindly accept these models as the only way of integrating problem solving strategies into your program; rather, tailor them to the needs and abilities of your students.

**DID YOU KNOW?** _____

The sun rotates faster at its equator (approximately 25 days for a complete rotation) than it does at its poles (approximately 35 days for a complete rotation).

**Classroom Activity** Challenge students to create a model (using styrofoam balls, for example) an illustration, or a physical representation (using several students holding props) that illustrates the sun's external rotation patterns. Invite students to create more than one depiction of the sun's rotation and to decide which is most representative. Afterward, have students speculate on the reasons the sun rotates at different rates in different areas. Invite a professor from the science department of a nearby college to offer explanations (in language students can comprehend). ∎

## New York State Education Department Model

Figure 4.1 presents a model of problem solving developed in 1985 as part of the New York State Education Department's Elementary Science Syllabus. The model begins by helping students identify a problem using the sequence illustrated on the top left side of the figure. Students should use their *experiences* to make them aware of *discrepancies*. The discrepancies should lead them to raise *questions*, and the questions will help them define the problem.

*Experiences* comprise both spontaneous events and teacher-planned activities. They can include direct

experiences with concrete, hands-on materials; out-of-class experiences; and indirect experiences such as reading, writing, listening, and speaking. Many of these experiences will emanate from students' prior knowledge and backgrounds of experiences.

*Discrepancies* are differences, inconsistencies, disagreements, or disharmonies that students encounter. A discrepancy is evident only when children have had some prior experience or basis for comparison. Discrepancies can be grouped into six general categories:

1. A goal to achieve without a means to achieve it (e.g., raising a box that is too heavy to lift).
2. A difference between what the student expects to observe and what the student actually observes (e.g., a light bulb does not go out when the switch is turned off).
3. A lack of knowledge; others may know the information, but the student does not (e.g., seeds need moisture and heat to germinate).

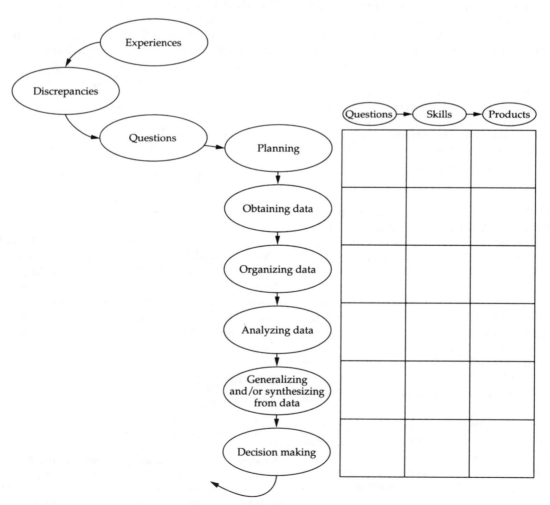

FIGURE 4.1    New York State Education Department Problem Solving Model

4. A difference between what the student has been told is true and what the student has verified personally (e.g., wood floats in water).

5. A conflict (internal or external) between interpretations, opinions, attitudes, or values (e.g., two students want to use the same piece of equipment at the same time).

6. A difference between an existing set of conditions (what is) and desired set of conditions (what should be) (e.g., a littered school playground needs cleaning).

*Questions* play a significant role in problem solving since they help to identify and define the problem as well as guide the systematic search for a solution. Once students recognize a discrepancy, you should encourage them to construct many questions about it (see Chapter 3). It is important that students have opportunities to construct precise questions so that the problem is clearly identified.

Once students have identified a problem by formulating a precise question, they can proceed with problem solving as outlined in Figure 4.1. The model is organized into a sequence of steps, with specific tasks for each step, and you can isolate each step for instruction. Once students learn the tasks for each step, they can use them, either intentionally or automatically, to solve their own identified problems.

1. *Planning.* A problem solver uses a sequence of focus questions to construct and organize precise questions. The focus questions are:

a. What is the problem?
b. What background information do I have?
c. What new information do I need?
d. What procedure or sequence of actions do I need to follow?
e. How will I know when I have solved the problem?

Students should be taught that when they construct a plan, they must always assume that it may have to be revised in light of new information.

2. *Obtaining data.* In this step, the problem solver gathers data that may have an impact on the solution to the problem. The problem solver is guided by the following focus questions and question stems:
a. What new information do I need?
b. What are the properties of . . . ?
c. What are the names of . . . ?
d. How long (wide, big, etc.) is it?
e. How much does it weigh?
f. What color is it?
g. How hot is it?

Quantitative as well as qualitative data may be needed.

3. *Organizing data.* Here the problem solver establishes some pattern for the data obtained. The procedure is guided by the following focus questions and question stems:
a. In what useful way(s) can the information be organized?
b. Which ones belong to this group?
c. In what order do these belong?
d. What categories are there?
e. How can this be graphed?
f. What is the result of this calculation?

It may be possible to organize the data in many different ways. Thus, the form chosen should be considered tentative.

4. *Analyzing data.* This step requires the problem solver to seek patterns and relationships in the data, to recognize characteristics that suggest cause and effect, and to state inferences. The procedure is guided by the following focus questions and question stems:
a. What useful analyses can be made of the organized information?
b. In what ways does . . . compare/contrast with . . . ?
c. What was the apparent effect of . . . ?
d. What seemed to cause . . . ?
e. What must have been the sequence of events?
f. What factors (variables) are involved?
g. What assumptions were made?

Analysis of data must be careful and reasoned for effective problem solving.

5. *Generalizing or synthesizing from data.* Here the problem solver creates conclusions or alternative choices (potential solutions to the problem) to use in the

next step, decision making, guided by the following focus questions and question stems:

**a.** What can be drawn from the analyses of information?

**b.** How can I explain...?

**c.** How can I show that I need to...?

**d.** What is the principle of...?

**e.** If this continues, what is likely to happen?

**f.** What can I predict?

**g.** What might happen if I...?

**h.** What model shows what we know about...?

**i.** What new problems does this suggest?

**j.** How does...apply to...?

The conclusions or alternative choices may lead to the same solution (convergent thinking), or they may suggest a number of different solutions (divergent thinking).

**6.** *Decision making.* In the final step, a problem solver uses a sequence of focus questions to arrive at a decision. The focus questions are:

**a.** What decision needs to be made?

**b.** What are the alternative choices and the reasons for each?

**c.** What are the consequences of each alternative?

**d.** Who will be affected by each possible choice, and in what way?

**e.** What values are directly related to each choice, and how do they relate to it?

**f.** Which choice is the best choice?

**g.** Do I have any other data to support my decision?

**h.** Do I have a follow-up if my decision is not correct?

The decision may lead directly to the solution to the problem. It may point to new directions in pursuit of the solution, or it may suggest new problems to be solved. In any case, the decision should lead to action, and the action should be freely chosen by the problem solver.

The solving of problems is not always orderly or sequential. It may be necessary to move back and forth between steps in arriving at appropriate solutions and strategies for problem solving. Students need to understand that problem solving does not necessarily begin at point A and end at point B. Determining an adequate solution may entail a series of "leapfrog" maneuvers back and forth between the steps outlined.

At each of the preceding steps it is necessary for students to participate in the following tasks, as indicated at the top of Figure 4.1:

**1.** *Questions.* The problem solver should construct many precise questions that will help clarify the problem and the steps that must be taken to solve it. This may be done in a brainstorming-style activity. The student should view each precise question as a little piece of the problem to be solved. There is no initial need for the student to organize the questions; that is part of the planning step.

**2.** *Skills.* The problem solver can obtain an answer to each precise question by applying appropriate skills or processes (see Chapter 2). Students should be taught to select and apply the best skills or processes for the specific task implied by the question.

**3.** *Products.* The problem solver creates a tangible product by applying the appropriate skills to the specific task. For example, by applying the skill of recording data, the problem solver may create the tangible product of a chart or graph. The product contains an answer to the question.

## TEACHER TO TEACHER

If three cats can kill three rats in three minutes, how long will it take one hundred cats to kill one hundred rats? Solving brainteasers like this one requires the ability to break away from conventional thinking patterns in order to look at problems in new ways. I like to foster such thinking skills in my students by challenging them with mind benders on a regular basis. Over the years I have collected dozens of brainteasers and mental puzzles. I keep them stored in a file box on my desk, and whenever I have a few spare minutes I select one to pose to my students. I advise them to look beyond the obvious answer and to illustrate their ideas. I love to watch my students frantically scratching away, hoping to be the first one to find the solution. By the way, have you solved the brainteaser above? If you answered "100 minutes," try again!

Laura Candler
Edgewood Elementary School
Fayetteville, NC

## Creative Problem Solving

The second problem solving model, designed by Sandra Abell (1990), is known as creative problem solving (CPS). It allows for the integration of the contemporary issues of science/technology/society (STS) and higher-order thinking skills. Students are given the opportunity to think creatively about hypothetical dilemmas and apply that information to current environmental issues. The focus is on decision making, and the model includes problem defining, understanding relationships, observation of details, and a systematic approach to finding solutions.

CPS is based on five essential steps: fact finding, problem finding, idea finding, solution finding, and acceptance finding. Throughout the entire process students are provided with many opportunities to brainstorm, arrange and rearrange ideas, and evaluate a number of potential conclusions to arrive at a suitable one.

CPS is initiated by presenting students with what Abell calls "a mess" (a statement of conflict in need of a resolution). It can be a hypothetical situation or a current issue. What is important, however, is that there be a certain degree of ambiguity surrounding the situation, with the problem poorly defined.

What follows is a hypothetical dilemma that could be presented to a class of third- or fourth-grade students. Using Abell's model, notice how students are actively engaged in examining many perspectives of the situation (keeping an open mind) and reach their own self-initiated conclusion(s).

> Bay City sits in the foothills of the Cascade Mountains in the Pacific Northwest. Located close to the Pacific Ocean, it has long been a mecca for visitors who just want "to get away from it all." Fishing is plentiful, water sports are in abundance, and the lifestyle is relaxed. However, plans for a major new power plant have been proposed. The location of the plant, upstream on the river that runs through Bay City, has residents concerned. At a town meeting the owners of the plant assure residents that there will be minimal effects on the environment and on the town. Yet concerns still abound.

### Step 1: Fact Finding

During the initial step students brainstorm for an abundance and a variety of questions that will help clarify the "mess." Following are some possible questions:

- Will the quality of water in Bay City diminish?
- Will the wildlife be affected in any way?
- How will the power plant affect the aesthetics of the region?

- Will there be an increase in the amount of contaminants in the air?
- Is the power plant too big for a city the size of Bay City?
- Will the migration of salmon upstream be affected by the power plant?
- Who will monitor the activities of the power plant to ensure that it is in compliance with EPA regulations?

Once students have generated some preliminary questions, they can begin to consult reference sources, audiovisual materials (films and filmstrips), and experts to locate answers to their queries.

### Step 2: Problem Clarification

As students collect data related to their original questions, the problems confronting Bay City will become more clearly defined. Their objective at this point is to begin narrowing their focus so that they can deal with a single question. Abell (1990) suggests that this can be done by having students complete the following question stem: "In what ways might we . . . ?" Possible questions for the Bay City problem might end as follows:

- Stop the power plant from being built?
- Maintain the economic survival of the community?
- Maintain the present level of air quality?
- Ensure the delicate ecological balance of the river?
- Obtain an adequate supply of power?

After several questions have been posed, students should be challenged to combine their ideas into a single focus question, which can serve as the basis for solution finding. For the present example, the following might serve as the focus question:

- How can we preserve our way of life and that of the indigenous wildlife while providing for the power needs of the larger region?

### Step 3: Brainstorming

Next students begin their search for all the possible answers to their focus question. Lots of ideas are encouraged, and everyone has an opportunity to contribute a variety of potential solutions. No value judgments are attached to any suggested solution; the object here is to look at all sides of the issue *before* reaching any decisions. The following examples are presented as potential solutions to the Bay City situation.

- Require the power plant to submit annual environmental impact statements.
- Build the power plant in another location.

- Reroute part of the river to ensure the annual migration of salmon.
- Require "scrubbers" on all the power plant smokestacks.
- Create a team of townspeople to monitor the activities of the plant.
- Pass zoning laws prohibiting the construction of industrial or power plants.
- Require the plant to shut down during the tourist season.
- Have townspeople serve on the plant's board of directors.
- Petition the plant owners to scale down their initial plans.

## Step 4: Critiquing the Solutions

The next step is for students to critique and evaluate their list of solutions. It will be beneficial to have them decide on several criteria by which to conduct their evaluation. They can then rate each solution against the established criteria. It will also be helpful to have students create a chart or grid on which comparisons can be made. They can give a numerical value to each solution after discussing the various solutions among themselves, with their parents, or with people in the local community. As responses are collected, the solutions are assigned numerical values (1 to 5—low to high) based on the established criteria and given a place on the grid.

Students should then begin to see a potential solution emerging from their grid. In many cases, however, they will discover that a combination of solutions offers the best response to the initial problem. For example, in the Bay City problem students may arrive at the following plan of action:

> The plans for the power plant will be scaled down so that the ecology of the area is preserved. A representative group of townspeople will serve as a monitoring board to gauge the activities of the power plant relative to the annual salmon run and the tourist industry. The recommendations of the "townies" shall supersede those of the plant operators.

## Step 5: An Action Plan

In the final stage of CPS, students develop a workable plan of action for carrying out their solution. This step involves anticipating difficulties, getting assistance, and developing a step-by-step ordering of the activities necessary to reach the final goal (Abell, 1990). It is important for students to look back at the resources (people, printed materials, etc.) they used earlier in the process and consider them as assets in putting their plan into effect.

Because of the nature of the hypothetical Bay City situation, it will not be possible to enact the suggested plan. However, it can serve as a model for what students can do with real-life issues that affect their community and their lifestyle. Such issues abound in the local media (newspapers, television, radio) as well as on the national scene. Students can locate current problems and issues with which they can employ the five steps of CPS and seek potential solutions. Provide students with the opportunity to select issues that are of interest to them or that may have a significant impact on their lives, both present and future. Students will then begin to realize that problem solving is an important and effective element in daily living, not just in the classroom.

## DID YOU KNOW? _____

Throwing away one aluminum can is equivalent to wasting 6 ounces of gasoline.

**Classroom Activity** Using CPS as a model, direct your students to convert this particular fact into a "mess." Encourage them to go through the five steps—generating questions, conducting research, brainstorming for potential answers, critiquing the suggested solutions, and designing an appropriate plan of action—relative to the use and disposal of aluminum cans. Challenge students to create a plan for their school as well as plans for their individual households. What similarities do they note between the two plans? What major differences?

For example, encourage students to get involved in saving aluminum cans at school. Put a committee in charge of counting the number of cans collected; a chart can be kept in the main entrance of the school. Each month the student committee can notify the school how many gallons of gasoline were saved.

## Polya's Four-Step Plan

A general-use problem-solving model developed by George Polya (1973) has many applications across the elementary curriculum. It is a model that can be easily memorized and put into action by most children, and it has direct applications to many areas of science as well as everyday life. It is not, however, a panacea for all problems; it will be necessary for students to select the problem-solving skills that best meet the specific demands of a challenge and are in keeping with their abilities and attitudes.

Polya's (1973) problem-solving plan comprises four separate yet interrelated steps:

1. Understanding the problem
2. Designing a solution strategy
3. Carrying out the strategy
4. Evaluating the results

## Step 1: Understanding the Problem

It is important that children understand the nature of a problem and its related goals. It is vital that youngsters comprehend what is known about a problem as well as the complicating factors involved. This involves more than just reading or talking about a problem; it includes a knowledge of all related facts and other, associated problems.

Following are some techniques that help children understand the nature of a problem and the conditions that surround it.

1. List all related relevant facts.
2. Specify all the given information.
3. Restate the problem in your own words.
4. List the conditions that surround a problem.
5. Describe known related problems.
6. List implicit conditions.
7. List given conditions.

## Step 2: Designing a Solution Strategy

Once the nature and parameters of a problem are understood, it is necessary for students to select and design one or more appropriate strategies to help resolve the problem. This is not always an easy process for students, particularly those who are prone to guess at answers with only a modicum of success. Problem solving must be presented as a systematic approach based on sound decision making.

Students need to understand that there are many strategies available to them and that no single strategy will work for all problems. Not only do students need to be made aware of the various problem-solving strategies that follow, so too do they need to be aware of the fact that a combination of strategies can be used. Initially, this may involve a process of trial and error in selecting the proper strategy or combination of strategies. However, when this takes place in a supportive atmosphere, children will be more apt to investigate all potential problem-solving strategies rather than relying on just one or two.

**Create Visual Images.** Many find it useful to create "mind pictures" of a problem and its potential solutions prior to working on the problem. Mental imaging allows them to map out many parameters of the problem and "see" it clearly. Children can do the same thing very effectively when they are encouraged to close their eyes and create a mental picture of the problem.

**Guesstimation.** Children should be given opportunities to engage in some trial-and-error approaches to problem solving. It should be understood, however, that this is not a singular approach to problem solving but rather an attempt to define the limits of the problem and to gather some preliminary data toward its solution.

**Creating a Table.** A table is defined as an orderly arrangement of data. When students have opportunities to design and create tables of information, they begin to understand that most data relative to a problem can be grouped and organized into an orderly format.

**Using Manipulatives.** By moving objects around on a table or desk, students can uncover patterns and organize elements of a problem into recognizable components. Creating manipulatives and actively moving them can be an important aid in defining the limits of a problem and in structuring potential solutions.

**Working Backward.** It is frequently helpful for youngsters to start at the end of a problem and work backward. In other words, students can take the data presented at the end of a problem and use a series of computations or approximations to arrive at the data presented at the beginning of the problem.

**Brainstorming.** One of the most effective problem-solving strategies is to have students engage in a process of brainstorming—collectively generating as many different possible solutions as they can. The emphasis in brainstorming is to generate a *quantity* of ideas without regard to the *quality* of those ideas. Brainstorming allows students to be inventive, divergent, and open-minded about a problem and a host of possible solutions.

### DID YOU KNOW? _____

Bricks and windows are made from the same principal ingredient, sand.

**Classroom Activity** Ask students to brainstorm for all of the various uses of bricks (buildings, door stops, window breakers, sidewalks, etc.) and all of the possible uses for windows (observation, barriers, insulation, etc.). Next have students brainstorm for the similarities that exist among other objects constructed of the same material (clay, brass, paper, etc.). Have students list all the uses of the objects made from a certain material. How do the various lists compare? What conclusions can students draw from their lists? ■

**Simplifying.** Many problems seem overwhelming to youngsters due to the large number of variables, the amounts involved, or the sheer numbers. Allowing children to simplify complex problems into manageable terms may reveal a pattern that can be used to solve the problem.

**Using Logic.** Although it should be understood that problem solving is a constant process of using logical reasoning, specific conditional statements can be used in the design of solution strategies to help students approach a problem from a new perspective. For example, students can be asked if/then or either/or questions:

"If . . . is true, then is . . . true?"
"If . . . is not true, then is . . . true?"
"Would either . . . or . . . be used in this situation?"

**Looking for a Pattern.** Looking for patterns is an important problem-solving strategy since many problems are similar and are based on predictable patterns. A pattern, by definition, is a systematic repetition and may be numerical, visual, or behavioral (Goodnow & Hoogeboom, 1987).

**Creating a Systematic List.** Recording information in list form is a process used quite frequently by scientists to map out a "plan of attack" for defining and solving problems. Students should be encouraged to record their ideas in list form to determine regularities, patterns, or similarities among problem elements.

**Drawing a Picture or Diagram.** Illustrations are helpful in organizing data, manipulating information, and outlining the limits of a problem and its possible solution(s). Most children enjoy drawing pictures and this can be used in helping them look at a problem from many different perspectives.

## Step 3: Carrying Out the Strategy

It's important to keep in mind that the steps and strategies just illustrated are often not approached in sequential order. That is, problem solvers may engage in several steps at the same time (particularly as they become more proficient) or may mix up the steps to solve a new problem in a unique manner. The steps are highly interdependent and interrelated, allowing students an abundance of possible approaches to use in problem solving.

In working through a strategy or combination of strategies, students should:

1. Keep accurate and up-to-date records of their thoughts and procedures. Recording the data collected, the predictions made, and the strategies used is an important part of the problem-solving process.
2. Work through a selected strategy or combination of strategies until it becomes evident that they are not working, they need to be modified, or they are yielding inappropriate data. As students become more proficient problem solvers, they should feel comfortable in rejecting potential strategies at any time during their quest for solutions.
3. Monitor the steps taken with great care. Students have a natural tendency to rush through a strategy to arrive at a quick answer, and it is incumbent upon the teacher to encourage them to carefully assess and monitor their progress.
4. Feel comfortable in putting a problem aside for a period of time and tackle it later. Scientists rarely come up with solutions the first time they approach a problem; students, too, should feel comfortable in letting a problem "rest" for a while and returning to it at a later time.

## Step 4: Evaluating the Results

It is vital that students have multiple opportunities to assess their own problem-solving skills and the solutions generated from using those skills. Frequently, students are overly dependent on teachers to evaluate their performance in the classroom (see Chapter 10). It is critical that students take time to discuss and evaluate the strategies used and the success or lack of success they had in using various approaches to a problem.

The process of self-assessment is not easy, however. It involves risk taking, self-assurance, and a certain level of independence. But it can be effectively promoted by asking students questions such as: "How do you feel about your progress so far?" "Are you satisfied with the results you obtained?" "Why do you believe this is an appropriate response to the problem?" Students who are actively engaged in evaluating their own problem-solving strategies will begin to feel a sense of control in arriving at and believing in the solutions they generate. Of course, this may take time because an attitude is being developed—one that ideally will be incorporated as an automatic response on the part of the student.

Here are some additional questions to help students self-assess throughout problem solving:

1. How do you feel about your work so far?
2. Where do you think this approach will lead you?
3. Are you investing sufficient time and effort in this problem?
4. What are you doing to ensure a satisfactory solution?
5. Do you have any idea where this will lead you?
6. Is this the only possibility?
7. What else could you suggest at this stage?
8. Do you anticipate problems or delays further on?
9. Why is this procedure important at this stage?
10. Are you satisfied with your progress?

## IDEA BOX

Students frequently base their answers on the tone of voice used by the teacher rather than on the question. Students have also learned that if a teacher questions them they must be wrong and should change. The implications are that you must be aware of the tone of voice you use in conversing with and questioning students and must monitor the types and number of questions you ask. Have a colleague record your questioning procedures during a science lesson, and analyze them together at a later date. Did you "give away" information solely through your tone of voice? Did you ask too much of one type of question? The answers may surprise you and provide you with some food for thought in designing lessons.

## TEACHER TO TEACHER

Sometimes, in spite of our careful planning, there are instances where student investigations do not move at the pace we'd intended, or what we thought the children would observe does not happen. We are tempted to bring the group together at a large table, demonstrate what we'd thought would occur, and provide answers so that the class can turn its attention to other matters.

In science, worthwhile activities for children should focus on answering questions and solving problems. When we close a lesson prematurely, the opportunity to provide them with experience that develops the kind of knowing required to function well in like situations may be lost.

From the start, they will need to know that problems may arise during investigations and, when they do, finding solutions will require both puzzling and patience. Talk about "fair tests" and the feelings that accompany events that have gone awry. If they become frustrated, help them see that one cause may rest in their expectation to find *the* answer the first time around. Use the opportunity to model your problem-solving skills. Help them build on others' strategies and ideas. And, as they work, praise their ingenuity and encourage pride in their discovered solutions.

Applaud their discoveries, for those events are the heartbeat of science. The "ah-ha" of discovery can transform simple activities into exciting events and inspire students far beyond what we teachers hope to accomplish during a single year.

Lillian Phillips McKeel
Radio Park Elementary School
State College, PA

## CRITICAL THINKING

What day follows the day before yesterday if two days from now will be Sunday?

How did you do with this question? Were you able to arrive at an answer very quickly? Did you need to use a pencil and paper and map out a plan of attack? Or did you give up altogether? When this question (and others like it) was asked of college students, most did not know how to proceed in figuring out an answer. They either guessed at an answer or gave up on the question (Whimbey, 1977).

There is a twofold issue involved here. That is, what did you do to try and solve the problem, and why did you choose to proceed or to give up on finding a solution? The answers to these questions have a lot to do with how we can integrate critical thinking skills into the elementary curriculum in general and into our science programs specifically. Studies conducted by the National Assessment of Educational Progress (NAEP) support the contention that thinking, particularly critical thinking, is not an inherent element in the day-to-day instruction of children.

Promoting thinking skills can be made part of the daily instruction of children and can help them develop independence in cognitive functioning. Critical thinking is not a frill or "add-on" to the curriculum but a process of investigation and discovery that incorporates the skills of analysis, observation, hypothesizing, imagination, interpretation, generalization, reasoning, logic, classification, synthesizing, and comparing/contrasting. Indeed, comparing these skills with the skills and processes discussed in earlier sections of this text reveals a host of relationships between effective science instruction and critical thinking.

The objective of the science curriculum is to help students become fair-minded, objective, and committed to clarity and accuracy. Such is the nature of critical thinking. When students are provided with opportunities to engage in critical thinking (the word *critical* is used here in its most positive sense), they can effectively look for evidence, evaluate potential sources, and weigh information before taking any action (Pasch et al., 1991).

Critical thinking involves both convergent and divergent reasoning and extends beyond basic knowledge. The components of critical thinking include:

- Analyzing precise meanings of words and ideas
- Perceiving and inferring relationships
- Weighing facts, values, and generalizations
- Finding the logic within given material
- Creating new products
- Making evaluations

Brookfield (1990) has posited a series of indicators that determine whether critical thinking is going on.

1. The student is contextually flexible; he or she sees cultural or situational limits, not global ones.
2. The student is able to get inside another person's head and discern the way that person sees the world. In other words, the student can stand outside his or her own frame of reference.
3. The student has the ability to tolerate ambiguity, is not thrown by the unexpected, knows that perfection is rarely encountered, and looks for origins of problems in the self rather than in others.
4. The student entertains the possibility of change in situations other than crises and will look for alternative ways of thinking and action even without the strong stimulus of a crisis.
5. The student displays a readiness to challenge "group think." (Groups tend to erect a conventional wisdom about how things should be done. Individuals who challenge it run the risk of being seen as troublemakers and outsiders.)
6. The student displays a healthy skepticism about final solutions or ultimate truths touted as applicable in all situations.
7. The student has a view of the future that is open and malleable rather than fixed. This is an affective criterion and an emotional disposition.

It is clear from this list that critical thinking is a complex subject and one not easily taught. Not only does it involve the use of "mental muscles"; it involves emotional factors and attitudes. In short, teaching critical thinking can be viewed as helping students become more open-minded and evaluative about their own science education and about learning in general.

Now let's look at two aspects of critical thinking in more detail.

## Discrepant Events

- A teacher places a glass of water on a table. She takes a piece of metal and drops it gently into the glass. The metal floats on the water.
- A teacher puts a pile of books on a desk. He leans a board against the books to form an inclined plane. He then takes a tin can and places it on its side at about the midpoint of the board. He lets go and the tin can begins to roll *up* the board!
- A teacher gives a student a glass of liquid and a handful of raisins. The student drops the raisins into the liquid, and after a few moments the raisins begin to rise. When they reach the surface of the liquid they fall to the bottom only to rise to the top once again. The cycle is repeated over and over.

- A teacher lights a small candle and places it upright on a table. He blows the flame out, yet moments later the flame mysteriously reappears. The flame is blown out again, only to reappear once more.

These examples illustrate discrepant events—events in which there is an inconsistency between what one reasonably expects to happen and what actually happens. Discrepant events are based on Piaget's theory of equilibrium (see Chapter 1); that is, there is a conflict between what was thought to be known (equilibrium) and what was experienced (disequilibrium). Resolution of this conflict can occur through the process of *assimilation* or *accommodation* (Leyden, 1991).

Discrepant events can be valuable learning activities when used judiciously in science lessons. They are most effective when students have had some background experiences related to the event; that prior knowledge is what creates the conflict between what one expects and what actually happens. There are many ways to present discrepant events. George, Dietz, Abraham, and Nelson (1974) suggest the following:

1. *Silence:* Use exaggerated movements and conduct the entire presentation of the discrepant event in silence.
2. *In progress:* Have the event be in progress when students enter the classroom.
3. *Pictures and film loops:* Use visual aids that show inconsistent observations or present information that is inconsistent with past experiences of the students.

### IDEA BOX

The use of discrepant events can be a wonderful introduction to science lessons. Not only do they serve as motivating devices, but they also provide a vehicle for discussion and interaction among students. They should not, however, be made part of every science lesson. To do so would diminish their impact and make them seem less than amazing.

Work with your colleagues to design a variety of discrepant events. They can be collected in a three-ring binder and kept in the faculty room or science center. Refer to the list when designing science lessons and be sure to add more discrepant events to the notebook periodically.

## Logic

The use of logic is a key component in developing critical thinking skills. Logic may be defined as the science that investigates principles governing correct and reliable inference. The following list identifies behaviors associated with logic.

- Using details to prove or refute a statement
- Identifying details needed to solve a problem

- Relating information to a previous experience with a similar theme
- Rearranging events to develop an accurate sequence
- Perceiving associations (time, place, cause and effect)
- Obtaining information implied in pictures
- Comparing and contrasting reactions among events
- Predicting outcomes
- Drawing conclusions
- Identifying ideas implied but not directly stated
- Determining the most appropriate action in a given situation
- Assessing the adequacy of information to support a conclusion
- Classifying terms, facts, and ideas under headings or in categories
- Differentiating relevant and irrelevant information

(Baltimore County Public Schools, 1985)

**DID YOU KNOW?** _____

Antarctica is sunnier, windier, and colder than any of the other continents.

**Classroom Activity**    Divide the class into seven groups and assign to each group the name of a continent. Charge each group with the responsibility of locating facts and figures that are unique to their continent. Each group can prepare a piece of posterboard in the shape of its continent and record on it the facts obtained via library research, interviews with experts, or audiovisual means. Students may wish to focus on a particular characteristic—climate, for example—and collect as much data about that area as they possibly can. The "continents" can be posted around the room and referred to throughout the year.                                    ■

Incorporating logical reasoning and thinking into the science program can lead to enormous benefits for your students. Not only will it provide them with opportunities to assess the range of data available to them, but will also allow them to select information that builds on their prior knowledge and facilitates their critical interpretation of scientific data.

·····························  **CREATIVE THINKING**  ·····························

Many children have the mistaken notion that science, because of the facts and figures that seem to drive it, is the least creative subject in the elementary curriculum. This assumption is usually based on their extensive experiences with "book learning" or the memorization of scientific principles.

Yet science can and should be one of the most creative subjects you will teach. Indeed, by approaching science as a creative venture for yourself, you can demonstrate the inherent creativity of science to your students. A creative vision of science opens up students' minds to all sorts of possibilities and enhances the promotion of divergent thinking strategies.

Creative thinking can be defined as the formation of new ideas to satisfy an immediate need. In fact, creative thinking and critical thinking go hand in hand. Ideas are generated through processes associated with creative thought, and those same ideas are evaluated or put into practice through critical thinking processes. This presupposes that we can teach youngsters the processes that produce ideas as well as the processes that will lead them to assess the appropriateness of those ideas. It is certainly possible to do this, and nowhere is it more possible than in the science curriculum.

Before we explore some strategies and techniques that will help you become a creative teacher of science and your students become creative thinkers in science, we need to take a look at some of the factors that inhibit creative thought. As we examine the events that hinder students' thinking, we urge you to

consider these factors as potential inhibitors of your own creative thinking, too.

## Inhibitors of Creative Thinking

A science program that promotes creative thinking allows children opportunities not possible in more "traditional" programs. However, it is not an easy matter to make students into creative thinkers. In fact, it becomes more difficult the older children are (adults may have the most difficulty reshaping their thought processes to become more divergent thinkers).

It is an unfortunate fact of life that much of our educational system is built on the concept of guiding students toward accepted modes of thinking. That is to say, children's thinking may be predetermined by curriculum guides and teacher's manuals that present information in logical and sequential order for memorization or manipulation according to established procedures. As Sarason (1982) has pointed out, students traditionally make very few decisions about their own learning. In short, many students are teacher-dependent in their thinking (i.e., the teacher determines the content and what students must think about that content), and helping students become independent thinkers may not be a high priority for the elementary classroom. Following are a few of the reasons for this; you should consider them when designing your own science curriculum.

1. Teachers often feel "married" to the teacher's manual or curriculum guide. That is, there is a sense that all of the material in the guide/manual must be covered during a specific time frame (the school year). To break away from that material may invite retribution from colleagues or administrators.

2. Teachers sometimes feel as though they are under some sort of administrative pressure to adhere to a preestablished curriculum, one that has been "approved" by a governing body at the local, regional, or state level.

3. Teachers may feel that commercial science materials (textbooks, packaged programs, manipulatives, funded programs, etc. [see Chapter 11]), having been created by experts and professional scientists, contain all the answers and designs they need for their elementary science curriculum.

4. Teachers may feel constrained by an ever-expanding curriculum squeezed into an ever-decreasing amount of time in the school day. With so many things to teach during the course of one day, many teachers believe there is no room to include anything else in the program.

5. Teachers may feel pressure from parents and other "outsiders" to teach the "basics" and to leave the "frills" out of the curriculum.

6. Teachers may believe that their students' performance on the traditional end-of-the-year achievement tests will suffer if they do not stick to an established curriculum. Concurrent with that perception is the belief of some untenured teachers that if their students do not perform well on those tests, then their job security is at risk.

The promotion of creative thinking may also be hampered by students' own perceptions of their thinking. Roger von Oech (1983, 1986), a creativity consultant for industry and business, argues that knowledge is the stuff from which new ideas are made, that knowledge alone won't make a person creative. He points out that the key to being creative lies in what one does with one's knowledge. In other words, creative thinking requires an outlook that allows one to search for ideas and manipulate knowledge and experience.

> Discovery consists of looking at the same thing as everyone else and thinking something different.
>
> Albert Szent-Gyorgyi
> Nobel Prize, medicine

Von Oech (1983) has described some of the mental blocks that tend to inhibit creativity. His listing has been modified here for the science curriculum because these roadblocks to thinking have a great deal of impact on students' thinking performance.

1. *The right answer.* As mentioned throughout this text, it is an unfortunate result of many elementary science programs that students get a sense of science as nothing more than the memorization of specific facts and figures. Thus, students may believe that getting the right answer is more important than thinking about a diversity of possibilities. By focusing on single right answers, we may inhibit the creative thought process.

---

**THINKABOUT #1**

Five letters are shown below. Select the one that is different from all of the others.

A     B     C     D     E

---

2. *Follow the rules.* True, there are principles and rules that are essential to science comprehension, such as the laws of gravity, photosynthesis, and cloud formation. Unfortunately, children may believe that all of scientific exploration is built on an inviolable foundation of laws, rules, and principles. Children often feel inhibited because they believe that if they don't know the rules, they can't play the game (of sciencing). This may occur because students perceive rules as something created by adults. When students are provided with opportunities to invent *and* try out their own rules, they can develop a scientific attitude similar to that used by professional scientists. That is, students should not feel "bound" by others' rules but should have opportunities to invent their own rules to explain a phenomenon or investigate a situation.

---

**THINKABOUT #2**

Using only four straight lines, and without lifting your pencil from the paper, connect all nine dots in the pattern below.

```
    •      •      •


    •      •      •


    •      •      •
```

**THINKABOUT #3 (Bonus Question)**

Using fewer than four straight lines, and without lifting your pencil from the paper, connect all nine dots in the pattern.

**THINKABOUT #4 (Extra Bonus Question)**

Come up with more than one right answer to Thinkabout #3.

It didn't work that time, but what if...

3. *Be practical.* Children can be inventive, creative, and imaginative in most subjects (notice the response you get when reading a fairy tale to a group of primary-level youngsters). However, for some reason, students believe that science is a logical and practical way of looking at the world. Providing children with opportunities to ask their own questions, pursue answers to those questions, and deal with both answerable and unanswerable questions, can stimulate their natural curiosity about the world around them.

**THINKABOUT #6**

Cross out five letters so that the remaining letters, with their order unchanged, will spell a familiar English word.

S F I C V E I L E E T N T E C R E S

**THINKABOUT #5**

A woman goes into a store to buy something for her house. When she asks about the price, the clerk replies, "The price of one is thirty-nine cents. The price of twenty-five is seventy-eight cents. And the price of one hundred and forty-four is a dollar and seventeen cents." What does the woman want to buy?

5. *I'm not creative.* Many children, "conditioned" by an educational system built on rote memorization and low-level thinking skills, believe that they cannot be creative. Students commonly have the impression that success in school is built on the ability to memorize bits of information and regurgitate that data on a seemingly endless series of paper-and-pencil assessment measures. This can be a self-fulfilling prophecy: children will behave and perform as they are expected to behave and perform. In other words, if teachers believe that children can achieve only a certain level of intellectual or creative competence, that tends to be the level those children achieve. On the other hand, if teachers believe that students can perform at high levels of investigation, discovery, and exploration, children will tend to fulfill that perception.

4. *To err is wrong.* Many children have a fear of failure. That is, these youngsters' self-concept is affected when they get too many wrong answers (the same holds true for college students), so they are reluctant to venture any type of answer. Their creativity and thinking shuts down, and they are hesitant to suggest a solution to a problem. Von Oech (1983) reminds us that in the normal course of events we may actually fail more than we succeed. It's important for young children to understand that scientists don't succeed every time they try an experiment or examine the principles surrounding a natural phenomenon. Children need to work in an atmosphere that supports their efforts and encourages them to work through their mistakes. They need to know that scientists make mistakes all the time, and that those mistakes can serve as catalysts for later discoveries and inventions.

**THINKABOUT #7**

A frog falls into a bucket that is filled halfway to the top with cream. Without using any artificial assistance (sticks, rocks, human help, etc.) how might the frog get out of the bucket?

**THINKABOUT #8**

How many different ways can you think of to connect A with B?

A          B

_____

**DID YOU KNOW?** _____

Your foot measurement is the same as the length of your arm between the elbow and wrist.

**Classroom Activity**   Provide students with all sorts of measuring instruments and allow them to measure various parts of their bodies. Have each student make an extensive list of measurements (you may wish to challenge them to come up with 50 or 100 different body measurements). Have each student look over his or her list to see if there are ways that body parts can be measured (or compared) using other parts of the body, as in the preceding example. You may wish to introduce students to the fact that some of the earliest measuring devices were body parts (thumb, arm, foot, etc.). Provide opportunities for students to chart the results of their studies.   ■

## Enhancers of Creative Thinking

Teachers sometimes make the mistake of assuming that exercises and activities designed to strengthen creative thinking "muscles" are appropriate only for gifted or creative students. Nothing could be further from the truth. Creative thinking can be promoted in any subject area for all students when it is presented as "an ongoing cyclical process which can be taught by providing an enriched content, a nonjudgmental environment, and a strong foundation of questioning and critical thinking skills" (Baltimore County Public Schools, 1985, p.105).

Table 4.2 is a self-evaluative instrument to assess the environment you provide in your classroom regarding the encouragement of creative thinking. It is suggested that you use this instrument at the beginning of the school year as well as at the midpoint of the year to gauge the degree to which you stimulate creative thinking throughout the science program.

**TO INVESTIGATE** _____

Duplicate Table 4.2 and ask one or two classroom teachers to complete the form. Later, observe them teaching one or more science lessons and make notes on the level of creativity you perceive in those classrooms. With your classmates, compare teachers' self-reports on science creativity and the observed levels of creativity during a science lesson. Are there any discrepancies? Is the self-evaluation comparable to what was observed? To what can you attribute any differences? How do your perceptions compare with the perceptions of your fellow classmates?   ■

TABLE   **4.2**

.......................................................

## PROMOTING CREATIVE THINKING: A SELF-EVALUATION

.......................................................

_____ 1. I provide stimuli for as many of the senses as possible.

_____ 2. I guide students to recognize that creativity can be improved by working in a disciplined manner.

_____ 3. I verify that students understand the instructional objectives for the creative activities we do.

_____ 4. I teach a variety of strategies for overcoming blocks to creativity.

_____ 5. I make a conscious effort to provide opportunities for students to be creative, to be original, and to try to think of new ways to solve a problem.

_____ 6. I provide a nonthreatening atmosphere in which students are encouraged to raise questions.

_____ 7. I encourage students to develop criteria to judge the work of both their peers and themselves.

_____ 8. I encourage students to apply affirmative judgment and to make positive self-statements about their creativity.

_____ 9. I help students to defer judgment and to keep an open mind when new ideas are being presented.

_____10. I attempt to integrate divergent production into as many areas of science as possible.

_____11. I help students to recognize and value the components of convergent and divergent thinking in creative production.

_____12. I model creative thinking and apply it to the science curriculum whenever possible.

_____13. I provide opportunities for students to share their creative products with appropriate audiences.

Fredericks (1988) outlines four creative thinking strategies, all of which can be incorporated into the science curriculum:

1. *Fluency*. This is the ability to create a potpourri of ideas. It involves the generation of many thoughts without regard to quality. Brainstorming is a good way to enhance fluency.

   Brainstorming is designed to produce many ideas and can be used in small or large groups of students. However, it should not be considered an end in itself but rather a prelude to further investigation and discovery. To be effective, brainstorming should adhere to the following guidelines:

   • *No negative criticism*. Defer judgment until a large number of alternatives have been produced.
   • *Freewheeling is desired*. Offbeat and unusual ideas are encouraged.

- *Quantity is stressed.* Include the obvious alternatives as well as the unusual and clever ones.
- *Combine alternatives.* Piggyback ideas to produce new ones.
- *Stress a continuous flow of ideas.* No value judgment or evaluation of ideas is permitted during brainstorming.
- *Structure a way for students to share ideas.* Have students list ideas on the chalkboard, share ideas verbally, or discuss all the alternatives generated by all groups.

**FIGURE 4.2**  Brainstorming

## TEACHER TO TEACHER

One of the favorite activities of my students is brainstorming. It is such fun that they don't really care if they are stretching their brains by breaking away from the ordinary and looking for new associations and categories. When there are a few odd moments at the end of a class, I will quickly divide my class into two teams and give directions: (1) Each side take turns naming something that is _____. (I supply the topic, such as red, round, comes in pairs, kinds of dogs, boats, kinds of transportation, foods, starts with the letter *B*, words with double letters, etc. The list is endless and can relate to recently studied topics.) (2) Each person must listen carefully to be sure no one repeats what others have said or what he/she has said. (3) Repeaters or no answer in the called time take one step back but continue to play so they don't lose interest, or sit down but continue to listen for repeaters. (4) The team with the most people left standing (or in the original line) is the winning team when time is called.

Sometimes I have students write all the things they can within the three or five minute time I set. The one with the most answers calls out his/her list. We talk about how thinking of different categories helps generate ideas (for example, *foods*: green, red, yellow; then fruits, vegetables, meats, nuts; then tree-grown, underground, etc.). This is a good time to award a special ribbon or praise for originality to the person who names the one (or most) items that no one else named.

We need to foster the skills of creative thinking so students of all ages will come to accept and respect the fluent ideas of others and hopefully become more adept at those skills themselves. These are fun activities for any age student, but they really do improve as they practice and hear how others think.

Marion M. Sebastian
Berkeley Lake Elementary School
Duluth, GA

2. *Flexibility.* This skill involves drawing relationships between seemingly unrelated ideas (for example, how is a rubber band like a dictionary?). Locating common elements between items helps students look for many possible answers to a problem.

Another productive method for stimulating flexibility is attribute listing. Attributes may be defined as the qualities, characteristics, factors, features, traits, or structural or functional properties of an object, person, or situation (Baltimore County Public Schools, 1985). In the process of attribute listing, students examine and record the features of an idea or situation in order to redirect their thinking. An analysis of attributes allows students to identify new relationships that will aid problem solving. (See Table 4.3.)

3. *Originality.* This refers to the creation of ideas that are unique—those that are different from all others. It involves the willingness to take risks, to be unconventional, and to deviate from common patterns. The original thinker is able to analyze known information, to manipulate and transform it to reveal new and different relationships, and to recognize which ideas are the most original. The original thinker uses divergent strategies to create ideas and convergent thinking to evaluate ideas and refine them into a desirable outcome (Baltimore County Public Schools, 1985).

4. *Elaboration.* This is the process individuals go through to expand an idea until it is workable or feasible. It is a process of multiplication or addition that builds ideas into their final form. Ideas that require elaboration must be closely scrutinized for the interrelationships of component parts, for the complexity of detail, and for the integrity of the product or outcome as a whole. This procedure necessitates the simultaneous processing of these components so that a harmonious balance of analysis and synthesis is maintained.

TABLE 4.3

## MORPHOLOGICAL FORCED CONNECTION

Morphological forced connections is a variation of attribute listing designed to promote inventive thinking through forced associations. Students list the attributes of a concept or problem and brainstorm to come up with as many alternatives for the attribute as they can. They then select alternative attributes randomly from the chart to create new forms of the original subject.

**Example**

Directions:    Improve a thermometer

Attributes:    Glass      Round      Mercury      4″

Alternatives:  Metal      Square     Soda pop     2′
              Chocolate   Oval       Perfume      1″
              Mosaic      Rectangular Oil         15′
              China       Circular   Water        1′
              Tin         Figure-8   Soap         6″

Creation:      A chocolate, circular thermometer filled with soda pop that could be completely inserted in a person's mouth to record body temperature. Afterward, the thermometer could be eaten and swallowed.

## POINTS OF DISCUSSION

1. Add several entries to Table 4.1. What other types of activities do you believe can foster a thinking curriculum?
2. In terms of your projected teaching style, which of the problem-solving models presented would you be most comfortable using? Why?
3. Given the fact that most basal series in science do not emphasize problem-solving skills, how will you integrate problem solving into your classroom science program? Throughout your entire curriculum?
4. How has problem solving been treated in your college courses in education? In other fields? How has the inclusion or exclusion of problem solving helped you understand, appreciate, or use the principles or concepts of a course in the sciences? In history/political science? In the humanities? In English/speech? In the behavioral sciences?
5. Provide an example of how Polya's model would be used with a lesson on plant reproduction, static electricity, world climates, or the solar system.
6. Work with your classmates and design a series of discrepant events for the life, physical, and earth and space sciences.
7. What inhibits your creativity? What enhances your creativity?
8. What do you think you need to do to become a creative teacher? How can you ensure that you will follow through on those goals?

## REFERENCES AND SUGGESTED READINGS

Abell, Sandra. (1990, October). "The problem-solving muse." *Science and Children, 28*,(2), 27–29.

Baltimore County Public Schools. (1985). *Strategies for differentiating curricula.* Towson, MD: Author.

Barell, John. (1991). *Teaching for thoughtfulness: Classroom strategies to enhance intellectual development.* White Plains, NY: Longman.

Brookfield, Stephen. (1990, October). *Teaching critical thinking.* Paper presented at Harrisburg Area Community College, Harrisburg, PA.

Chaffee, John. (1991). *Thinking critically.* Boston: Houghtoin Mifflin.

Ennis, R. H. (1987). "A taxonomy of critical thinking dispositions and abilities." In J. Baron and R. Sternberg (Eds.),

*Teaching thinking skills* (pp. 9–26). New York: Freeman.

Fredericks, Anthony D. (1986, October). "Mental imagery activities to improve comprehension." *The Reading Teacher, (40)*(1) 78–81.

Fredericks, Anthony D. (1991). *Science brainstretchers: Creative problem-solving activities in science.* Glenview, IL: Scott, Foresman.

Fredericks, Anthony D. (1988). *The gifted reader handbook* Glenview, IL: Scott, Foresman.

George, K., Dietz, M., Abraham, E., & Nelson, M. (1974). *Elementary school science: Why and how.* Lexington, MA: D.C. Heath.

Goodlad, John. (1984). *A place called school.* New York: McGraw-Hill.

Goodnow, Judy, and Hoogeboom, Shirley. (1987). *The problem solver—4.* Sunnyvale, CA: Creative Publications.

Halpern, D. F. (1984). *Thought and knowledge: An introduction to critical thinking.* Hillsdale, NJ: Earlbaum.

Leyden, Michael. (1991, February). "Discrepant events." *Teaching K–8, 21*(5), 25–28.

National Assessment of Educational Progress. (1981). *Reading, thinking, and writing.* Princeton, NJ: Educational Testing Service.

Pasch, Marvin, Sparks-Langer, Georgea, Gardner, Trevor, Starko, Alane, & Moody, Christella. (1991). *Teaching as decision making: Instructional practices for the successful teacher.* White Plains, NY: Longman.

Polya, George. (1973). *How to solve it.* Princeton, NJ: Princeton University Press.

Pratt, Harold. (1981). "Science education in the elementary school." In Norris C. Harms and Roger E. Yager (Eds.), *What the research says to the science teacher: 3,* (pp. 76–77), Washington, DC: National Science Teachers Association.

Rath, Louis, Wassermann, Selma, Jonas, Arthur, & Rothstein, Arnold. (1986). *Teaching for thinking: Theory, strategies and activities for the classroom.* New York: Teachers College Press.

Sarason, Seymour. (1982). *The culture of the school and the problem of change.* Boston: Allyn & Bacon.

Schuncke, George. (1988). *Elementary social studies: Knowing, doing, caring.* New York: Macmillan.

Silverstein, Shel. (1974). *Where the sidewalk ends.* New York: Harper & Row.

Souviney, Randall J. (1981). *Solving problems kids care about.* Glenview, IL: Scott, Foresman.

Von Oech, Roger. (1983). *A whack on the side of the head.* New York: Warner.

Von Oech, Roger. (1986). *A kick in the seat of the pants.* New York: Harper & Row.

Wassermann, Selma, & Ivany, J. W. George. (1988). *Teaching elementary science: Who's afraid of spiders?* New York: Harper & Row.

Whimbey, Arthur. (1977). "Teaching sequential thought: The cognitive skills approach." *Phi Delta Kappa, 59,* 255–259.

# 5

# THE TEACHER'S ROLES
# AND RESPONSIBILITIES

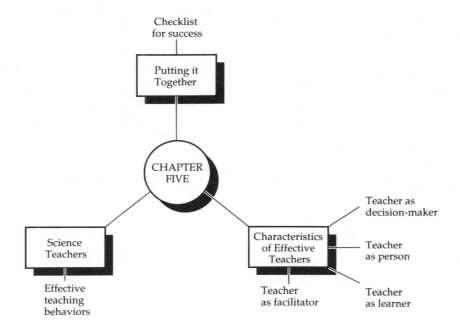

## Chapter Objectives

After reading this chapter you should be able to:

1. Identify the personality elements of good teachers of science.

2. Elaborate on the classroom requisites for effective teaching.

3. Define effective and ineffective teaching behaviors.

4. Explain the four major characteristics of effective teaching.

5. Understand the nature of motivation in science education.

It was early August, and Karen Manderbach was fever-ishly poring over all the teacher's manuals, curriculum guides, and class notes she could find in preparation for her first year of teaching. Karen had recently graduated from the state university with a degree in elementary education. Her student teaching experience had been wonderful. Her cooperating teacher had guided her into some exciting discoveries about herself and about the ways she could best teach students. Her supervisor at the college consistently gave her high marks on her classroom performance during the student teaching experience. The building principal had made two sep-arate evaluations of Karen's teaching and had sent a strong letter of recommendation for inclusion in her placement file. After graduation Karen had interviews with seven school districts before landing her first job—as a third-grade teacher in a suburban school district near her home. Her first year was about to start, and she was scared!

As Karen went over all the guides, notes, and manuals she began to realize that there was a lot she still needed to learn about being a good teacher. Her college classes had provided her with some of the attributes and attitudes necessary for effective teaching. The manuals and course guides given to her by her principal contained a wealth of data that had to be taught during the course of the school year. The teacher's manuals offered a plethora of facts and information pertinent to each area of the curriculum. It soon became apparent to Karen that her effectiveness as a teacher would go far beyond the information in these guides and books. She would have to be as much a learner as her students.

Karen's bewilderment is not unusual; it is quite common among many first-year teachers (and among teachers with many years of experience, too). First-year teachers often discover that their college courses provided only the fundamentals of various curricular areas and that it is up to the individual teacher to put them into motion and to make those facts and figures meaningful to children. This often means lots of on-the-job training. In other words, being a good teacher does not always depend on the grades you get in your college courses or the amount of knowledge you've crammed into your head during your four years of study; it may

be more dependent on how much you are willing to learn along with your students. In fact, the best teachers are those who have as much to learn as they do to teach.

One of the great misperceptions teachers have is the belief that they must be scientists to effectively teach science. Even the best scientists of this country will freely admit that they have only a whisper of knowledge about their chosen areas of expertise. But they do have an unsatiable desire to learn more, and that factor is what separates the average scientists from the great ones. Becoming a scientist is not a process of learning all there is to know about a subject but an ongoing process of adding to one's knowledge base. The same holds true for the classroom teacher. Science education is a partnership between teachers and students that stimulates inquiry and investigation rather than rote memorization.

Cohen, Staley, and Horak (1989) have developed a series of statements dealing with teacher perceptions of science. In Table 5.1 their list has been modified into a self-analysis questionnaire which you may wish to administer to yourself. After you have completed this questionnaire, you are encouraged to compare your perceptions with colleagues in your class. How do your views differ from those of your peers? What similarities do you note? What do the results of this survey indicate regarding science education in elementary classrooms? The answers to those questions may provide you with some interesting discussion points (see the points of discussion at the end of this chapter) to share in class.

## TO INVESTIGATE

Make several copies of Table 5.1 and visit several classrooms in your local area. Ask some teachers to complete the form (you may want to tell them that their responses are confidential and will not be sent to the principal). Once you and some of your classmates have several completed forms, bring them back to the class. Discuss any similarities or differences in the responses gathered. Do you note any widespread beliefs about the teaching of science? Are there major differences between the responses of more experienced teachers (more than 10 years) and those of novice teachers (less than 3 years)? Try to arrive at some generalizations about your collective data. ∎

## ATTRIBUTES OF GOOD TEACHERS OF SCIENCE

There are several features that contribute to one's effectiveness as a teacher of science. You may wish to consider the following factors in terms of your own personality dynamics and characteristics. They are purposely generic in nature and may offer you some in-

sights in terms of your approach to teaching science at the elementary level.

*Science teachers are creative.* They are willing to explore new dimensions and seek new possi-

## TABLE 5.1

................................................

### TEACHER PERCEPTIONS OF SCIENCE

................................................

| True | False | | |
|------|-------|---|---|
| ____ | ____ | 1. | Science is a body of accumulated knowledge. |
| ____ | ____ | 2. | The teacher must have a strong background in science to teach science. |
| ____ | ____ | 3. | Science is learned by reading and listening to others read from the science book. |
| ____ | ____ | 4. | Every child should have a science book. |
| ____ | ____ | 5. | All children should do the same experiments and get the same results. |
| ____ | ____ | 6. | A science demonstration is something that never seems to work, so it is better to ignore those in the teacher's guide. |
| ____ | ____ | 7. | Any science concept can be taught at any grade level. |
| ____ | ____ | 8. | All noise in the classroom is detrimental to learning. |
| ____ | ____ | 9. | Science need be taught only when there is nothing else to do in the day. |
| ____ | ____ | 10. | The purpose of elementary school science is to prepare children for junior high school and high school science. |

### Questions

A. Which of the statements do you support the most?
B. Which of the statements would *your* former elementary schools teachers have supported the most?
C. Which of the statements is most similar to your own philosophy about teaching science?
D. Which of the statements would your professor subscribe to the most? Which one would he or she argue against the most?
E. Based on your classroom observations, how do you think most teachers would respond to these statements?

bilities, never sure of what lies down the next path. They are willing to experiment with new approaches to learning simply because they've never been tried before.

*Science teachers are inquisitive.* They continuously ask questions, looking for new explanations and a myriad of new answers. In so doing, they serve as positive role models for students. They do not aim at finding all the answers but rather are content to develop a classroom environment in which self-initiated questioning (by both teacher and students) predominates.

*Science teachers are joyful.* They relish the thrill of discovery and the natural curiosity of children. They are excited about learning and transmit that excitement to their students. They are stimulated by the unknown and are amazed at what can be learned, not just at what is learned.

### DID YOU KNOW? _____

It has been calculated that in one 24-hour period all the people in the United States collectively grow a total of 6 square miles of new skin.

**Classroom Activity** Encourage students to develop growth charts for various parts of their body (e.g., hair, fingernails, toenails, arms, legs). Students may wish to create individual diaries of the growth patterns of their own bodies or develop a bulletin board display of the growth patterns of the class as a whole. Be sure to have students make some predictions about the rates of growth of the various body parts in addition to different ways those growth patterns can be measured (e.g., rulers, calipers). ■

*Science teachers are success-oriented.* They know that students should spend 60 to 70% of their time in moderate- to high-success activities (Borich, 1988). They are aware that this level of success will provide students with practical applications of the information learned in class and will enhance the development of self-concepts.

*Science teachers are change makers.* They know that change can be a positive element in every classroom. If something is not working, they will eagerly strike out into new territories for exploration. They are never content with status quo; their classrooms are always evolving.

*Science teachers are listeners.* They are aware of the "rule of two-thirds" which states that, irrespective of grade or subject, two-thirds of class time is taken up by talking, two-thirds of that time is taken up by teacher talk, and two-thirds of the teacher's talk consists of telling or demonstrating rather than interacting with students. These teachers know that children have much to contribute to the curriculum and to each other, and they provide numerous opportunities for them to do so.

*Science teachers are engagers.* They provide opportunites for emotional, mental, and physical engagement in all learning activities. They permit students to participate in a variety of ways, a variety of formats, and a variety of assignments. Students assume a measure of independence because they have a host of options available to meet their individual needs and interests.

*Science teachers are involved.* They are eager to work alongside their students, rather than giving out assignments, to discover and explore all the dimensions of science. They are willing to get their hands dirty ("hands-on") and keep an open mind ("minds-on") as to what could be, not just what is.

*Science teachers are decision makers.* They decide that children are capable of making their own decisions and living by those decisions. They offer students an arena in which self-selection and personal decision making is encouraged. They know that students will develop a sense of "ownership" about the science program when given opportunities to formulate directions and set individual goals.

*Science teachers are childlike.* They embrace the naturally inquisitive minds of children and their inherent quest for knowledge. They know that learning can be fun as well as instructive. They are not afraid of falling down and scraping their knees. They are playful yet determined. They engage in a multitude of interactive discussions and group decisions. They ask all kinds of questions—silly, irrelevant, nonjudgmental, exploratory, creative, provocative, and even those without any answers. They are adventurous and bold.

## TEACHER TO TEACHER

There I was, in slight heels, freezing and slightly angry at this science supervisor who had mandated that we participate in a workshop which involved hiking, crossing a creek, and completing a water quadrant survey, in the cold spring rain. To add injury to insult, we all had to wear garbage bags as raincoats and were given film cans to put our ashes in case we smoked. The beauty of the scenery did not calm me. I was uncomfortable. I won't even mention the outhouse or the three mile hike. And the tree I walked into on the night star hike to lie down in the meadows to look at the stars (I think the tree survived). I saw stars before we got to the meadow, but who knew the constellations in the night sky? I could rattle them off in the planetarium, but this was the real sky. I was lost.

Years later I reflected back on that experience. I now know the outdoor lab area like the back of my hand and have taken children there in winter (once in the snow) as often as possible. I got over thinking that glow worms were wild animals waiting to get me when I went to the outhouse. I learned to follow game trails and to teach students the patterns of nature. I can locate the plants of interest to a season and have even taught a lesson that I consider a great experience.

The children and I sat around the pond in the quiet to observe nightfall—using our five senses. We watched the tiny glimmer of the first stars and listed to the animal noises at night as the sky became inky dark. We splashed in the pond and heard dogs barking somewhere far away. A chorus of frogs started and we quietly got up and went in to write and draw about watching the night fall. Then, we wrote a book.

I became an amateur naturalist. I took classes at the Smithsonian and learned to teach children how to keep a naturalist's notebook of their visits. I've even taught at the outdoor laboratory in the summer and worked as a camp counselor for several weeks. And I have been to the Audubon Summer Camp and any other outdoor adventure that appeals to me. Sometimes, it's a matter of being exposed to ways of doing things or new ways of seeing how to teach something—even in cold spring rain—that makes you a better teacher. So try the training offered by uncommon places like museums and organizational societies. You have everything to gain.

Bonnie Bracey
Ashlawn Elementary School
Washington, D.C.

# CHARACTERISTICS OF EFFECTIVE TEACHERS

Table 5.2 lists 25 attributes of an effective teacher as specified by the Dallastown, Pennsylvania, Area school district.

## TO INVESTIGATE

Visit several teachers in some local schools. Make observations and create a list of those characteristics you feel the outstanding teachers display. What characteristics seem to turn up most often? Is there a pattern to those characteristics? Do the characteristics have more to do with teacher personality or with teacher training? After you have had an opportunity to share your list with some of your classmates, write a definition of a good teacher. How will you become such a teacher? How does your view compare with the views of your classmates? Share and discuss any similarities or differences. ■

TABLE  **5.2**

## DALLASTOWN, PA. AREA SCHOOL DISTRICT EFFECTIVE TEACHER BEHAVIORS

1.  Alert, appears enthusiastic
2.  Appears interested in pupils and classroom activities
3.  Cheerful, optimistic
4.  Self-controlled, not easily upset
5.  Likes fun, has sense of humor
6.  Recognizes and admits own mistakes
7.  Is fair, impartial, and objective in treatment of pupils
8.  Is patient
9.  Shows understanding and sympathy in working with pupils
10. Is friendly and courteous in relations with pupils
11. Helps pupils with personal as well as educational problems
12. Commends effort and gives praise for work well done
13. Accepts pupils' efforts as sincere
14. Anticipates reactions of others in social situations
15. Encourages pupils to try to do their best
16. Classroom procedure is planned and well organized
17. Classroom procedure is flexible within overall plan
18. Anticipates individual needs
19. Stimulates pupils through interesting and original materials and techniques
20. Conducts clear, practical demonstrations and explanations
21. Is clear and thorough in giving directions
22. Encourages pupils to work through their own problems and evaluate their accomplishments
23. Disciplines in quiet, dignified, and positive manner
24. Gives help willingly
25. Foresees and attempts to resolve potential difficulties

Students who are actively engaged in the processes of science are those who sense the significance of science in their everyday lives and their role in maximizing their own scientific growth. Helping pupils master the concepts and principles of science is not entirely dependent on good materials and lots of time. The classrooms where science is valued and mastered are those in which the teacher assumes the interrelated roles of *humanist, decision maker, learner,* and *facilitator.*

You should consider these four roles in terms of your own personality dynamics as well as in terms of your reasons for becoming a teacher of children.

## DID YOU KNOW?

When people sleep their capillaries expand, which speeds the spread of nutrients. That's why children tend to grow faster when they're asleep than when they're awake.

**Classroom Activity** At the beginning of the year direct each student in your classroom to lie down on a sheet of newsprint. Have another student trace a line around the student lying down. Then ask each student to cut out his or her outline. Within the borders of the outline have students record all their vital physical data ( height, weight, temperature, waist size, shirt size, length of right foot, length of left foot, etc.). Post these outlines in a prominent place. At several times during the year ask students to take new measurements of themselves and record the new data on their individual outlines. Plan some time at the end of the year to discuss the growth patterns of individuals within the classroom as well as the class as a whole (How much total weight did the entire class gain? How many inches did the entire class gain in the measurements of their left feet?). ■

## Teacher as Person

The reasons you are in a teacher preparation program are undoubtedly manifold. One's personality and how it is shared with children are significant determinants for choosing the profession of teaching, and for success in the classroom. The personality of a teacher is also a major factor in the success of students within that teacher's influence.

Who you are and what you believe are as important to the success of your science program as the information you share and the activities in which your students participate. Teachers with strong personality characteristics such as those in the following list can ensure that their instruction is sincere, personal, and creative.

1. *Teachers should be enthusiastic.* Your enthusiasm and excitement about teaching will rub off on your students. If you are "energized" about the teaching of science, your students will be "energized" about the learning of science. Your expectations for teaching and your expectations for your students must be high.

### IDEA BOX

Start off each of your daily lessons with a "focus question." A focus question is designed to stimulate students' imaginations and tune them in to the concepts and content of a particular lesson. For example:

"Have you ever thought about what would happen if there were no gravity?"
"How would your life be different if you were allowed to eat only plants?"
"Did you know that when it's summer in the Northern Hemisphere, it's winter in the Southern Hemisphere?"
"What kind of damage would a severe earthquake cause in our town?"

Focus questions alert students to the information to be presented in the lesson and make them inquisitive. You may even want to pose a focus question at the start of the school day and save the answer till later in the day when the science lesson is presented.

2. *Teachers should have a sense of humor.* Sure, science is serious, but you and your students can also have a lot of fun as you experience all the dynamics of science. Plan to collect jokes, riddles, and quips from all kinds of sources. (For an example of appropriate science-related humor, see Table 5.3.) Keep a classroom journal and make regular entries for everyone to enjoy. Be willing to laugh at yourself when you make a mistake or goof up. Let students see the lighter side of science.

TABLE **5.3**

### SCIENCE DEFINITIONS NOT IN YOUR USUAL DICTIONARY

| | |
|---|---|
| Announce | One-sixteenth of a pound |
| Archeologist | A scientist whose career lies in ruins |
| Arthritis | Twinges in the hinges |
| Bacteria | The rear of a cafeteria |
| Bass | A fish with a deep voice |
| Bigamist | A dense fog |
| Caterpillar | An upholstered worm |
| Climate | What you do to get to the top of a hill |
| Coffee | Break fluid |
| Decomposing | What Beethoven is doing |
| Deliver | An important body organ |
| Eclipse | What a barber does |
| Iceberg | A permanent wave |
| Illegal | A sick bird |
| Liter | A nest of kittens |
| Meteorologist | A man who can look in a woman's eyes and tell whether |
| Myth | A small moth |
| Nightingale | A very windy evening |
| Paradox | Two physicians |
| Propaganda | A socially correct goose |
| Quartz | Two pints |
| Seismologist | Fault finder |
| Tears | Glum drops |
| Tin | Not fat |
| Vitamin | What you do when someone visits |
| Zinc | Where you put the dirty dishes |
| Zookeeper | A critter sitter |

3. *Teachers should be encouraging.* Think of the first time you tried to ride a bicycle. Did you get up on the bike and ride continuously for 10 miles? Of course not! You probably fell down a few times, skinned your knees, scraped your hands, and collected an assortment of bumps and bruises. But eventually you learned how to ride a bike. The same process applies in science. Children may not be able to master all the concepts and principles the first time around (just as you probably did not master the pedals, brakes, steering, and gear shifting during that first bike ride). Your encouragement to help children persevere and try again can be a significant factor in their success in science.

4. *Teachers should be passionate.* Good teachers are good because they not only have a love for children, but they also have a passion for the subjects they teach. If you're passionate about teaching, students will recognize it immediately. If you're less than excited about what you are doing, children will perceive

that very quickly. Your passion for teaching science must be evident in everything you do with the children.

**DID YOU KNOW?** _____

Crows are known for their loud and raucous cawing. One major reason for all that noise is that it helps to cheer up depressed members of the flock.

**Classroom Activity** Have students make several bird feeders. Simple ones can be made from plastic milk cartons. Cut a hole or square from one side of the carton (about 3″ × 3″). Hang three or four of these cartons outside the window of your classroom or in some nearby trees. Sprinkle some bird seed in the bottom of each feeder. Provide students with notebooks and ask them to record the different varieties of birds that visit the feeders, the time of day they visit, the behavior patterns, and how long they feed. Have students keep these notebooks throughout the year and note any changes in bird behavior from season to season. ■

## Teacher as Decision Maker

Making decisions, particularly about the scope and direction of the science curriculum, is never an easy process. Obviously, good decisions come from a combination of self-assurance and practice. If you are not confident in your own abilities as a science educator, you may not be able to inspire confidence in your students. Consider some of the following decisions, which may need to be made prior to or during the teaching of a science lesson. The answers will change from lesson to lesson; there are no quick and easy answers. Rather, they are presented in order for you to consider a small fraction of the choices you will need to make throughout every science lesson you teach.

- How do I provide for individual needs?
- What materials shall I use?
- When should I start the lesson?
- What are my objectives?
- How shall I arrange the room?
- What grouping patterns should I use?
- How shall I terminate the lesson?
- What kinds of extending activities should I use?
- How many activities should there be?
- Should I use audiovisual materials?
- What audio-visual materials are available?
- How much material from the text should I use?
- How can I provide for the needs of the less able students?
- What happens if the experiment doesn't work?

- Where should I put all the materials?
- What are some of the responsibilities of students?
- How can I inject some humor into this lesson?
- What will keep excitement and enthusiasm high?
- What should students do after the lesson is over?
- Do I need help?
- Is there another way of teaching this lesson?
- What questions should I ask?
- Will students need to do any writing or recording?
- Why didn't I become a doctor like my mother wanted me to?

It should be evident that you will be making decisions all the time. Some will be easy, some difficult. Nevertheless, your ability to face the decision-making process with confidence and enthusiasm will have many positive effects on your ability to engage students in the learning process.

## Teacher as Learner

No doubt you're looking forward to the day when all your college classes are over and you've secured that first teaching position. That will be an exciting time in your life. However, as your professors may have suggested, that is just the beginning of your education rather than the end. Good teachers add to their knowledge base throughout their entire teaching career. If you are to provide the best possible education for your students, you need to provide yourself with a variety of learning opportunities, too. It is erroneous

to think that four or five years of college are all that is needed to be successful in the classroom. There are too many developments within the field of education and especially within the field of science for you to think that your college degree is the summation of all the skills and knowledge you'll need for the rest of your career. Indeed, what you learn throughout your teaching career may be significantly more important than the courses you've taken in college.

Good teachers of science will keep current, stay active, and continually seek out new answers or new questions for exploration. Your desire to find out more about effective teaching methods and new discoveries within the scientific community can add immeasurably to your talents as a teacher and also to your students' appreciation of science in their own lives. Following are some selected resources for you to explore during your teaching career. Additional resources can be found in the appendices.

1. *Professional Organizations.* Joining a professional organization—whether on a national, regional, or local level—can provide you with some important contacts. This "sharing of kindred spirits" is important not only for keeping current in the field of science, but also for sharing ideas and opportunities about the teaching of science. It provides you with wonderful opportunities to remain active throughout the whole sphere of teaching. Following are the addresses of some of the major organizations.

   American Association for the Advancement
     of Science
   (AAAS)
   1333 H Street, NW
   Washington, DC 20005

   National Center for the Improvement
     of Science
   Teaching and Learning
   The NETWORK, Inc.
   290 South Main St.
   Andover, MA 01810

   National Science Teachers Association
   1742 Connecticut Ave. NW
   Washington, DC 20009

2. *Conferences and conventions.* Attending a professional conference or convention on a regular basis provides you with first-hand experiences and contacts available nowhere else. You can interact with other teachers and science professionals from throughout the country. This sharing of knowledge is essential if you are to stay current with the processes and discoveries of science education. Conferences are an exciting way to learn about new products, discover new strategies, and investigate new happenings.

3. *Journals for teachers.* There are several professional journals with which you should familiarize yourself as part of your career development. Your college library, a local public library, or the school library probably subscribes to these journals or can acquire them. You may also wish to consider a subscription for yourself. These periodicals are an invaluable source of information on the teaching of science as well as discoveries throughout the scientific community. They are an essential part of your professional growth. Some of the better-known titles are:

   *Science and Children* (National Science Teachers Association, 1742 Connecticut Ave., NW, Washington, DC 20009)

   *The Universe in the Classroom* (Teacher's Newsletter Department, Astronomical Society of the Pacific, 1290 24th Street, San Francisco, CA 94122)

   *IConnect* (Teacher's Laboratory, Inc., P.O. Box 6480, Brattleboro, VT 05301)

4. *Popular Magazines for Teachers.* There are several popular magazines and periodicals that can also be part of your professional library. It is not necessary to subscribe to all of them, but a subscription to one or two will give you some intriguing insights into the wide world of science that can make your classroom program more exciting. The following are some of the more familiar titles:

   *Omni* (1965 Broadway, New York, NY 10023)

   *Discover* (P.O. Box 420105, Palm Coast, FL 32142-0105)

   *Popular Science* (2 Park Ave., New York, NY 10016)

5. *Magazines for Children.* As part of your professional growth you may also wish to consult science magazines geared to children. These periodicals are designed to offer youngsters a "painless" approach to the subject, one that underscores the excitement and challenges of the world of science. Children's magazines offer interesting ideas on how children can learn and appreciate science. Following are a few examples:

   *National Geographic World* (17th and M Streets, N.W., Washington, DC 20036)

   *Owl* (Young Naturalist Foundation, 59 Front St., Toronto, Ontario M5E 1B3 Canada)

   *3-2-1 Contact* (E = MC Square, P.O. Box 2932, Boulder, CO 80321)

   *Science World Magazine* (902 Sylvan Ave., Englewood Cliffs, NJ 07632)

## IDEA BOX

Contact several elementary school librarians and ask them if they have some old science magazines they would be willing to donate to your classroom (many schools discard magazines that are five years old or more). Work with your students in removing articles of particular interest from the magazines and collecting them in thematic books (home-made books containing articles about a single subject, e.g., animals, ocean exploration, or space travel). Relate these "books" to your science curriculum and you'll have some interesting reference materials for your students to use as supplements to the textbook. (You may also be able to obtain some old books or magazines from your college professors.)

## TEACHER TO TEACHER

The key to successful hands-on science teaching is sharing and scavenging. No single basal text has enough appropriate activities for a truly hands-on approach. Whenever possible, avail yourself of the opportunities to find more activities which you can use to supplement and enhance your curriculum. Those opportunities might include: attending workshops at state, regional, and national conventions; subscribing to science education journals, such as *Science and Children*; participating in in-sevice courses within your district; or simply saying to a colleague, "What activities do you use to teach this concept?" You'll be amazed at the wealth of good ideas that do exist, and by constantly adding new ideas to your own "bag of tricks," you will be keeping your teaching fresh and your students excited about "the magic of science."

Marilyn A. Richardson
Hawthorne Brook Middle School
Townsend, MA

## Teacher as Facilitator

Many people have the misconceptions of a teacher as one who dispenses massive amounts of information and of students as individuals who are supposed to soak up that information. Such people regard educators as those members of society who have all the answers to all the questions (perhaps they are perceived as having all the questions, too).

Experience has taught us that the best and most difficult role teachers can assume is that of facilitator. Teachers should provide opportunities for learning rather than simply providing all the learning. Giving students an arena in which they can make their own discoveries and chart their own explorations through the world of science will yield higher numbers of active learners.

## DID YOU KNOW?

If it were possible to weigh all of the land animals on the surface of the earth, ants would constitute 10 to 15% of the total weight.

**Classroom Activity** All students are interested in classroom pets and animals. Your students may wish to set up their own ant farm. You can obtain the Critter Condo®from Nasco (901 Janesville Ave., Fort Atkinson, WI 53538), which includes certificates for ants, butterfly larvae, cacti, and frogs. Better yet, have students create their own animal housing and collect species indigenous to your local area. Obtain a copy of *Pets in a Jar: Collecting and Caring for Small Wild Animals* by Seymour Simon (New York: Viking, 1975). ∎

As a facilitator, you must be willing to provide opportunities for learning. Consider the following guidelines as part of the facilitative process.

## Know What Your Students Know

Say you are experiencing some mechanical problems with your car. You take it to your local mechanic for repair. Usually, your mechanic will ask you to describe the problems you're having. You'll mention the knocks, pings, grinds, and other sounds and difficulties with the car. The mechanic will write down your description of the trouble on some sort of repair list. That information is vital in helping your mechanic pinpoint the difficulty and repair it properly. Without that information the mechanic may have no idea where to begin or what to look for in performing the necessary repair work.

The same holds true in your classroom. It is essential that you know the strengths and weaknesses of your students, the knowledge they have about a particular topic, and how you are going to fill any gaps in their knowledge base. Awareness of your student's background knowledge is the one of the most critical factors in your success as a teacher of science. You need to be consistently sensitive to what your students know, how they learned what they know, and what they are doing with what they know.

It is imperative that you know the individual differences among your students so that you can provide a learning environment that capitalizes on the specific strengths of each student. The significance of this factor becomes clear when you consider that 60 to 80 percent of the differences in students' achievement scores is due to differences in students' prior learning (Bloom, 1976).

## Stimulate Responsible Students

During your tenure as a teacher, you will undoubtedly be asked some of the following questions several times each day:

"Is this what you wanted?"
"How did I do?"
"What do you want me to do now?"
"What should I be doing here?"

Such questions send a strong message that students are overly reliant on the teacher to make decisions for them. These queries indicate that students have not been given adequate opportunities to make their own choices based on their own needs and interests.

One of the traps we fall into as teachers is to tell students everything they must do or learn. In so doing, we help to create "irresponsible learners"—students who depend on the teacher for their direction and decision making. These students are teacher-dependent instead of student-independent.

It is vital that we provide students with opportunities to chart the course of their learning. In this way we are saying to them that they are capable of making decisions and living by the consequences of those decisions. This means relinquishing some of the control we have in the classroom. It does not entail telling students everything they must do or think, but rather working alongside of them to help them in making decisions. The locus of control must lie with the student. Learning is an individual matter; no one can do it for us.

## IDEA BOX

When a student asks you "How did I do?" or a similar question, turn the question back on the student and ask the child to make some personal decisions about his or her own work or progress. For example, consider the following responses:

"How do you feel about your work so far?"
"Do you feel this represents your best effort?"
"What else do you think needs to be done?"
"What is another possible way of looking at this?"
"What have you learned from this activity?"
"Why do you think your conclusion is appropriate?"
"Is there another way of approaching this?"

Such questions give students opportunities to think about what they are doing or have done as opposed to having the teacher make those decisions. When students can internalize their work, that work becomes more meaningful to them.

Table 5.4 Outlines several tips and strategies you can incorporate in your classroom routine to assist students in assuming more responsibility within the science program. These practices will help students become more independent thinkers. Never do for students what they themselves can do when they're taught.

TABLE **5.4**

......................................................................................

## HELPING STUDENTS BECOME MORE RESPONSIBLE

......................................................................................

| Process | Value |
| --- | --- |
| Give infrequent praise. Ask students to evaluate their own work. | Students often become overly dependent on teacher recognition. They need to recognize the worth of their own efforts. |
| Point out the positive results of students' actions ("Your contribution was important in helping your group complete the task"). | Students need to know that their efforts are valued by others in the classroom and that responsible learning has a positive *affective* side, too. |
| Let students decide on various ways to approach an assignment or task. | Inviting student input gives students a sense of "ownership," a feeling that the task is theirs and is not done for the convenience of the teacher. |
| Let students know that you need their contribution, that you will be counting on them to decide on several courses of action within a lesson or unit. | Students need to know that they *can* make contributions, that the program is not driven by a dictatorial teacher's manual. |
| Don't just assign tasks and have students complete them. Work alongside students, encouraging, prodding, and stimulating when necessary. | Students need to feel that teaching and learning is a partnership, that they have just as much to say about what can be learned as the teacher. |
| Let students teach you. | Don't assume that you are the repository of all science knowledge at your grade level. Students (indeed, all of us) need to know that they have something of value that can be shared. |

## Be Passionate About Science

During the first few years of teaching there are many routines and subjects to master. Science is only one of many areas you will need to master, and it is the area in which many novice teachers feel the least competent. The point stressed throughout this text, is that you do not need to know everything there is to know about science or science teaching. Indeed, a certain amount of ignorance can be a blessing in disguise.

More important than content is the passion and desire with which you approach science. You serve as a most influential model for your students, and your enthusiasm and energy will have an enormous impact on how your students approach science education.

### DID YOU KNOW? _____

Scientists have determined that the common housefly hums in the key of F.

**Classroom Activity**   Insects have always fascinated children. Extend the learning opportunities for your students by sharing one or more of the following books: *Backyard Insects* by Millicent Selsam and Ronald Goor (New York: Four Winds, 1981); *Wasps* by Sylvia Johnson (New York: Lerner, 1984); and *Where Do They Go: Insects in Winter* by Millicent Selsam (New York: Four Winds, 1982). For a humorous look at the insect world, get *Insects All Around* by Richard Armour (New York: McGraw-Hill, 1981).  ■

## Be a True Motivator

One of the questions you may be asking yourself now — and will certainly ask yourself during your first few years of teaching — is "How can I motivate my students in science?" Motivation is defined as the stimulation for a human action. People can be encouraged to pursue a task to a satisfactory conclusion. For example, you are probably motivated to complete your college courses and your student teaching experience so that you can obtain your certificate. You may also be motivated to get a job, to complete an assignment, or to join your friends for a weekend social engagement. Typically, your motivation takes one of two forms: *intrinsic* motivation and *extrinsic* motivation.

Extrinsic motivation comes from outside the individual. Other people (e.g. parents, teachers, friends) tell the person what to do or how to do something. Intrinsic motivation comes from within the individual. The individual makes decisions on what will be done and how it will be accomplished. For example, take a look at the following two statements and mark each one "true" or "false."

_____ My parents told me what college I should attend.
_____ I decided to become a teacher. Nobody made that
        decision for me.

As you might expect, the first statement reflects extrinsic motivation, and the second involves intrinsic factors. Your motivation to attend this particular college and to become a teacher may have been determined by others, or it may have been the result of your own choosing. Observations of children have shown that those students who are more intrinsically motivated tend to do better academically, or, conversely, a larger proportion of "below average" students are extrinsically motivated. This certainly does not imply a cause-and-effect situation but, rather, a need to be aware of the procedures and methodologies we can use in our classrooms to promote a more intrinsic orientation to learning.

Table 5.5 on page 87 provides some dos and don'ts for promoting higher levels of intrinsic motivation in your classroom.

Hooper and Miller (1991) found that there is a direct relationship between the types of tasks teachers give students and their level of motivation to complete those tasks. Their findings indicate that teachers traditionally provide high-level students with more challenging, open-ended, and creative assignments whereas lower-level students are provided with less creative, "fill-in-the-blank" type assignments. What is most interesting about their study is the finding that students, no matter what their ability level, were more intrinsically motivated when provided with more complex assignments. This has significant ramifications for the teacher of science who wishes to help students achieve a form of motivation that is self-initiated and self-perpetuating. In short, it means that a process approach to science, one in which students are given numerous opportunities to ask their own questions

TABLE **5.5**

. . . . . . . . . . . . . . . . . . . . . . . . . . . . . . . . . . . . . . . . . . . . . . . . . . . . . . . . . . . . . . . . . . .
## MOTIVATIONAL STRATEGIES
. . . . . . . . . . . . . . . . . . . . . . . . . . . . . . . . . . . . . . . . . . . . . . . . . . . . . . . . . . . . . . . . . . .

| Do | Don't |
|---|---|
| Solicit lots of student ideas. | Give lots of stickers, certificates, and the like. |
| Encourage students to pose lots of questions. | Continually tell students what they should or must do. |
| Give students a sense of belonging in the classroom. | Always call on the "brightest" students to provide answers. |
| Allow students some degree of choice in selecting activities, projects, and experiences. | Use grades as a form of "punishment." |
| Throughout a lesson, encourage students to verbalize what they are doing and why. | Follow the scope and sequence of the teacher's manual explicitly. |
| Provide many opportunities for students, at all ability levels, to experience success. | Promote a competitive atmosphere that pits one student against another. |
| Invite students to "design" lessons or components of lessons. | Emphasize grades over learning. |

and pursue the answers to those questions, will result in higher levels of intrinsic motivation for *all* students. On the other hand, science assignments that rely on workbooks, text-based experiments, and other forms of convergent thinking may actually be detrimental to your efforts in motivating students. A diversity of complex and divergent tasks is the key to a successful (and motivational) science program.

Table 5.6 on page 88 lists a number of questions you should ask yourself in the course of a science lesson to ensure that you are providing an environment in which students are motivated.

. . . . . . . . . . . . . . . . . . . . . . . . . . . . . . . . . . . . . . . . . . . . . . . . . . . . . . . . . . . . . . . . . . . .
# PUTTING IT ALL TOGETHER
. . . . . . . . . . . . . . . . . . . . . . . . . . . . . . . . . . . . . . . . . . . . . . . . . . . . . . . . . . . . . . . . . . . .

Undoubtedly, by this time you are beginning to wonder if you'll ever learn all this material and be an effective teacher as well. With so many skills and so much information to master, with so many different kinds of students in the classroom, and with so many other things taking place in your personal life, the first few years of teaching may seem daunting.

This section presents a design that incorporates several of the ideas presented in this chapter in an "easy-to-swallow" format. Constructed by Shier and O'Brien (1990) it is a plan of action that provides numerous learning opportunities for students and takes advantage of their natural curiosity. Entitled the Activity-Based Primary Science Project, it is geared to the introduction of science to primary-level (grades 1–3) students. However, in reviewing this plan you will quickly see

that it also has many ramifications for intermediate-level (grades 4–6) students.

This approach to science education is structured on nine key elements:

- Students are given the opportunity to encounter natural phenomena through first-hand experiences.
- Students can use familiar objects in real-life settings.
- Students are encouraged to actively construct knowledge and explanation.
- Students can integrate science processes and problem-solving skills.
- Student activities are developmentally appropriate and capitalize on early childhood experiences.
- Students employ risk taking, divergent thinking, and self-initiated questioning.

TABLE   **5.6**

......................................................................................................

## QUESTIONS TO ASK YOURSELF DURING SCIENCE LESSONS

......................................................................................................

### Before the Lesson

| | | |
|---|---|---|
| YES | NO | Have I provided opportunities for students to relate this lesson to past experiences? |
| YES | NO | Have I identified the purpose of this lesson for students? |
| YES | NO | Do students understand why this information is important to them? |
| YES | NO | Will students have opportunities to work collaboratively to solve problems and pursue questions? |
| YES | NO | Will I need to consult additional resources before beginning this lesson? |
| YES | NO | Am I enthusiastic about this lesson? |
| YES | NO | Will students have sufficient opportunities to become actively engaged in all dimensions of the lesson? |
| YES | NO | Have I prepared a sufficient number of high-level thinking questions as well as several critical thinking procedures? |
| YES | NO | Have I provided opportunities for students to set and pursue their own self-initiated objectives? |

### During the Lesson

| | | |
|---|---|---|
| YES | NO | Am I explaining things simply? |
| YES | NO | Am I conducting the lesson at an appropriate pace—not too fast, not too slow? |
| YES | NO | Are students able to understand the relationship of these concepts to other areas of the curriculum? |
| YES | NO | Am I learning new things along with the students? |
| YES | NO | Am I encouraging peer listening and responsive interaction? |
| YES | NO | Am I providing sufficient examples and explaining procedures appropriately? |
| YES | NO | Do students have multiple opportunities to ask their own questions and direct their own courses of investigation? |
| YES | NO | Am I making this lesson enjoyable, informative, and interesting? |
| YES | NO | Am I learning some new information? |
| YES | NO | Am I providing opportunities for students to monitor and evaluate their own discoveries? |
| YES | NO | Am I probing for clarification, extension, and/or expansion of responses? |
| YES | NO | Am I providing adequate thinking time throughout the lesson? |
| YES | NO | Am I encouraging and supportive of *all* students? |
| YES | NO | Am I using humor as a vehicle for enhancing students' enjoyment of the lesson? |
| YES | NO | Am I doing all the work for students? |
| YES | NO | Am I accepting students' contributions nonjudgmentally? |
| YES | NO | Am I on the same level with the students (based on Bloom's taxonomy)? |
| YES | NO | Am I communicating with the students? |

### After the Lesson

| | | |
|---|---|---|
| YES | NO | Are students able to summarize the lesson in their own words? |
| YES | NO | Do students have some unanswered questions about the lesson? |
| YES | NO | Have I provided opportunities for students to extend their knowledge of the topic through additional resources or materials? |
| YES | NO | Are students encouraged to pursue the lesson concepts in other areas of the curriculum? |
| YES | NO | Are students encouraged to seek alternative answers? |
| YES | NO | Would students want to pursue this lesson again? |
| YES | NO | Was the lesson well planned and well organized? |
| YES | NO | Did I provide students with opportunities to work through their own problems? |
| YES | NO | Do students have multiple opportunities to evaluate and assess their own performance? |

- Students are engaged in a motivating classroom environment based on success, encouragement, and frequent student-teacher interaction.
- Students are involved in varied classroom settings, including individualized instruction, cooperative learning, whole class demonstrations, and interest centers.
- Students are provided with activities organized around seasonal themes and traditional life, earth, and physical science topics.

You should notice in these descriptors that much of the learning that takes place is initiated by and geared toward students and their penchant for satisfying their own curiosity. The learning does not necessarily come from books or other material, but rather is built around a "hands-on, minds-on" approach to science education. In many ways, this is what "sciencing" is all about.

The Activity Based Primary Science Project is founded on a six-stage activity pattern. Again, you will note that these stages are in agreement with the qualities of an effectively organized science program. Lessons are structured on the following sequence:

1. Ask a question requiring reasoning (estimate/ predict).
2. Engage in activity (real-life experience).
3. Measure/count (make computations) and record.
4. Graph information.
5. Find a pattern, rule, relationship, generalization, or formula.
6. Extend activity; ask new questions.

Note how the investigation presented in Table 5.7 utilizes many of the attributes cited as important in science lessons. Note particularly the degree to which the teacher is involved (or uninvolved) in this activity.

The Activity Based Primary Science Project focuses on discovery learning in its truest sense. Students are provided with opportunities to ask their own questions and initiate their own investigations in an atmosphere that supports their natural curiosity. This approach does not rely on the memorization of lifeless facts and figures but rather depends on students taking charge of their learning.

In many ways, plans such as this exemplify the best kind of science education. Your role in this effort is to provide an arena conducive to this and encourage students to pursue knowledge in keeping with their interests and needs. It is a responsibility you should not take lightly and should promote enthusiastically.

**DID YOU KNOW?** _____

Several medical research studies have shown that the higher the altitude the lower the cancer rate.

**Classroom Activity**   Organize the students into small groups of medical researchers. Ask them to chart the course of diseases and illnesses contracted by members of the class. What illnesses seem to be most prevalent? Which ones last the longest? Which individuals seem to get sick the most? The least? How does one's lifestyle or diet affect the number or severity of illnesses contracted? Based on the data they collect throughout the year, what types of prevention methods would they suggest? This information can be collected in a brochure and distributed to other classes.  ■

The checklist in Table 5.8 on page 90 can be used to gauge the effectiveness of your science lessons. No teacher will get all 5s on this list, and you will undoubtedly note one or more areas for improvement. It is suggested that you complete this list at the beginning of the school year as well as at the midpoint. You can thereby identify specific areas for strengthening.

TABLE   **5.7**

..................................................................................................................

## HOW FAR CAN A MEALWORM CRAWL?

..................................................................................................................

| | |
|---|---|
| Question | How far will a mealworm crawl into two minutes? Cut pieces of string or yarn to show predictions. |
| Activity | Place four or five mealworms on a large piece of white chart paper and trace their path for two minutes. |
| Collect and Compute | Cut a piece of string or yarn to match the mealworm's path. Compare that piece with the prediction piece. If desired, compute the difference. |
| Graph | Make a three-column graph with all the path strings. Label columns "too long," "too short," and "just right." Distances can also be graphed by comparing each string to a nonstandard unit of measure (e.g., attribute blocks or mealworm body lengths), and the units can be used for a real, pictorial, or symbolic graph. |
| Interpret | Did all the mealworms crawl? Did all the mealworms crawl the same direction? How would you describe the way the mealworms crawled? What kind of path do most mealworms make? Did most mealworms crawl shorter distances, longer distances, or the same distance as predicted? Did all mealworms crawl the same distance? What was the typical distance crawled by the mealworms? What did you find out about how far mealworms crawl? |
| Extend | Would a mealworm crawl twice the distance in four minutes? Would a mealworm crawl the same distance every time? What would make a mealworm crawl further? Not as far? |

TABLE   **5.8**

......................................................................................

## CHECKLIST FOR SUCCESS

......................................................................................

*Key:* 5 = Always
   4 = Mostly
   3 = Sometimes
   2 = Infrequently
   1 = Never

| | | |
|---|---|---|
| 1. | I am enthusiastic about my lessons. | 5  4  3  2  1 |
| 2. | I relate science to students' everyday lives. | 5  4  3  2  1 |
| 3. | "Hands-on, minds-on" science is stressed. | 5  4  3  2  1 |
| 4. | I have equal expectations for all students. | 5  4  3  2  1 |
| 5. | Exercises do not require single "right" answers. | 5  4  3  2  1 |
| 6. | Lectures and "book learning" are kept to a minimum. | 5  4  3  2  1 |
| 7. | Activities are designed to foster the development of process skills. | 5  4  3  2  1 |
| 8. | A variety of questioning methods are utilized. | 5  4  3  2  1 |
| 9. | Students can interact with one another in various ways. | 5  4  3  2  1 |
| 10. | Students are provided with numerous opportunities to make their own discoveries. | 5  4  3  2  1 |

......................................................................................

## POINTS OF DISCUSSION

......................................................................................

1. Complete Table 5.1. Discuss any similarities or differences between the data you generate and the data generated by your classmates. What can you infer from this information?

2. Interview a first-grade teacher and a sixth-grade teacher on the role of motivation in the science program. Are their motivation levels higher or lower for science than for other subjects? What about their students' levels of motivation? How do they each motivate students?

3. Interview several parents of elementary students. What do they feel their role is in promoting science in the school or in the home?

4. Recall some of your elementary teachers. What characteristics did they have that were positively or negatively related to your success in science?

5. Survey several of your classmates. What characteristics of their professors do they identify as crucial

their success in and enjoyment of college science courses? What implications are there for the elementary classroom?

6. Interview several students who plan to take this course in the future. What personality characteristics do they want in the professors that would make the course enjoyable and profitable for them?

7. How would you gauge yourself as a learner? What will you do after you leave college to continue being a learner?

8. How important is a sense of humor in maximizing the learning opportunities for students?

9. Has your passion for science changed as a result of taking this course? To what do you attribute any changes?

......................................................................................

## REFERENCES AND SUGGESTED READINGS

......................................................................................

Bloom, B. *Human characteristics and school learning.* (1976). New York: McGraw-Hill.

Borich, G. D. (1988). *Effective teaching methods.* Columbus, OH: Merrill.

Cohen, H. G., Staley, F. A., and Horak, W. J. (1989). *Teaching science as a decision making process.* Dubuque, IA: Kendall/Hunt.

DeVito, A., and Krockover, G. (1976) *Creative sciencing: A practical approach.* Boston: Little, Brown.

Hooper, M. L. and Miller, S. (1991). *Motivational responses to simple and complex classroom assignments by high, average, and low achievers: classroom implications.* Unpublished manuscript, University of North Carolina at Greensboro.

Shier, P., and O'Brien, G. (1990, April). *The Activity Based Primary Science Project.* Paper presented at the National Science Teachers Association Annual Convention, Atlanta, GA.

CHAPTER

# 6

# RESOURCES, MATERIALS, AND THE SCIENCE TEXTBOOK

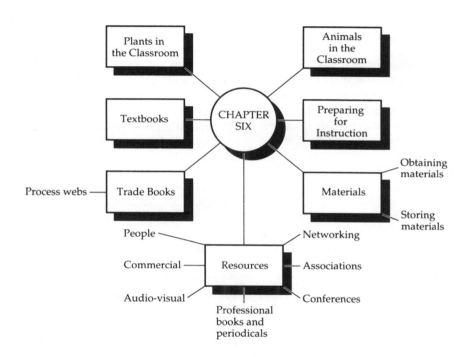

## Chapter Objectives

After reading this chapter you should be able to:

1. Explain the variety of resources available in the design of a complete science program.

2. Elaborate on the wealth of materials that can be located, constructed, and used in the science program.

3. Describe the steps necessary in preparing for instruction.

4. State how and when living organisms can and should be used in the classroom.

5. Detail the advantages and disadvantages of typical science textbooks.

6. Illustrate how science trade books can be used as valuable components of the overall science curriculum.

Even though, as this text has stressed, science is very much a "people activity," you will need some assistance in helping students gain an appreciation for science learning. That assistance usually takes the form of the resources, materials, and texts available in the classroom. What you use and how you use it will be a major factor in the construction of your classroom science program, just as it will be a major element in the overall success of your program.

This chapter provides an overview of some of the resources, materials, and textual items available to you and your students. Consider them as possibilities, not absolutes, for the design of your individual science program.

# RESOURCES

A science program can be as broad and as detailed as you wish it to be. It need not be constrained by the dictates of the science text or district-planned curriculum in order to be effective. And it does not need to be hampered by your unfamiliarity or uncomfortableness in teaching science. There is a wealth of resources at your disposal that can be powerful adjuncts to the classroom program and can provide wonderful insights for your students. By taking advantage of the many resources both in and outside of the classroom, you can help students appreciate the universality of science and its applications to their daily lives.

You probably have some fears, perhaps even some misgivings, about your ability to teach science. These fears may be related to your own experiences as a former elementary student as well as to the wealth of data you will be expected to share with youngsters. However, you need not do it all yourself. There is an abundance of resources at your disposal that can become important components of your science program and can help you build a program that is both dynamic and meaningful. The following list, which is not intended to be complete, contains items that you may wish to consider as possible elements of your entire program.

## People

One very valuable resource that is often overlooked by classroom teachers is the people in their local communities. No matter whether you live, in a large city or a small community, there are people who can add a measure of relevance and authenticity to your science program. These individuals can serve as guest speakers, panel members, slide-tape presenters, seminar leaders, and the like. People resources you may want to consider for your classroom program include:

| | |
|---|---|
| Druggists | Sanitation workers |
| Nurses | Nursing home workers |
| Environmentalists | High school science |
| Professors | teachers |

| | |
|---|---|
| Park rangers | Electricians |
| Plumbers | College students |
| Astronomers | Veterinarians |
| Musicians | High school students |
| Gardeners | Zoologists |
| Meteorologists | Zoo personnel |
| Scientists | Ecologists |
| Doctors | Factory workers |
| Medical laboratory workers | Farmers |
| Airplane pilots | Biologists |
| Cartographers | Conservationists |
| Cooks | Mechanics |
| Geologists | Telephone engineers |
| Nuclear plant workers | Flight controllers |

## Commercial

Often it will be necessary for you, your school, or the school district to purchase materials from one or more commercial science supply companies (see Appendix H). Even though many needed materials can be scrounged from storage closets, flea markets, hardware stores, and parents of students, it is often necessary to obtain supplies from a commercial source.

**FIGURE 6.1** Resource people for your science program.

Commercial catalogs feature an array of colorful and interesting equipment and supplies of all kinds. Reading a science catalog can lead to ideas for constructing less expensive, home-made equipment that does the job quite well. For example, one catalog lists a "bug house" (a plastic container with screened sides for keeping grasshoppers, crickets, and other insects) for $5.65. A similar device can be constructed from an oatmeal box, with sections of the sides and top cut away and pieces of old nylon stockings glued over the openings. Such a device costs virtually nothing (just the donation of the oatmeal box, a discarded pair of pantyhose, and a bottle of school glue). With a little inventiveness and creativity, you too may be able to build some (but certainly not all) of the devices offered in a science supply company's catalog.

## Audiovisual

The predominance of videocassette recorders (a recent study reports that more than 60 percent of American homes have one) makes the use of audiovisual (AV) materials a valuable part of any classroom science program. AV materials catalogs that are exceptional because of their outstanding quality and breadth of coverage are the National Geographic Society Educational Services Catalog (Educational Services, Washington, DC 20036) and the Corporation for Public Broadcasting's catalog of its "3-2-1 Contact" programs (Office of Education, 1111 Sixteenth St. NW, Washington, DC 20036) The National Geographic Society's catalog is also distinguished by an impressive collection of relevant filmstrips.

**IDEA BOX** _____

As you meet with teachers in the schools near your college, as well as teachers in your home town, ask them about the audiovisual materials they use in their classes. Write the information down on index cards (including titles, subject matter, and distributors) and file them by title or science discipline (life science, physical science, etc.) in a recipe box. Have your classmates do the same and exchange the information with each other. Then, when you are teaching and it becomes time to decide on a potential AV source, you'll have some choices at your fingertips. Obviously, it would be a good idea to add to your files throughout your professional career.

Although many commercial companies offer a variety of videos and filmstrips for your science program, you may also wish to consider producing your own. Many schools and school districts have their own video-recording equipment. If yours does not, perhaps you can borrow the necessary equipment from a parent of one of your students. Students can design and film their own experiments and projects, a trip along a river's edge or the seashore, or a guest lecture. With a little bit of editing your students can begin building a classroom library of self-initiated, self-produced videotapes that not only can supplement this year's science program but also can be used in future classes. Most important, students will be provided with another opportunity to become actively involved in the science program. In addition, they will be provided with a chance to combine their science curriculum with other subject areas, including language arts (writing and practicing scripts) art (designing signs and backdrops), music (selecting appropriate background music), and reading (conducting necessary research in the school or public library) (also see Chapter 8).

**DID YOU KNOW?** _____

During one 24-hour period your heart pumps over 1,850 gallons of blood.

**Classroom Activity** Set up several charts with students' names and ask each student (either working alone or with a partner) to take his or her pulse at various times throughout the day (upon arriving in the morning, just before and right after lunch, just before and right after recess, etc.). An easy way for students to take their pulse is as follows: Push a small thumbtack into the base of a wooden matchstick. Have a student lay his or her arm on a table, palm up. Balance the matchstick on one of the veins on the student's wrist. Have other students look from the side, and they will see the matchstick bounce up and down with each heartbeat. Have students record the number of "bounces" in 30 seconds and multiply by 2 to find the number of beats per minute. After some time ask students to make predictions on their heartbeats under different conditions (after a strenuous physical activity, for example) based on past experiences. Have students maintain their charts over a long period of time (several weeks) to note any trends. ∎

## Professional Books and Periodicals

In order to keep your science program current, it is strongly suggested that you keep abreast of happenings in the field through professional publications. Science activity books and professional journals (see Appendices E and F) allow you to stay current on recent developments in the field of science education and can stimulate you to try new approaches to familiar presentations and demonstrations. These printed resources are invaluable in "energizing" your overall program and providing you with new ideas and strategies. A subscription to *Science and Children* (National Science Teacher Association, 1742 Connecticut Ave., NW, Washington, DC 20009-1171), the preeminent science education journal for elementary teachers, is worth its weight in gold. Not only will you discover some of the latest viewpoints on science instruction; you will find a wealth of techniques and other resources for use in your classroom.

## Conferences and Conventions

As mentioned in Chapter 5, attendance at conferences and conventions of the National Science Teachers Association can be a sound investment in your own career as well as in the success of your classroom program. Not only can you hear some of the leading experts in the field of science education, but you will have numerous opportunities to rub elbows with teachers from around the country. Conferences are a wonderful opportunity to gather the latest information on science teaching and can be one of the most valuable resources you will use. It is not the conference itself that is the resource, but the information and other printed materials you gather at the conference, which can be exciting supplements to your overall science curriculum. Listings of the dates and locations of state, regional, and national conferences can be found in current issues of *NSTA Reports*, the bimonthly newspaper of the National Science Teachers Association.

### TEACHER TO TEACHER _____

Through the years, I have found that many elementary science teachers feel very isolated. As a result, science programs often wither and die out completely. The cure is as simple as it is enjoyable . . . discover your local, state, and national science teacher's associations—attend the conferences and get involved!

As a veteran of many local, state, regional, and national science teacher's conferences I have found that both attending and teaching sessions provides teachers with an extra charge for the classroom, develops networks of battle-tested ideas and information, as well as allowing opportunities for teachers to share success.

Robert G. Guy
Big Lake Elementary School
Mount Vernon, WA

## Professional Associations

Joining a professional association (see Appendix D) can provide you with a host of contacts and resources that will enhance classroom teaching. Associations allow you to stay current in science education and provide a form of revitalization and renewal through professional contacts. Most organizations and associations offer a variety of printed materials (including a journal, books, pamphlets, brochures, and curriculum guides) that can add immeasurably to your competency as a teacher of science.

## Networking

Throughout your career as a teacher you will have numerous opportunities to meet with other teachers—not only within your own school or district, but from other areas as well. Establishing and maintaining contacts with teachers from other areas can be a valuable resource for your classroom program. You will have a chance to share your successes and disappointments, and you can exchange strategies, ideas, and techniques. Your networking can start with the teachers in your own school and move outward. Attending local and state science conferences can provide you with opportunities to link up with other teachers in your area. Attendance at a national convention will allow you to network with educators from many different regions and perspectives.

Another avenue for networking is through professional teacher magazines such as *Teaching K–8, Learning, Instructor,* and *Teacher.* Addresses of teachers from around the country are frequently listed in these magazines (in classified ads, data on authors of articles, or pen pal listings). Taking the initiative to contact some of these individuals may be productive in terms of the information they send you and the support system you can establish with them.

## TO INVESTIGATE

As you visit some of the schools and classrooms in the area around your college campus, take along a camera, if possible. Take photographs of classrooms, bulletin boards, science projects, display tables, and special equipment; in fact, take photos of everything you can find that relates to science education. When the photos are developed, bring them to class and share them with your classmates. What do the photos tell you about science education in the local schools? What elements look exciting? Which elements don't look so exciting? See if you and your classmates can assemble a scrapbook of photos on the ideal science-oriented classroom. How is that classroom set up? What does it have? What types of materials or supplies are there? How is it organized? Discuss the implications of this activity in terms of your future classroom. ∎

Although the preceding discussion is intended to provide you with as much data as necessary for you to become an effective teacher of science, this text cannot provide you with everything. The school you teach in, your areas of expertise and interest, the students you teach, and current discoveries about science teaching and learning will all dictate the course of your science program. Much of your competency will come through on-the-job training, through teaching science every day. Designing and constructing a functional science program is not an overwhelming task, however; there are a number of resources at your disposal. Taking some time to investigate these resources (and making them part of your overall science program) can be one of the most important things you do as a professional educator.

············································································
# MATERIALS
············································································

To conduct a successful science program you will need many different kinds of materials. Depending on the school you teach in, you will probably be provided with textbooks for your students, a teacher's manual for the textbook series, and a collection of various materials, which may be found in cabinets in your classroom or stored in a central location in the school. Some of the materials you use will be from commercial sources, and others will be home-made adaptations of more expensive equipment. The chances are, however, that you will not have sufficient materials for every aspect of your science curriculum.

This can be a blessing in disguise. Few schools, and certainly few teachers, can afford the enormous array of materials offered by education supply companies. Therefore, to adequately supply your classroom with the necessary supplies and materials, you will need to be inventive and creative (but teachers are known for that anyway!). In short, you may have to scrounge for some materials, beg and borrow others, and create a host of contraptions for other portions of your program. (By the way, getting your students involved in creating some of the needed materials can be a powerful adjunct to your overall program.)

You will certainly want to take advantage of the materials your school offers, but be mindful of other materials you can find or make yourself. Here are some strategies to use for your particular science program.

## Obtaining Materials

Materials for your science program can be located anywhere. You need not restrict yourself to publisher cat-

alogs, although that may be a good starting point to research the availability of special equipment or apparatus. With a little bit of ingenuity and a modicum of cash and time, you should be able to equip your science program with all sorts of materials, equipment, and supplies.

You should consider the following sources as sites for the collection and accumulation of materials. You will probably discover others within your town or community that are not included in this list. What is important is that you keep an open eye and an open mind to any location as a potential site for science materials.

- *Yard sales, garage sales, flea markets, and junk stores.* Visit a junk shop or yard sale every so often to see what you can find in the way of possible science materials for your classroom. Several teachers have created an entire science program with just the equipment and materials gathered from yard sales. Keep in mind the enduring maxim of yard sales: "One person's junk is another person's treasure!"

  *Examples:* bowls, muffin tins, knives, watering can, thermometer, plastic dishes, fur, buttons, foam rubber, clothespins, bricks, and pans.

- *Hardware stores.* Hardware stores are repositories for all kinds of fascinating equipment. Although it will require the outlay of some of your own money, a good hardware store can offer a variety of objects and paraphernalia found in no other location. You are urged to look into the old country variety as opposed to the large chain hardware stores.

  *Examples:* ball bearings, nuts and bolts, iron filings, sockets, metal sheeting, glass cutters, dry cells, doweling, flashlights, switches, and wire.

## TO INVESTIGATE

Photocopy the "materials and supplies" list from any teacher's manual of a science textbook series. With a group of classmates visit a local hardware store (the large, all-purpose hardware store is ideal). Divide the list among yourselves and see how many of the items you can locate in the store. If it is a relatively well-equipped establishment, most of the items should be easily located. With a little creativity, other necessary materials can be "invented" by using available items in an unusual fashion (for example, a small electromagnet can be made by taking apart an inexpensive doorbell; and pulleys can be constructed from doweling, cut into 1 ½-inch lengths, and large metal washers, fastened to each end of the dowel sections with an epoxy glue). Compare notes and prices and figure out what it would take to "stock" a typical classroom using the local hardware store as the major "supplier." ■

- *School storerooms and closets.* Locate all the storerooms in the school and spend some time looking through them. Storerooms may house materials and equipment that no one is currently using or that has been forgotten about over the years. Of course, your best friend in this venture will be the school custodian. Make sure you get to know this person and enlist him or her in your quest for supplies.

  *Examples:* balance scales, paper punch, knives, microscopes, tuning forks, wedge, straws, thermometers, thumbtacks, trays, sponges, tape recorder, and glass jars.

- *Variety stores, large drugstores, and supermarkets.* Some of the large stores in your neighborhood or a local shopping mall can offer an abundance of possibilities for classroom science supplies. Keep an eye out for all sorts of usual and unusual materials that can become part of your science program. A roll of first-aid tape, for example, can serve many purposes, including a temporary "holding area" for a crawling mealworm, a device for rolling down an inclined plane, material to assist in the construction of a bird feeder, or an object to use in a demonstration of magnetism. You will discover that many objects can be used in several different areas of the science program.

  *Examples:* balloons, birdseed, needles, iodine, shades, comb, ice cube trays, pitcher, wooden beads, sticks, yeast, salt, plastic dishes, food coloring, measuring cups, balls, and alcohol.

## DID YOU KNOW?

All the bacteria in your body outnumber all the people in the world by about 22 to 1.

**Classroom Activity**   Have each student take a flat toothpick and scrap some saliva from the side of his or her mouth. Place each scraping on a slide and dye it with one or more food colors. Have students look at the organisms in their mouth through a classroom microscope. Ask them to make drawings of what they see through the microscope. Are there similarities in the organisms found in the students' mouths? Are there major differences? Ask students to determine other body locations (between the toes, an oozing wound) where scrapings could be taken for microscopic observation. ■

- *High school science department.* One place you should not ignore is the science department of your district's high school. By working closely with one or more of the science teachers at the secondary level, you may be able to borrow materials and supplies throughout the school year. Also, keep in mind that the science teachers themselves can serve as a valuable resource for your classroom. Invite them occasionally to visit your room and share some information with your students. Not only does this cement the bonds between elementary and secondary educators'; it gives your students a peek into the workings of scientists at another level.

  *Examples:* telegraph key, tuning forks, prisms, skeleton, pendulum, collecting trays, buzzers, motors, maps, glass, flywheel, batteries, and balance scales.

- *Pet stores and garden stores.* It is logical that if you're going to spend any amount of time on the life sciences, you should take advantage of two of the most obvious "life science stores" in your community: a local pet store (animals) and a garden store or nursery (plants). Not only will you locate a wealth of live organisms, but you will find an array of materials and equipment used to maintain the organisms over extended periods. Pets and plants should definitely be part of any elementary classroom, and you should visit these establishments on a regular basis.

*Examples:* fish, gerbils, parakeets, lizards, mice, turtles, hamsters, chicks, animal food, bedding, cages, fertilizer, potted plants, potting soil, gardening tools, and watering cans.

- *Toy stores.* Don't overlook one of the most valuable suppliers in your community: the toy store. The large toy stores (e.g., Toys R Us, Kiddie City, and Kay Bee) typically carry many different kinds of scientific apparatus as well as other items that can be adapted and used in the science program. It's not unusual to find inexpensive microscope sets or other types of science kits in a toy store.

  *Examples:* harmonica, bubble pipes, electric motors, prisms, pinwheels, marbles, table tennis balls, whistles, stethoscope, wooden balls, Slinky®, and suction cups.

- *Donations from parents.* One of the most important sources of materials and equipment can be the parents of your students. By asking them to contribute to your science program, you help to maintain open lines of communication and allow students to extend their science lessons beyond the classroom and into their homes. Sending the request well in advance of the time you need the supplies will allow parents to obtain some of the supplies during weekly or biweekly shopping trips.

  *Examples:* flour, yeast, gelatin, boxes, bowls, beans, muffin tins, flower pots, extension cords, cardboard tubes, colander, tin cans, teapot, potatoes, wheels, and cloth fabric.

- *Local industries.* A key source of supplies and equipment may be in your own backyard: the local industries in your town or community. Many of these businesses are happy to work along with the local schools and would be delighted to share ideas and materials with you. Such establishments may include the local electric company, a lumber mill, the dairy council, a municipal water company, and a natural gas supplier.

  *Examples:* fuses, fuel pump, oil, ball bearings, tools, tubs and pans, sockets, switches, iron filings, sheet copper, pipes, water and milk samples, and valves.

**TEACHER TO TEACHER** ⎯⎯⎯⎯⎯⎯⎯⎯⎯⎯

So what, if your school system or department doesn't have money? Seek out foundations and grant funding proposals. The first time I wrote, it was discouraging. I got nothing. Polite thank yous, and letters that started off: "I regret to inform you...." So the next year I wrote grants, got all three, and applied for institutes. My record year was the year I attended a science institute at the Richmond Science Museum, attended the National Geographic Summer Institute in Washington, DC, and then went to Spain as an Earthwatch Expedition member. If I could, I would do them all again.

I became more confident, I enjoyed myself, and new worlds were opened to me. More importantly, I met a lot of like-minded people. We worked hard, learned a lot, and we had fun! I can attribute my continuing academic success to my involvement in this type of experience.

Bonnie Bracey
Ashlawn Elementary School
Washington, DC

## Constructing Equipment and Materials

From time to time it may be necessary for you to build something or construct a special piece of apparatus. Perhaps you'll need to build a series of pulleys for a demonstration on simple machines. You may need to put together a terrarium for the arrival of some lizards. Or you may need to have students attempt to make a homemade telescope for viewing the stars. Although these devices need not be elaborate or complex, you will need to have some tools on hand with which to construct them. The following is a list of several items you should have in your classroom:

| | | |
|---|---|---|
| Hammer | Sandpaper | Wrenches |
| Pliers | Steel wool | Screwdrivers |
| Metal shears | Small wood saw | Paring knife |
| Metal saw | Various files | Glass cutter |
| Plane | Coping saw | Leather punch |
| Can opener | Yardstick | Tape measure |

## Storing Materials

With all the subjects you need to teach and with the limited amount of space you have in your classroom, it may seem as though there is never enough room to keep all the equipment and materials "at the ready" for various parts of your instructional program. For science this is especially true given the fact that it requires more space and materials than all the other subjects put together.

In deciding how and where to store your science materials, keep the following points in mind:

1. Materials must be readily accessible by both teacher and students. Students need to know exactly where materials are kept so that they will be able to obtain those materials on their own.
2. Materials and equipment that require safety precautions (hotplates and other electrical devices, slides, crockery, etc.) must be kept out of the reach of inquisitive youngsters.

3. There should be a selection of "free play" materials within easy access of students who desire to investigate an area of interest on their own (for example, a hand lens and tweezers for a small group wishing to examine a worm found during recess, or some metal balls and fishing line for a student who wishes to create her own version of Folcoult's pendulum).

4. Materials and equipment kept in containers, storage cabinets, or lockers must be labeled on the outside for easy and quick identification by both students and teachers. For younger students or those lacking adequate reading abilities, an illustration or photograph of the object(s) may be posted on the outside of the container.

5. Supplies and materials should be kept in a variety of locations in the classroom so that they are readily accessible at all times and are evenly distributed throughout the room. It is important to let students know that the entire classroom is a science classroom.

6. Some supplies will be in constant use and must be obtained quickly and easily. Paper towels, scissors, chalk, pens and pencils, and string are items used fairly often and should be supplied in several locations throughout the room.

7. Science centers can be established throughout the room (see Chapter 9) for housing and supplies as well as for the independent exploration of science concepts and principles. Multiple units of various supplies can be maintained at each center so that students can use them on their own.

8. You may wish to set up a "museum shelf" or "museum corner" in your classroom to display artifacts and materials associated with one area of the science program (e.g., birds, non-green plants, electrical devices, or simple machines). These can be maintained by students and used to exhibit particular objects for a predetermined length of time.

How you store your supplies and equipment will be limited only by your imagination and the design of your classroom.

## TEACHER TO TEACHER

One of the most common difficulties of implementing hands-on science into the general classroom or dealing with new classes trooping into the science specialist's lab is how to be set up for lessons, and how to avoid "downtime" handing out materials.

If you arrange your classroom so that children can work in cooperative groups of four, most equipment or supplies for hands-on lessons can be placed on a small tray for each group that can be placed at the side of the room until they are needed.

Classroom teachers can set trays up during prep time, or the day before, so they can place them on the children's tables when needed. Clean-up is easier, too, because each group of children is responsible for restoring their tray back to the condition it was in at the beginning of the lesson.

As a science specialist, I have all my lessons for the week set up on trays, and I have shelving placed around my room, so the trays do not have to be dismantled. Sometimes I am able to leave sample trays set up from year to year, so I do not have to reconstruct lessons from scratch each year.

Esther B. Weiner
E.M. Baker School
Great Neck, NY

## PREPARING FOR INSTRUCTION

It is one thing to have all your materials and quite another to be able to use them and have students use them to their fullest advantage. It would be helpful to lead your students through some simulation exercises in which they can locate necessary equipment, set it up, use it productively, put it away, and do the needed housekeeping chores to allow the same materials to be used again or to make the science area ready for other activities. Wasserman and Ivany (1988) suggest the following sequence of activities, which will allow students to assume an active role in not only learning science but in "doing" science. This is not an inviolable list, and it has been modified somewhat; it is subject to the demands and structure of your own science program.

1. Talk to your students about the science program. Help them understand that "sciencing" is an active process that requires work prior to an activity, work during the activity, and work upon completion of the activity. Students need to understand the materials they will be using, how they can work together in large or small groups, and how they can find answers to their questions.

2. Identify procedures for handling any problems that may arise. You can't predict *all* the problems that may arise, you can anticipate many of them. You know that some equipment will break, liquids will spill, and materials will be used up. Students need to know what *they* can do on those occasions.

3. Be explicit about the way materials are to be cared for. You may wish to discuss with your students the special procedures necessary for specific items. If necessary, post a short list of care directions next to or on a piece of equipment and ask students to review the directions regularly.

4. Be explicit about cleanup procedures and about how and where materials are to be stored. If you are interested in helping students become more responsible individuals, you need to provide some instruction on standard cleanup procedures and about cooperation in the return and storage of science materials. Again, it would be valuable to lead students in one or more simulation activities so that this process becomes automatic.

5. Invite the students' ideas and suggestions for making the working procedures more effective. The most successful science programs are those in which youngsters feel a sense of "ownership" that is, they have a personal stake in the equipment and materials used as well as the procedures for using them. Soliciting their input and advice can be powerful motivators for the duration of the science program.

### DID YOU KNOW?

About 4½ million years ago, during the primal stage of the earth, a day was only about 4½ hours long.

**Classroom Activity**  Have students collect as many items as they can that relate to time (e.g., calendars, digital watches, sundials, egg timers, and alarm clocks). Have students collect time-related items that were used in the past as well as items currently used. Ask them to set up a museum-type display with appropriate labels and signs (a good art activity). If there are display cases available in the school, get permission for your students to put together an attractive exhibit for the entire school.  ∎

6. Where students are to have choices about who handles the equipment and supplies, make the procedures for making these choices explicit. In other words, ensure equity across the activities as well as throughout the entire science curriculum. For example, do not make the mistake of having only boys handle the larger equipment with the girls put in charge of cleanup. Parcel out the roles and assignments as equitably as possible.

7. Undertake a "trial run" with four or five students working at a science center or simple activity. Then have the students participate in an evaluation of the trial run. Have other class members (each of whom observed the trial run) participate in the evaluation, too. Ask for ideas and suggestions from all students on how procedures could be improved or modified for future activities, demonstrations, or experiments.

8. Supervise the students' work closely at first, and taper off the supervision slowly as you observe children's increased ability to work together on their own initiative. Provide opportunities for students to assume greater control over the completion of selected activities. As the year goes by your role should change from that of a dispenser of information (the traditional role of a teacher) to that of a facilitator—one who provides the conditions and opportunities for learning to occur, and allows students to pursue an area of interest on their own initiative.

9. Always emphasize: SAFETY FIRST! Make sure students wear safety goggles when appropriate, use asbestos gloves when necessary, and wear face masks when air pollutants are released. Plan time to discuss the safety factors associated with electricity and the use of sharp instruments. When in doubt, it is always better to demonstrate an activity than to expose students to dangerous situations.

What is important is that students have some direction within the science program and also be able to establish their own directives. Achieving that balance will not be easy, particularly during your first few years of teaching. However, as you become more proficient in the teaching of science, you will become more proficient in helping students "take charge" in science.

### TO INVESTIGATE

Visit several elementary classrooms and observe the level of student involvement in each. Assign a percentage to each room in terms of the level of student participation (i.e., 100 percent would indicate that students are completely in charge and thoroughly engaged in all aspects of the science pro-

gram; 0 percent would indicate that the teacher was completely in charge, allowing no student intervention). Compare your data with that of your classmates. What can you infer about some of the teachers in the local schools? What can you infer about their respective science programs? Based on your own experiences and philosophy about the teaching of science, what percentage would you assign yourself? Why? How does your assigned percentage compare with those of other students in the class? To what can you attribute any differences? ∎

## TEACHER TO TEACHER

When I have several brief activities on the same subject I now use the "expert" system for moving groups through stations. Previously, I would set up each station with printed directions and materials. I would explain all stations to the entire class and then let them rotate through the stations group by group.

I found I was needed to help at almost every station. By contrast, I have one person from each base group meet with me at the first station, and I demonstrate how they are to follow the written directions. The next person in each group meets with me at the next station, and so forth. While I am meeting with these "experts" the rest of the class is preparing data sheets or doing preliminary reading. Then we rotate each base group through the stations. Each student has a chance to lead his or her base group at one station. They are excited and proud to do so. Almost no help is required from me during the rotation as I monitor students' activity on task. To summarize, I usually ask a different person from the group to explain to the whole class how the activity relates to our topic.

Elaine S. Heine
Ocean Breeze Elementary School
Indian Harbour Beach, FL

## ANIMALS IN THE CLASSROOM

The well-stocked classroom should provide an abundance of learning opportunities for students. It is important to have not only the proper equipment and supplies, but examples of living organisms, too. Flora and fauna are important to any child's comprehension of science, particularly the life sciences (see Chapter 12). With so much emphasis now being placed on the state of the environment, it is important for *all* students to realize that humans are the true caretakers of the earth. How we provide for and take care of the plants and animals we live with has a lot to say about who we are and what we envision for the future—the future our students will inherit.

Quite naturally, students enjoy having living organisms in the classroom, particularly animals. Not only do animals represent the first experiences most students have with science, they are present in the students' homes and usually in the surrounding environment. You should have a collection of animals in your classroom so that your students can gain some firsthand experiences with science. It is important, however, that proper care be taken so that animals are not subjected to conditions that are detrimental to their health or safety. The Humane Society of the United States recommends that teachers adopt the "24-hour-rule" to serve the needs of both animals and students:

> Small animals, such as insects, turtles, frogs, and salamanders, may be kept for a period not exceeding 24 hours, if the habitat in which they were found is simulated as closely as possible in captivity. Children should not handle but observe the

animals. They should research information about identification, characteristics, feeding habits, values, etc. The animals should then be released, unharmed, in the same area they were found so they can carry on their environmental activities.

Obviously, a great deal of teacher discretion is necessary before any animal or organism is introduced into the classroom. Although small animals are certainly not as complex as humans, they do require care and attention to their living conditions and feeding during the time they are in the classroom.

The selection of animals for the classroom will be based on the activities you wish to provide students, the availability of adequate housing, and feeding requirements. It is important to keep in mind that the classroom is unlike any animal's natural habitat, just as it is unlike the homes of your students. Also, remember that the school is closed from dismissal time at the end of the day until the morning of the following day and that care is generally not available for classroom animals during the weekends or holidays.

Table 6.1 lists some of the animals typically found in a well-stocked classroom as well as their sources, food requirements, and living needs. Those items marked with an asterisk can be obtained through commercial sources. You may wish to check out the most current "Hands-On Science Catalog" available from Delta Education, Inc. (P.O. Box 950, Hudson, NH 03051 [800-442-5444]) or a local pet store.

TABLE **6.1**

## CLASSROOM ANIMALS: THEIR CARE AND FEEDING

| Animal | Source | Food | Container |
|---|---|---|---|
| Birds* | Pet store (do not obtain wild birds) | Birdseed* | Cage* |
| Mealworms* | Pet store, grain storage areas | Bran cereal,* grains | Wide-mouth jar, plastic container* |
| Fruit flies | Rotting fruit | Rotting fruit | Glass jar with lid |
| Lizards* | Pet store | Mealworms, insects | Wire cage* |
| Butterflies* | Pet store, catalog | Sugar water | Butterfly kit,* mesh cage |
| Tropical fish* | Pet store | Commercial food* | Aquarium* |
| Frogs* | Pet store, catalog, ponds | Worms, insects (live if possible) | Terrarium, aquarium* |
| Earthworms | Moist soil, humus | Nutrients obtained from soil | Glass jars filled with soil |
| Snails (land) | Forests, logs, rocks | Lettuce, fish food,* ant eggs* | Terrarium, large glass jar |
| Ants* | Under logs, pet store, catalog | Food scraps, dead insects | Glass jar filled with soil, ant farm* |
| Rats and mice* | Pet store | Commercial food,* grains* | Metal animal cage* |
| Turtles* | Pet store, lakes, ponds | Worms, lettuce, vegetables | Aquarium,* terrarium* |
| Crickets* | Under boards and rocks, pet store | Soft fruit, crushed seeds | Plastic boxes, cages* |
| Chameleons* | Pet store, near river banks | Live insects | Wire mesh cages* |
| Hamsters,* gerbils* | Pet store | Grain, lettuce, vegetables, commercial food* | Wire cages* |
| Snakes* | Barns, grain areas, pet store | Live mice,* live insects | Terrarium* |
| Spiders | Plants, trees | Live insects | Wire mesh cage* |
| Rabbits* | Pet store | Grains, lettuce, commercial food* | Metal cage* |
| Grasshoppers | Grassy areas | Leaves, grasses | Mesh cage,* large glass jar |

# PLANTS IN THE CLASSROOM

Just as you will want to have a variety of animals in your classroom, so too will you want a variety of plants. The obvious advantage of plants is that they require minimal care and can be used in many different kinds of science experiments and demonstrations. In addition to an abundance of plants in the classroom, there should also be many opportunities for students to grow their own plants from seed. Letting children learn about the growth cycle first-hand is an obvious advantage of having plants in your classroom.

In deciding on the plants to have in your classroom, probably one of the first places you will want to visit is your local garden center or greenhouse. Check out the wide variety of plants they have on display and ask for information on the varieties that interest you the most. Keep in mind the temperature of your classroom and the amount of care specific varieties will need (a great deal, some, or very little). Plan to select varieties that can tolerate tending by children and, in the event of overwatering or overfertilizing (as will sometimes happen), can maintain some degree of vigor. The person you talk with at the garden center will need to know the conditions under which the plants will be maintained in order to recommend the best varieties for your particular classroom.

You must also give some thought to the supplies you will need to maintain classroom foliage. Consider some of the following items as essential equipment for the plants in your classroom (most of these items can be obtained at your garden center or through a science catalog):

Grow lamps
Fertilizer
Watering cans
Terrariums
Potting soil
Flower pots
Peat pots
Small garden tools (hand shovel, hand rake)
Small greenhouse
Starter cups
Thermometer
Water gauge
Plastic trays
Soil test kit
Vermiculite
Charcoal
Pebbles
Topsoil
Soda containers (for making terrariums)

**IDEA BOX** ⎯⎯⎯⎯⎯⎯⎯⎯⎯⎯⎯⎯⎯⎯⎯⎯⎯⎯⎯

Two of the best books on the care and maintenance of houseplants are *Sunset House Plants: How to Choose, Grow, and Display* (Menlo Park, CA: Lane Publishing, 1983) and *The Instant Guide to Healthy Houseplants* (Columbus, OH: Field Publications, 1989).

Although, you will want to begin at your local garden center, don't rule out plants that may be found in their natural habitats. These include plants found in a pond, stream, outdoor garden, vacant lot, wooded area, or other location specific to your area. Some of the plants you might obtain in these areas include:

| | |
|---|---|
| Grasses | Eelgrass |
| Algae | Coleus |
| Moss | Sundew |
| Lichens | Elodea |
| Ferns | Euglena |
| Mushrooms | Duckweed |

Be careful to take no more plants than absolutely necessary for classroom use. Be sure students understand that the plants taken from their natural environments are samples only, and that they will not be taken if it would significantly diminish the amount of that variety in the area.

Another source for plants is the catalogs of many seed companies. Providing opportunities for students to grow their own plants from seeds is a necessary part of your science program. Contact one or more of the following companies and request their latest seed catalog(s):

W. Atlee Burpee Co.
Warminster, PA 18974

Gurney Seed and Nursery Co.
1448 Page St.
Yankton, SD 57078

Burgess Seed and Plant Co.
P.O. Box 82
Galesburg, MI 49053

Miller's Nursery, Inc.
Canandaigua, NY 14424

Plants can be grown and maintained quite easily in most classrooms. You may wish to obtain a greenhouse or terrarium from a commercial vendor or make your own. Illustrated below are two examples that can be constructed from common household items.

**TEACHER TO TEACHER** _____

As part of our "Seeds and Plants" unit, I took my kindergarten students on a "sock-walk" through the weeds on the outskirts of our school campus. The children pulled Dad's old socks on over their own shoes and socks, and we explored the many different kinds of seeds and weeds that like to stick to socks. At the conclusion of the activity, each child placed one sock on a plate and soaked it with water. I explained that now we would see if any of the seeds in our socks would sprout. The next day the principal visited our classroom, and upon seeing all the seedy socks on plates, she asked "What in the world are you boys and girls studying in this class?" One serious little girl spoke right up and said, "We've been studying dirty socks!"

Dianne Benham
Pomerado Elementary School
Poway, CA

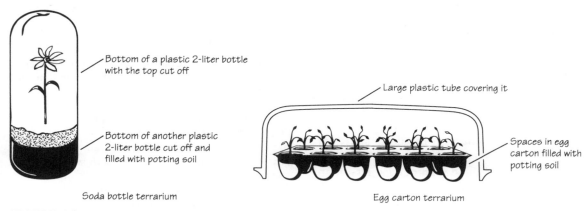

**FIGURE 6.2** Soda bottle and egg carton terrariums

## SCIENCE TEXTBOOKS

As you might imagine, some students' recollections of their elementary textbooks are not very flattering. Here are some typical comments:

"It was boring."
"We read the chapter and did the questions at the end. We never got to do any activities."
"The material wasn't very interesting."
"The teacher read to us and asked us a whole bunch of questions."
"It was boring."
"Only the smartest kids in the class got to read out loud; the rest of us just had to sit and listen."
"The material wasn't very interesting and for the most part was too difficult to understand."

"I remember that the textbook we used was at least 15 years old and filled with old photos of rocket ships."
"It was boring."

If your recollections of your old science textbooks are similar to those of there students, you probably did not view textbooks with a great deal of affection. In years gone by, the basic elementary science program was one in which students were asked to read selections from a textbook and answer questions (found at the end of each chapter) on a separate sheet of paper or orally in class. Later editions of textbooks contained some demonstrations and experiments, most of which were performed by the classroom teacher with very little if any hands-on investigation by students. In short, science education was often the most passive part of the elementary curriculum: students were asked only to absorb lots of factual data and "regurgitate" that data on a series of workbook pages or mundane assignments. In many ways, traditional methods of teaching science were actually extensions of the reading curriculum, with students performing the same tasks they did in the reading basal text.

Science textbooks have come a long way since those days. Equipped with knowledge about how children learn, the need to integrate process and product, and the supportive research for a discovery approach to science education, we are seeing some dramatic changes in science texts.

As you visit elementary classrooms, you probably notice that most, if not all, of them use a standard science textbook series. The reasons for this are many and relate to the design and focus of the science curriculum, the mandates of the administrations, and the level of expertise and "comfortableness" of classroom teachers. Cain and Evans (1990) offer several reasons that teachers typically rely on textbooks as a major part of their science program:

1. *Textbooks are especially helpful for beginning teachers.* The beginning teacher can find security in the pages of a teacher's manual. With so many things to do and so little time to do them all, the novice teacher finds some degree of solace in the daily plans and activities that are detailed for him or her. The material to be covered and the design of each lesson are spelled out in exquisite detail.
2. *Textbooks provide teachers with organized units of work.* Many teachers like to teach by the unit method, and a textbook provides all the plans and lessons needed to cover a topic in some detail. Also, because each unit is specific to a particular grade level, teachers know that they will not be covering material that will be taken up in a later grade or that has already been covered in a previous grade.
3. *A textbook series provides the school system with an organized science program.* School administrators, who usually make the final decision on which materials will be used in the classroom, know that a science series will have a balanced, sequential presentation of science data. They also know that a series has been written by experts in the field of science education from throughout the country. Since many school districts do not have the financial or personnel resources to create their own individual science curriculum, they must rely on the expertise of a commercial publisher, who typically has access to many more resources than a single school district.
4. *Textbooks are popular with some teachers because they feel insecure with any other program.* Many teachers are unsure of their competencies in science, particularly their competency to teach science. They appreciate a detailed and sequential science text that tells them what to do and when to do it. In short, there are no surprises; everything is carefully spelled out. Whatever information the teacher needs to teach a concept or a lesson is included in the science text. All the teacher needs to do, essentially, is "give it" to the students. Of course, this can also be a major limitation of any science textbook.
5. *Textbooks are popular in many schools because the teachers and administration do not know that other programs exist.* By purchasing a science textbook series, administrators and teachers know that it is a complete science program. That is, the series has (presumably) been based on the latest science information and teaching strategies. What may happen, therefore, is that the series becomes the only source of science information for the classroom, and other sources may be eliminated, ignored, or forgotten.

## DID YOU KNOW? _____

According to some scientists, the approximate weight of the earth is 6,588,000,000,000,000,000,000,000 (or about 6.5 sextillion) tons.

**Classroom Activity**   You'll certainly want to introduce your students to rocks and minerals. Here's an interesting collection of trade books for all the amateur geologists in your classroom: *Rocks and Fossils* by Rhoda Ritter (New York: Watts, 1977); *Rock Hunter's Guide* by Russell P. MacFall (New York: Crowell, 1980); *The Young Rockhound's Handbook* by W. R. C. Shedenhelm (New York: Putnam, 1978); *Guess What Rocks Do* by Barbara Rinkoff (New York: Lothrop, 1975); and *First Look at Rocks* by Millicent Selsam (New York: Walker, 1984).   ∎

6. *Good textbooks are excellent teaching aids.* A major advantage of textbooks is that they are a resource for both teachers and students. Everything to know and present to students is contained in the textbook series: information about specific topics, demonstrations, experiments, materials, designs, and all manner of facts and figures. In short, a textbook serves as a repository for many different kinds of science information and instructional techniques.
7. *Kits are available from the publisher or outside suppliers to supplement the textbook.* Many commercial textbook publishers provide kits and other supplementary materials that can be used in conjunction with a lesson or unit. Because the kit was produced by the publisher that created the textbook, teachers know that the materials and components of the kit will match the science content of the textbook. This saves the teacher from scrounging around to locate hard-to-find materials.

8. *Textbooks may be less expensive to purchase and use than some of the kits or kitlike materials.* Unfortunately, many schools and school districts need to consider the financial restraints of their curriculum over pedagogical needs. In other words, if money is an issue, it may be far easier for a school district to purchase a textbook series than to purchase a series of kits and laboratory equipment. Unfortunately, what school districts have to work with may be dictated by budgetary consequences rather than instructional needs.

## TO INVESTIGATE

Visit several elementary schools in the area near your college. Observe several science lessons over an extended period of time. What do you observe about how the science textbook is used? Do teachers tend to rely on it a great deal, somewhat, a little, or not at all? Ask teachers who use the textbook a lot for the reasons they depend on the textbook. Ask teachers who tend to use the textbook very little why they decided to use it so infrequently. Do you notice anything in the classrooms that demonstrates a relationship between students' attitudes toward science and the amount of time they are required to spend with the science textbook? What might be some implications for your future classroom?   ∎

The adequacy of a textbook depends on the teacher who uses it. In other words, if a teacher uses a textbook exclusively, his or her students may miss some essential components of a well-rounded science program. On the other hand, if a teacher decides to reject a textbook approach to science education, his or her students also may miss some necessary instruction or information. Thus, for the question of how much the science textbook should be used, the answer is: "It all depends."

As a teacher of science you will need to make many decisions, and one of those will be the degree to which you wish to use the science textbook. That will depend on your level of "comfortableness" in teaching science and the specific needs and attributes of the students in your classroom. Early in your teaching career you will probably rely on your science textbook series a great deal more than you will later on. As you become more proficient and practiced in the teaching of science, you will want to strike out on your own, trying new experiments, investigating different modes of instruction, and looking for interesting activities and demonstrations in resource materials and science conferences. You will wean yourself from total dependence on the textbook and begin to establish a program that meets not only your needs but those of your students as well.

However, it is important to recognize the limitations of science textbooks. Table 6.2 on page 106 presents some of the difficulties associated with science textbooks and suggests ways of overcoming those difficulties.

Textbooks are tools; they are only as good as the person using them. A hammer in the hands of a competent carpenter can be used to create a great cathedral or an exquisite piece of furniture. In the hands of someone else the result may be a run-down shack or a rickety bench. However, do not make the mistake of basing your entire science curriculum on a science textbook series. A carpenter doesn't just use a hammer to build a magnificent oak chest. He or she may use a plane, chisel, saw, sander, and any number of other tools to create the desired masterpiece. A great science program, just like a great piece of furniture, requires many tools for its construction. What tools you use and how and when you use them will be the ultimate determinants of the success of your science curriculum.

## TEACHER TO TEACHER

It's important to realize that many basal texts do not need to be started on page one. Science texts fall among this group. I have learned that there are advantages obtained by starting in the middle or even the last unit of a text. One of the biggest advantages is the availability of equipment and audiovisual material. Since the majority of teachers are page-bound and start at page one in a book, there is a great deal of competition for materials throughout the year. When you start in another part of the text at the beginning of the school year, you find that many of the materials needed for teaching science are readily available at the times you want them.

Arthur D. Dempsey
Anthony Elementary School
Anthony, NM

Here is a list of guidelines for you to consider in using the science textbook as one of the tools for your science program:

1. Use the textbook as a resource for students, but not the only resource.
2. Use the textbook as a guide, not a mandate, for science instruction.
3. Strike a balance between the traditional "minds-on" approach to science, as may be reflected in the textbook, and the "hands-on" approach of discovery learning.
4. Be free to modify, eliminate, or augment the material in the textbook.
5. Supplement the textbook with lots of outside readings, particularly science trade books.
6. Supplement teacher information in the textbook with science activity books (see Appendix E); attendance at local, regional, or national science conferences; articles in periodicals such as *Science and Children*; and conversations with experienced teachers.

TABLE **6.2**

......................................................................................................................

## TEXTBOOK WEAKNESSES AND DIFFICULTIES

......................................................................................................................

| Weakness | Student Difficulty | Ways of Overcoming Problem |
|---|---|---|
| Science textbook is designed as the sole source of information. | Students see only one perspective on a concept or issue. | Provide students with lots of information sources, including trade books, encyclopedias, and teacher resources. |
| Textbook is old or outdated. | Information shared with students is not current or relevant. | Obtain up-to-date materials or use textbook sparingly. |
| Questions from textbook tend to be fact-oriented. | Students get the impression that science is simply a collection of facts and figures. | Ask higher-level questions and critical/creative questions. |
| Textbook doesn't take the background knowledge of students into account. | Teacher does not tailor the curriculum to the particular attributes and interests of students. | Discover what students know about a topic prior to teaching. Ask questions and discuss their ideas before the lesson. |
| Activities; demonstrations, and experiments are presented as optional parts of the textbook. | Students may not see the relationships between "knowing" science and "doing" science. | Base the science program on a process or discovery approach to learning. Make science more hands-on. |
| Text is difficult to read. | Students cannot adequately read the material or understand important concepts. | Use lots of trade books that tap students' interests and individual reading abilities. |
| The science text provides inadequate or shallow coverage. | Students do not have opportunities to pursue a topic in great depth. | Spend more time on fewer topics to develop deep-rooted conceptual understanding. |
| Textbooks have all the answers to all the questions. | Students tend to see science as nothing more than the accumulation of right answers. | Encourage students to elaborate their responses and clarify their understanding through a host of extending activities. |
| The science textbook has everything carefully mapped out for the teacher. | Teachers are not allowed to take advantage of "teachable moments" or include explorations based on student interests. | Allow students to investigate areas of science they wish to pursue. |
| Textbooks are designed as extensions of the reading program. | Students do not see science as a hands-on, minds-on subject. Their view of science is distorted. | Include lots of hands-on activities for students throughout the science program. |

7. Encourage students to move beyond the pat answers given in the textbook and develop their critical and creative thinking skills (see Chapter 4).
8. Feel free to eliminate sections or units in order to provide more in-depth coverage of other topics.
9. Integrate science lessons in the text with other areas of the curriculum (see Chapter 8). Let students see the relationships that exist between science and art, music, math, social studies, reading, physical education, and other subjects.

10. Remember, no textbook is perfect, and no textbook is complete. It is but one resource at your disposal—a blueprint, a guidebook, an outline, but certainly not the entire science program.

Figure 6.1 is a chapter from an elementary science series, *Discover Science—Grade Four* (Glenview, IL: Scott, Foresman, 1989). It will provide you with a look at how typical science texts are set up. As you review these materials, think about how you will use a science textbook series in your own classroom.

## INTRODUCING CHAPTER 6

### Major Concepts
*Lesson 1* Forces make things move.
*Lesson 2* Work is done when a force makes an object move in the direction of the force; energy is needed to do work.
*Lesson 3* Machines make work easier.

### Vocabulary
chemical energy, complex machine, compound machine, efficiency, energy, friction, gravity, inertia, kinetic energy, mechanical energy, potential energy, simple machine, work

Chapter 6

# Work and Energy

Muscles in the bicycle rider's legs provide the energy to move the bicycle quickly. The simple machines that make up the bicycle let the rider do the most work while using the least energy.

142

## Teaching Options

### Cooperative Learning ◆

**Jigsaw Format** (See page T23.)
Assign the following topics at random to your cooperative learning teams.
   *Topic A:* How can friction be harmful? helpful?
   *Topic B:* What is a machine?
   *Topic C:* Can a machine produce more force than is put into it? Explain.
   *Topic D:* Name and describe the six simple machines.
Have students search for information on their topic as they read the chapter. Then let all students with the same topic meet in an expert group to discuss the information. When students return to their teams, they may take turns presenting their topics to the team. Then give students a test covering all topics to complete individually (Chapter 6 Test A or B in the *Test Book*). Award Superteam certificates to teams whose average test scores exceed 90%, and Greatteam certificates to teams whose average test scores exceed 80%.

## Introducing the Chapter

How would you compare the amount of work you have to do to get a stopped bicycle going and to keep a moving bicycle moving?[1] What happens to you if you are riding along and your bicycle stops suddenly?[2] In the activity below, you will observe moving and still objects. In this chapter, you will learn about motion, energy, and work.

[1] more work to get bicycle going
[2] keep moving, fall off

### Observing Moving and Still Objects

Place a sheet of paper on a desk or table. Then, place a heavy book, such as a dictionary, on the paper. Pull the book quickly across the table or desk by pulling on the paper. Suddenly stop pulling the paper. Observe what happens to the book.

Keep the same book on the paper. The book should be still—not moving. With a sudden movement of your hands, jerk the paper toward you. Observe what happens to the book.

**Talk About It**

1. Which of your observations shows that an object that is still tends to stay still?
2. Which of your observations shows that an object in motion tends to stay in motion?

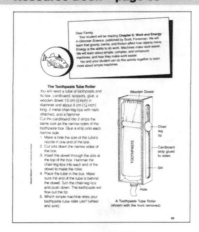

143

---

**Resource Book    page 63**

---

### SCIENCE BACKGROUND

Isaac Newton formulated three laws of motion. The first law is sometimes called the law of inertia and is based on ideas of Galileo. The law of inertia states that a body at rest tends to stay at rest unless an outside force acts on it and that a body in motion tends to stay in motion unless an outside force acts on it.

# TEACHING PLAN

## LESSON 1
pages 144–146

### Lesson Objectives
- *Explain* what causes motion.
- *Compare* speed, velocity, and acceleration.
- *Describe* the effect of friction on motion.

### Lesson Vocabulary
friction, gravity, inertia

## 1  MOTIVATE

### Demonstration Activity ◆
Set up several dominoes on end to form a design. Allow a volunteer to push the first domino.

### Discussion
Questions: **How is each domino able to move?** (The first domino moved because of the force exerted by the student. The others fell because the domino before it knocked it down.) **What would happen if I tossed one domino in the air?** (It would fall to the ground.) **What causes it to fall to the ground?** (Guide students to *infer* that gravity causes the domino to fall to the ground.)

---

### LESSON GOALS

You will learn
- what makes things move.
- how motion is measured.
- how friction changes motion.

---

**gravity** (grav**ʹ**ə tē), a force that pulls any two objects together, such as you and the earth.

Using a force to rake leaves.

# 1  What Makes Things Move?

The world is filled with moving objects. Cars, buses, trucks, and trains move. People move through the halls of your school. The leaves on trees move as the wind blows. The earth and the other planets move around the sun.

### Force

The boys in the picture are raking leaves. As the boys pull the rakes, the leaves are moved into piles. The leaves move because the boys are using a force. A push or a pull is a force.

Only a force can change the motion of an object. A force can move something that is standing still. A force can make a moving object move faster, slow down, or stop. The direction of a moving object changes only when a force acts on it.

When you sit at the top of a slide, you slide down. Gravity pulls you down. **Gravity** is the force that pulls objects toward the center of the earth. Gravity made the leaves in the picture fall to the ground.

144

# Teaching Options

## SCIENCE BACKGROUND

Motion is measured in terms of speed, velocity, and acceleration. Speed indicates how fast an object is moving per unit time. Velocity measures both speed and direction. Acceleration indicates the rate of change in velocity.

Newton's second law of motion describes what happens when a force is applied to an object. The force changes the object's motion. The change depends on the size of the force and the mass of the object. Newton's third law of motion states that for every action, there is an equal and opposite reaction. This law explains how jet engines work.

### Reading Strategies ◆

**1.** Guide students' pre-reading by asking: What two or three questions do you have for each subheading?
**2.** Assign these strategies: Visualizing Information and Finding and Writing Sentences for Vocabulary Words (See pages T26–T29.)
**3.** Pair students to share what information is clear and unclear and initiate discussion using students' unanswered questions.

### How Motion Is Measured

Have you ever wondered how fast an airplane flies? If you have, you wondered about the airplane's speed. To know what an object's speed is, you need to know how far the object moves each second, minute, or hour.

The speedometer in a car measures the car's speed. Look closely at the speedometer in the picture. Find the speedometer and the numbers labeled km/hr. Imagine that the car is moving at a speed of 88 kilometers per hour. The car will move 88 kilometers in one hour if its speed does not change. How far will the car move in 30 minutes?

### Inertia and Friction

About three hundred years ago, the scientist Isaac Newton realized that a moving object will keep moving unless a force acts on the object. Newton also realized that a still object will remain still unless a force acts on the object. The tendency of an object to stay in motion or to stay still is called **inertia**. You observed inertia if you did the activity on page 143.

**inertia** (in ėr′shə), the tendency of a moving object to stay in motion or a resting object to stay still.

¹ 44 kilometers

A speedometer measures speed.

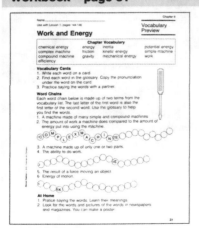

145

## 2  TEACH

### Teaching Tips

● *Metric-English Equivalent:* 88 kilometers/hr = about 55 mi/hr
● Show students three objects of different mass such as a pencil, a shoe, and a chair. Question: **Which object would take the most force to lift? the least?** (the chair, the pencil) Discuss how objects of different mass require different amounts of force to move them.
● Have students describe examples of the action gravity they have experienced in their lives. (jumping, dropping objects, diving, and so on)
● Encourage students to *describe* what it would be like without gravity. (Answers will vary, but most students should state that objects and people would float.)
● Obtain two toy cars. Push the cars at different speeds, then let go. Questions: **What can I do to make one of the cars stop?** (Use a force, such as placing your hand on one of them.) **Will both cars stop eventually? why?** (Yes, friction, an outside force, will cause the cars to stop.)

---

**Workbook    page 31 \***

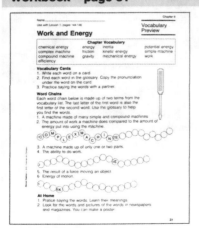

**Enrichment**

Encourage interested students to use reference sources to find out about the gravity on the surfaces of the various planets and the moon. Assist students in calculating their weight on different planets.

**Special Education**

Have students with learning disabilities find five objects in the classroom that move or can be moved. Ask them to name the force that causes the movement.

## TEACHING PLAN

### Teaching Tips
- **Possible Misconception:** Some students may think that moving objects will eventually slow down of their own will.
- Have students *describe* situations illustrating how friction can be both helpful and harmful. (helpful: slowing down a bicycle or roller skates; harmful: machine parts wear out)

### 3 ASSESS

### Lesson Review
1. Forces cause objects to move.
2. An object's speed is how far the object travels within a certain period of time.
3. Friction slows down motion.
4. **Challenge!** Answers might include oiling the surfaces or sandpapering the surfaces to make them smoother. **Thinking Skill:** *Applying information to new situations*

### Find Out On Your Own
Static friction results when two surfaces touch but do not move against each other. Sliding friction results when one surface slides over another surface. Rolling friction results when an object rolls over another. **Thinking Skill:** *Collecting and communicating information*

## Teaching Options

---

*SCIENCE IN YOUR LIFE*

Friction helps you do things every day. The friction between your shoes and the sidewalk helps you walk. Without friction, you would slip and fall. Friction makes cars stop. Friction helps keep tires from slipping on the road.

---

**friction** (frik′shən), a force that slows the motion of moving objects.

¹ The checker will stop.

Look at the girl playing with the checkers. When the girl pushes a checker, it slides across the board. As the checker moves across the board, it slows down. What will happen to the checker when it reaches the carpet?¹

**Friction** is a force that slows down or stops moving objects. When an object rubs against another object, friction results. The friction between smooth surfaces is less than the friction between rough surfaces. The friction between the checker and the board was less than the friction between the checker and the carpet.

Friction slows down the checker.

**Lesson Review**
1. What causes objects to move?
2. What is the speed of an object?
3. How does friction change an object's motion?
4. **Challenge!** How can you reduce the friction between two objects rubbing together?

Study on your own, pages 386–387.

---

**FIND OUT ON YOUR OWN**

Use an encyclopedia to find out about different kinds of friction. Make a poster that describes what you learned. Include pictures that illustrate the different types of friction.

146

---

**Reteaching Suggestion ♦**

Take the class to the gym or playground to play a game of kickball. After the game, discuss examples of force, gravity, speed, and friction that occur during the game.

**Workbook    page 32 ***

---

♦ *Suitable as a language development activity*

### Observing Friction

Suggested grouping: pairs

**Purpose**
*Observe* how the kind of surface and the weight of an object affect friction.

**Gather These Materials**
• flat wooden board, abut 25 cm long and 15 cm wide • enough sandpaper to cover half the board • 4 thumbtacks • thin rubber band • masking tape • small paper cup • 20 large metal washers

**Follow This Procedure**
1. Use tables like the ones shown to record your observations.
2. Tack the sandpaper to half of the board. Use a tack in each corner so the paper lies as flat as possible.
3. Tape the rubber band near the bottom of the paper cup as shown in the picture. Put ten washers in the cup.
4. Drag the cup slowly and steadily across the smooth surface of the board by pulling the rubber band. Friction between the cup and the surface causes the pull. Record whether the rubber band stretches a little or a lot and whether the cup is easy or hard to pull.
5. Pull the same cup slowly and steadily across the sandpaper. Observe how much the rubber band stretches and how much you pull. Compare these observations with your observations of the smooth surface. Record any differences.
6. Repeat step 4 using ten washers and then using twenty washers in the cup. Record any differences.

*Wear cover goggles for this activity.*

**Record Your Results**
**How Stretch and Pull Compare**

|  | Smooth surface | Rough surface |
|---|---|---|
| Ten washers | See results below. | |

|  | Ten washers | Twenty washers |
|---|---|---|
| Smooth surface | See results below. | |

**State Your Conclusion**
1. How does the roughness of a surface affect friction?
2. How does the weight of an object affect friction?

**Use What You Learned**
Why is sand put on icy roads in the winter?

147

---

**Resource Book    page 67**

*\* Answers to masters on pages 142E–142H*

---

## ACTIVITY PLAN

**Concept**
The type of surface and the mass of an object affect friction.

**Objectives/Process Skills**
• *Observe* how the roughness of a surface affects friction.
• *Observe* how friction changes when more washers are added to the cup.
• *Record* observations.

**Time Allotment**
Allow 20 minutes.

**Safety Tip** (See page T24.)
• Students should be very careful when using the thumbtacks. Count the number of thumbtacks at the end of the activity.
• If hand lenses are used to compare surfaces, direct students not to use lenses to concentrate the sun's rays onto skin or paper.

**Teaching Tips**
• **Helpful Hint:** Use large metal washers so that the mass difference between five and ten is significant.
• Students can use hand lenses (if available) to *compare* the surfaces of the board and sandpaper.
• To illustrate the function of lubricants, have students rub petroleum jelly on half of the board instead of sandpaper, and repeat steps 4 and 5.

**Answers**
*State Your Conclusion*
**1.** The rougher the surface, the greater the friction between the surface and the object moving over the surface.
**2.** The heavier an object, the greater the friction between the object and the surface over which it is moving.

*Use What You Learned*
The sand increases the roughness of the ice surface, producing enough friction to keep tires from skidding. **Thinking Skill:** *Applying information to new situations*

---

**Activity Results**

The friction between the cup and the sandpaper is greater than the friction between the cup and the smooth board. Increasing the mass of the cup increases the amount of friction between the cup and the surface over which it is moving.

With 10 washers, the rubber band stretches a little and the cup is easy to pull on the smooth surface. The rubber band stretches more and the cup is harder to pull on a rough surface.
With 20 washers, the rubber band stretches more and the cup is harder to pull.

# SCIENCE TRADE BOOKS

Many references to science trade books have appeared throughout this text. When trade books are made an important part of the science curriculum, children will be more inclined to embrace science as an important subject of the elementary curriculum as well as an important part of their lives. Indeed, many teachers have found that a literature-based science program is intrinsically more interesting and relevant to students.

Not only do trade books open up new avenues for discovery and exploration on the part of students; they also compensate for some of the weaknesses in science textbooks. Science texts tend to approach topics in a general way. That is, a large amount of information is presented superficially, with no significant detail. The reason for this is obvious. A textbook, by its very nature, must offer large quantities of data to a large segment of the student population. As a result, most topics are covered lightly. Another disadvantage of textbooks is dated information. Because it takes so long to produce a new edition of a textbook series, some of the information may be out of date by the time the text is used. Also, the fact that many schools keep their textbooks for many years (it is not unusual to find textbooks in use for 8 to 10 years) compromises the currency of some of the information presented. Another factor to keep in mind is the fact that in trying to be all things to all people, some textbooks fail to arouse student interest. Students may reject textbooks simply because of what they are: compendiums of large masses of data for large masses of readers. Students may find it difficult to understand the relevance of so much data to their personal lives.

The use of trade books in the science class has many benefits for students, including the following:

1. Trade books can be geared to the individual interests and needs of children. Since not all students are interested in the same topic, teachers can direct individuals to the books that can answer their personal questions and satisfy their curiosity.
2. Trade books provide youngsters with up-to-date information that may not be available from any other source. Although textbooks may become outdated, the large number of trade books published annually ensures that students have access to current information and scientific knowledge.
3. Students, particularly those with reading difficulties, may find the textbook too demanding or challenging. Trade books, on the other hand, can be keyed to the reading abilities of all students in the classroom. Teachers can find a variety of books on a subject

from the easiest of readers to the most challenging. Thus, the information in the text can be effectively supplemented with a book that provides a measure of reading success for an individual student.
4. Trade books also have the advantage of offering different points of view on a variety of topics. Textbooks must present a "homogenized" view of many topics, particularly those that are controversial. The inclusion of several different trade books as part of a specific science unit can help students formulate their own opinions and see how scientists differ in their interpretations of various data.
5. Trade books allow students to work individually on a particular topic. Students can pursue an area of interest through any number of trade books, immersing themselves in all aspects of a single topic. In so doing, they obtain valuable information that may not be available in the general text, which must tackle a wider range of information.
6. Many trade books present information on a particular topic in an engaging and invigorating format. Indeed, all of the books recommended throughout this text have been chosen on the basis of their appeal, simplicity of language, colorful use of photos and illustrations, and accuracy. The intent is to extend youngsters an invitation to explore science in all its beauty and grandeur; this is a unique advantage of integrating trade books throughout the science curriculum.

Your use of trade books can become a very positive element of the curriculum. It can provide youngsters with a host of possibilities not available from the basal text. Following are some instructional ideas for incorporating trade books as a relevant part of your science curriculum:

- *Single book.* Each student should frequently be given the opportunity to select his or her own book. This selection should be based on the interests of the child and be correlated with the topic or topics under discussion. As each child reads a personally chosen book, he or she can select a variety of extending activities and projects (see Appendix B).
- *Thematic units.* Several books on a single topic can be combined into a thematic unit (see Chapter 8). Thematic units allow youngsters to compare and contrast many different viewpoints on a single topic. Moreover students have a chance to follow a topic in greater depth, looking at it from many different sides and for many days.

- *Multiple copies.* If possible, obtain multiple copies of a single book and design a mini-lesson in which several students read the same book and discuss its content. For example, you may wish to set up a temporary discussion group about the solar system. After a little investigation you may discover that your school district (if it is one that has several elementary schools) has multiple copies of the book *Mars* by Seymour Simon (New York: Crowell, 1988). You can obtain those copies and have several students at the same time read the book, discuss it, and design some extension activities that allow them to relate the book to the content of the science text. You thereby offer youngsters literary extensions that would not be available if you were to stick to the textbook.

You're probably wondering where you can locate and obtain the necessary trade books. Following are some places, people, and resources for you to consider.

1. *Printed resources.* The following resources will provide you with some good leads in locating appropriate literature for your classroom. Consult Appendix C for additional sources.
   a. *Eyeopeners* by Beverly Kobrin (New York: Penguin, 1988) is an annotated bibliography of more than 500 nonfiction books in a variety of areas. Included are activities and projects for each book as well as suggestions of how nonfiction books can be effectively incorporated into any curriculum.
   b. "Outstanding Science Trade Books for Children" is an annotated bibliography of the best science books of the year. This list is included in the March issue of *Science and Children*, a publication of the National Science Teachers Association (NSTA). Included are write-ups on a variety of science-related books in several different areas.
   c. Publisher catalogs offer a panorama of children's books in science. Two of the most complete catalogs are: Scholastic, Inc., *Literature-Based Classroom Catalog* (P.O. Box 7502, 2931 East McCarty St., Jefferson City, MO 65102) and Perma-Bound, *Master Catalog* (Vandalia Road, Jacksonville, IL 62650). Write and obtain the current issue.
   d. "Children's Choices" is published each year in the October issue of *The Reading Teacher*. This list is a compendium of the most popular books of the past year as selected by students themselves. More than 10,000 youngsters are surveyed on the fiction and nonfiction books they enjoyed most during the past year. An annotated bibliography is prepared, and reprints can be obtained

free of charge from the International Reading Association (P.O. Box 8139, Newark, DE 19714-8139).
   e. *Science Through Children's Literature* by Carol Butzow and John Butzow (Englewood, CO: Teacher Ideas Press, 1989) offers the classroom teacher a plethora of specific activities for each of 33 fiction books with science themes (for example, *The Very Busy Spider* by Eric Carle [New York: Putnam, 1985] and *The Magic School Bus at the Waterworks* by Joanna Cole [New York: Scholastic, 1986]). Opportunities for extending science into other areas of the curriculum are also offered.

2. *Librarians.* Librarians can provide invaluable information on both fiction and nonfiction science books. In addition, they can keep you up to date on some of the latest releases in children's literature. You should consider utilizing the services of some of the following individuals:
   a. *Your school librarian.* This is probably the person you will want to contact first. He or she not only will be familiar with the holdings of the school library but will be eager to work with you in designing appropriate book-related activities. For example, if you let your school librarian know of a particular unit you will be using in your classroom two or three weeks in advance, he or she will be able to assemble a collection of relevant science books for your use.
   b. *The public librarian.* One very valuable resource person that many teachers fail to utilize is the local public librarian. This individual, particularly if your public library is large enough to have a children's section and attendant children's librarians, can be worth his or her weight in gold. Many public libraries have extensive collections of children's literature that school libraries cannot match, because of funding or other budgetary restrictions. Frequent contacts with the public library can add an exciting dimension to your science program.
   c. *College librarian.* Many colleges maintain curriculum libraries that you'll want to take advantage of in selecting appropriate materials and literature. If you teach near a college, make sure to contact the head librarian or the librarian in charge of the educational materials and arrange to use books and other items.

## DID YOU KNOW? _____

Louisiana and Hawaii are the only states that continue to grow in physical size.

**Classroom Activity** If you're interested in obtaining an extensive teaching packet of free materials about the geology and topography of your particular state, write (on school stationery) to the Geologic Inquiries Group, 907 National Center, Reston, VA 22092. This organization will also respond to any specific questions you or your students may have about the geology of your state. ∎

3. *Book clubs.* Several clubs provide all sorts of books (often at very low prices) for students. Many clubs have incentive programs, in which after students have purchased a certain number of books, they or their teacher are entitled to a selection of free books for the classroom library. Here are four of the most popular book clubs:
   a. Scholastic Book Clubs, 2931 East McCarty St., P.O. Box 7500, Jefferson City, MO 65102
   b. Troll Book Clubs, 320 Route 17, Mahwah, NJ 07498
   c. The Trumpet Club, P.O. Box 604, Holmes, PA 19092
   d. Weekly Reader Paperback Clubs, 4343 Equity Dr., P.O. Box 16628, Columbus, OH 43272

4. *Neighborhood sources.* One of the easiest ways to obtain books for your classroom is not only inexpensive but fun as well. This is through garage sales, yard sales, and neighborhood flea markets. In many parts of the country an abundance of these "clearance sales" take place in the spring and fall months. It can be worth your while to stop by these sales every to often so see what you can find in terms of science books for your classroom (one of the authors obtained a 20-book science encyclopedia for $5 at a local garage sale).

Sources for science trade books are unlimited. By taking advantage of the variety of books available as well as the number of places in which these books can be obtained, you can enliven your science program and infuse it with relevance and excitement. Trade books also stimulate students to pursue topics of significance for them as individuals. Trade books allow you to promote science as an exploration of knowledge that extends beyond the walls of your classroom.

# PROCESS WEBS

Chapter 2 discussed the value of process skills as elements of the classroom science program. Not only should students understand the processes of science; they must be able to initiate their own discoveries and investigations with their process skills. In so doing, they will develop an appreciation of their role in science learning and see science as an ongoing exploration of the world.

One strategy teachers can use to underscore the importance of process activities and encourage the use of relevant trade books throughout the elementary science curriculum is known as "process webbing." This teaching technique was developed by teacher education students at York College. The technique is adaptable to many different types of nonfiction books and many different teaching situations. It can be used with individuals, small groups, large groups, or the entire class. However, it is most useful as a small group activity that immediately follows the reading of a particular trade book.

Table 6.3 is a description of how a process web was developed for one book: *Volcanoes* by Seymour Simon (New York: Morrow Junior Books, 1988). Note the inclusion of both process questions and process activities. Also noteworthy is the fact that several options are available for any child or any group of children to pursue at their choosing. Process webs can be constructed by teachers as important components of the overall science program. They can be used in many situations and with many books to enhance elementary science instruction.

You may wish to create your own process webs. The following steps will be helpful:

1. Obtain a trade book that relates to a unit of study (consult your school librarian; the listings at the end of Chapters 12, 13, 14, and 15 in this text, or the list of resources in Appendix C).
2. Share the book with your students by reading it aloud or having selected students read the book independently.
3. Encourage students to discuss the information in the trade book that applies to the unit under study or to their own interests.
4. Work with your students to brainstorm potential activities and questions for each of the seven major processes of science (even first-grade students are capable of doing this).
5. Allow students to select one or more of the brainstormed activities and questions for each process. Encourage them to work with other students on selected activities.
6. Hold a "debriefing session" upon completion of the activities and questions to help students relate those activities back to the trade book and to any textbook material.
7. Display any resulting products along with a copy of the trade book.

TABLE   **6.3**

......................................................................................................

### PROCESS WEB: *VOLCANOES* BY SEYMOUR SIMON

......................................................................................................

#### Observing

1.  Bring in samples of volcanic ash or lava (these can be obtained through science supply companies) and show them to students. Ask students to discuss the feel of these substances and relate them to the descriptions in the book.

2.  Ask students to draw their own interpretations of the two gods Vulcan and Pele. Post the pictures throughout the room or gather them in a class scrapbook.

3.  Ask students to compare volcanic ash to the ash from other types of materials (paper, wood, etc.). What is similar? What is different?

4.  Students may be interested in creating a flip book illustrating the sequence of activities during a volcanic eruption.

5.  Have students watch the filmstrip "Earthquakes and Volcanoes," available from the National Geographic Society (Washington, DC 20026) as part of the "Discovering the Powers of Nature" series (catalog no. 03237). Ask them to generate a list of adjectives (which can be recorded in a class book) to describe the actions they observed.

#### Classifying

1.  Have students place the titles of the four different kinds of volcanoes on separate sheets of poster board. Ask them to draw illustrations of selected examples (from around the world) of each type of volcano on the poster board.

2.  Have students create a scrapbook classifying volcanic rocks (lava, pumice, etc.) and types of lava (aa, pahoehoe).

3.  Ask students to construct comparative charts of volcanoes according to different climatic regions of the world (e.g., how many active volcanoes are located in tropical regions vs. polar regions?).

4.  Have students make charts of the dormancy periods of selected volcanoes. Which volcanoes remained dormant the longest? Which volcanoes had the most recent eruptions? Where are the most dormant volcanoes located? Where are the most active volcanoes located?

#### Inferring

1.  Have students compare the photographs in this book with volcano photos in other books. What similarities are there? What differences are notable? How can they account for differences in photos of the same volcano?

2.  What happens when you shake a bottle of soda pop? How is that similar to the action of a volcano? Why?

3.  Ask students to develop a pantomime in which students simulate the actions of the volcano, lava, surrounding territory, and so on.

#### Communicating

1.  Divide students into several small groups and ask each group to list as much background information as possible about volcanoes. Have each group chart their data in the form of an outline or semantic web (see Chapter 8).

2.  Have students watch a video of a volcano erupting (e.g., "The Violent Earth" [National Geographic Society, Washington, DC 20036 catalog no. 51234]). Have students pretend they are at the site of one of the eruptions, and videotape their reactions.

3.  Have students draw pictures of what their geographic area would look like after a volcanic eruption.

4.  Have students study famous volcanoes in history (Krakatoa, Mt. Fuji, Vesuvius, etc.).

5.  Ask students to write letters to people who have lived in the area of a volcanic eruption (the people who lived near Mt. Saint Helens, for example) and solicit information about their experiences (names and addresses can be obtained from phone books available at large public libraries).

6.  Have small groups of students investigate the myths and legends regarding volcanoes compared with modern scientific knowledge.

7.  Ask students to develop a "volcano drill" in the event a volcano were to erupt in close proximity to their school. What precautions should be taken? What preparations should be made? How would a volcano drill be similar to or different from a fire drill or earthquake drill?

---

Process webs provide numerous opportunities for students to tie together scientific concepts and relevant trade books. Students will begin to understand that the processes of science are not restricted to the science classroom but can be applied in many different situations throughout their lives. The linkage of process skills with literature also provides students with an opportunity to make science more relevant to other areas of the elementary curriculum.

TABLE **6.3** (*Continued*)

..........................................................................................................................................................
### PROCESS WEB: *VOLCANOES* BY SEYMOUR SIMON
..........................................................................................................................................................

#### Measuring

1. Ask students to locate information on the "eruption rates" (i.e., the length of time from the start of the eruption until the volcano settles down) for different volcanoes. How can they account for the wide variation in rates?

2. Ask students to measure the temperatures of different household items (boiling water, microwave dinner, etc.) and compare those temperatures with the temperature of molten lava (comparative charts can be constructed by student groups).

3. Have students investigate the heights of different active and inactive volcanoes around the world. During a volcanic eruption, how much of the mountain is lost? (Mt. Saint Helens, for example, lost more than 1,100 feet in height when it erupted in 1980.)

4. Have students compare the time periods of volcanoes and earthquakes. Why do volcanoes tend to last longer? Why do active volcanoes and major earthquakes occur in the same areas of the world?

5. Have students obtain data on the relative speeds of different types of lava. How fast does quick-moving lava flow? Slow-moving lava?

#### Predicting

1. Have students make some predictions on the length of time it takes for an area surrounding a volcano to recover after an eruption.

2. Show one of the "before" photos in the book and have students predict what the volcano will look like after an eruption (they may wish to draw illustrations). Afterward, compare their predictions with a posteruption photo in the book.

3. Ask students some of the following questions: How long will it take for animals and plants to return to an area of a volcanic eruption? Which animals will return first? Which plants will return first? How long will it take to clean up an area?

#### Experimenting

1. Take two paraffin blocks and cut them into the shape of earth crust plates. Put them on a hot plate and slowly move them in opposite directions (using heavy-duty gloves) to examine how plates move and react.

2. Boil several eggs until they crack. Ask students to explain the similarities between the egg shells and the crust of the earth.

3. Obtain some volcanic ash. Mix different amounts with equal amounts of potting soil. Fill several compartments of an egg carton with the different mixtures and plant several vegetable seeds in each compartment. Have students compare the relative growth rates of the vegetables. In which mixture do the seeds germinate first? Which one is most conducive to healthy growth? How does the amount of volcanic ash affect the germination and growth of plants?

..........................................................................................................................................................
## POINTS OF DISCUSSION
..........................................................................................................................................................

1. The National Science Teachers Association (1742 Connecticut Ave. NW, Washington, DC 20009) has a pamphlet entitled *How to Care for Living Things in the Classroom* (1978). Write and obtain a copy. While you await the arrival of the pamphlet, work with a group of your classmates and develop your own list of Dos and Don'ts for plant and animal care in the classroom. When the NSTA pamphlet arrives, compare your list with theirs.

2. Survey all the other students in your class. Determine everyone's hobbies, interests, and free-time activities. Put together a master list of avocations for the class as a whole. How would you utilize the talents of your classmates as resources for an elementary science program?

3. Read several back issues of *Science and Children*. Elaborate on how you would use information from four of the articles to "*energize*" a standard classroom program. Based on your observations of nearby classrooms, how could the science program be improved in one or more of these classrooms using information from *Science and Children?*

4. What do you see as one of the major advantages of joining a professional organization such as NSTA. Can you see any advantages of joining while you are still in college?

5. Your first year of teaching will be filled with many procedures to memorize and many new things to do. What will help to make your classroom a child-centered classroom? What will you need to do before students walk in the door the first day of school? What will you need to do the first few weeks of school? How will you be able to maintain a child-centered classroom throughout the year?

6. Obtain the teacher's manual for a science textbook series. With a group of your classmates, analyze the contents of the book. How comfortable would you be in using that particular series? What would you want to change or modify?

7. What do *you* think is the chief disadvantage of science textbooks? Why? What do you think is the chief advantage of science textbooks? Why?

8. How can the school librarian help you in your overall science program? What are three major advantages of a close working relationship with that individual?

9. Work with a partner and create a process web on a single science trade book. Share your information with other classmates.

## REFERENCES

Cain, Sandra E., & Evans, Jack M. (1990). *Sciencing: An involvement approach to elementary science methods.* New York: Merrill.

Wassermann, Selma, & Ivany, J. W. George. (1988). *Teaching elementary science: Who's afraid of spiders?.* New York: Harper & Row.

# 7

# UNIT AND LESSON PLANNING

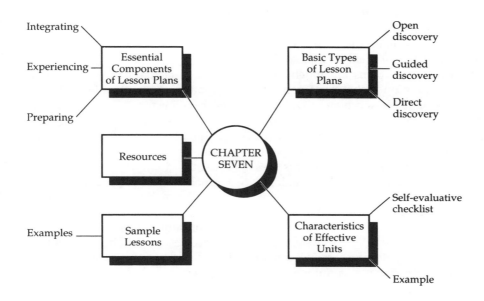

## Chapter Objectives

After reading this chapter you should be able to:

1.  Describe the three major elements of a lesson plan.

2.  Prepare a series of cyclical lesson plans on a specific topic.

3.  Describe several different varieties of lesson plans, including their similarities and differences.

4.  Understand the characteristics of effective units in science.

"Why should we learn how to write lesson plans when the textbook has all the information we need to teach our students?" This question is one typically asked by prospective teachers and reflects their concern not only about the content of their methods course in science, but also about the content and context of their future science programs.

This is a valid question that is asked frequently and for which there is no easy answer. Nevertheless, when teachers realize that a lesson plan is just that—a plan—they can begin to understand that it is a blueprint subject to modification from year to year and from one group of students to another. A lesson plan is not an inviolable design but rather a sketch that provides a sense of direction and the means to help students achieve appropriate levels of understanding for certain science objectives.

No textbook or set of printed materials can be written to serve the needs of all students. Your students will have their own particular learning styles, attitudes, and aptitudes. No textbook publisher can plan for that. Your experience in teaching science, in knowing your own strengths and weaknesses, and in tailoring lessons to the special qualities of your class will be important to the success of your science curriculum. Your effectiveness as a teacher of science will be determined not by the type or number of prepared materials you use, but rather by how you provide youngsters with the cognitive and affective opportunities they need to make science a personal part of their lives.

There is no ideal lesson plan. There are as many different lesson plans as there are teachers. According to Orlich et al. (1990), lesson plans are much more than a response to the question "what am I going to teach today?" A well-designed lesson plan provides an outline for the accomplishment of specific tasks while allowing for a measure of flexibility in terms of student interests and needs. Lesson plans should provide learners with an interactive relationship between themselves and what they can learn. A lesson should be tailored to what students know, how they can best process new information, and how they can integrate that knowledge into their lives.

Lesson plans can take many different designs and allow for a variety of options. However, a lesson plan should be built around three essential components:

1. Preparing
2. Experiencing
3. Integrating

These three components may be described as the beginning, middle, and end of the lesson plan. The implication here is that a well-designed lesson plan will move students from the unknown to the known. However, good science instruction is cyclical in nature; each science lesson is built on the concept of previous lessons and serves as a foundation for science lessons to follow. Such lessons are more challenging than the lessons many of us experienced in elementary school. The following chart compares linear (traditional) and cyclical (interactive) lessons:

| Linear | Cyclical |
| --- | --- |
| Focus on factual data | Focus on concepts |
| Emphasizes memorization | Emphasizes problem solving |
| Teacher-directed | Student-oriented |
| May be text-based | Learner-based |
| Competitive | Cooperative |
| Unimaginative | Creative |
| Pedantic | Motivational |
| Formal | Informal |
| Isolated experiences | Interrelated experiences |

One of your greatest challenges in designing effective science lessons will be determining how the lesson relates to other learning and to other instructional possibilities.

## ESSENTIAL COMPONENTS OF A LESSON PLAN

As mentioned earlier, the basic elements of preparing, experiencing, and integrating provide the structure for the effective science lesson. Let's take a look at each element in detail.

### Preparing

It is important to adequately prepare students prior to the teaching of a lesson. The preparation stage is the one most often neglected by classroom teachers, yet it may be the most significant stage in terms of the success of a science lesson. Many teachers are inclined to provide their students with a collection of facts, figures, and data with little regard for the ability of students to assimilate that information. Students need to be adequately prepared for receiving the concepts and gen-

eralizations they will be taught. Indeed, when teachers ignore the preparation stage in the design of their lessons, they cheat children out of valuable learning opportunities.

The preparation stage of a lesson includes several elements. Some of these are outlined next.

- *Tapping background knowledge.* It is important for the teacher to know the extent and level of the children's background knowledge before beginning any lesson. (See Table 7.1.)
- *Self-questioning.* Unfortunately, most of the questions asked in a typical classroom are teacher-directed. When children are given opportunities to generate their own questions about a topic, they will be motivated to seek the answers to those questions.

TABLE 7.1

................................................................................

## THE NO BOOK DR-TA

................................................................................

The "No Book DR-TA" (Gill & Bear, 1988) is an activity designed to elicit students' background knowledge. Based on an inquiry model of reading comprehension, it offers teachers data on what students already know about a topic while helping students establish a purpose for exploring the body of knowledge to be presented. This strategy can be conducted with the whole class, a large group, or a small group. The following four steps make up the "No Book DR-TA."

1. Students (in groups) list everything they can think of that might pertain to a designated topic. Students may wish to generate ideas on their own or brainstorm in subgroups for all the background information they have on a particular topic. A master list is maintained for each group.
2. Students group the items in their lists into categories. This step can be conducted as a whole class activity, with each group sharing the items (and their designated categories) from their list. It may be necessary for you to model the categorizing behavior for students initially.
3. Students assign a name to each group of items and arrange them as though they were a table of contents for a book. This should be done as a class activity until students have sufficient practice in assigning titles to their respective categories.
4. Students write a "book" about the upcoming topic using the categories as chapter titles. They are encouraged to write as much about each topic as they can, summarizing what each section is about. If students get stuck, they are allowed to make up what they don't know. This step can serve as a homework assignment for older students or can be conducted in class as an oral dictation activity for younger students. The "books" are then kept on file. They can be edited as the lesson progresses or rewritten at the conclusion of the lesson.

The following example of a "No Book DR-TA" was used in a second-grade classroom. The topic was "changes in weather," and the teacher, Chris Montgomery, wanted to find out how much background knowledge her students had on this topic. Her students came up with the following list during the first three steps of the "No Book DR-TA."

| Seasons | Hot Weather | Cold Weather | Temperature | In the Sky |
|---------|-------------|--------------|-------------|------------|
| Winter | Sunny | Snow | Hot | Clouds |
| Summer | Warm | Ice | Warm | Rain |
| Fall | Sun | | Cool | Lightning |
| Spring | | | Cold | |

It was evident to Chris that her students had some knowledge about the weather, although their backgrounds were not strong. After her students had finished dictating a class book (which Chris wrote on chart paper for the entire class to see), she was able to tailor her lesson on weather according to the gaps in her students' background knowledge. At the conclusion of the lesson Chris and her students wrote another "book" and compared it with the one generated via the "No Book DR-TA." Students were delighted to learn that some of their previous perceptions about the weather had changed and were amazed at the new information they had learned during the lesson.

---

- *Predictions.* Predictions are educated guesses about what may happen. A prediction may be thought of as "an investment of self," in the sense that when one makes an investment that individual wants to find out the results of the investment. Not only is predicting an important process skill; it's also valuable in providing students with some self-initiated directions for a lesson.
- *Brainstorming.* Brainstorming is an active search for many possible answers to a single question. The emphasis in brainstorming is on gathering a quantity of ideas with little regard for their quality. Brainstorming allows students to share much of their prior knowledge in a supportive arena.
- *Setting goals.* It is vital that you provide youngsters with opportunities to establish their own goals and directions. In so doing, you give them a chance to "buy into" their own learning and an impetus to pursue information because they have a stake in the information that is to be pursued.

- *Previewing.* Many students perceive science as a topic that consists of facts and data known only to the teacher. Their job, then, becomes one of guessing what teachers already know or figuring out the important points in the textbook. Keying students into the knowledge they may gain through the lesson is an important part of the lesson.
- *Relationships.* It's important for teachers to demonstrate how a lesson is related to other lessons. Students must understand that no lesson exists apart from other lessons.
- *Classifying.* Classifying is a process of showing children the various relationships that exist among elements of a lesson as well as relationships between lessons. Understanding the various ways in which data can be classified is an important part of any lesson.
- *Graphic organizers.* Graphic organizers are charts, graphs, or outlines of the essential information in a lesson. They serve to provide students with a pic-

torial representation of the major points in a lesson and how those points are related to each other.

- *Gaining attention.* Often referred to as a motivational device, attention getting is how we stimulate students interest in a topic. It may involve asking students thought-provoking questions such as: "How would you like to sleep for four months every year?" "Did you know that white light is actually a combination of seven colors?" "Did you know we can measure any tree on the playground without climbing it?" Other attention-gaining devices are models, maps, globes, scientific apparatus, and demonstrations. It is important that every lesson include some method to stimulate students' interests.

- *Stating the lesson objectives.* Many students perceive a lesson as something the teacher concocts on the spot. Unfortunately, this perception signals youngsters that lessons are not designed with their needs and interests in mind. It is vital, therefore, to let your students know exactly what you plan to have them learn. When students are aware of the objectives, they will be able to understand the direction and scope of a lesson and work with you in achieving those objectives.

### DID YOU KNOW? _____

The hair on your head grows at a speed of 0.00000001 miles per hour.

**Classroom Activity** Have students brainstorm for all the parts of their bodies that are growing (fingernails, leg bones, etc.). Ask them to make some predictions on the rates of growth for those body parts, and have them chart that information. Then set them loose in the library to investigate the growth rates and patterns for those body parts. Be sure to add that information to the original chart. ■

### TO INVESTIGATE _____

As you visit elementary classrooms in your area, note how much time teachers devote to the solicitation of the background knowledge of their students. What methods or procedures are used? Can you suggest other possibilities? How is students' knowledge or lack of knowledge related to the lessons being taught? What procedures can you suggest to provide the teachers with more data concerning students' background knowledge? How would you initiate those lessons differently? ■

## Experiencing

Experiencing is the stage of a lesson in which students obtain valuable information, manipulate data, and engage in active discovery through total involvement. The following elements can be included in this stage:

- *Processing.* The processes of science (detailed in Chapter 2) are valuable explorations into how science operates. They provide students with opportunities to investigate scientific principles first-hand. Science becomes not just an accumulation of finite answers but an application of processes that aid in discovery and learning.

- *Assimilating new ideas.* Students need to be able to tie new ideas to those they already have. It is important for students to manipulate ideas in such a way as to draw relationships between previously learned information and new discoveries.

- *Problem solving.* As discussed in Chapter 4, problem solving is an inherent part of scientific discoveries. Letting students solve their own problems in their own way is a valuable motivational technique.

- *Creative thinking.* Science is much more than the memorization of facts. Any science lesson must allow kids chances to work with data in new and unusual ways—often in ways that cannot be planned by the teacher. A supportive environment must be provided that enables students to initiate and follow through on their own discoveries.

- *Hands-on activities.* It is critical to encourage students to use all of their sensory powers in learning about the world of science. Teachers need to consider activities that allow students to touch, smell, see, hear, and taste science in as many ways as possible.

- *Lesson methodologies.* Not only is it important to give some thought as to *what* you are going to teach youngsters, the methods of presentation must be considered as well. You have probably sat through a class that consisted of nothing more than dry, stale lectures. Chances are you found the class boring and wearying and something less than intellectually stimulating. The same fate awaits your students if you concentrate on one type of teaching methodology to the exclusion of others. Table 7.2 demonstrates that it is important to consider a variety of formats in presenting effective lessons to pupils.

TABLE  7.2

## LESSON METHODOLOGIES

Least Impact →————————————————————————————————→ Greatest Impact
and Involvement                                         and Involvement

```
                                                    Guided practice
                                                 Skill practice
                                              Gaming and simulation
                                           Modeling
                                        Role playing
                                     Debriefing
                                  Buzz sessions
                               Projects
                            Problem-solving activities
                         Playing
                      Experimenting
                   Small group discussions
                Brainstorming
             Interviewing
          Round robin
       Field trips
    Observation
 Demonstration
Audiovisual presentation
Illustrated lecture
Reading information
Lecture
```

Knowledge ————————————————→ Synthesis ————————————————→ Performance

1. *Lecture.* Often the most misused and abused form of presentation, a lecture is an arrangement in which the teacher speaks directly to students.
2. *Reading information.* In this format the teacher assigns material from the textbook for students to read independently or aloud to the class.
3. *Illustrated lecture.* This is similar to a regular lecture, except that the teacher presents information orally in addition to including pictures or photographs.
4. *Audiovisual presentation.* In this format the teacher uses slides, movies, filmstrips, or overhead transparencies.
5. *Demonstration.* Students witness a real or simulated activity in which the teacher uses materials from the "real world" of science.
6. *Observation.* This format allows students to watch an event take place. The teacher may have little control over the content or method of presentation.
7. *Field trips.* The teacher takes the students out of the classroom and into a new learning environment (see Chapter 9), usually for only a short period of time.
8. *Round robin.* In this methodology students have an opportunity to share information or ideas in a small-group format. Everyone participates equally.
9. *Interviewing.* This format includes the personal interview in which one person talks with another person, and the group interview, in which several people talk with a single individual.
10. *Brainstorming.* This is the process in which students share as many ideas as possible on a single topic. The object is to generate a quantity of ideas without regard to quality.
11. *Small group discussions.* The class is divided into small groups of two to four, and each group is assigned a specific task. The group works together, and members are responsible for each other.
12. *Experimenting.* In a planned experiment, students manipulate materials in order to discover some scientific principle or truth.
13. *Playing.* Often not considered an appropriate science event, playing allows students to experiment on their own with a limited set of conditions. Answers or results are not usually known in advance.
14. *Problem-solving activities.* In this situation the class, small groups, or individuals are given a problem or a series of problems and are directed to find an appropriate solution. It is important to include problems for which the teacher does not have a pre-determined answer.
15. *Projects.* Students are allowed to create their own designs, models, or structures to illustrate an important point or science fact.
16. *Buzz sessions.* Temporary groups are formed for the purpose of discussing a specific topic. The emphasis is on verbal interaction among group members.
17. *Debriefing.* Usually conducted at the conclusion of a lesson, debriefing allows students to condense their knowledge as a group or class. It is an active thinking process.
18. *Role playing.* In this methodology a student takes on the role of a specific individual and acts as if he or she were actually that person. The intent is to develop a feeling for and an appreciation of the thoughts and actions of another individual.
19. *Modeling.* The teacher models the behavior students are to employ within an activity. Students may model appropriate behavior for each other, too.
20. *Gaming and simulation.* This is a procedure in which individuals are given real-life problem situations and asked to work through those situations.
21. *Skill practice.* Students are provided with an opportunity to apply newly learned skills in a real-life experience.
22. *Guided practice.* Here students are allowed to experience all aspects of a learning situation. Usually the work is done individually, although it can be done collectively. The teacher remains an impartial observer.

- *Eliciting the desired behavior.* A good science lesson must provide opportunities for students to become actively involved in the dynamics of the lesson and to demonstrate their comprehension of the information. There are several ways in which students can demonstrate the desired behavior. Rosenshine and Stevens (1986) have suggested several:
  a. Preparing a large number of oral questions beforehand
  b. Asking many brief questions covering main points, supplementary points, and the process being taught
  c. Calling on those students whose hands are not raised in addition to those who volunteer
  d. Asking students to summarize a rule or process in their own words
  e. Having students write their answers (on paper or on the chalkboard) while the teacher circulates
  f. Having students write their answers and check them with a neighbor (a method frequently used with older students)
  g. At the end of a lecture or discussion (especially with older students), writing the main points on the chalkboard and then having the class meet in groups to review the main points

- To that list may be added the following:
  h. Having students critique the directions or setup for an experiment or demonstration
  i. Directing students to verbalize the steps they are taking in the completion of an activity
  j. Engaging students in the manipulation of objects or devices and having them discuss their feelings about their actions
  k. Allowing students to work in small groups to share the information learned and how it relates to prior knowledge
  l. Having students graph or illustrate significant points on the chalkboard for class critique.

## TEACHER TO TEACHER

Often students are not prepared sufficiently for a hands-on experience. If the students have been afforded the opportunity to watch their teacher and a student perform the hands-on activity, they will be better prepared to complete the activity successfully and sequentially as well as to enjoy the process. To capture the interest of my students, I use a homemade orange lab coat. One student is "the scientist for the day" and wears the student lab coat, performing the pre-lab activities as I model the steps of the process and asking questions pertaining to the procedure and equipment to be used. This activity helps me with the clarification of the process and the students with following directions. Being the "scientist for the day" motivates the students to attend to the lesson with a more meaningful purpose.

Faye Neatherly
San Jacinto Elementary School
Deer Park, TX

## Integrating

Integration is a critical stage in the development of an effective lesson. It signals to students that what they learn in a planned lesson is also applicable outside that lesson. It demonstrates that knowledge is not confined to the scientific world but has applications throughout the elementary curriculum and throughout each students' life.

The following events may be included in the integration stage:

- *Summarizing.* Most teachers assume that they should provide some sort of summarization at the end of a lesson, but such a process may deny students a valuable opportunity to summarize the lesson on their own. Teachers may have students submit a capsule report, in either written or oral form, on what was learned in the lesson and how that information applies to other lessons or other areas of learning.
- *Criterion checks.* Periodically throughout a lesson teachers should give students a criterion check, which consists of raising a question or a concern to make sure students are on task and are understanding the concepts being presented. It behooves teachers to take time out at regular intervals to make sure students are processing data in productive ways.

## IDEA BOX

Involving children in the dynamics of a lesson can be accomplished through the use of criterion checks. A criterion check is a question, situation, or mini-activity offered periodically throughout a lesson that lets children assess their progress and lets the teacher monitor their progress. These are not formal evaluation tools but monitoring devices to ensure that sufficient progress is being made.

The following list of examples is not intended to be all-inclusive or universally applicable. The nature and scope of your lessons will determine which of the suggestions are appropriate for your students. You should provide a criterion check every 10 to 15 minutes during the lesson. Students must understand that these checks are not for grading purposes but are meant to serve as guideposts for the progress of the lesson.

1. Ask students several open-ended questions such as the following:
   "What have you learned so far in this lesson?"
   "Why is this information important?"
   "How does this information relate to anything we learned previously?"
   "How do you feel about your progress so far?"
   "How does this data apply to other situations?"
   "Where else could this be used?"
   "What do you think might happen next?"
   "How do you think this lesson will turn out?"
   "Is there something you don't understand at this point?"

2. Have students provide a brief oral summary (25 words or less) about what they have learned up to a specific point.

3. Direct students to prepare brief written summaries and to keep a record of these summaries in a journal for review after the lesson.

4. For small group work, have each group appoint a reporter to briefly summarize the work of the group.

5. Have students make a preliminary sketch of a major piece of information they have learned.

6. Individual students can make a tape recording of information learned or struggles encountered periodically throughout a lesson.

7. Ask students to each make a prediction of how the lesson will conclude.

8. Ask students to describe what information they would need at a particular point if they were teaching or tutoring other students about the lesson concepts.

9. Appoint individual students to take on the role of teacher and instruct others on what to do next in the lesson.

Criterion checks should be "dropped into" a lesson periodically to make sure the lesson is progressing smoothly and is in line with your stated objectives. Information gained from criterion checks allow you to make any necessary changes within a lesson rather than at the end of a lesson, when it may be too late.

- *Cross-curricular activities.* One of the most valuable functions teachers can perform is to demonstrate to students how science is involved in other areas of study. The relationships between science and language arts, social studies, art, music, health, and physical education help students appreciate science as a universal subject.

## IDEA BOX

Linda Cassill, a third-grade teacher in a small school in Arizona, was planning a lesson on pigs. The textbook contained information on the uses of pigs, some data on farm life, a listing of the products humans get from pigs, and a brief excerpt about Wilbur from *Charlotte's Web*. Linda believed that the lesson could be extended, not only because kids are naturally attracted to pigs but also because she felt that children's experiences with pigs could be applied throughout the curriculum.

Linda used a procedure known as theme webbing which is simply the integration of a science topic into other areas of the elementary curriculum. This gives students an opportunity to use skills normally associated with other subjects to broaden their experiences with a science topic. The following plan, briefly outlined, is how Linda expanded the topic of "pigs" into a cross-curricular subject.

### Language Arts/Reading

1. Write a story on "A Day in the Life of a Pig" from the pig's point of view.
2. Debate: Are pigs smart or dumb?
3. Create a movie on the life cycle of a pig.
4. Make up pig riddles.
5. Journals: "What do pigs think about all day?"
6. Write a pig diary (shape book).
7. Write a class poem about pigs.

### Art

1. Create paper-plate pigs.
2. Design a pig collage.
3. Make a clay piggy bank.
4. Create finger-puppet pigs.
5. Make drawings of different breeds of pigs and classify them by personality type.
6. Design pig placemats.
7. Create bleach-bottle pigs and display them in the room

### Science/Health

1. Why are pigs messy? Study their environment.
2. How and why do we raise pigs?
3. Draw and label the features of pigs.
4. What are some pig products?
5. Interview a farmer about raising pigs.
6. Investigate the intelligence of pigs.

### Social Studies

1. Research the importance of pigs to humans.
2. Create a map of an imaginary pig farm.
3. Study the uses of pigs in other countries.
4. Investigate pig-producing areas of the country.
5. Trace the domestication of pigs throughout history.

### Physical Education

1. Play "pig tag"—the farmer is "it" and puts pigs in a "pen."
2. Students act out movements of pigs.
3. Play "Simon Says" with farm animals.
4. Students do different animal walks (waddle, trot, etc.).

**Math**

1. Measure the room in "pig units."
2. Graph the number of pigs found in selected illustrations.
3. Have students create word problems using pigs.
4. Design pig flash cards.
5. Invent recipes using pig measurements.

**Music**

1. Make up a class song about pigs.
2. Play "Farmer in the Dell" and create a dance.
3. Sing "Old MacDonald Had a Farm."
4. Work with the music teacher to collect pig-related songs.

- *Evaluation.* Chapter 10 addresses the topic of evaluation in greater detail. Suffice it to say here that the well-designed lesson provides opportunities for both teacher and students to evaluate progress within the lesson. Have students mastered the objectives established for the lesson? How is that mastery to be measured?
- *Metacognition.* Metacognition is defined as thinking about one's thinking. Students need opportunities to consider their thought processes within a science lesson and how to correct any deficits in those processes (see Table 7.3).
- *Extending projects.* Consider both short-term and long-term projects that students can participate in according to their interests and ability levels. You may wish to include a variety of activities within a lesson as well as some activities that can extend beyond the lesson.

- *Closure.* Public speakers are often told that there are three essential rules that should guide any presentation (Orlich et al., 1990): (1) Tell the audience what you're going to tell them. (2) Tell them. (3) Tell them what you've told them. These rules are important to the well-designed science lesson, too. It is essential in the cyclical lesson plan to incorporate some sort of closure. This may mean a few minutes at the end of the lesson in which you or your students summarize the significant points, an activity in which students share perceptions with each other, or a session in which students recall their positive or negative perceptions of the lesson. No matter how you conduct it, it is vital that students have an opportunity to identify the major points of a lesson—not to define the end of the lesson but to demonstrate the fullness of a body of knowledge and its relationship to any information that follows.

The preceding list is a selection of possibilities to consider in the design of a lesson plan. The outline that follows is a possible sequence of those procedures. It represents a potential plan of action for developing lesson plans. Of course, no teacher would want to include every element of this outline in a single lesson. It may be appropriate, however, to consider using specific methods in the order in which they are presented here.

**Preparing**

1. Gaining attention
2. Tapping background knowledge
3. Brainstorming
4. Classifying

TABLE 7.3

......................................................................................................................

## METACOGNITIVE QUESTIONING

......................................................................................................................

Following are two lists. One provides you with some questions to ask your students as they participate in a science activity, and the other contains examples of questions students should come to ask themselves as they progress through a lesson. You can facilitate this process by encouraging students to think out loud as they engage in various parts of the lesson. Listen to what they are saying and ask them to consider all the options available in terms of thought within a lesson.

| **Teacher-posed** | **Student-posed** |
|---|---|
| Is this activity similar to anything you may have done before? | Why is this information important for me to know? |
| What were you thinking when you did this activity? | Is this similar to something I already know? |
| What have we learned so far? | Do I understand what's happening? |
| What is the major point of this process? | How does this information differ from other things that I know? |
| Did you change your mind about any prediction you made? | Why is this difficult for me to understand? |
| Do you have any personal questions at this point? | Do I need additional data to help me understand this procedure? |
| What did you do when you didn't understand that part of the lesson? | Can I write a summary of the lesson now? |
| What makes you feel your interpretation is correct? | What do I know so far? |
| What new information are you learning? | What did I do to cause me to think this way? |
| How did you arrive at your interpretation? | Am I satisfied with my conclusions? |

5. Graphic organizers
6. Relationships
7. Predictions
8. Previewing
9. Setting goals
10. Self-questioning
11. Stating lesson objectives

### Experiencing

1. Creative thinking
2. Hands-on experiences
3. Problem solving
4. Processing

5. Lesson methodologies
6. Eliciting the desired behavior
7. Assimilating new ideas

### Integrating

1. Criterion checks
2. Cross-curricular activities
3. Metacognition
4. Summarizing
5. Extending projects
6. Evaluation
7. Closure

## RESOURCES

To prepare effective lessons, you should make use of the wide variety of resources at your disposal. If you are uncomfortable in teaching science, you will be happy to learn that there is an endless assortment of printed materials you can consult in designing purposeful and exciting lessons. You may wish to consider some of the following:

- *Textbooks.* Most textbook series come with a teacher's manual that provides plans and activities that can be incorporated or modified for a particular lesson.
- *Commercial science programs.* Your school library or the curriculum library at a nearby college will have examples of commercial materials. Consult Appendix H for a list of publishers and suppliers of commercial materials.
- *National Science Teacher Association publications.* The NSTA has a catalog of exciting and up-to-date science publications that can become part of your professional library.
- *State or local curriculum guides.* Most states and local school districts publish curriculum guides. Although objectives will differ from guide to guide, these publications can serve as a valuable resource in the planning of your classroom science program.
- *Other textbooks.* You may find it advantageous to consult other texts in the field of science education to obtain necessary information.
- *Teacher resource books.* Many publishers offer resource books (see the Appendix) that can be purchased in local bookstores or teacher supply stores. These books offer fresh ideas to incorporate into your science curriculum.
- *Colleges and universities.* Take advantage of a local college or university and ask members of the science department or teacher education department for any resources they may have for your use. It would also

be helpful to consult with several professors on ideas and activities they have found to be successful in the classroom.

- *Science periodicals.* Magazines such as *Science and Children, Teaching K–8, Learning, Instructor,* and *Teacher* provide readers with exciting ideas and activities for your science program. A subscription to one or more of them is a good investment (see Appendix F for additional titles).
- *Film and book catalogs.* A careful reading of the many catalogs teachers receive over the school year can reveal some intriguing approaches to lesson preparation as well as literary and audiovisual resources for those lessons.
- *Newspapers and popular magazines.* These resources offer current information on many issues and concerns. They are a ready resource for exploring recurring events (e.g., space shuttle launchings, biotechnology research, and eradication of common diseases). Chapter 9 provides suggestions on how these resources can be effectively integrated into the curriculum.

**DID YOU KNOW?**

Approximately 99 percent of all species that ever lived are now extinct.

**Classroom Activity** Popular magazines frequently carry articles on the environment and its effects on plant and animal life. Depletion of the ozone layer and the greenhouse effect are examples of continuing stories that many magazines cover on a regular basis. Encourage your students to collect related environmental articles into several different scrapbooks. These scrapbooks can be maintained over the course of the school year and related to specific chapters in the science text. ■

# SAMPLE LESSONS

Examples of lesson plan forms used in various school systems are presented in Tables 7.4–7.7. For an example of an actual lesson plan, let's take a look at a plan for a lesson on soil that was written and conducted by Bill Burdett for his fourth-grade class (page 130). Note the sequence of events in this plan and how Bill has designed a lesson that moves his students from preparation to experiencing to integration. Although Bill could have designed this lesson in several possible ways, he felt that the following plan was best suited to the needs of his students and the resources available.

TABLE 7.4

## LESSON PLAN FORM USED BY MESA PUBLIC SCHOOLS, MESA, ARIZONA

**Lesson Plan #**

Title:

Objective:

Process Skills:

Integration:

Session Time:

Materials:

Teacher Background:

Procedure:

1.

2.

3.

4.

5.

6.

Extended Activity:

TABLE 7.5

## LESSON PLAN FORM USED BY YORK COLLEGE, YORK, PA

**Lesson Plan #**

Class/Subject:                    Date:

Period:                           Time:

Behavioral Objectives:

Materials/Equipment:

Procedures:

1) Motivational Technique/Opening:

2) Development of Lesson:

a)

b)

c)

d)

e)

3) Closure/Outside Work:

Evaluation:

TABLE 7.6

......................................................

# LESSON PLAN FORM USED BY SHECKLER ELEMENTARY SCHOOL, CATASAUQUA, PA

......................................................

**Lesson Plan #**

Competencies:

  a) Processes:

  b) Attitudes:

  c) Science Discipline:

Text:

Supplemental Resources:

Background Information:

_____

Activity #_____:

Grade Level:

Purpose:

Focus Question:

Materials:

Procedure:

_____

Activity #_____:

Grade Level:

Purpose:

Focus Question:

Materials:

Procedure:

_____

TABLE 7.7

......................................................

# LESSON PLAN FORM USED BY COHEN, STALEY, AND HORAK

......................................................

**Lesson Plan #**

Objective, Purpose, Aim:

Content:

Lesson Logistics:

  a. Time alloted:

  b. Materials required:

  c. Social/physical structure:

Procedures/Activities:

  1.

  2.

  3.

  4.

  5.

  6.

Evaluation:

_____

**Unit:**
**The Earth's Surface**

*Lesson:*
*Changes in Landforms*

## Preparing

1. *Gaining attention.* Two days before the lesson, Bill mixed several cups of sand with a large amount of white glue. He shaped the mixture into cubes and allowed them to dry. He gave a cube to each student along with a plastic butter container, several small pebbles, and some water. He instructed each student to put the cube, pebbles, and water into the butter container; cover the container with a lid; and shake it for several minutes. Afterward, Bill instructed his students to remove what was left of the cube from the container and to speculate on why the cubes were considerably smaller.

2. *Tapping background knowledge.* Bill wrote the phrase "Changes in Landforms" on the chalkboard. He divided the class into four groups and asked each group to generate as many ideas as they could about that topic. He then asked the recorder for each group to write the group's ideas on the chalkboard and put them into categories. Bill then developed a semantic web (see Chapter 8) to demonstrate the relationships between students' prior knowledge.

3. *Predictions.* Bill told his students that they would be learning about some of the changes that take place in the surface of the earth. He asked each student to predict what changes are normal and what changes may be caused by humans. Each student recorded his or her predictions in a journal, which was used as reference guide throughout the remainder of the lesson.

4. *Stating lesson objectives.* In the upper right-hand corner of the chalkboard, Bill wrote the following lesson objectives:
    We will learn:
    a. The three layers of the earth
    b. How volcanoes and earthquakes change the shape of the land
    c. How weathering changes the earth's surface

## Experiencing

1. *Creative thinking.* Bill had prepared and now began to ask his students several "what if" questions:
    "What if there were no volcanoes on the surface of the earth?"
    "What if rocks never wore down?"
    "What if the surface of the earth were perfectly smooth?"
    "What if it were possible to accurately predict earthquakes?"
    "What if the earth were solid all the way through?"

    Bill then asked members of the class to develop a news report on the creation of the Grand Canyon as if they were actually there and could film the entire process in fast motion. Students later presented their news report to another fourth-grade class.

2. *Hands-on experiences.* To provide his students with first-hand experience with each of the designated objectives, Bill developed the following activities:

**a.** Bill provided students with three different colors of modeling clay. He instructed each student to create a ball about ½″ in diameter using one color of clay, to surround that ball with clay of another color, and then to put a third layer of clay around the first two. Students were then told to use a kitchen knife to cut their clay balls in half and describe what they saw in terms of the three layers of the earth.

**b.** The class constructed a salt map (a mixture of flour and water with a few teaspoons of salt, combined into a claylike consistency) of the western United States. Several mountains were formed in the salt map, including Mt. Saint Helens in Washington. A small depression was left in the top of this mountain. When the salt map was dry, Bill put 1 teaspoon of baking soda in the top of Mt. Saint Helens and carefully added 1 tablespoon of vinegar. Students had an opportunity to observe and describe what took place. Bill provided materials for students to create their own volcanoes.

**c.** Students were divided into several small groups, and each group was given a baking pan filled with soil. Students held the pans at an angle and poured some water into the top of each pan. They then made observations on how the water carried dirt to the bottom of the pan. Students planted some grass seed in other pans and repeated the experiment after the grass had sprouted. They recorded their observations in their journals.

**3.** *Processing.* Throughout each of the demonstrations Bill posed several questions and provided several collateral activities for his students. He also provided opportunities for students to ask questions of each other. The responses to these queries were recorded in the students' journals.

**a.** *Observation:*
"How do your observations differ from (Mindy's)?"
"Would your observations be similar if you were to do this activity again?"

**b.** *Classifying:* Students created a collage of pictures depicting volcanoes from around the world. Students also created graphs of twentieth-century earthquakes according to their measurements on the Richter Scale (0–3, 4–6, 7 and above).

**c.** *Inferring:* Using toy houses and other models, students created a make-believe town located on a fault line. They put the town on a piece of plywood and made a video of the effects of an earthquake. This film was compared with a film of the 1989 San Francisco earthquake, which Bill showed his students at the end of the lesson.

**d.** *Measuring:* Students measured the amount of soil that was eroded in the pans with no grass in comparison to pans containing grass. Measurements were also compared for the different inclinations of the pans. Trials were also conducted using various types of grasses.

**4.** *Lesson methodologies.* Bill knew that an effective lesson on changes in the earth's surface would require the use of various instructional methodologies. He provided his students with a minimum amount of lecture. He included some audiovisual presentations on earthquakes and rock formations in the Southwest. He included some demonstrations on the destructive power of volcanoes and earthquakes. A geology professor from the local college was invited to give students an opportunity to ask self-initiated questions. Students also had opportunities throughout the lesson to engage in buzz sessions to consolidate their data and record it in a class scrapbook. In addition, Bill shared with the class the book *50 Simple Things Kids*

*Can Do to Save the Earth* (Kansas City, MO: Andrews & McMeel, Earthworks Group, 1990) and developed a simulation in which students had to make some decisions on how humans can prevent the destruction of the earth's surface.

### Integrating

1. *Criterion checks.* Throughout the lesson Bill included a number of criterion checks. The following questions were posed to his students periodically throughout the lesson:

   "What is the most important thing we have learned so far?"

   "What data do you think you need to carry on with this experiment?"

   "How comfortable are you with this procedure?"

   After each of the three major demonstrations, Bill had his students write a 25-word telegram summarizing the events of the lesson. Bill then asked his students to send those telegrams to his colleague Terry Breslin's fourth-grade classroom. Terry was able to use those telegrams in the design of his own lesson plan on "Changes in Landforms."

2. *Cross-curricular activities.* Bill created a number of cross-curricular activities in which students were able to link their knowledge about the earth's surface with lessons in other subjects.

   a. *Reading/language arts:* Bill read the book *Volcanoes* by Seymour Simon to his class and then asked each student to create a fictional story about the time a volcano appeared in his or her home town.

   b. *Art:* Each student created a mobile based on some of the significant events in the history of the earth's surface.

   c. *Physical education:* A local Red Cross volunteer was invited to demonstrate CPR and its importance in saving lives during emergencies such as earthquakes.

   d. *Social studies:* Bill shared information on how soil and water erosion has affected the lives of various civilizations. People who lived along the Nile River, along the Ganges River in India, and along the Missouri River in the United States were compared and contrasted.

   e. *Math:* Students compared the thicknesses of the layers of the earth in term of feet and yards, and centimeters and meters.

   f. *Music:* Bill played some Pete Seeger records for the students. Discussions afterward centered on the environmental conditions that existed at the time Seeger's songs were written as compared with current conditions.

3. *Summarizing.* Bill asked students to summarize all the information they had gathered in their journals. Each student was directed to prepare an overview of the entire lesson, which was recorded on a sheet of construction paper. Each student's summary was then posted in the front of the classroom for discussion. Students then added their new knowledge to the background knowledge on the semantic web created prior to the lesson. Bill engaged the students in an active discussion on the differences between what they knew prior to the lesson and what they knew now.

4. *Extending projects.* Bill provided his students with a selection of individual and small group projects, including the following:

   a. Students could put together a mini-lesson to present to another fourth-grade classroom.

   b. Students could organize a debate on the practicality of warning citizens prior to a predicted earthquake as opposed to keeping that information from the media.

**c.** Students could interview several professors at the local college concerning the events most destructive to the surface of the earth. Decisions would be made as to whether human-caused conditions or natural conditions are more destructive.

**d.** Students could write a letter to their local congressperson on the need for changes in insurance practices related to natural disasters.

**e.** Students could establish a plan of action for their own families to reduce injuries in the event of an earthquake.

What is evident from Bill's lesson plan is that he came up with a number of options to explore with his students. The plan allowed students to broaden their comprehension of the topic, guided by their interests and needs. Bill was able to actively involve his students in a plan that had some structure yet also provided some options for mastering the stated objectives.

**DID YOU KNOW?** _____

The Mississippi River delta is expanding into the Gulf of Mexico at a rate of nearly 360 feet per year.

**Classroom Activity**  Have students create a salt map of the Mississippi River delta. Periodically ask them to add materials in the delta region to indicate the amount of silt buildup over the years. Invite a geologist or professor from a nearby college to explain the reasons for the buildup and any appropriate measures for curbing the expansion of the delta region.

The following sample plan was developed as part of a larger unit on *arthropods*. You will notice that it underscores the three major elements of all plans: preparing, experiencing, and integrating.

**Unit:**
**Arthropods**

*Lesson:*
*Insects—Up Close and Personal*

## Objective
After a close look at insects, the student will be able to identify them and list their identifying characteristics.

## Materials
- Overhead transparency ("What Is an Insect?")
- A preserved grasshopper
- Containers with ventilated lids to hold insects
- Hand lenses or magnification boxes
- Overhead projector
- "Arthropod Safari Chart"
- Collected insects for short-term observations
- Selected films about insects (see the National Geographic catalog)

## Teacher Background
Imagine a world without silk, honey, most flowers, fruits, and vegetables. Dead plants, animals, and many waste products would remain mostly intact where they fell, unable to return their nutrients to the soil. Gone would be many opportunities for valuable scientific discoveries. Natural shellac, varnish, and some dyes would not exist. Gone too would be many vectors of diseases that have ravaged mankind from time immemorial. No longer would we be able to watch with wonder the metamorphosis of a caterpillar into a beautiful butterfly. Such would be a world without insects.

*Insects*—the very word usually brings a grimace and a "Yuck!" response, yet these animals are a vital, fascinating, and aesthetically delightful part of our daily life. For these reasons, this activity takes a close look at this group of arthropods.

This largest of all animal groups is composed of creatures displaying almost unimaginable variety in structure, function, shape, color, life habits, and other adaptations. In spite of this incredible diversification, all insects share certain identifying characteristics. Like all other arthropods, they have an *exoskeleton* and *jointed legs*. In addition, insects have *three body parts, six legs, two antennae,* and *two or four wings.*

## Procedure
1. The very best way to observe and learn about insects is to have some live ones to study. Give each pair of students the following materials and have them spread out, *within defined boundaries,* on the schoolyard looking for specimens. (It's OK if they bring in non-insects; in part of the activity they will determine which animals are insects and which aren't.)

---

Be sure to avoid arthropods that sting or bite!

- A container with a ventilated lid (for larger specimens)
- A magnification box (for smaller specimens)
- A copy of the "Arthropod Safari Chart"

Films about insects can show aspects of insect life that are very difficult to illustrate in any other way. Also, if the students are unable to find living specimens, due to weather or season of the year, films can provide a "vicarious field experience."

**2.** Project the transparency "What Is an Insect?" Point out the characteristics of an insect. In addition to *antennae, wings,* and *compound eyes,* there are the *three main body parts:*

*Head:* Antennae and eyes are located here.
*Thorax:* Legs and wings are attached here.
*Abdomen:* This is the animal's stomach.

If the students have live specimens available, have them look at the animals using hand lenses. Can they find all three main body parts of their animal? Is it an insect, or is it another arthropod? Is it another kind of animal altogether? Is it an immature or larval stage of an insect? Can they find the name of the animal in a field guide identification book?

Have the students examine the preserved grasshopper. Can they find all the main body parts? Has anyone caught a live grasshopper? Compare and contrast the living animal with the preserved one.

**3.** *Extended activity: Creative writing and art.* Have the students respond in creative writing and/or another art form to the following classical Japanese haiku poems:

You can see the morning
breeze blowing the hairs
of the caterpillar.
*—Buson*

Alas! The firefly seen by
daylight, is only a bug
with a red neck.
*—Basho*

Even among insects
in this world, some are
good at singing, some bad.
*—Issa*

**Arthropod Safari Chart**
**1.** Describe where you found this animal and what it was doing when you found it.

_____

_____

**2.** What kind of arthropod is this animal?

_____

_____

**3.** Make up a name for this animal based on what it looks like and how it moves.

_____

**4.** Could you find its real name in a reference book? What is it?

_____

**5.** Make a drawing of the animal you found.

The preceding lesson plan incorporates the following components:

**1.** Objectives
**2.** Materials
**3.** Teacher background
**4.** Procedures
**5.** Films and transparencies
**6.** Extended activities
**7.** Record sheet

This lesson is a good example of how children can develop an appreciation for science by actively collecting and examining a piece of the scientific world. The teacher does not know beforehand what types of insects or other creatures students will bring to the classroom. However, the teacher has an outline of the characteristics by which students will be able to identify insects.

The lesson is also distinguished by the fact that there are no process activities or higher-level questions built in. These components would be developed according to the information or specimens students re-

trieve from the field. Obviously, this means that the teacher must be confident in his or her own teaching abilities to carry out this lesson. In short, the thinking and questioning strategies would be done "on the spot" according to what students found in the field. Although this plan may be more appropriate for an experienced teacher, it certainly has a lot of possibilities for the novice teacher as well.

Consider some of the following points regarding this lesson:

**1.** The record sheet allows students to record information as it is collected. These sheets can be compiled into an ongoing scrapbook of information on insects. This permits the lesson to extend over a longer time period.
**2.** The writing and art activities illustrate the relationship of insects to other portions of the curriculum. These opportunities demonstrate the universal application of science throughout children's lives.
**3.** This lesson lends itself to cooperative groups in which students work in teams to discover information and arrive at mutual decisions.
**4.** Obviously, this lesson is dependent on the weather, season of the year, and local environment. It may be difficult (but not impossible) to do near an urban school.

**DID YOU KNOW?** _____

In order to make a pound of honey, bees must collect nectar from approximately 2 million flowers.

**Classroom Activity** Encourage students to collect information on the beneficial aspects of insects. Ask them to locate data on how insects help preserve the environment as well as on some of the products we get from insects. You may wish to invite an entomologist into your classroom to explain all the benefits of insects. Students may wish to prepare an informational book or brochure summarizing their findings. This guide can be shared with other classrooms.

# CHARACTERISTICS OF EFFECTIVE SCIENCE UNITS

An effective science unit is the result of careful planning, a sensitivity to the needs and interests of your students, and an awareness of the strategies and techniques that allow students to make personal discoveries throughout the science curriculum. As a beginning teacher, with all the new tasks and responsibilities you must learn, you may be tempted to rely on the plans and designs provided in the science text. However, the information and directions provided in the textbook series reflect a particular point of view and may not be consistent with the needs and abilities of your students. This is not meant to disparage the use of basal texts; however, you need to be aware of how those texts fit into the overall science program in your classroom.

Zeitler and Barufaldi (1988) have suggested that the following characteristics should be part of the design of all science units:

1. *Active involvement of the learner in the learning process.* A science unit succeeds when children are allowed to actively participate in all aspects of that unit. Also, students should be provided with opportunities to shape and guide the direction of science unit according to their needs and interests.
2. *Problem-solving orientation.* Sufficient time must be allotted to any science unit to allow children to set their own purposes and seek answers to their own inquiries. Children need to realize that science is a continuous process of problem solving, not the memorization of discrete facts or the completion of experiments for which the answers are already known.
3. *Relevance to the learner's interests and needs.* A science program must reflect of the interests, needs, and abilities of students in a particular classroom. Therefore, a program may change from year to year depending on the students using it.

## TEACHER TO TEACHER

Several years ago one of my life science classes was dissecting crayfish. Unknown to me at the time, one of my best students was quietly collecting the pinchers from all the crayfish and taping them to his fingers. When the bell rang he quickly dashed into the hall. Pandemonium broke loose with students (and staff) screaming, laughing, and shouting as he did a rather amusing monster imitation.

Subsequent conversations with the student and the entire class in general revealed that they were bored silly with hacking open rubbery, smelly specimens that looked like mush on the inside and had no relevance to their everyday lives.

Because of that student's mischief, I was motivated to develop what would eventually become an award-winning program of live animal laboratory activities in which the animals are observed and then released unharmed.

Always be alert to what your students can teach you. Students can sometimes give us that "whack on the side of the head" that forces us to evaluate our methods and try new and better approaches.

Dennis Holley
Shelton Public Schools
Shelton, NE

4. *Consistency with the underlying goals and philosophy of science education.* Students need to understand that science involves the processing of data rather than the memorizing of information. A hands-on approach to science reflects the developmental stages of children in the program and allows them to take responsibility for much of their own learning.
5. *Open-ended nature, free of built-in "correct" solutions.* Students must understand that science is much more than a series of "right" versus "wrong" responses. Science education is effective when children learn that there are few absolutes.
6. *Open approach that allows students freedom to inquire, to develop a personal method of solving the problem, and to test the solution and judge its correctness individually, without the imposition of an outside judgment from any source—and freedom to be wrong as well as right.* Children should be provided with sufficient opportunities to chart the course of their own learning. In addition, children must be allowed to make mistakes and learn from those errors, rather than having the teacher say, "That's wrong" and move on to another point.
7. *A conceptual framework designed to build knowledge of broad concepts using specific scientific information.* Many children have the perception that science is a random collection of facts and data. It is important for the teacher to demonstrate that science content is often sequentially arranged; the mastery of one concept is often predicated on the mastery of other concepts. In short, the well-designed unit is a series of lessons, each dependent on the others for the attainment of a particular goal.
8. *Continuity with previous and future lessons.* Students should understand that the processes of science are universal. Skills are not lesson-specific but can extend throughout the science curriculum and beyond.

9. *Opportunities for each student to succeed as a result of his or her own learning activities.* Teachers need to be sensitive to the learning styles of their students and cognizant of the activities and strategies that will enable students to take advantage of their individual learning styles. In other words, use of a single method of presentation or delivery should be the exception rather than the rule.

10. *Flexibility.* The key to the success of any science unit is flexibility. Teachers must be willing to consider modifications in time allotment, variations in student interests, alterations in the scope of demonstrations and explanations, and changes in the activities planned. What drives the successful unit is the degree to which teachers are willing to adapt a unit as it is being taught. It's not always easy, but it can result in a unit that is oriented to the needs of *your* students rather than someone else's.

The preceding guidelines are generic in nature but can provide you with a structure with which to design a meaningful and purposeful unit. Your unit will reflect your own teaching style as well as the learning styles of your students. For that reason, the units you design may be significantly different from those developed by colleagues teaching the same concepts or content. There is certainly no point in developing identical science units for several different classrooms, even at the same grade level. The units you create must be tailored to your knowledge of your students' strengths and weaknesses, as well as the processes necessary to help them develop an appreciation for their role in the world of science. You are the best-qualified person to design a science unit for your students.

## Self-Evaluative Checklist

The following checklist can serve as a guide (and a guide only) in terms of evaluating the units you design. It is not intended to be an all-inclusive list of requirements for every unit but should serve as a collection of benchmarks to aid in appropriate decision making in terms of the design, direction, and delivery of effective units.

1. Have I provided opportunities for students to access their background knowledge?
2. Have I provided means whereby students can link their prior knowledge with the information in the lessons?
3. Have I included a variety of discovery options for students?
4. Have I included a number of questioning strategies utilizing both divergent and student-generated questions?

5. Have I allowed for criterion checks periodically throughout the lessons?
6. Have I included a variety of presentation options that offer students opportunities to take an active role in the lessons?
7. Have I provided students with a sense of self-responsibility?
8. Are there opportunities for students to explore problems for which there may be no predetermined answers?
9. Are a variety of process skills included throughout the lessons?
10. Are the activities appropriate to students' interests and ability levels?
11. Is the text used as a resource rather than the focal point of the lessons?
12. Are cross-curricular activities included throughout the lessons?
13. Are students provided with a multitude of resources within as well as outside the classroom?
14. Do students have opportunities to apply what they have learned rather than merely recall it on evaluative instruments?
15. Do students have opportunities to generate their own problems and seek solutions to those problems?
16. Are the lessons cyclical in nature, each one building on and related to others?
17. Are students given opportunities to arrive at their own decisions and solutions rather than just mimicking my conclusions?
18. Is each lesson related to the real world of students, either individually or collectively?
19. Will students be "energized" about science as a result of participating in this unit?
20. Am I "energized" about teaching this unit?

### DID YOU KNOW?

The swift (a small bird similar to a swallow) may fly a million miles in the first three years of its life—without ever landing.

**Classroom Activity** Many children take birds for granted. Yet birds can offer students some spectacular insights into the animal kingdom. You may wish to develop an entire unit on birds, including lessons on different bird types, habits and habitats, flightless birds, bird world records, and the benefits of birds to humans. A visit to an aviary or a lesson by an ornithologist would be an exciting adjunct to the unit. If possible, attend a meeting of the local bird-watchers' club. ∎

Following is a unit developed to provide primary-level youngsters with an appreciation for the forms and states of matter. The lessons (or activities in this case) are designed to help students discover the principles of matter in a nonthreatening and investigative way. Notice how the teacher assumes the role of a facilitator for this unit, guiding but not directing students in their inquiries.

## Unit:
## Investigating Mystery Boxes

### Competencies
**A.** Processes
  **1.** Observing
  **2.** Classifying
  **3.** Inferring
  **4.** Predicting
  **5.** Communicating
**B.** Physical science
  **1.** Form/state of matter

### Text
No correlation

### Supplemental Resources
None

### Background Information
This set of activities is designed to develop skill in and appreciation for the use of *indirect* evidence in drawing and supporting inferences. Therefore, observations children make with their senses rather than lucky or superficial "correct" guesses should be given approval. Observations to strengthen or reject an inference about the unseen object should be encouraged. Also, encourage and respect contradictory inferences that are supported by observations.

In other words, being "right" means producing observations that support or reject an inference. All children who infer different objects for the same mystery box are "correct" if their inference is supported by the observations.

Objects in the list are only suggestions; alternative items may be substituted. The objects should, however, produce some clearly identifiable clues by indirect observation. (For example: Balls and cylinders both roll, but cylinders roll only along one surface. A short sliding sound usually indicates the object is longer than an object which has a long sliding sound.)

It is not necessary for all boxes to be identical. However, if they are alike in size and shape, then one can compare observations when similar operations are performed on different boxes.

For easy reference, boxes should be marked. Assorted colored stripes may be added with paints or crayons. Pictures of animals might be pasted to the boxes. Numbers or letters might add to the learning or review function of the lesson.

## ACTIVITY I

·················································
·················································

*Grade level:* 1

*Purpose:* The students will describe like and unlike characteristics of objects.

*Focus question:* In how many ways can we describe objects?

*Materials:* Table tennis balls, golf balls, wooden blocks, plastic lids, bars of scented soap, bean bags.

*Procedure:* Arrange children in a semicircle around a table. Place the set of assorted objects on the table and ask the children to describe the objects in as many ways

as they can. Discuss the characteristics of each object in turn. Then choose objects in pairs or in groups of three and discuss similarities and differences. Guide the discussion to characteristics that might be useful in later activities, such as:

> "The balls roll."
> "The golf ball is heavier than the Ping-Pong ball."
> "The soap smells."
> "The bean bag squishes."
> "The lid slides when it's one way and rolls when it's another way."

## ACTIVITY II

·················································
·················································

*Grade level:* 1 and 2

*Purpose:* The students will infer the identity of an object based on observations.

*Focus question:* What observations can be made to guess a hidden object?

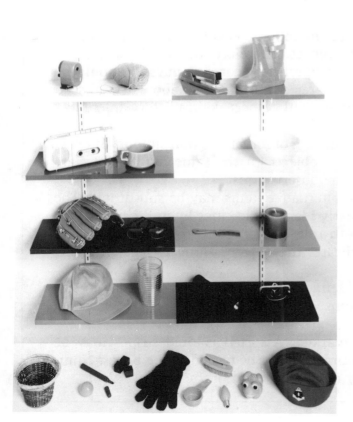

*Materials:* Two identical shoe boxes, tape, two pencils or pens.

*Procedure:* While the class is watching, put a pencil in one box and a roll of tape in the other. Tape each box so the lids are secure. Behind your back, switch the boxes several times so that the children cannot associate a box with its contents. Then mark them A and B.

Give each box to a different child. Tell the children to think about what is in each box but not to guess out loud. Instruct them not to squeeze the box but to move it in any way that will help them decide which object is in the box. After one or two minutes, have each child pass his or her box to another child. Continue until all have had a turn. Encourage other children to listen and watch for clues.

Then have the children discuss their ideas about what is in each box. Whenever possible, ask the children to state the observations that they felt were good clues.

Discuss clues in terms of their relationship to inferences about an object. Avoid comments or facial expressions that support or reject student observations or inferences.

Encourage the children to demonstrate anything they did that yielded a helpful clue. Allow one or two other children to repeat the action and see if they agree.

When observing and inferring wanes, open the boxes so that the children can check their inferences. Then repeat any observations that yielded productive clues, such as:

- A rolling sound versus a sliding sound
- A long slide versus a short slide
- A difference in weight

ACTIVITY   **III**

..........................................................................................

..........................................................................................

*Grade level:* 1 and 2

*Purpose:* The students will infer the identity of hidden objects.

*Focus question:* In what ways can we observe hidden objects?

*Materials:*

| Grade 1 | Grade 2 |
|---|---|
| Table tennis balls | Worksheet for |
| Golf balls | recording |
| Identical wooden or | Rolls of masking |
| plastic blocks | tape |
| Plastic or metal jar lids | Rolls of cellophane |
| Identical bars of scented soap | tape |
| Identical bean bags | Boxes of crayons |
| Shoe boxes | (with one or two |
| Chart for recording responses | crayons missing) |
| | Sets of pencils |
| | Sets of coins |
| | Shoe boxes |
| | Modeling clay |

*Procedure:* Before beginning this activity, prepare the mystery boxes. Place one object in each box and tape the boxes closed. Mark on each box an identifying number, letter, or colored geometric shape. Prepare enough boxes so that there is at least one for each small group of children. To prevent the scent of soap from spreading to other boxes, keep the scented soap boxes in a separate place until it is time to distribute the boxes.

Arrange the children in groups and give one box to each group. Explain that they are to find out enough about the object to infer (figure out) what it is. Caution them not to crush or open the boxes.

As you circulate, encourage productive observations (i.e. slowly tilting the box, listening for sounds as the box is manipulated, smelling, hefting for some sense of the object's weight).

Have children tell you what they think is in their box and why. Check to see if they made productive observations. Record their decisions on the chart or worksheets and give them a new box to study.

After most children have worked with the boxes, collect all the boxes. Gather the class into a semicircle to discuss their decisions. When each box has been discussed, open the box and show the object.

*Note:* It might be interesting to have an extra set of objects and an extra box on hand during the discussion. Conflicting inferences might be checked by placing the suspected objects, in turn, in the extra box to see if they produce the same observations. This is a simple example of constructing a model in science.

**RECORD SHEET FOR "MYSTERY BOXES"**

| Box | Observations | Predicted Object | Actual Object |
|---|---|---|---|
| 1 | | | |
| 2 | | | |
| 3 | | | |
| 4 | | | |
| 5 | | | |
| 6 | | | |

Planning effective lessons and units requires a commitment to the processes and methodologies that can be shared with students. Initially, you may find lesson planning to be tedious, yet you should investigate all the options at your disposal for "energizing" a science lesson. Keep in mind the lessons you experienced as an elementary student. Are they models for your lessons? Can they be used as springboards for some dynamic, invigorating, and enlightening lessons that your students will enjoy and remember for some time?

.................................... **POINTS OF DISCUSSION** ....................................

**1.** Given your style of learning, which type of lesson plan would you want a teacher to use with you? What is your rationale?

**2.** Given your style of teaching, which type of lesson plan would you feel most comfortable in using with your students? What is your rationale?

3. Select a topic from a current science text. Prepare a lesson using one type of lesson plan and another lesson (on the same topic) using another type of lesson plan. What similarities or differences do you note?

4. Choose a lesson plan and develop a mini-lesson to present to your classmates. Ask them for an evaluation.

5. Why is the "preparing" stage such a critical one in the design of effective lessons?

6. Choose one of the following topics and describe how you would integrate it into all areas of the curriculum:

a. The solar system
b. Simple machines
c. Weathering and erosion
d. Plant reproduction
e. Reptiles and amphibians
f. Magnets

7. How does a "hands-on" approach to science differ from more traditional models that rely exclusively on a text? What are the advantages? What are the disadvantages?

## REFERENCES AND SUGGESTED READINGS

Abruscato, J. (1988). *Teaching children science.* Englewood Cliffs, NJ: Prentice-Hall.

Carin, A., & Sund, R. (1989). *Teaching science through discovery.* Columbus, OH: Merrill.

Cohen, H., Staley, F., & Horak, W. (1989). *Teaching science as a decision making process.* Dubuque, IA: Kendall-Hunt.

Earthworks Group. (1990). *50 simple things kids can do to save the earth.* Kansas City, MO: Andrews & McMeel.

Fredericks, A., Cressman, B., & Hassler, R. (1987). *The science discovery book.* Glenview, IL: Scott, Foresman.

Gill, J. T., & Bear, D. (1988, February). No book, whole book, and chapter DRTA. *Journal of Reading, 31,* 444–449.

Orlich, D. C., Harder, R. J., Callahan, R. C., Kauchak, D. P., Pendergrass, R. A., Keogh, A. J., & Gibson, H. (1990). *Teaching strategies: A guide to better instruction.* Lexington, MA: D.C. Heath.

Otto, W., & Ericson, L. (1973). *Inservice education to improve reading instruction.* Newark, DE: International Reading Association.

Rosenshine, B., & Stevens, R. (1986). Teaching functions. In M. C. Wittrock (Ed.), *Handbook of research on teaching* (3rd ed.) (pp. 376–391). New York: Macmillan.

Smith, B., Sprague, S., & Smith, B. (1989). *Arthropods* (teacher's ed.). Mesa, AZ: Mesa Public Schools.

Wood, K., & Mateja, J. (1983). Adapting secondary level strategies for use in elementary classrooms. *The Reading Teacher, 36,* 492–496.

Zeitler, W. R., & Barufaldi, J. P. (1988). *Elementary school science: A perspective for teachers.* New York: Longman.

# 8

# SCIENCE ACROSS
# THE CURRICULUM

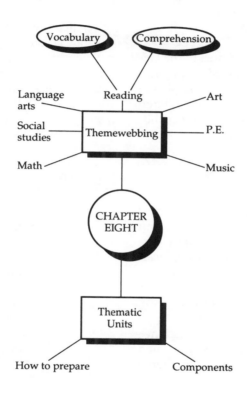

**Chapter Objectives**

After reading this chapter you should be able to:

1. Describe "theme-webbing" and its utility for the elementary science program.

2. Delineate the activities and techniques by which science can be incorporated into every aspect of the elementary curriculum.

3. Suggest alternative ways of integrating science into other curricular areas.

Students often have the following one or all of the following perceptions regarding science:

- Science is a subject that lasts for a preconceived length of time (e.g., 30 minutes twice a week).
- Science is a subject that exists in a textbook labeled "Science" or a similarly identified workbook.
- Science is a part of the curriculum that is taught by teachers using clearly identified objectives, experiments, and materials.
- Science is less important than math or reading because it is usually taught at the end of the day or can be eliminated for special programs, such as an assembly or a visit from the state trooper.
- Many teachers are afraid of science.

Teachers indicate that science is the area of the elementary curriculum they find easiest to reduce or eliminate to make time for special programs or completion of other assignments. Unfortunately, this leads children to perceive that science is not as important as other subjects but is a block of knowledge that can be changed or eliminated at will.

An intrinsically wonderful aspect of science is that it can be integrated into all aspects of the elementary curriculum. By perceiving science as a verb rather than a subject and by including it as a vital component of every other area of the curriculum, teachers can promote science as a vital element of the educational program of each and every youngster. Science should be a part of the math program, the social studies curriculum, physical education, the reading series, and language arts activities. When science is integrated into all aspects of the curriculum and all parts of the day, youngsters come to appreciate the value of science not just as an integral part of their school day but as an integral part of their lives. Pupils will not perceive science as something that can be eliminated at will or shortened because of some special program. Science will become a pulsating and energetic component of all aspects of their education and their lives.

# THEME WEBBING

Theme webbing is a procedure by which teachers can blend science into every aspect of the elementary curriculum. It enables students to develop an appreciation for the universal applicability of science and provides teachers with an opportunity to make decisions on how science can be taught throughout the day and throughout the curriculum.

The following example illustrates how a science unit dealing with the earth's surface was integrated throughout an elementary curriculum using theme webbing.

## Objectives

1. Students will understand the nature and composition of the earth's surface.
2. Students will comprehend the changing nature of the earth's surface.

## Student Activities

Reading    Put together a bibliography of books in the school library dealing with geology.
Read about famous geologists and some of their contributions.
Write your own book about some of the geological features in your home town.

Math    Stake out a plot of land one foot square in the back of the schoolyard and calculate the quantity of different rocks in the plot.
Calculate the different periods of time it takes an earthquake to run through a complete cycle.
Plot the distances between the last five major volcanic eruptions in the world.

| | |
|---|---|
| Health | Investigate how volcanic eruptions can affect the health of residents in a specific area. |
| | Develop a chart listing several natural occurrences in the surface of the earth and the health conditions affected by those events. |
| Social Studies | Investigate the history of your town and how geological conditions may have affected its settlement. |
| | Discover the oldest area in your town and create a salt map of it. |
| | What is the history of earthquakes in the United States? |
| Physical Education | Make the movements of a miner digging for coal. |
| | Create an obstacle course around the school using only natural items. |
| | Create a dance showing how rocks are eroded by the water action in streams. |
| Language arts | Write a fantasy story about how the earth was formed. Take on the role of narrator. |
| | Create a cartoon about the environmental impact of wind erosion. |
| | Conduct a debate on the need for controlling sand bars in rivers. |
| Art | Create a collage of all the environmental forces that affect your area of the country. |
| | Make a mobile of different types of rocks using pictures cut from magazines. |
| | Build a working model of a volcano. |
| Music | Record the sounds of rocks rolling in a stream or river. |
| | Turn a popular song into a tune about different types of rocks. |
| | Locate folk songs from this country and others that call for environmental action. |

**DID YOU KNOW?** _____

Every day, meteors weighing a total of 15,000 tons rain down on the earth. Most are smaller than a grain of rice.

**Classroom Activity** Work with your students in creating a theme-webbing mini-lesson on meteors. For example, you may wish to consider these activities as elements in the lesson:

*Reading:* Read Seymour Simon's *Long Journey from Space* (New York: Crown, 1982).

*Math:* Calculate how many ounces, pounds, or kilograms of meteors strike the earth each day, week, or month.

*Health:* Predict what might happen if the meteors contained virulent diseases.

*Social studies:* Investigate what life was like during the impact of the meteor at Meteor Crater, Arizona.

*Physical education:* Have students develop a variation of dodge ball in which the balls simulate meteors.

*Language arts:* Have students write about the life of a meteor from the meteor's perspective.

*Art:* Have students create a mobile of facts and illustrations about meteors.

*Music:* Have students research collections of classical music that would simulate the sounds of meteors in space. ∎

The remainder of this chapter relates the concept of theme webbing to each area of the elementary curriculum. Illustrated are practices and strategies for extending the learning opportunities for children to make science a dynamic component of the entire elementary program. The emphasis is not on science as a finite subject but rather as an interplay of ideas and as the interaction between what children know and what they can learn.

## Science and Reading

Much of the instruction in elementary science classrooms centers on the use of selected reading materials. Most classrooms use basal science programs that provide students with carefully sequenced and selected lessons over the year or over all the grades. Although science should not be text-dependent, teachers need to provide youngsters with background data and information as well as supportive materials that require some degree of reading competence. Whether the purpose is to obtain new information, collect necessary background information, or clarify concepts learned through experiments and projects, students will need to use reading skills to solidify science principles and designs.

We will take a look at some procedures by which teachers can promote the development of reading and science skills in tandem. These procedures, primarily focused on the areas of vocabulary and comprehension, provide means whereby teachers can facilitate the development of reading abilities in concert with science concepts.

## Vocabulary

It goes without saying that of all the elementary disciplines, science has the largest number of new words that students must master. Many teachers feel just as intimidated by the mass of words as do students. Helping students incorporate words into their everyday conversations and vocabularies may be an intimidating process, but it can be an exciting part of a science lesson.

Vocabulary instruction can be effective when a variety of word exercises are integrated into science lessons. When children are provided with many approaches to word study, words can become valuable tools for learning more about the scientific world. Following are several strategies for making vocabulary an intrinsic part of any science lesson.

**Semantic Webbing.** Semantic webbing is a graphic display of students' words, ideas, and images in concert with textual words, ideas, and images. It helps students comprehend text by activating background knowledge, organizing new concepts, and discovering the relationships between the two. Its value for vocabulary work lies in helping students begin to draw relationships between words and concepts and see that all words have a relationship to all other words in a chapter or unit. Semantic webbing is appropriate for use as a prereading or postreading activity in all types of science material.

Semantic webbing allows you to focus on the relationships between words and how words are used prior to, during, and after reading. The following procedure allows you to guide children into higher levels of thinking and comprehension.

1. A word or phrase central to the science lesson is selected and written on the chalkboard.
2. Students are encouraged to think of as many words as they can that relate to the central word. These can be recorded on separate sheets of paper or on the chalkboard.
3. Students are asked to identify categories that encompass one or more of the recorded words.
4. Category titles are written on the board. Students then share words from their individual lists or the master list appropriate for each category. Words are written under the category titles.
5. Students are encouraged to discuss and defend their word placements. Predictions about the lesson content can also be made.
6. The chapter is read, and then new words or categories from the lesson can be added to the web. Other words or categories can be modified or changed depending upon the information gleaned.

7. Discussion centers on the relationships among all the words in the web.

The following example of a semantic web concerns a second-grade teacher who wished to facilitate students' vocabulary awareness in a lesson on weather. Before beginning the lesson, she wrote the word "weather" in the center of the chalkboard and asked students to think of all the words they knew that related to "weather." The following words were recorded on one side of the board:

storms
rain
fog
snow
lightning
hurricane                          **WEATHER**
thunder
flood
drizzle
sunny
sleet
cloudy

Students were then directed to note any words that belonged together. The students identified a category name for each group of words, which was recorded on the board as follows:

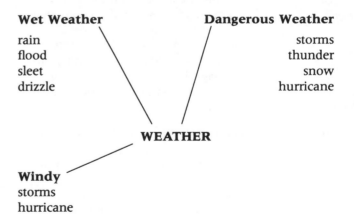

Students decided that some words (e.g., "storms," "hurricane") could belong to more than one category, whereas other words (e.g., "sunny") were a category unto themselves. The teacher then led the students through a chapter on weather. Afterward, students added words from the chapter to the web on the board:

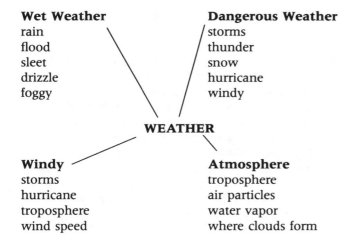

**Wet Weather**
rain
flood
sleet
drizzle
foggy

**Dangerous Weather**
storms
thunder
snow
hurricane
windy

**WEATHER**

**Windy**
storms
hurricane
troposphere
wind speed

**Atmosphere**
troposphere
air particles
water vapor
where clouds form

Discussion centered on how the words students knew before reading the chapter were matched with words learned during the chapter to aid in their understanding of the chapter concepts.

The advantage of semantic webs is that students have an opportunity to see how words are related to each other in a graphic format. In this way students begin to understand that words do not exist in isolation but are related in recognizable patterns. Helping students to see the patterns among words can be a powerful vocabulary strategy that facilitates science instruction throughout a single lesson or throughout the entire curriculum.

**Semantic Feature Analysis.** Semantic feature analysis is a procedure for helping pupils see how words within a category are alike or different and to relate the meanings of new words to prior knowledge. Vocabulary is presented in a logical manner:

1. A topic is selected from the textbook or some other source of interest to students.
2. Words related to the topic are listed on the chalkboard or on an overhead transparency. It is preferable to list words down the left side of the board or sheet.
3. Features shared by some of the words are listed across the top of the chalkboard or transparency.
4. Discussion is initiated by the teacher on the similarities or differences in the listed words. A check mark or "X" is placed on the chart to indicate whether or not a word in the left-hand column has one of the features listed the top.
5. Pupils are encouraged to add features or words to the chart either before the reading selection is tackled or during the reading of the material.

As students examine the checkmarks placed on the chart, they discover that no two words have exactly the same meaning, but that several words are related. Table 8.1 is an example of a semantic feature analysis of "water animals."

TABLE **8.1**

## SEMANTIC FEATURE ANALYSIS OF WATER ANIMALS

| | Dangerous | Friendly | Mammal | Fish | Amphibian | Insect | Edible | Inedible | Fresh water | Salt water | Feet | Fins | No appendages |
|---|---|---|---|---|---|---|---|---|---|---|---|---|---|
| Shark | X | X | | X | | | X | | | X | | X | |
| Guppy | | | | | | | | | | | | | |
| Trout | | | | | | | | | | | | | |
| Dolphin | | X | X | | | | X | | | X | | X | |
| Whale | | | | | | | | | | | | | |
| Sea horse | | | | | | | | | | | | | |
| Eel | X | X | | X | | | X | X | X | X | | | X |
| Frog | | | | | | | | | | | | | |
| Diving spider | | | | | | | | | | | | | |
| Narwhal | | | | | | | | | | | | | |
| Seal | | | | | | | | | | | | | |
| Salamander | | | | | | | | | | | | | |

The advantage of semantic feature analysis is that students come to see how words are related as well as unrelated. They thereby develop important conceptual frameworks that will help them understand ideas in a reading selection. Obviously, when this is done as a whole-class activity, there will be disagreements. Such disagreements can be healthy, particularly when students are allowed to defend the placement of their checkmarks. In the long run, this process allows students to tie together their experiences with information shared in a text. Such a process encourages an appreciation for new vocabulary words as something more than simple definitions.

**DID YOU KNOW?** ───────────────

Recycling just one run of the Sunday *New York Times* would save 75,000 trees!

**Classroom Activity**  Have students bring in several editions of your local newspaper. Ask them to read through the various sections and locate science-related words. Tell them that science words will be found in almost every section of the paper, including the comics, sports page, business section, and fashion page. Direct students to put together a scrapbook of science words cut from the newspaper. Afterward, they may wish to create word games, crossword puzzles, or word searches using science vocabulary found in the newspaper. ■

## Comprehension

The ultimate goal of any area of the elementary curriculum is to help students comprehend more of that subject. Providing youngsters with opportunities to develop their comprehension strategies helps them appreciate science as an integral part of their lives. Given the wide variety of materials students have to read in school, it behooves teachers to facilitate comprehension development in all subject areas, not just in the reading class.

**K-W-L.**  K-W-L is a reading comprehension strategy developed by Donna Ogle (1986) that assists students in dealing with expository material. It helps students to organize their background information, determine what they need to find out from reading the textual material, formulate their own questions about the material, and match what they have learned from reading the material to what they knew prior to the reading. It is an ideal strategy for use with all types of science materials and can assist students in developing their own strategies for learning through text.

The following six steps make up K-W-L:

1. *Discuss.* Determine what students already know about the topic of the chapter. Spend enough time in this activity to identify their knowledge and areas of confusion. As students volunteer information, list it on a class sheet or on individual sheets (see Table 8.2 on page 149).

2. *Categorize.* Ask students to find information that is related and to identify the category names. Provide them with examples as needed.

3. *Anticipate structure.* Ask students to think about the categories of information they would expect a chapter on this topic to cover. Encourage them to think about the kinds of information they anticipate.

4. *Question.* Ask students to use their own worksheets and write down any questions that come to mind during the class discussion of the topic. They should look for these as they read.

5. *Read and learn.* Suggest to students that, as they read, they jot down answers to their questions on their worksheets. Some may prefer to do this upon completion of the reading.

6. *Reflect.* When the reading and worksheets are completed, discuss what students have learned from reading. Review their questions to find out if any of them have not been dealt with satisfactorily. Suggest ways in which students can continue their search for information (library books, encyclopedias, etc.).

## TEACHER TO TEACHER ───────────────

I have found that one of the best creative exercises for a science class combines observational skills and poetic expression. I have students select a common object or phenomenon such as a place, person, a particular tree, rock, wind, or sunset, etc. and write specific, detailed observations about their selection.

Both structured and unstructured styles of poetic expression are briefly discussed and students are asked to reformulate their observations using one of them as a model. Generally these are not graded, but instead are shared in readings, handouts, or bulletin boards.

This can become an excellent interdisciplinary project with teachers of the language arts, who might discuss poetic forms or analyze professional poems similar in subject matter to what the students have written. In this way students can see similarities between their perceptions and those of professional poets.

Using and studying creative expression helps students to see that science is not just a collection of cold data isolated from the aesthetic. A good scientist must be an excellent observer; perceptions of meaning in everyday observations and phenomena often result in powerful poetic expressions.

Inez Fugate Liftig
Fairfield Woods Middle School
Fairfield, CT

## Science and Language Arts

The language arts offer a host of possibilities for integrating science throughout the curriculum. By utilizing

TABLE **8.2**

........................................................................................................

## K-W-L STRATEGY SHEET

........................................................................................................

| 1. *K* — What we know | 3. *W* — What we want to find out | 6. *L* — What we learned and still need to learn |
|---|---|---|
| | | |

2. Categories of information we expect to use:

A.                                                                     E.

B.                                                                     F.

C.                                                                     G.

D.                                                                     H.

4. Questions:


5. Read and learn:


the language arts of listening, speaking, reading, and writing, teachers can assist students in extending their learning opportunities throughout the scientific world.

The primary objective, however, is not to provide isolated activities in each of the four critical areas, but to demonstrate to students the integration possible when all the language arts are used in concert. Students should be provided with opportunities to develop all of the language skills together, each reinforcing the others. This helps both teachers and students gain an appreciation for the "marriage" that can occur between language arts and science.

## Whole Language

The philosophy of whole language has received considerable attention of late. There are several different interpretations of whole language, but this text will use the following definition:

Whole language instruction is the simultaneous, integrated teaching of reading, writing, speaking, and listening within a context that is meaningful to the language-learner (Baumann, 1985).

The characteristics of a whole-language program include the following:

- Students are exposed to meaningful language. That is, they are not confined to the language of textbooks but are immersed in language that has personal meaning for them.
- Students engage in written composition regularly. Opportunities are provided for students to be authors, editors, and publishers of their own work.
- Students are provided ample opportunities to develop and refine oral language abilities. A host of speaking opportunities are provided for children, including (but not restricted to) oral readings, plays, storytelling, drama, and debates.
- Speaking, listening, reading, and writing are not viewed as discrete entities but as interrelated, intertwined elements of the entire elementary curriculum.
- Teachers are positive role models who read to students, write regularly, speak in clear and exciting tones, and listen intently when spoken to.

- Students are given ample opportunities to practice and exercise their literacy skills throughout the entire curriculum, not just within the block of time devoted to language arts.
- Underlying the entire whole-language movement is the idea that the purpose of language is to communicate in meaningful and thoughtful patterns of expression and reception.

The following guide illustrates how some whole-language activities can be incorporated into a unit on dinosaurs—a topic frequently studied in second grade.

1. An overview of the text chapter is presented to students. Students are asked to share whatever information they know about dinosaurs.
2. A semantic web focusing on various types of dinosaurs is written and developed on the chalkboard.
3. Students are provided with a journal and asked to record their thoughts about the relative fierceness of specific dinosaurs as they are encountered in the chapter.
4. A written passage (with 10 selected words deleted and replaced with blanks) is prepared for students to fill in the blanks using words learned from the chapter.
5. Each student is instructed to create a story about a day in the life of a specific dinosaur. These stories will be shared with the other class members.
6. Several critical thinking questions are posed to the class, with answers recorded in individual journals. For example

    "What are some differences between dinosaurs and animals that live today?" "What type of climate do you think dinosaurs would enjoy most?"
7. Students can create their own dictionary of dinosaur terms. Words and their definitions will be written on dinosaur shapes cut from colored construction paper.
8. Students participate in several cross-curriculum projects such as:
    a. *Music:* Students create an original song using dinosaur terms and a popular children's song.
    b. *Reading:* Students make up an annotated bibliography of dinosaur books found in the school library.
    c. *Social studies:* Students investigate the geography of areas in the United States where dinosaur bones have been discovered.
9. Students can make plaster casts of animal prints found near the school or around their homes (see the following Idea Box).
10. Students can draw outlines of selected dinosaurs, cut them into several pieces, place the pieces in an envelope, and give them to a classmate. The classmate will reassemble the dinosaur puzzles and check with the creator of the puzzle for accuracy.

A whole-language approach to science stimulates language use and facilitates comprehension through student-initiated activities. When children are immersed in a language-rich environment, learning can be enhanced in any subject area, not just science. The goal of a whole-language approach to science is to develop an understanding of basic concepts through a variety of communication activities.

## IDEA BOX

One of the ways scientists are able to study dinosaurs is by examining the tracks they left behind. Most of these tracks were left in soft mud or clay, which eventually hardened, preserving the prints for millions of years. By closely observing these prints, scientists are able to determine the heights and weights of dinosaurs as well as other pertinent information. Examples of dinosaur prints can be found in Dinosaur National Monument in Colorado and Great Swamp in New Jersey.

**Organization and Materials**  This activity can be done shortly after it has rained or whenever animal tracks are likely to be found near the school or in the neighborhood.

Students will need a large bowl, water, a strip of cardboard that can be formed into a ring, a small ruler or tape measure, tape, a box of plaster of paris (which can be obtained at any hardware store), paper, and a pencil.

**Procedure**

1. Have each student prepare a ring by joining the ends of the cardboard strip with tape. A good size for the ring is about 5–6″ in diameter.
2. Gather the other supplies and take students outside to look for animal prints. If you live in a city, you may discover prints of dogs or cats. If you live in the suburbs or the country, prints of other animals may be available.
3. Share some observations about any prints discovered:

    "What types of animals do you think made this print?"
    "Why do you think that?"
    "What do you notice that is special about this print?"
    "How is it similar or different from our pets at home?"
4. Have children carefully measure the prints (length, width, and depth) and record that information on a sheet of paper.

    "What do we know about the conditions when this animal walked here?"
    "What else can we learn about this animal?"
5. Ask students to carefully place their cardboard rings around the prints and press each ring into the ground. Mix the plaster of paris according to the package directions.

    "Why is it important for us to follow the directions on the package?"
    "What might happen if we didn't follow those directions?"

6. Pour the plaster of paris mixture into each ring and let it dry for about 30 minutes.

"Why should the mixture dry before we lift it up?"

7. Pick up the casts and take them back to the classroom. If you wish, your students may want to make casts of other nearby prints that are different.

8. In the classroom, brush off the dirt and remove the ring from each cast. Examine the impressions with students. Record any information on sheets of paper.

"What do you notice about this print?"

"Are there some things you see now that you didn't see when we looked at the original print?"

**Conclusion**    Scientists take plaster casts of animal prints in order to study them in the laboratory. A cast is an accurate record of an animal's footprint and yields valuable data for the scientist. Although dinosaur prints may be millions of years old, we can obtain a great deal of information from them.

## Book Webbing

Book webbing is a process through which you can tie children's literature into the science curriculum. A variation of semantic webbing, it integrates all dimensions of the curriculum with a science-related book and develops and clarifies concepts for students in an enjoyable way. Above all, it provides you with an opportunity to extend the learning opportunities of children beyond the textbook into fascinating new discoveries.

To begin the process of book webbing, select a book that relates to a chapter or unit in your text. Initially, choose a nonfiction book, although as you become more proficient with this strategy you may wish to turn to fiction. It is important for you to become thoroughly familiar with the book before sharing it with your class. Although it may not be possible to provide a book for every member of the class, you can share the book in a host of presentation modes, such as reading it aloud to the entire class, recording the book on cassette tape for individuals or small groups to listen to during free time, or inviting a guest speaker in to share the book with a small group of students. Whichever presentation procedure you use, be sure to keep your enthusiasm and interest high, as you will want your students to do.

After the book-sharing process, brainstorm with students for curricular ideas that relate to the selected book. During this brainstorming process, develop a web on the chalkboard or on a separate sheet of paper. Then begin to develop lesson plans based on the connections recorded on the completed web. Each lesson plan should encompass at least one day's worth of activities but no more than three days. This allows students to get involved the activity for an extended period of time but

does not extend it beyond their attention span. Prior to presenting a lesson plan you should present or share portions or chapters of the selected book to the class.

After the book-webbing exercises, engage students in a discussion on how the concepts presented in the books could be extended or elaborated. In other words, provide students with an opportunity to share additional activities that relate to their personal world and individual interests.

Table 8.3 is an example of how one book—*How Did We Find out about Dinosaurs?* by Isaac Asimov—was developed into a multi-day unit using book-webbing as the instructional strategy.

TABLE   **8.3**

...............................................

## BOOK WEBBING: *HOW DID WE FIND OUT ABOUT DINOSAURS?* BY ISAAC ASIMOV

...............................................

| **Math** | **Art** |
|---|---|
| •Students will measure playground in sections according to the length of different dinosaurs. | •Students will make a collage of dinosaur pictures and words. |
| •Students will estimate the number of dinosaurs in a given geographical area. | •Students will make a cast of simulated dinosaur prints. |
| **Health** | **P.E.** |
| •Students will speculate on diseases that plagued dinosaurs. | •Students will move around the room as different dinosaurs. |
| •Students will investigate health reasons for the disappearance of dinosaurs. | •Students will create a dinosaur "obstacle course." |
| **Drama** | **Social Studies** |
| •Students will write a play based on a fictional encounter between two dinosaurs. | •Students will research areas of the country containing dinosaur bones. |
| •Students will invent a dance for dinosaurs. | •Students will create a "Dinosaur Bill of Rights." |
| **Language Arts** | **Reading** |
| •Students will write a new chapter for the book. | •Students will research other dinosaur books. |
| •Students will write and sing a song about dinosaurs. | •Students will read other I. Asimov books. |

This is the way I like to be with dinosaurs. Two-dimensional!

## DID YOU KNOW?

Despite what some movies would have you believe, no human being has ever seen a live dinosaur. The last of the dinosaurs died out 60 million years before humans appeared on the face of the earth.

**Classroom Activity** Rent several different dinosaur-related movies from your local video shop and show portions of them to your students. Ask students to keep track of appropriate as well as inappropriate portrayals of dinosaurs. What features or facts about the dinosaurs were realistically depicted in the movies? Which ones were "stretched" somewhat for the sake of interest? Based on their observations, students may wish to construct a guidebook on the "facts and fallacies" of movie dinosaurs. ■

## TEACHER TO TEACHER

Bring fun and excitement back into your teaching. How? Read a good book or do an author study. Link science with reading, language, and math by using literature. You will not only save time by integrating your science program, you will help children remember concepts and relate them to other experiences and also promote thinking. Problem solving is required by both literature and science. Spend some time in a bookstore or library and find literature you're really excited about. There are many wonderful books and authors to study for all ages. The hard part is narrowing down the choices and keeping focused. Be sure to combine both fiction and nonfiction. Use that literature with your students. That excitement rubs off. By having a variety of activities throughout the day for a concept and integrating it into your day, you reach all learning styles. Literature can support both the content and the processes of the sciences and provoke interest so that science can become a daily experience. Nurture the whole child—link science and literature.

Sandra J. Cobb
Brookside Elementary School
Worthington, OH

## Reflective Sharing

The reflective sharing technique is a language arts activity that allows students to bring their experiences into a lesson or unit and share that information in a mutually supportive environment. The following steps make up this strategy:

1. Identify the general subject area of a science chapter or unit.
2. For approximately three to five minutes have students brainstorm for all of the concepts they can think of that relate to that topic. The emphasis here is on the creation of a quantity of ideas.
3. Ask each student to choose one of the brainstormed ideas from the class list and write about that subject without stopping for about five minutes.
4. Sharing what each person has composed is the most important part of this strategy.
   a. Students are divided into groups of four. It is very important to have groups of four for the sharing process. In each group, members take specific roles:

   Person 1 reads what he or she wrote.
   Person 2 summarizes what person 1 read.
   Person 3 tells what he or she liked about the reading.
   Person 4 tells what else he or she would like to know.
   Note: If you can't get four students in every group (even with you participating), eliminate role 3 or 4.

   b. After one round of sharing, the process is repeated. Person 2 ("summarizer") of the last round now becomes person 1 ("reader"). Person 3 ("liker") now takes on the role of person 2 ("summarizer"), and so on.
   c. Complete four rounds so that everyone has a chance to assume all the roles.
5. Provide groups with an opportunity to share their thoughts about their subjects with the entire class (it is not necessary to have every group share, since some ideas will be redundant). Point out the wealth of information already known about the topic before students begin reading about it in their text. Discussions should be directed at helping students focus on how their ideas may match the content of the chapter.
6. After the chapter has been read and discussed, give students an opportunity to compare their original ideas with the new information gained from the text. A chart or list on the chalkboard may be appropriate for this activity.

The positive aspects of this activity are that students are encouraged to write and talk about ideas they know something about and react in positive ways to each other. In addition, readiness for the chapter is established as each student is allowed to share his or her experiences utilizing all of the language arts. Also, new concepts are presented and discussed as they relate to an upcoming topic. Most important, interest is stimulated and purposes for reading the selection are established beforehand.

## TO INVESTIGATE

Visit several classrooms and observe how different teachers integrate science into other subjects or how different subject areas are melded into the science program. What processes or procedures do teachers use to blend science with another subject? How do students react? What strategies can you suggest to help teachers integrate science into *all* areas of the elementary curriculum? How comfortable are teachers in blending science and another subject? Interview some teachers and elicit their reactions to an integrated curriculum. How do their perceptions affect your beliefs of how science should be taught? ∎

## Science and Social Studies

Annabelle Green teaches fourth grade in a small coastal town in southern Delaware. A popular tourist center, the town experiences an influx of vacationers each summer and the peacefulness of the winter months when the tourists have left. During the 14 years Annabelle has taught at her school, she has seen many changes, both in the geography of the beaches that border the town as well as in the public's perception of how those changes affect the town's major industry— tourism.

Annabelle wondered whether her students, many of whom will stay in the town to raise their own families, were aware of the changes taking place less than 200 yards from their school. One summer found waves of garbage, medical supplies, and raw sewage floating up on shore. For several weeks tourists stayed away from the town fearing contaminated beaches and health problems. Most town residents feared they were at the mercy of big cities far removed from their seemingly isolated community. But Annabelle didn't think so. She believed that if the ecology and economics of the area were to be preserved for future generations, action must be taken by this generation.

Annabelle began the following school year discussing the problem confronting the town. Lists of concerns were written on the chalkboard and shared by all members of the class. Possible solutions and responses were also generated. The class decided to take a field trip to view the problem first-hand. Even with all the

These medical supplies may have helped some, but they can create a lot of problems for others.

publicity in the local paper, several class members were surprised to discover the extent of the problem. Two became physically sick when they saw discarded syringes and bags of blood on one section of the beach.

After returning to the classroom, the energy level was high, discussion was hot and heavy, and emotions were at a fever pitch. Solutions and remedies were proposed, and the class decided to take an active role in seeing what could be done.

A letter-writing campaign to town officials and the local newspaper was initiated to alert townspeople to the seriousness of the problem. Letters were also written to newspapers in the larger cities up the coast. Students put together an "Ecology Newswatch" newsletter, which was inserted into the town's weekly newspaper periodically. Students attended town meetings and voiced their concerns about the pollution damaging their beach. In class, lessons were devoted to the environmental impact of pollution on the beaches. "Observation posts" were set up along the beach to detect major changes in the populations of wildlife visiting the beaches. Records were kept and the data was compared with a similar study conducted by another class several years before. The children studied the different types of pollution and drew charts and diagrams on the long-term effects of pollution. Much of this information was shared with the town council, townspeople, and other students in the school.

Although the students were not able to change the amount of pollution washing up on their beaches, they did alert residents to the seriousness of the problem and its implications for their community. Students from throughout the community began to realize that the things they do in their community may have an effect on other communities far removed. In short, students began to understand the interdependency of humans and nature not only within their community but between communities as well.

What Annabelle Green and her class did was to take advantage of local conditions and concerns to develop an integrated curriculum incorporating social studies and science. Annabelle wanted to drive home the importance of science as something more than facts and figures extruded from a textbook. She portrayed science as a human response to conditions that affect every organism on the planet. Her curriculum became one in which science and social studies were integrated into a project that not only utilized the processes of science but helped children relate those processes to their personal lives.

We typically think of social studies as the study of human relationships and how those relationships can be facilitated. Nowhere are these relationships more significant than in the elementary science curriculum. It is in this arena that children begin to understand the implications of scientific work and the utility of that work for this and succeeding generations. In short, what we discover today will have ramifications extending far beyond our classrooms and the facts and figures in textbooks.

Social studies is typically divided into six disciplines, each of which can be combined with scientific principles and practices to give students a well-rounded perspective on the world.

## Anthropology

Anthropology is the study of how people live and behave. Following are several activities teachers can use to promote the relationships between this branch of social studies and elementary science.

- Many ancient cultures, such as the Mayans, Incas, and Aztecs, were quite well developed scientifically. Direct students to investigate some of the science principles practiced during the times of these empires and how some of those principles are maintained today. What beliefs did those peoples have that we know to be false today?
- Many immigrant groups make up the American culture. Ask students to investigate their own family lines, tracing them back as far as they can. What physical features predominate in their family lines? Which features are destined never to appear in their

individual families? Take time to discuss how principles of genetics determine the physical attributes of some groups of people.
- Many cultures are distinguished by the types of foods they eat, either on a regular basis or for particular holidays. Ask students to investigate the foods regularly consumed by certain ethnic groups and determine which of those foods provide essential nutrients or include all of the basic food groups.

### DID YOU KNOW?

The Hunza, a group of people living in northwest Kashmir, are the only people totally free of cancer in any of its forms.

**Classroom Activity** Students may be interested in putting together a book or brochure on cancer. They may wish to do some library research, interview doctors, or talk with their parents about this disease. Direct them to investigate the different forms of cancer, which types are prevalent in men, which are common in women, the number of deaths attributed to cancer each year, and some possible preventative measures (e.g., diet). What aspects of the American culture can be related to certain forms of cancer? Do Americans suffer from some forms of cancer more than people from other countries? ∎

## Sociology

Sociology focuses on how humans participate in group activities—specifically, how people affect the groups to which they belong. Helping youngsters understand and appreciate the applications of sociology throughout the scientific world can be accomplished through some of the following projects:

- Groups of people usually settle in a particular region of the country for a number of reasons. Ask students to investigate the environmental factors that led to the settlement of a specific area of the country. For example, what types of wildlife encouraged settlers to live in a certain area? What landforms or geographical features were involved in the determination of the location of a settlement? What climatic conditions contributed to the decision to settle in a certain area of the country?
- To study the responsibilities of various occupations, have students investigate different groups of scientists and the duties they perform on a daily basis. What are some of the roles scientists play as a group or as members of a specific branch of science?
- Although many scientific discoveries have been made by individual men and women, others have been made by groups of people working together. Direct students to develop a list of scientific discoveries made by individuals in the last 50 years and compare it with a list of discoveries made by groups of people working together. What similarities or differences do they note between the lists?

## Political Science

Political science refers to the decisions people make relating to the activities of a group. Some of the following projects may assist children to develop an understanding of how science and political science are tied together.

- Political science is the study of how laws are made. In science, study focuses on how the laws of nature affect the way the world operates. Encourage students to discuss the differences and similarities between natural laws and man-made laws. Which are more powerful? Which are more lasting? Which are more influential?
- There are several universal laws of science such as "matter can be neither created nor destroyed." Ask students to determine if there are any universal laws specific to the political science arena. In other words, are there laws or regulations under which people must live, laws that cannot be modified or altered?
- The Bill of Rights is an important document. Ask students to create a bill of rights for the scientific community. What scientific rights should be guaranteed to all individuals? What rights are important for scientists to follow? What procedures must all scientists follow in investigating this world or other worlds beyond ours?

## Economics

Economics focuses on how groups and individuals use resources available to them. The following activities can be used to promote scientific principles and economic ones in tandem.

- Colonists brought many supplies with them to the New World. Ask students to determine what foodstuffs the early settlers should have brought with them to provide basic nutrition. Students may also wish to assess our knowledge of basic nutrition against the knowledge that prevailed in those days. Ask them to chart any differences.
- Many countries are experiencing a "brain drain"; that is, prominent scientists are leaving their homelands and working in the United States to take advantage of the technological advances in this country. Ask students to discuss the ramifications of scientists leaving their countries and working here.
- What climatic conditions affect the production of specific food items? Direct students to investigate weather patterns that occur in certain parts of the country, particularly those producing a large amount of food (e.g., California's Imperial Valley, Nebraska's wheat fields). Direct them to chart weather patterns over the last 20 years and relate those patterns to the production of food in a specific area of the country.

## Geography

Geography is more than a study of the earth. It also involves how the earth changes from time to time, the effects of humans on the earth and vice versa, and relationships between landforms, climate, soils, and vegetation. Teachers will find some of the following activities appropriate for illustrating these principles.

- Ask students to keep a daily log of the weather conditions in your area. Direct them to investigate how specific geographical features influence weather patterns. Ask them to also determine how weather affects some of the geographical features in your area.
- What environmental concerns predominate in your area of the country? How can individuals make a difference in deciding how resources will be preserved for future generations? Are there some environmental issues influenced by the geography of the area that cannot be changed for one reason or another? Can some environmental concerns affect a beach community as much as a mountain community?
- How is the geography of the earth being influenced by human actions? Ask your students to compare human actions and natural actions in terms of their effects on the geography of this country. Which are more damaging? Which are more beneficial?

## History

History is more than the events that took place in the past; it is also the recording of those events by humans and the influence of those events on current events. History is an understanding of how circumstances, conditions, and concerns affect all human beings, whether they lived many years ago or are living today. Following are some ideas to help meld science and history.

- Ask students to construct a "self-history" scrapbook. Direct them to include photographs of several stages in their growth as well as the growth of other family members. Students should record their physical appearance for each photo and indicate the changes that took place between stages in their development.
- Direct students to investigate the life of a scientist from 50 years ago, one from 100 years ago, and one from 200 years ago (for example: Salk, Edison, and Newton). What similarities or differences were there in the lives of these individuals?
- Direct the class to create a time line of significant scientific discoveries. A large sheet of butcher paper can be posted on one or more walls of the classroom, with each student contributing several events to the time line. Contributions can be prose or illustrations.

Integrating science and social studies can assist children to expand and elaborate their scientific concepts. By focusing on the "humanness" of science, students can develop a healthy awareness of science as more than simply facts, theories, and figures. Combining science and social studies illustrates that science

involves an understanding of how humans deal with the natural world and how they use that knowledge in their interactions with each other.

## Science and Math

Science and mathematics are two disciplines that should be taught interchangeably. Although students in the primary grades have not been introduced to various units of measurement, they can be made aware of differences in size, quantity, depth, height, volume, and distance through qualitative adjectives.

Throughout the grades, you should introduce students to a variety of units of measurement, including time, linear distance, and volume. Terms related to these measurements should replace the more general concepts of "large," "tiny," "huge," and "small." Charts can be maintained in the classroom, with new words added periodically.

By the time children reach the intermediate grades they should realize that general terms are relative. Pupils should be encouraged to use definitive units of measurements in order to make precise observations, comprehend significant information, and adequately report their scientific findings.

The integration of mathematics and science assumes a high level of significance when you engage students in the dynamics of scientific research. Celeste Penfors, a third-grade teacher, demonstrated this dramatically when she involved her students in learning about the changing position of the sun in the sky. A two foot square of oaktag posterboard was placed on a window sill located on the south side of the school. Masking tape marked the four corners of the oaktag to ensure that it would always be in the same location when measurements were taken. A mound of clay was placed in the center of the oaktag, and a 7-inch pencil was placed upright in the center of the mound. At noon on every sunny day, the class marked the end of the pencil's shadow and recorded the date of the marking. At the end of four weeks, the students disassembled their instrument and measured the length of each shadow. Then they plotted their findings on a chart with which they readily observed the shadow's lengthening from September 25 to October 28. This data was then compared with the findings of another group, whose data indicated that the sun's location was at a lower angle in the sky each day. The findings from the two experiments helped children understand why the duration of the daylight hours changes, the significance of the earth's tilt on our climate, why we have seasons, and a host of other concepts concerning the relationship of the earth and the sun. They were asked to predict what would happen between January 10 and February 10, and these predictions were recorded and a follow-up experiment planned for the second semester.

To demonstrate the value of math in the science program, select areas of student interest and extend them throughout the day. The following experiment is a suggestion.

Children regularly observe the results of evaporation—from clothes drying, to the need to add water to an aquarium, to pools of rainwater drying up. After a discussion of the phenomenon of evaporation suggest an experiment. Take a few jars with openings that differ significantly in size, with each jar having the capacity to hold at least a pint of water. Have students place the jars in the same location and fill each with a pint of water. Five days later have students measure and record the amount of water in each jar. Have students make a chart illustrating the size of the opening and the amount of evaporation from each jar. Ask students to determine a pattern or ratio defining the relationship between the surface area of water and the amount of evaporation.

By focusing on the importance of mathematics in any scientific experiment, teachers can demonstrate the close relationship between these two areas of the elementary curriculum. By measuring precise growth patterns, volume, time, distance, and size, students develop an appreciation of measurement throughout scientific discovery or investigation. It is also important for you to encourage students to transfer the skills they learn from doing their scientific projects to all aspects of their environment. For example, quantitative measurement is significant to their health in terms of caloric intake, blood pressure, blood sugar count, and cholesterol readings. Students must realize that they live in a scientific world in which precise measurements and accurate observations go hand in hand in each discovery they make.

**DID YOU KNOW?** _____

A total of 60,000 miles of vessels carry blood to every part of the human adult body.

**Classroom Activity**  Direct students to set up a "measuring station" in which they measure various parts of each other's bodies. Identify, for example, which student has the longest thumb, the shortest eyelashes, or the widest big toe. Discuss the various units of measurement that might be used for each of several body parts. Students may wish to develop a book of "Body World Records" in which they record the measurement records of selected body parts within the classroom. The following books would be appropriate to share with your students: *The Human Body* by Jonathan Miller (New York: Viking, 1983), and *Blood and Guts: A Working Guide to Your Own Insides* by Linda Allison (Boston: Little, Brown, 1976). ■

## Science and Music

The prime ingredient of music is sound. It is sound that sets music apart from all other artistic expressions. Sound is important to all human beings who have the capacity to hear. It is vital for survival whether one lives in a metropolitan area, a primitive jungle, or the vast, frozen arctic regions. It also enables cultures to express their feelings, attitudes, and values through chants, dance, hymns, and other musical forms.

Sounds of nature and the immediate environment have always held a fascination for humans. We have tried to reproduce the sounds of cities, technology, birds and animals, movement of air, and countless other elements from our surroundings. In fact, some of the great musical compositions were inspired by the natural environment:

- The sea was the inspiration for Debussy's "La Mer."
- Semetana wrote about "The Moldau" ("The River").
- Clouds were the inspiration for Griffes.
- Ives selected the environment for his "Three Outdoor Scenes."
- And, of course, there is the pastoral section of Beethoven's Symphony no. 6.

These compositions demonstrate that music can be used as a perfect introduction to the study of nature. Select a composition, play it, and discuss it with students. Ask them if they can feel what the composer experienced as he wrote the music. You may want to take students outside and help them relate to their environment as they listen to the sounds all around them. If your school is in an inner city, help children appreciate the noises and tempo of the city. On a quiet playground, the muted sounds of a bird, a squirrel running up the trunk of a tree, a small stream flowing gently over rocks, and the movement of the leaves can all be used to demonstrate the relationships we have with the sights *and sounds* of nature. Drawing students' attention to these sounds is important, for without the ability to distinguish one sound from another a child is unable to sing in tune, clap or play a rhythm pattern accurately, or recognize a common orchestral theme.

Questions to ask students include:

- What patterns do you note, what tempo, and what rhythms?
- Does each sound have a characteristic quality?
- What is the duration of each sound?
- Is the sound high, low, or middle-range?
- How loud is the sound?
- Does a sound or group of sounds reflect how you feel at a given moment?

To apply some of these thoughts to children's investigations into the world of science, consider the following ideas:

1. Have children create their own orchestra. Encourage students to make new and distinctive instruments. Anything in the environment can be used as an instrument or to help build an instrument. A few possibilities are a discarded crate, a hand-operated eggbeater, bottles filled to different levels with water, coffee cans of various sizes, plastic lids, wooden spoons, and rubber bands stretched over rulers. These and other creative instruments can form a classroom orchestra and demonstrate sound, pitch, vibration, and tone.
2. Ask children to record the sounds of nature. What differences do they note between the sounds recorded in one part of town and sounds recorded in another part of the city? Direct students to create a chart of high-, middle-, and low-range sounds obtained from their recordings.
3. What is the sound of silence? Challenge students to create an environment in their classroom or their bedrooms at home that is completely devoid of sound. What characteristics must that environment have? What difficulties do children experience in creating a completely soundproof environment? What are the implications for the world of nature?

Again, science is a verb! It is listening, moving, and creating. There are many vehicles for these actions; music is one. When we lead children to realize that sound, rhythm, pitch, and tempo occur both in nature and in music, we help them understand that the various areas of the curriculum do not exist in isolation but are part of the totality of our understanding of the universe. We enjoy music because of its relation to our attitudes and emotions. We understand music because of our knowledge and appreciation of science. This enjoyment and understanding should be experienced by children in their explorations through their environment and through their lives.

## Science and Physical Education

As children move through the science curriculum, they come to understand the importance of concepts such as gravity, stability, leverage, and force in the physical sciences. In the biological sciences, students are required to become familiar with the structure and functions of the skeletal, muscular, and cardiovascular systems of animals, including humans. As children are introduced to these concepts, an excellent referent is their own bodies. Physical education is an excellent opportunity to coordinate the psychomotor domain with the cognitive domain as the following examples demonstrate.

1. Children in the elementary grades frequently learn about gravity as it applies to our solar system. It may be more appropriate to introduce this concept through a group of activities in physical education. For example, have some students stand with their feet together and another group stand with their feet 8 inches apart. Ask students to lean to either side, back and forth. Ask them to decide which students were better able to retain a stationary position. This brief exercise introduces the concept of stability, or the ability of the body to maintain a stationary position or to perform purposeful movements while resisting the forces of gravity.

   *Gravity:* A natural force that pulls everything toward the center of the earth. Gravitational pull always occurs through the center of weight or mass of an object.

   As students perform a number of activities, including standing with their feet together or 8 inches apart, have them sway from side to side, catch a ball, or throw a ball. They will begin to comprehend to effects of gravity on their bodies. Ask students to try and locate their center of gravity and explain why one group of students has better control of their bodies. Their answers should reflect these principles:
   a. The wider or broader the base of support, the more stable the body.
   b. The lower the center of gravity to the base of support, the greater the stability.
   c. The nearer the center of gravity to the middle or center of the base of support, the greater the stability.

   Students will want to engage in some applications of these principles, such as kicking and catching a football, throwing a baseball, tumbling, and getting in a starting position for a running race.

2. As children participate in a variety of sports, they become aware of the importance of force. When they swim, throw a ball, hit a volleyball, serve a tennis ball, or kick a soccer ball, they know that their "force" has an effect on the end result.

   - Some balls roll faster than others.
   - At times, a swift return is required in volleyball.
   - Some balls in baseball are hit for distance; some are not.

   Children soon realize that force is not directly proportional to effort. This realization is an excellent opportunity for you to explain force as it applies to the human body. A few demonstrations of jumping, throwing, or swinging a tennis racket will help students observe that achieving maximum results in any forceful movement requires continuity of flow from one part of the body through another.

   - The basketball player does not jump from an upright position; he or she crouches to lower the center of gravity in his body (for more stability) and to use the stronger muscles of his legs. As the legs are extended, the body and arms are extended upward. Have children act as basketball players and jump from a crouched position. Then ask them to jump from an upright position and notice the difference. Direct them to measure the heights they achieved in each position.
   - Have a student hit a tennis ball or swing a baseball bat while assuming various positions—initially with the bat or tennis racket extended from the trunk of the body, and then with the instrument moved closer to the body with each swing. Have students measure the results each time. Similar activities can be done with kicking and throwing a ball.

3. *Newton's first law:* An object at rest will remain at rest; an object in motion will remain in motion unless disturbed by an outside force.

   The force of a body in motion is directly proportional to the size or mass of the body and its velocity. It is difficult for heavy objects to stop or change directions (e.g., an ocean liner). Have students roll a tennis ball toward some upright books and see how many books it will knock over. Then have them roll a basketball and observe how many books are knocked over. Ask them to apply this observation to other moving objects: cars, themselves, thrown objects, softball bats hitting a ball, or swings on the playground.

4. Another physical activity revolves around the lever, which is one of the simple machines all students study. Most children, however, are not aware that they are using a lever when they throw a ball. Have students throw a ball from various positions:
   a. Just snapping the wrist
   b. Snapping the wrist and moving the elbow
   c. Throwing the ball with the arm extended and with the shoulder serving as the fulcrum.

5. The key to the circulatory system is the heart. One way children can be made aware of the function of the heart is to listen to it with a stethoscope. Have students locate each other's heartbeat and listen to it for a minute or so. Help students locate the pulse in their wrists and record its rate. Ask several students to run around the playground and record their pulses on their return. Record the pulses of the runners again after 1-, 2-, and 3-minute intervals. Have another group of students walk the same distance as the runners, and record their pulses, too. This information can be recorded on charts similar to the one shown in Table 8.4.

Discuss with students the heart as a muscle and the effects of physical exercise on this and other muscles in the human body.

6. The human body provides other opportunities for children to explore aspects of their world. For example, you may wish to discuss the story of "The Three Little Pigs" with your class. Ask students why two of the houses were blown down and one was left standing. Show them pictures of buildings being constructed with steel girders. Explain that although we do not have steel girders in our bodies, we do have a strong support system—the skeleton. Have students describe how it is both similar to and different from a building. Encourage them to construct a chart that lists features of the human skeletal system in comparison with features of a building. Describe the function of muscles to the skeletal system.

Science has real value to children when they are actively engaged in every dimension of the science curriculum. When students have numerous opportunities to use not just their cognitive skills but their psychomotor skills throughout the science program, then science achieves personal meaning for every child. Melding science and physical activity can make scientific concepts meaningful and long-lasting.

## DID YOU KNOW?

During the winter months, arctic ground squirrels temporarily chill their bodies to subfreezing temperatures without turning their blood into ice. These squirrels are the only mammals known to do this.

**Classroom Activity** Invite a laboratory technician or volunteer from the Red Cross to explain the nature of blood to your students. Ask the individual to share data on the composition of blood (including red blood cells, white blood cells, platelets, and fibrin), diseases of the blood (anemia, AIDS, hemophilia, etc.), and why it's necessary for hospitals and blood banks to have adequate supplies of blood on hand. Have students discuss why healthy blood is necessary to a healthy lifestyle. You may wish to share with them the book *The Human Body* by Jonathan Miller (New York: Viking, 1983) or *Your Wonderful Body* by Donald J. Crump, ed. (Washington, D.C.: National Geographic, 1982). ■

## Science and Art

Art can be an intrinsically valuable part of the entire science curriculum. Indeed, it would be difficult to develop effective and motivational science lessons without incorporating a host of art activities and processes. Consider the following as necessary components of your science program.

- Bulletin boards can be created by students to illustrate a unit of study in any science area.

TABLE  8.4

## PULSE RATE CHART

**Group I: Runners**

|  | Immediately | 1 Minute | 2 Minutes | 3 Minutes |
|---|---|---|---|---|
| Child 1 | _____ | _____ | _____ | _____ |
| Child 2 | _____ | _____ | _____ | _____ |
| Child 3 | _____ | _____ | _____ | _____ |
| Child 4 | _____ | _____ | _____ | _____ |
| Child 5 | _____ | _____ | _____ | _____ |

**Group II: Walkers**

|  | Immediately | 1 Minute | 2 Minutes | 3 Minutes |
|---|---|---|---|---|
| Child 1 | _____ | _____ | _____ | _____ |
| Child 2 | _____ | _____ | _____ | _____ |
| Child 3 | _____ | _____ | _____ | _____ |
| Child 4 | _____ | _____ | _____ | _____ |
| Child 5 | _____ | _____ | _____ | _____ |

- A series of dioramas can be created and set up on window sills or shelves of the classroom bookcase.
- Students should be encouraged to create original posters dealing with specific science topics. These posters should be displayed in the classroom or throughout the school.
- Mobiles allow students to select important words, ideas, and illustrations of a science topic and display them in interesting and creative ways.
- Students may enjoy creating salt maps (made from a mixture of water, flour, and some salt in a paste-like consistency) of geological formations (e.g., volcanoes, river deltas).
- Encourage students to create their own puppets and use them in original plays about scientific discoveries in a specific unit.
- Collages can be developed pertaining to a unit of study. Have students cut out pictures from old magazines specific to a particular concept (e.g., space exploration, animal homes) and glue them in a random pattern on sheets of newsprint.
- A photo board can be established in the classroom with students contributing photographs of specific science-related objects.

Aside from the typical kinds of displays just described, the art curriculum offers a host of other possibilities for blending art and science. Consider some of the following:

- Have students study several different paintings. What do they notice about the use of color? How are colors blended together? Why do some colors complement each other while others do not? Do paintings need to use all colors of the spectrum to be good?
- If possible, obtain some archeological artifacts, either from your local area or from museums or science supply houses. Discuss with students the materials that were used to create and design these objects. How has technology changed today?

- Observe several statues in your local parks or playgrounds. Ask students to decide on how statues should be designed to allow for gravity, weight, and mass.
- You may be able to take students to an art museum for a field trip. Ask students to compare the displays in an art museum with those found in a natural history museum. What similarities and differences do they note?
- Invite a local artist to visit your classroom. Ask that person to discuss color theory (prisms), the uses of colors, and how colors are mixed to create new shades.
- Start a unit on art in nature. Have students examine rock formations (e.g., Window Rock, Arizona), geological structures (e.g., Zion National Park, Utah), or natural coloration (e.g., Painted Desert, Arizona) and discuss how they were created.
- Have students explore the chemical reactions artists depend on for their work. Examine how plaster of paris is mixed and how it solidifies. Look at how linseed oil breaks down the fibers in a painter's canvas.

What becomes apparent from such activities is the fact that art and science are natural partners and should be emphasized throughout the entire day and entire curriculum. Art not only provides students with "hands-on" experiences in science; it also helps students appreciate the beauty and aesthetic value of science.

## TO INVESTIGATE

Make arrangements to visit a local classroom and observe a teacher presenting a science lesson. With your notes, create a "theme web" of the lesson, tying it into all of the other areas of the curriculum. Try to come up with three activities related to the science lesson for each of the other subject areas. Gather your lists of these activities, photocopy them, and share them with others. ∎

# THEMATIC UNITS

Teachers wishing to incorporate science into all aspects of their curriculum can do so through the creation of thematic units. A thematic unit is an interrelated series of lessons, activities, projects, readings, and explorations centered around a single topic. For example, "Staying Healthy," "Life Cycles," and "Dinosaurs" would all be appropriate thematic units. Each topic is broad enough to allow for the utilization of a variety of resources and learning opportunities, yet specific enough to give pupils some in-depth experiences within a particular area of the science curriculum.

Thematic units are beneficial for students because they provide multiple opportunities for them to engage in decision making and critical thinking. They offer a host of meaningful learning opportunities tailored to their needs and interests. Children are given the chance to make important choices about what they are learning as well as how they wish to go about learning it. Most important, thematic units provide youngsters with hands-on learning opportunities in dealing with real-life issues and problems. Science forms the basis for these investigations, but the entire curriculum is interrelated and integrated to involve students in a multiplicity of learning opportunities and ventures.

Thematic units are beneficial for you as a teacher in that they give you a chance to expand on the concepts and issues in your text. If your students have a great deal of interest in environmental issues, for example, the development of an appropriate thematic unit allows them to explore this topic in greater detail than would be possible if you relied solely on the textbook. Thematic units are also valuable because they provide you with multiple opportunities to match the skills, attitudes, and varying knowledge levels of your students with the resources, information, and scientific data available in and outside your classroom. In short, thematic units integrate many resources, all areas of the elementary curriculum, and the interests of your students into a meaningful and balanced approach to the world of science. Above all, thematic units demonstrate the varied relationships that exist between science and other aspects of the elementary curriculum in a positive, nonthreatening format.

As you might imagine, the development of thematic units takes some time and effort, simply because they are specific to the needs of *your* students and *your* available resources. However, you can overcome this limiting factor in a number of ways. First, you may want to consider creating only two or three units each school year. The development of a few well-planned units each year will provide you and your future students with a wealth of learning opportunities without taxing your "midnight oil" or creativity. Also, you may find it beneficial to work with several colleagues to design and develop some thematic units together. This team approach offers the advantage of tapping the creative spirit of many individuals and incorporating those ideas into a well-thought-out and purposeful thematic unit. Another plan of action is to utilize some commercial materials as a base for your thematic units and then expand on those materials in terms of your students' interests. Suffice it to say that there are many ways to plan and execute thematic units, and the enormous benefits to your students and your science program more than outweigh the effort involved.

## Designing a Thematic Unit

Following is a plan of action to consider in developing your own thematic units. It is presented not as the only way or the best way to organize a unit but as a workable outline that can be tailored to the needs of your students and the resources available. As you become proficient in creating thematic units, you will probably eliminate some of these steps and include others. The beauty of a thematic unit lies in the fact that it can be adapted based on teacher competence, students' skills, and classroom/community resources.

*Theme:* Select a theme in keeping with the topics offered in your science text, the interests or needs of your students, or your own experiences.

*Focus:* Develop a one-sentence focus statement summarizing the intent of the theme. This statement will help you stay on track with the activities and projects you consider.

*Materials:* Although this element is listed near the beginning of the design plan, it is advantageous to decide on all the materials you need for a unit after it has been written. In this way, you will not limit yourself to a few familiar items.

*Brainstorming:* You will want to brainstorm for all the possible resources, materials, projects, and options that could be incorporated in the unit. In this stage it is important to consider *everything* that could possibly be integrated, and it would be helpful to have students suggest potential activities for the unit.

*Initiating activity:* Select one of the brainstormed activities to start off the unit. This activity should be highly motivational and should get students excited about participating in the unit.

*General activities:* This list includes all the various activities identified in the brainstorming stage. It should include cross-curricular activities as well as activities that last for various periods of time. For example, it would be appropriate to have a selection of short-term (ST) projects (lasting less than one day), mid-term (MT) projects (lasting two or three days), and long-term (LT) projects (lasting one week or longer).

*Discussion questions:* Include a variety of open-ended questions that will help children think about the topic in varied ways. The intent is not to ask questions with single right answers but rather to help children consider all the possible interpretations of the unit.

*Literature selections:* You will need to do some research to select appropriate literature to be incorporated into your thematic unit (see Appendix C). You should give some thought to both fiction and nonfiction sources. Included with each literature selection will be: (1) a prereading activity, (2) a journal-writing activity, (3) a variety of learning activities that tie the book to various areas of the curriculum, and (4) some open-ended discussion questions.

*Culmination:* The culminating activity of the unit will be some project or activity that provides youngsters with an opportunity to summarize their discoveries in a meaningful format.

*Evaluation:* You will need to give some thought as to how you will evaluate student progress throughout the unit. This does not imply the need for formal pencil-and-paper tests but, rather, the provision for a variety of evaluative options (see Chapter 10).

*Related works of literature:* This section offers your students additional literature options through which they can explore the topic of the unit in greater detail.

Following is a thematic unit created for a class of second- or third-grade students. Notice how all aspects of the curriculum were integrated into this unit and how it provides a variety of learning options. This unit is offered not as an ideal thematic unit, but as an illustration of the potential of thematic units for bringing science into every dimension of the elementary curriculum. By creating your own units you will help students understand the universal application of science throughout your instructional program and throughout their lives.

**Thematic Unit:**

*Second/Third Grade*

**Theme: Dinosaurs**

~~**Focus:**~~ *Standard*

Students will be able to comprehend prehistoric concepts about dinosaurs and will be able to understand ways to expand their knowledge on dinosaurs.

~~**Objectives:**~~ *Performance expectations (Know & be able to do)*

On completion of this thematic unit, students will:

1. Define various dinosaur terms such as "extinct" and "fossil."
2. Give examples of animals from the past that are now extinct.
3. Explain how scientists learned about life long ago.
4. Compare and contrast life today with life when the dinosaurs existed.

**Materials:**

1. Three or four medium-sized watermelons
2. Drawing paper, construction paper, posterboard, butcher paper, index cards, yardstick, lunch bags, shoe boxes, cardboard strips
3. Crayons, markers, pencils, paste/glue, scissors, string/yarn, colored chalk, masking tape, tempera paints
4. Plaster of paris, clay, flour and water, food coloring
5. Oven, videocassette player
6. Cassettes "The Little Blue Brontosaurus" and "Dinosaur Rock," dinosaur stencils, 30 T-shirts
7. Student copies of *Digging Up Dinosaurs* by Aliki (New York: Crowell, 1981), *The Smallest Dinosaurs* by Seymour Simon (New York: Crown, 1982), *Ranger Rick's Dinosaur Book* by Howard F. Robinson, ed. (Washington, DC: National Wildlife Federation, 1984), and *Dinosaur Days* by Joyce Milton (New York: Random House, 1985).
8. An example of a real fossil, seashells
9. Videos *Dinosaur* and *The Land Before Time*
10. Chicken or turkey bones

**Note to Teachers:**

Paint the watermelons long enough in advance so that the paint is dry for the initiating activity. Measure the string to be the exact size of the dinosaurs before starting activity #2. Get permission from the principal before drawing a dinosaur on the playground in activity #2. The dinosaur T-shirts should be made before Dinosaur Day. The dinosaur poll in activity 16 could be a classroom- or building-wide survey.

~~**Initiating Activity:**~~ *Anticipatory set / motivation*

Purchase three or four medium-sized watermelons and paint them white. These are to be hidden in a "dinosaur nest" somewhere on the playground before the start of

the lesson. Tell the students that they must find the dinosaur nest in order to begin the dinosaur unit. Once the "eggs" are found, they can be cut open and shared with the group. After returning to the classroom, have the students draw pictures of imaginary creatures that may have laid those "eggs."

## Activities:

It is not necessary, nor is it suggested, that you use all the activities listed. They are intended to illustrate the scope of activities that can be developed. Selection should be based on student needs, interests, and objectives.

**Learning Activities (across the curriculum)** *(at least 2 other areas)*

*(Procedure)*

1. (Language arts) Through the taped story "The Little Blue Brontosaurus," students will learn that although scientists know a lot of information on dinosaurs, some things can't be proven—such as exact shapes and colors. After the tape, use imagery to have students develop their own kind of dinosaur and then make the dinosaur out of construction paper pieces. (ST)

2. (Math) Prior to the lesson, use string to measure out the heights and lengths of various dinosaurs. Line the class up by height and choose the student in the center of the line as the average. Trace this person on heavy butcher paper to get a pattern. Go out to the playground and roll out the string for a dinosaur. Have the students guess how many bodies long and high that dinosaur is. Have a child record the estimate and then use the pattern to obtain an actual measurement. Do this for all the dinosaurs. Compare the sizes. Have the students draw a life-size dinosaur on the playground to show the other classes. (ST)

3. (Art) Provide students with plastic dinosaur figures, clay, construction paper, and so on. In small groups, students can create shoe box dioramas. (MT)

4. (Art, language arts) Allow each student time to construct a dinosaur puppet using paper bags and various kinds of paper. When the puppets are completed, separate the students into groups of four. In small groups, students can make up a play using their dinosaur puppets as the main characters. The plays can be shared with the rest of the class. (LT)

5. (Language arts) Play the cassette tape "Dinosaur Rock" to the whole class. This tape describes what life was like over 100 million years ago through songs and dance. When the tape is over, allow the kids to work in small groups to develop a short skit for their favorite part of the tape or let them can develop a commercial to promote the tape. (MT)

6. (Health) Have students develop different menus for various types of dinosaurs. What plants or meats must each dinosaur eat to stay healthy? How much food should a particular dinosaur eat each day? Use menus from local restaurants as examples. (MT)

7. (Art) Have students work in small groups to create a large wall mural showing life when the dinosaurs existed. The mural can be drawn on heavy butcher paper and decorated with paints, crayons, construction paper, or other art materials selected by the students. (MT)

8. (All subjects) Make arrangements to have other teachers become involved in the unit. Let the music teacher sing dinosaur songs and possibly do a dinosaur musical for the school. Have the art teacher make dinosaur T-shirts using stencils and paint. Let the gym teacher practice dinosaur movements in games. The librarian could read more dinosaur stories and show filmstrips or movies. (LT)

9. (Language arts) Have students write to a "dinosaur pen pal" explaining how modern life differs from the life of their "dinosaur pen pal." (ST)

10. (Math) Have students make graphs and charts recording the different heights, weights, and sizes of various dinosaurs. Some library research will be necessary. (MT)

11. (Science) Show the students an example of a real fossil. Review the definition and importance of fossils. Using clay, plaster of paris, cardboard strips, and seashells, allow each student to make his or her own fossil. (MT)

12. (Language arts) Invite a professor from a local college to make a short presentation on dinosaurs. Have your students prepare a list of questions beforehand to ask the visiting speaker. (ST)

13. (Language arts) Using known poems and songs, create frames and have the students make them into dinosaur poems and songs. For example, turn "Brown Bear, Brown Bear" into "Dinosaur, Dinosaur." The poems and songs can be combined into a class collection. (ST)

14. (Science, language arts) Discuss what the term "extinct" means. Make a list of extinct animals. Explain the theories on why dinosaurs disappeared. Read the story "What Happened to Patrick's Dinosaurs?" Have the students create their own books using titles such as "What Happened to _____ 's Dinosaurs?" (they insert their own names). Encourage them to create their own ideas and record them in their individual books. (MT)

15. (Language arts) Read the book *Tyrannosaurus Was a Beast* by Jack Prelutsky (New York: Greenwillow, 1988).

*Poems.* Using dinosaur shaped cutouts, allow the students to create their own dinosaur jokes, riddles, and rhymes. (LT)

Examples:

*Q:* Where did a Tyrannosaurus Rex sleep?

*A:* Anywhere it wanted to.

> The Brontosaurus is a funny beast
> His head goes west, his tail goes east
> He ate all day, he ate all night
> He was a monstrous, awful fright
> But this one thing is understood
> He'll not be found in your neighborhood

16. (Math) Take a poll of the students' favorite dinosaurs. Make a graph to show the group's favorites. (MT)

## Discussion Questions:

 1. Do you think dinosaurs would make good pets? Why or why not?
 2. What are some of the similarities between dinosaurs and animals that live today?
 3. Why are scientists interested in the bones of dinosaurs?
 4. How do scientists learn about animals that are no longer living?
 5. How do you think people would react if a dinosaur were living in your town?
 6. Where on our planet could dinosaurs live today?
 7. How can we tell if a dinosaur ate meat or plants?
 8. In what ways do you think dinosaurs were able to protect themselves from their enemies?
 9. How do you think cold weather would affect dinosaurs?
10. Why are people today so interested in learning about dinosaurs?

## Literature-Related Activities:

> *Title: The Smallest Dinosaurs*
> *Genre:* Nonfiction
> *Author:* Seymour Simon
> *Bibliographic information:* New York: Crown, 1982
> *Summary:* Many youngsters assume that all dinosaurs were big, lumbering creatures. Not so! Many dinosaurs were no bigger than the pets we have at home. Simon presents valuable data on what is known and what we still have to learn about dinosaurs that weren't so big.
> *Interest level:* 3–5

1. *Prereading activity:* Ask students whether it would be easier for a large dinosaur or a small dinosaur to survive. What special types of survival techniques would a small dinosaur need to compete with his bigger cousins? Ask students to create charts that compare the relative heights and sizes of the small dinosaurs with animals of today.
2. *Journal-writing activity:* Ask students to create a "testimonial" on the benefits of a small dinosaur over a large dinosaur. Their entries can focus on the attributes of various dinosaurs and why some attributes might be more desirable than others.
3. *Learning activities (across the curriculum):*
   a. (Reading) Direct students to research other books about dinosaurs (e.g., *The Largest Dinosaurs* by Seymour Simon) and compare and contrast the differences. (MT)

b. (Art) Have students create various dinosaur skeletons with pipe cleaners. Each student can include a complete description of his or her model, outlining its special features. (MT)

c. (Language arts) Have students write and illustrate make-believe stories about going back in time to observe the dinosaurs. Be sure they understand that dinosaurs died out long before humans appeared on the earth. (MT)

d. (Language arts) Using an old board game, have students create new rules and characters for a dinosaur game. Students can develop their own procedures and share the game during free time. (LT)

4. *Discussion questions:*
   a. What advantages did small dinosaurs have over large ones?
   b. What would you enjoy most about living in the time of the dinosaurs?
   c. What would you still like to learn about small dinosaurs?
   d. What is the most important thing we know about the small dinosaurs?

---

*Title:* Digging Up Dinosaurs
*Genre:* Nonfiction
*Author:* Aliki
*Bibliographic information:* New York: Crowell, 1981
*Summary:* This book presents valuable information on the painstaking process of digging up dinosaurs and reconstructing their skeletons. It provides data on the work of paleontologists in a light and easy tone.
*Interest level:* 2–4

---

1. *Prereading activity:* Provide small groups of children with a pile of chicken bones (be sure the bones have been boiled and dried thoroughly). Direct each group to arrange the bones in their original configuration. Ask them to discuss any problems they have in putting a chicken skeleton back together, even though most of them know exactly what a chicken looks like. Talk about the difficulties scientists have in putting a dinosaur skeleton back together, particularly when no human has ever seen a live dinosaur.

2. *Journal-writing activity:* Have several students pretend to be dinosaurs. Have them describe their bodies, outlining their size, configuration, dimensions, skeletal structure, and other important features. Ask each one to explain why his or her body is different from those of other dinosaurs.

3. *Learning activities (across the curriculum):*
   a. (Art, science) Have students create their own dinosaur fossils. Provide small groups of students with pie plates half filled with wet sand. Ask each group to place several chicken bones in the sand. Circular strips of cardboard can be placed around the bones and a plaster of paris mixture poured into the makeshift molds. After the plaster of paris has dried, have students examine their "fossils" to note any similarities with dinosaur fossils. (MT)
   b. (Art, language arts) Have students create their own dinosaur books. Ask each student to trace an outline of a dinosaur on a sheet of construction paper and cut it out. The student then traces that shape on another piece of construction paper as well as several sheets of newsprint and cuts them out. All the sheets should be put together (with the construction paper sheets on the front and back) and stapled. Have students write about their favorite dinosaur on the pages of their dinosaur book. (MT)

c. (Language arts) Ask students to write a story on a day in the life of a dinosaur. Instruct them to share important details about what a dinosaur would do during the course of a single day. (ST)

d. (Math) Locate a photograph or illustration of a dinosaur skeleton. Direct students to count the number of bones in a leg, in the chest, or in another section of the dinosaur body. Ask them to compare their count with the number of bones in a similar section of their bodies (you may want to provide an illustration of the human skeleton). Prepare graphs and charts of the similarities and differences. (MT)

4. *Discussion questions:*

a. What are some of the difficulties scientists have in reconstructing dinosaur skeletons?

b. Why do you think people are so interested in learning about dinosaurs? Defend your answer.

c. Would you want to spend some time looking for dinosaur bones and then putting them together? Why or why not?

d. What do you consider to be the most interesting part of a dinosaur skeleton? Why?

---

*Title: Ranger Rick's Dinosaur Book*
*Genre:* Nonfiction
*Author:* Howard F. Robinson, ed.
*Bibliographic information:* Washington, DC: National Wildlife Federation, 1984
*Summary:* With an abundance of illustrations and diagrams, this book provides young scientists with a captivating look at what we know about dinosaurs as well as what we postulate about dinosaurs.
*Interest level:* 4–6

---

1. *Prereading activity:* Ask each student to create an illustration of the "ideal" dinosaur. What would be its physical features? What size would it need to be in order to survive? What about its shape and color? Ask students to keep these illustrations and compare them with illustrations in this book later.

2. *Journal-writing activity:* Tell students that they are reporters who have been transported back to the time of the dinosaurs. Direct them to prepare a newspaper article on an event that happened between two or more dinosaurs as they foraged in a swamp.

3. *Learning activities (across the curriculum):*

a. (Language arts) Have students create an original dinosaur dictionary. Direct them to collect dinosaur-related words from various books and resources and compile those words into a dictionary (cut into the shape of a dinosaur). (LT)

b. (Art, science) Use a long roll of butcher paper or newsprint to cover one wall of your classroom or a section of the hallway outside your room. Have students create a time line (with illustrations) showing the emergence and disappearance of various dinosaurs. (LT)

c. (Art) Ask students to create a card game (based on the rules for "Concentration"). Draw illustrations of dinosaurs on separate index cards and write the names of those dinosaurs on other cards. Cards are placed face down, and students are encouraged to match an illustration of a dinosaur with its name. (ST)

**d.** (Language arts) Direct students to create a "Dinosaur Observation Manual," a guide to watching and observing dinosaurs (just in case anyone might happen to sight an unusual creature in his or her backyard). (MT)

**4.** *Discussion questions:*
   **a.** What dinosaur would have the greatest chance for survival if it were to appear on earth today? Why? Which one would have the most difficult time surviving today? Why?
   **b.** What features of dinosaurs are still evident in animals today?
   **c.** How does size affect a dinosaur's ability to survive or locate food?
   **d.** What is your favorite dinosaur? Why do you like that type of dinosaur more than any other?

---

*Title: Dinosaur Days*
*Genre:* Nonfiction
*Author:* Joyce Milton
*Bibliographic information:* New York: Random House, 1985
*Summary:* Brief and simple descriptions of the various kinds of dinosaurs that lived millions of years ago.
*Interest level:* 1–4

---

**1.** *Prereading activity:* Direct students to create paragraphs on some of the most distinguishing features of dinosaurs. What features were most useful for survival? For eating? For locomotion? For confrontations? Ask students to defend their choices.

**2.** *Journal activity:* Have students write summaries of what they think it was like when the dinosaurs lived. Each student could share his or her summary with another classmate.

**3.** *Learning activities (across the curriculum):*
   **a.** (Language arts) Provide each student with one of the dinosaur names and direct him or her to find information on the dinosaur and write a paragraph about it. Students with the same dinosaurs can be paired later to compare notes. Have the information combined into a class book. (LT)
   **b.** (Art, language arts) Have each student create an original dinosaur. Students can provide detailed descriptions of their invented dinosaurs and give them appropriate names. (MT)
   **c.** (Science) Although illustrations of dinosaurs show them with brown or green skin, scientists don't know exact color of dinosaur skin. Ask students to conduct some research and propose reasons why illustrations of dinosaurs show them with green or brown skin. Could dinosaurs have had blue skin? Red skin? (MT)
   **d.** (Music) Have small groups of students each choose one of their favorite dinosaurs from the book. Ask group members to take a familiar song and rewrite the lyrics using dinosaur words.

   *Example:*     (to the tune of "I've Been Working on the Railroad")

   I've been watching Stegosaurus
   All the livelong day
   I've been watching Stegosaurus
   Just to see what he would say
   Can't you hear him munchin', crunchin'
   Rise up and start to eat a tree
   Don't you ever want to meet him
   'Cause he will make you flee.

**4.** *Discussion questions:*
   **a.** If you lived when the dinosaurs did, would life be different?
   **b.** If you went out to play one day and found a dinosaur in your backyard, what would be the first thing you would say?
   **c.** What if the dinosaurs never became extinct?
   **d.** If you found a clue that led you to believe a dinosaur was still living, what would you do?

## Culmination:

*(doing @ end of unit — presentation, special day etc)*

The culminating activity will be "Dinosaur Day." This day could include all or some of the following activities:

1. Have students wear dinosaur outfits or T-shirts.
2. Have a dinosaur read-in; select and read only dinosaur books for the entire day.
3. Have students write experience stories from the perspective of a dinosaur.
4. Make dinosaur models out of clay or dough mixture.
5. Play dinosaur games and sing dinosaur songs.
6. Show a dinosaur movie such as *The Land Before Time.*
7. Write and perform a dinosaur play.
8. Have a dinosaur feast using dinosaur-shaped foods such as finger jello, cookies, and graham crackers.
9. Construct and break open a dinosaur piñata.
10. Create dinosaur coloring books to share with students in lower grades.
11. Have a guest speaker from a museum or local college come to visit.
12. Go on a field trip to a fossil site or local museum.
13. Create an enormous papier-mâché dinosaur.
14. Create a "Dinosaur Book of World Records" (largest, smallest, heaviest, smallest brain, longest lived, etc.).

*assessment/*

## Evaluation:

Throughout the unit, student journals and products should be evaluated based on criteria established by the teacher and students. Possibilities include one or more of the following:

**a.** Students can determine beforehand the number of books that should be read throughout the unit.
**b.** Each student should create an original language arts product such as a play, skit, narrative, diary, or other appropriate work.
**c.** Each student can create a bank of five to eight questions to be placed in a central location. All students can draw from this "bank" and respond to the questions of their classmates.
**d.** Small groups of students can each create an original quiz on the information shared in class. Duplicate and randomly distribute these quizzes to the groups for completion.
**e.** Have each student prepare a simple outline of the significant points covered in the unit. Post these on the bulletin board.

**f.** Have each student make a tape recording of the four or five most important pieces of information they have learned through this unit. The tapes can be evaluated according to predetermined objectives.

**g.** Take time occasionally to read students' journal entries to determine how students are organizing their thoughts, integrating new data, and drawing important conclusions.

**h.** Schedule frequent conferences with students or groups of students throughout the unit. Provide them with opportunities to share and discuss the information they are learning and using.

## Related Works of Literature  *other resources*

Aliki. (1981). *Digging up dinosaurs.* New York: Crowell.

Aliki. (1985). *Dinosaurs are different.* New York: Crowell.

Aliki. (1988). *Dinosaur bones.* New York: Crowell.

Arnold, Caroline. (1989). *Dinosaur mountain: Graveyard of the past.* New York: Clarion.

Barton, Byron. (1989). *Dinosaurs, dinosaurs.* New York: Crowell.

Barton, Byron. (1990). *Bones, bones, dinosaur bones.* New York: HarperCollins.

Branley, Franklyn. (1982). *Dinosaurs, asteroids, and superstars: Why the dinosaurs disappeared.* New York: Crowell.

Branley, Franklyn. (1989). *What happened to the dinosaurs.* New York: Crowell.

Carroll, Susan. (1986). *How big is a brachiosaurus?* New York: Platt and Monk.

Cobb, Vicki. (1983). *The monsters who died: A mystery about dinosaurs.* New York: Coward-McCann.

Cohen, Daniel. (1983). *Monster dinosaur.* New York: Lippincott.

Craig, Jean. (1989). *Discovering prehistoric animals.* Mahwah, NJ: Troll.

Daeschler, T. (1990). *The dinosaur hunter's handbook: Discover the traces of a lost world.* Philadelphia: Running Press.

Elting, Mary, & Goodman, Ann. (1980). *Dinosaur mysteries.* New York: Platt and Monk.

Freedman, Russell. (1983). *Dinosaurs and their young.* New York: Holiday.

Gibbons, Gail. (1987). *Dinosaurs.* New York: Holiday.

Gilbert, John. (1981). *Dinosaurs discovered.* New York: Larousse.

Gordon, Sharon. (1980). *Dinosaurs in trouble.* Mahwah, NJ: Troll.

Hopkins, Lee Bennett. (1987). *Dinosaurs.* San Diego: Harcourt Brace.

Jacobs, Francine. (1982). *Supersaurus.* New York: Putnam.

Lambert, David. (1982). *Dinosaurs.* New York: Watts.

Lasky, Kathryn. (1990). *Dinosaur dig.* New York: Morrow.

Lauber, Patricia. (1989). *The news about dinosaurs.* New York: Bradbury.

Peters, David. (1989). *A gallery of dinosaurs and other early reptiles.* New York: Knopf.

Prelutsky, Jack. (1988). *Tyrannosaurus was a beast.* New York: Greenwillow.

Sattler, Helen. (1981). *Dinosaurs of North America.* New York: Lothrop.

Sattler, Helen. (1984). *Baby dinosaurs.* New York: Lothrop.

Sattler, Helen. (1985). *Pterosaurs, the flying reptiles.* New York: Lothrop.

Sattler, Helen. (1989). *Tyrannosaurus rex and its kin: The Mesozoic monsters.* New York: Lothrop.

Sattler, Helen. (1990). *The new illustrated dinosaur dictionary.* New York: Lothrop.

Selsam, Millicent. (1982). *A first look at dinosaurs.* New York: Walker.

Simon, Seymour. (1990). *New questions and answers about dinosaurs.* New York: Morrow.

Thayer, Jane. (1964). *Quiet on account of dinosaur.* New York: Morrow.

Thomson, Peggy. (1985). *Auks, rocks and the odd dinosaur.* New York: Crowell.

Wexo, John Bonnett. (1985). *Dinosaurs.* Washington, DC: Wildlife.

# POINTS OF DISCUSSION

1. Observe a teacher for one day and make notes on the topics covered. Create a theme web of all those topics, integrating science with each area of the curriculum.

2. Discuss the way you were taught science while an elementary student. How do you think it ought to be taught? Describe your favorite teacher in elementary school and how he or she taught science.

3. Describe the value of teaching science throughout the entire day versus teaching it as an individual subject. Create a list of positive and negative features.

4. Do you support children working in small groups or individually on science projects? Why?

5. Select a chapter from any science series and construct a semantic web of vocabulary words and concepts to use in a classroom.

6. What do you perceive to be the role of encyclopedias, trade books, and basal textbooks in the elementary science curriculum?

7. List three of your favorite areas of science (e.g., rocks, magnetism, plants). Explain why they are your favorite areas and state five concepts you know about each area.

8. See how long it takes you to list 20 occasions in which you either used or observed something related to science in the last 24 hours.

9. Work with a partner and create a thematic unit on a topic selected from a current science series.

# REFERENCES AND SUGGESTED READINGS

Baumann, J. (1985). *Whole language instruction and basal readers*. Columbus, OH: Silver Burdett and Ginn.

Cohen, H., Staley, F., & Horak, W. (1989). *Teaching science as a decision making process*. Dubuque, IA: Kendall-Hunt.

Ogle, D. M. (1986). K-W-L: A teaching model that develops active reading of expository text. *The Reading Teacher* 39(6), 564–570.

Rothlein, L., & Meinbach, A. (1991). *The literature connection: Using children's books in the classroom*. Glenview, IL: Scott, Foresman.

Schunke, G. M. (1988). *Elementary social studies: Knowing, doing, caring*. New York: Macmillan.

# 9

# SPECIAL PROJECTS, PEOPLE, AND EVENTS

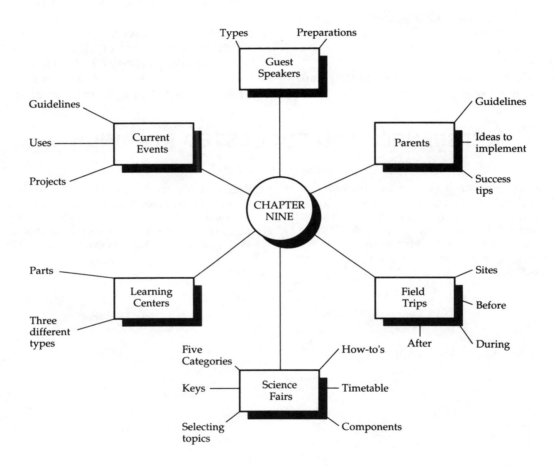

## Chapter Objectives

After reading this chapter you should be able to:

1. Describe the roles of current events, guest speakers, and parents in the science curriculum.

2. Elaborate on the utility of learning centers, science fairs, and field trips to students' appreciation of science.

3. Develop strategies to expand the science program within the classroom as well as beyond the classroom.

This book has focused on the processes that constitute a successful science program. The emphasis has been on the active participation of children throughout the science curriculum. In short, students must understand that science is more than the accumulation of facts and figures in a book; it entails the manipulation of information and the investigation of self-initiated questions.

Science is everywhere. It is part and parcel of everything we do from the time we wake up in the morning until we retire at night—and even beyond. Thus, science education is more than a series of science lessons; it is an attitude, a constant inquiry into things known and unknown. Therefore, the elementary science program can be enhanced considerably when other people, special projects, and timely events are incorporated into the curriculum on a regular basis. This will expand learning possibilities far beyond the limits of any textbook or curriculum guide.

Although some may argue that special projects and people should be considered as "add-ons" to the science program, the inclusion (as opposed to the addition) of a variety of outside experts, extending activities, and investigative projects within the science curriculum can be a positive part of any child's experiences with science. It is important, however, that

you consider the abilities and ages of your students in deciding which events to make part of your program. For example, it may not be necessary to invite a rocket scientist to lecture to your first-grade students on planetary exploration when a student from the local high school will do just as well. Also, if you have a heterogeneous class of third-graders, it may be appropriate to have them work in teams (cooperative learning) to tackle science fair projects as opposed to having them attempt projects individually. Above all, it is essential that you keep the needs, abilities, and interests of your students in mind when deciding on the appropriate strategies and activities to broaden their "book learning."

You should give serious consideration to the following possibilities for any science lesson or unit. These options might not be appropriate for *every* lesson, but they can add a certain measure of excitement to lessons when offered on a regular basis.

1. Current events
2. Guest speakers
3. Parents and community members
4. Learning centers
5. Science fairs
6. Field trips

## CURRENT EVENTS

To many children science seems to be a subject confined to textbooks and laboratories. Students frequently get the view that science occurs within the structure of school and is learned principally through experiments and demonstrations. Obviously, an important objective of the science curriculum is to show students the relationships between what is learned in the classroom and the world outside. By helping youngsters appreciate the universality of science, or any other subject for that matter, you provide them with positive experiences that can have a significant effect on their understanding and use of that subject well into adulthood.

The use of current events within the science program allows children to see how their knowledge base can be expanded in new directions. For example, the following media can be used to heighten students' awareness of current events.

1. *Television.* A host of science-related programs are available in most parts of the country. Programs such as "3-2-1 Contact" and "Nova," plus selections on "The Discovery Channel," are regular features in most viewing areas.

2. *Magazines.* You should subscribe to, or at least read on a regular basis, one or more popular science periodicals (see Appendix F).
3. *Radio.* Most PBS radio stations carry broadcasts of science programs and interviews with well-known scientists. Find out when science-related programs are to be aired and listen to them.
4. *Books.* Popular books are published on science topics every day (see Appendix E). Many books on dinosaur discoveries, space exploration, and genetic engineering find their way onto best-seller lists.

Introducing students to current events involves more than simply clipping news stories out of the daily newspaper. Some events may be appropriate for children to consider, whereas others may be outside their level of comprehension. Refer to the following guidelines in promoting current events throughout the science curriculum.

1. To be meaningful to children, a current event must be within their range of comprehension. Merely bringing in a news article or a recording of a ra-

dio program that has something to do with science may be inappropriate.

2. Current events should be selected based on the interests of children. Teachers should encourage children to keep an eye out for news-related science events that match their own interests, hobbies, reading habits, or free-time activities.

3. Current events achieve importance when they can be related to the personal lives of children. When students understand the relationships between their science curriculum and events in the outside world, valuable learning takes place.

4. There must be an element of concreteness in the events shared in class. Many science events and discoveries are too abstract for children to process and may tend to confuse students more than enlighten them. For example, the physics involved in using planetary gravitational fields to propel space probes into the far reaches of the solar system may be quite difficult for elementary students to comprehend. Such abstractness should be tempered with concrete information on the value of those space probes, the kind of information intended for collection, or the distances traveled.

5. Often, children see current events as a reporting of isolated facts. The "who," "where," "what," "when," "why," and "how" of news reporting may signal to students that this is how they should be sharing current events in the classroom. More important, children need to develop a conceptual understanding of an event—an understanding that moves beyond facts and figures and helps children see the relevance and importance of the event to their own lives.

As students share current events, you should pose the following questions to yourself. This list is not meant to be complete but rather is meant to help you integrate a variety of current events into the natural sequence of science lessons and activities planned for your students.

- What background information do students have about this topic?
- What information do I need to provide students before sharing the event?
- How can I relate this event to a topic recently discussed in class or scheduled for discussion in the very near future?
- Is this event within the conceptual capacity of all the students?
- What ancillary materials, media, or people can enhance the comprehension of this event?
- Is this event significant enough to be turned into a complete lesson, or should it be used as part of another lesson?
- How can I help students relate this event to their personal lives?
- How aware are students of this event? Is it an isolated event or part of a larger body of information?
- How can I incorporate the processes of science (i.e., classifying, communicating, inferring) into the discussion of the event?
- What will make this event of continuing importance to students?
- Can this event be expanded into other areas of the curriculum? That is, can I make it part of my reading lessons, social studies program, or math curriculum?
- How can I make this occurrence more than just a "one-shot" event? That is, how can I make it a natural and normal part of several lessons or discussions in class?

These questions are appropriate for all types of media and can provide you with some guidelines to help make current events a valuable adjunct to your science curriculum.

**DID YOU KNOW?** _____

By the time you've reached the age of 70, you will have shed nearly 40 pounds of dead skin.

**Classroom Activity**   Have students check the local newspaper and several current magazines for information on scientific discoveries concerning elderly people. What new information are we learning about older citizens, and what scientific advances may prolong the lives of all people? Students may wish to consider the social ramifications of increasing numbers of elderly people in our society.   ■

There are several ways to bring current events into the science program. You will need to decide which of the following suggestions fit your style of teaching and the needs of your students.

1. Students can bring in events collected from the media on a random basis. As soon as a student discovers an event of interest, he or she can bring it in to share with the class.
2. Students can be assigned to seek out specific events relating to a particular unit of study. For example, if the class is studying a unit on ecology, students can be assigned the task of looking for articles about the environment in the local newspaper or popular periodicals. These can become valuable additions to the topic as it is being shared in class.
3. Students can put together a scrapbook or notebook of selected current events. Provide students with a listing of the topics scheduled for discussion during the course of the year. Encourage them to keep a lookout for news items that relate to those topics. As events are reported in the media, they can be clipped or recorded and added to the notebook. Then when those topics come up for discussion, several current events will be available for you to use as part of the lesson. The notebook should be maintained throughout the entire year.
4. As you read or hear about events unfolding in the world of science, make it a point to share those happenings with your students. You may wish to start off the day discussing a news story or magazine article you recently encountered. Making this a regular part of the school day keeps students alert to the universality of science.
5. Many events in the world of science are predictable (most are not). The launching of a space shuttle or an undersea exploration is an example of a predictable event that can be a regular feature of daily science discussions. Children can get a sense of the progress of an event and follow it with interest if it is made part of the daily routine.
6. Students may write to science newsmakers, science TV consultants, or local science teachers about current events.

Current events should not be relegated to the social studies curriculum; they can be a vital element of the science program, too. Also, current events should extend beyond the bulletin board into other types of activities. Following is a sampling of activities that promote current events in different formats.

*Class newspaper.* Students can collect and summarize current news articles and events from the local media. These can be prepared in the students' own writing and assembled into a class newspaper to be distributed to students in the class or throughout the school.

*Parent newsletter.* To help parents keep abreast of what is happening in the science program, students can prepare summaries of news events from the media as well as current happenings within the classroom science program. These can be assembled into a regular newsletter to be sent home to parents.

*News show.* Have students prepare summaries of current events in science and share them with their classmates. This can be done in the form of a simulated news broadcast during the day, or it can be produced for a larger audience (other classes or the entire school) on a monthly basis.

*Electronic media.* If possible, students may wish to prepare news videos to be shown to other classes via the school's closed-circuit TV system or distributed to other classes for viewing on a VCR. These videos could contain collections of different items, including summaries of recent scientific discoveries, interviews with make-believe or actual scientists about their work, stories on science in our daily lives, demonstrations of experiments, interesting science facts, and any other pertinent information. These videos can also be made available for parents to watch at home.

*News calendar.* Provide students with a large wall calendar and ask them to record scientific discoveries—both current and past—on the squares of the calendar. Students can research events that occurred on specific days of the year and include other discoveries as they are made during the course of the school year.

*News scrapbook.* Prepare a scrapbook or notebook in which students collect examples of science events as they occur. (See Figure 9.1.) These events will then be available for inclusion in the science curriculum according to the topics scheduled for discussion over the year. Plan to take time to discuss these events as they are added to the scrapbook.

*News notes.* Have each student prepare a 3 × 5 index card with an important science fact, a recent discovery, an ongoing investigation, or an upcoming event. These cards can be sent to teachers in other rooms so that current events may be shared with other students.

*Presentations.* Direct students to produce a news program or presentation on a current event. The presentation which can be shared with students in another classroom, should pro-

# Students take crack at embryology

By MARGARET HOPKINS
*Daily Record correspondent*

Eighty Canadochly Elementary School students become embryologists recently as three dozen fertilized eggs were deposited into their classrooms.

The fifth-graders at that Eastern elementary school are participating in the York County Extension Service's 4-H Embryology Project.

Until the baby chicks hatch in about 17 days, the students will be responsible for caring for the eggs. This includes monitoring the temperature and humidity in each of three incubators and turning the eggs several times a day.

At least 10 to 15 minutes of each science class will be spent studying the eggs, said teacher John Wolizer who participated in the program last year.

"This is hands-on learning," Wolizer said. "If they were just reading (about embryology), they'd be lost."

In its sixth year, the embryology project this year will include 55 classrooms in 27 schools in York County, 4-H program assistant Jodi Myers said. The curriculum can be used with students in third through 12th grades.

Myers' responsibilities are to provide the eggs, incubators and 4-H booklets with activities and diagrams as well as three classroom visits. Some schools may combine their classes for the project.

During the first visit, she explains the parts of an egg and how incubators work.

Alisha Markel, a Canadochly fifth-grader, said although her family had raised day-old chicks, she had never studied the insides of an egg.

The albumen, or egg white, and membranes, other parts of the egg, also were new to Robert Brooks even though his family had hatched some chicks in a homemade incubator. Robert, also a fifth-grader at the school, said the em-

bryology project will allow students to watch how a chick grows and to compare that with human growth.

Myers was questioned closely by students about how they would know if an embryo had died and whether the eggs would become overheated when candled. Candling, the subject of Myers' second visit, is when an egg is held up to light. Because the shell is porous, the embryo becomes visible.

Not only does the embryology project provide hands-on learning, but it also teaches responsibility. Eggs must be turned daily to ensure the embryos have a continual source of food. Temperature within the incubators also has to be checked. If higher than 100 degrees, the embryos can die, which happened to one dozen eggs last year.

"We are trying to introduce kids to a new form of life, to teach responsibility and to show the complexity of life," Myers said.

**FIGURE 9.1**   Science-related news clipping for student scrapbook

vide information on the event as well as on how that event relates to the lives of students and the science curriculum. Students should be directed to respond to questions from the audience.

*Art projects.* Students can share current events via a number of art-related projects. For example, a small group of students can assemble a shoe box diorama of a current event. Using various art materials (construction paper, pipe cleaners, cotton balls, etc.), students can create a three-dimensional display inside a shoe box that illustrates a current event. Other students may wish to put together a mobile displaying the various elements of a current event. For example, students could clip various pictures of a recent shuttle launching and hang them from a wire coat hanger for display in the classroom.

*Telephone hotline.* Many schools maintain a telephone answering machine that provides parents with information of current school happenings. This can be turned into a science information hotline by making arrangements for students to record specified current events on the machine. Parents, other students, and members of the local community can then call in and receive some of the latest infor-

mation in the world of science via the telephone.

*Supplementary materials.* As students collect data on a variety of current events, challenge them to assemble these reports into supplementary curriculum materials. These materials—in the form of worksheets, brochures, or flyers—could be used to supplement outdated material or information in the science textbook. It also provides students with valuable opportunities to utilize their writing skills in a productive and meaningful manner.

Current events can have a powerful influence on how children approach science and how they view science as part of their lives. Achieving this, however, requires commitment and guidance from the classroom teacher. You must demonstrate your enthusiasm for the scientific events taking place and demonstrate how those events represent an important part of the overall curriculum. Your responsibility is to help students understand that science is not a static subject but rather is constantly evolving in many different arenas outside the classroom. Those arenas provide you and your students with important learning experiences and a host of stimulating forays into the wide world of science.

# GUEST SPEAKERS

People in the local community can add immeasurably to the classroom science program. Besides bringing in a variety of experiences to share with students, community people can demonstrate to children that science is an everyday part of their lives and can be enjoyed by all.

## DID YOU KNOW?

There are 50–100 billion bacteria and other organisms in your mouth.

**Classroom Activity** Invite a doctor, nurse, or laboratory technician into your classroom to describe all of the living organisms that inhabit the human body—on the outside as well as the inside. Students may wish to create a chart of the different types of creatures they carry around with them. ■

The following list contains suggestions for potential guest presenters.

| | |
|---|---|
| Doctor | Train conductor |
| Local authors | Engineer |
| Shop/store owners | Nurse |
| People with unusual | Travelers |
| hobbies | Exchange students |
| College professors | Newspaper reporters |
| 4-H club leader | County agent |
| Early inhabitants of the | Environmental |
| community | group leader |
| Representatives | Community workers |
| of local industries | Pharmacist |
| Commercial pilot | Electrician |
| Sanitation workers | College students |
| High school science | Veterinarian |
| teacher | High school students |
| Park ranger | Musicians |
| Plumber | Gardeners |
| Astronomer | Environmentalist |
| Computer operators | Factory workers |
| Zoologists | Medical labo- |
| TV weatherperson | ratory worker |
| Ecologist | Biologist |
| Farmer | Butcher |
| Construction worker | Auto mechanic |
| Cooks | Dietitian |
| Baker | Landscaper |
| Carpenter | Architect |
| Artist | Weaver |
| Pet store owner | Tree surgeon |
| Mason | Chef |
| Roofer | Restauranteur |

## IDEA BOX

Keep an index card box on your desk. Provide tabs in the box with the chapter titles and numbers (from the textbook) on separate tabs. As you read your local newspaper and come across the name of an important individual in your community, write his or her name, address, and phone number on an index card and file the card in the appropriate section of the box. Then, in advance of that chapter in your textbook, contact that individual as a possible speaker. Keep the card file up to date, and over the years you will build up a valuable resource file of community "experts" for your science program.

As you can see, the range of possible "experts" you can bring into the classroom is limitless. Each of the people listed above, as well as others from your community, can add substantially to your science program. It is important, however, that both the guest presenter and the class be sufficiently prepared prior to the visit. Consider the following items when inviting any speaker to your classroom.

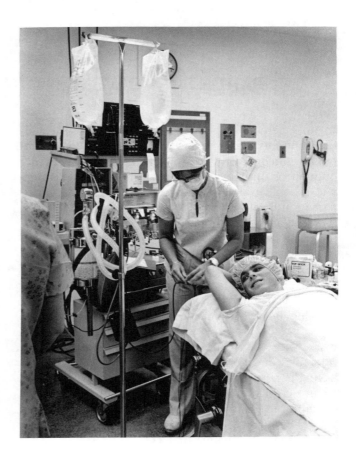

1. Make sure the people you invite not only are knowledgeable about their subject matter but are also able to present it in an interesting and informative manner. Outside speakers sometimes get caught up in their own jargon, not realizing that their level of vocabulary might not be understood by youngsters.

2. It is important that the person you invite addresses a topic relevant to a concept or issue currently being discussed in class. An airline pilot's discussion of wind and weather three months before the topic is to be addressed in class may have little carryover effect for students.

3. Plan to meet with the speaker in advance of his or her presentation. This will ensure that the speaker is aware of the objectives of the presentation and how it should relate to the topic(s) being presented in class.

4. Always confirm the date and time of a speaker's visit several days in advance. A phone call or short note is most appropriate.

5. Prepare students in advance. Ask students to suggest a list of possible questions that can be asked of the speaker either during or immediately after the presentation. These questions can be listed on a sheet of paper and duplicated for all students. Students should also be provided with some background data on a visiting speaker. The occupation, background, experiences, and topic of the speaker's presentation should be shared with students prior to the visit.

**TO INVESTIGATE** ⎯⎯⎯⎯⎯⎯⎯⎯⎯⎯⎯

As you visit elementary classrooms, observe how much the teachers use their textbooks. How many outside speakers, materials, or activities are incorporated into the science program? What methods do the teachers use to expand on the information in the text? Do teachers use all the information in the textbook or just some of it? How could those lessons be broadened through the use of current events or a guest speaker? ∎

## PARENT INVOLVEMENT IN THE SCIENCE PROGRAM

Inviting parents as partners in the education of children presents many interesting possibilities for educational enrichment. Soliciting parent involvement not only opens up lines of communication between home and school, it also provides a vehicle through which parents and educators can work hand-in-hand towards the scholastic success of all youngsters (Fredericks & Rasinski, 1990).

It seems reasonable to expect that the classroom science program can be enhanced considerably when parents and other family members are offered opportunities to support it and contribute to it. In fact, a growing body of educational research suggests that when parents are provided with true opportunities to work with teachers in promoting scholastic goals, the students' education is enhanced considerably. Indeed, having parents assume an active role throughout your science curriculum, as well as throughout other parts of your academic program, can extend learning far beyond the four walls of your classroom and can help to make science a dynamic subject.

Developing a successful effort to solicit parent involvement in your science program is not a simple proposition. It demands some planning and attention to specific factors. Rasinski and Fredericks (1988) have specified eight principles to guide the development of effective outreach programs. Those guidelines are

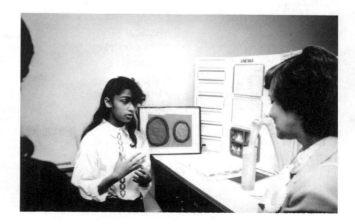

adapted here to apply specifically to gaining parent involvement in the classroom science curriculum.

- *Regular daily time.* Science is much more than a classroom subject. Students and their parents need to recognize that science is an integral part of our daily lives and needs to be promoted as such. It is therefore important that parents be provided with activities and designs to help them share science with their youngsters on a frequent basis. Table 9.1 shows a calendar of activities that can be prepared monthly and sent home to parents. Talking with children about a recent scientific discovery, an event in the national news, or an article in the local newspaper are other ways parents can help promote science as a viable subject.
- *Purpose and motive.* Both parents and their children must understand the relevance of home-based activities. How does science relate to the day-to-day lives of youngsters? Completing workbook pages may have little relevance to childrens' lives, but collecting water samples from a nearby stream can! For parents to take an active role in the classroom science program, it is important that they be provided with stimulating activities that are purposeful.
- *Real science activities.* Parents often conceive of science as simply the memorization of limitless facts and figures. In soliciting their support, it is vital to provide them with holistic activities that use viable information in meaningful contexts. When parents

help their children build a bird station, construct a model airplane, or track the habits of local wildlife, for example, science becomes much more than dry facts; it turns into an active exploration of the world around.

- *Internal interest.* No matter what efforts are expended to solicit parents as partners in the science program, the interests of the child should be kept paramount. Helping students develop a lifelong appreciation of science demands that parents and teachers begin with concepts and activities that are of interest to children. For example, if a child enjoys animal stories, an appropriate science activity might be to have the entire family visit a local game preserve or zoo to record the eating habits of a giraffe or gazelle. For a child who is interested in electricity, a visit to a local power plant or manufacturing firm might be in order. In short, parent-child activities in science need to be built on a foundation of student interests.
- *Tolerance and patience.* A certain degree of patience is necessary on the part of parents. Activities that place children or parents in confrontive or uncomfortable situations should be avoided. Parents need to keep in mind that children develop at different rates, and they should exercise appropriate levels of tolerance. Do not suggest extending activities that will cause parents to lose their patience.
- *Support and encouragement.* Parents should understand that the ideas you suggest to them are backed by a system of support. Parents like to know that

TABLE 9.1

## HOME SCIENCE CALENDAR

| Sun. | Mon. | Tues. | Wed. | Thurs. | Fri. | Sat. |
|---|---|---|---|---|---|---|
| | | | Plant radish seeds | Watch PBS special | Make terrarium | Collect leaves |
| Count robins, hawks | Collect different bugs | Draw garden map | Read garden book | Collect rocks | Write story on bugs | Plant bean seeds |
| Label plant parts | Observe spiders | Collect flowers | Build bird house | Identify four fruits | Dig for worms | Weed garden |
| Make bark rubbing | Measure tree height | Scatter bird seed | Find 2 flying insects | Make rock garden | Plant carrot seeds | Examine plant roots |
| Collect 5 seed packets | Make plant poster | Read bug book | Find 2 new plants | Chart radish growth | | |

should they have any concerns or questions, they are free to contact you. Simply giving parents a project to complete with their children is not the best way to solicit their participation. Parents need to understand that assisting their children in science requires not just a system of right answers but a foundation of mutual support and encouragement. Your outreach efforts should be designed not to turn parents into teachers but to help them promote the science program as a positive human activity.

- *Informality*. Don't formalize your outreach efforts too much. Spontaneity should be a prime consideration in any parent involvement effort. Parents should realize that science happens in many kinds of informal situations as well as formal ones. For example, when parents and children talk about the changing cloud patterns or the growth of seeds in the family garden, they are involved in informal science activities that can have far-reaching, positive effects on the children's science awareness.

- *Interaction*. Whatever activities or projects you suggest to parents as extensions of your classroom program, try to provide for a maximum of parent-child interaction in those activities. Parents should not be asked to tell their children what to do but should be encouraged to interact with their children in meaningful discussions. Providing parents with questions or ideas to discuss can contribute significantly to the promotion of science in the home.

## TEACHER TO TEACHER

Getting parents involved is one of the keys to a great science program! Parents can help with many aspects of the science curriculum, including: research reports, home-science experiments, and visits to local science museums.

Every Friday morning I have a "Science Day" to do something really fun with my class of fifth-graders. We do activities and experiments that are very much hands-on.

I got an idea one day to invite my students' parents in for a Friday morning to get them involved in a "Science Day."

We did a lesson called "Static Magic" and WOW!, the results were classroom magic! The parents not only got involved, they helped bring home the main points of the lesson with their wealth of experience and parental guidance.

I continue to run the weekly Friday science days, but about once a month, I invite the parents in to continue the magic.

Christian Heine
Cornwells Elementary School
Bensalem, PA

## Ideas to Implement

The number of opportunities to involve parents in the classroom science program is limited only by one's imagination. Following are some ideas and projects culled from many schools around the country. They are offered as suggestions and to stimulate you to create similar efforts within your science curriculum. Some of these ideas can be implemented by individual classroom teachers; others are more appropriate as schoolwide efforts. Providing parents with active opportunities to assist in the development of these programs will help guarantee their success.

- Set up a special series of workshops on the science program. Give parents an opportunity to be "students" once again.
- Write a letter to the editor of the local newspaper encouraging parents to assume an active role in the science curriculum. Include some relevant tips and ideas.
- Hold a monthly "parent tea" after school hours to share ideas with parents and discuss various parts of the curriculum.
- Ask the district superintendent to prepare a letter to be sent to the parents of students in your classroom.
- Invite parents to serve on a "curriculum council" to help select materials and supplies for the science program or to help establish directions for the curriculum.
- Call one parent each week to relay some good news about what the child is doing in science or to share some important happenings in the science program.
- Set up a lending library of resource books and extra science materials for parents to check out and use at home.
- Establish a special bulletin board in your classroom displaying some of the science-related activities that families participate in during the year. These may include visits to local museums, a list of literature shared at home, or new facts discovered by family members.
- Provide parents with lists of science-related literature to share with their youngsters at home. Also provide sources (library locations, teacher supply stores, bookstores, etc.) for that information.
- Invite parents into the classroom to discuss their science-related interests, trips, or hobbies.
- Encourage parents to schedule family field trips in which all members of the family travel to a particular site or exhibit. Consult local agencies or the Yellow Pages for locations of special places in the community.
- Keep abreast of upcoming TV shows on PBS or the Discovery Channel and provide parents with information on those programs.
- Have students prepare a calendar of upcoming events in the science text or program. These can be sent home on a regular basis—once a week or once a month.

- Interview parents about some of their interests, hobbies, activities, or vacations. Prepare this information in the form of a special classroom newsletter.
- Set up a classroom quiz show with parents and students participating together.
- Set up an exhibit in the local shopping mall including photos of parents and children working together on science projects, tips for parent participation, information sources, and other school-related activities.
- Develop a slide show or video program of classroom science projects and experiments to show parents periodically throughout the year.
- Work with a local college (how about your former professor?) to set up a parent awareness program on the science curriculum.
- Many popular magazines carry science-related articles. You may wish to clip these and distribute them to parents.
- Put a parent suggestion box in your classroom, a special location in the school, or somewhere in the local community.
- Every two weeks or so have your students prepare special "homework packets" consisting of science articles, games, pertinent worksheets, upcoming TV programs, museum exhibits, and the like.

## TEACHER TO TEACHER

I have always believed in involving parents and siblings in my kindergarten classroom activities. My project "Take Science to Lunch" has been very successful in accomplishing that goal. Each child is able to take a brown bag science project home each week with full instructions and materials to do a science experiment or activity with their family. The projects are reinforcement of the activities we have done in our classroom that week and involve very inexpensive materials. The great part of this project is that all children can take part and there is no pressure on the "busy" parents to get the project done and return it to school. Many students tell of taking their "lunches" to Grandma's or other relatives and sharing it with them. The emphasis is on the process skills of science and getting students actively involved in experiencing science.

Jim Olson
South Elementary School
Princeton, MN

## Success Tips

Parents can provide a measure of vitality and strength to your science curriculum. They can help their children understand how what is learned in the classroom relates to life outside the classroom. It is vital, therefore, that you encourage parents to take an active role in the programs and processes you implement within your science program.

### DID YOU KNOW?

Some types of fleas can leap 150 times their own length—either vertically or horizontally. That's equivalent to a human jumping 1,000 feet.

**Classroom Activity** Have students work with their parents to record the jumping and leaping abilities of family members. Who can jump the highest? Who can jump the farthest? Have students chart the results and bring them into class to share. Students may wish to discuss reasons why humans cannot jump as far or as high as many animals. ∎

Following is a compendium of techniques that are representative of successful parent outreach efforts—strategies that ensure sustained family involvement throughout the science curriculum.

- Encourage parents to participate continuously throughout the school year. Effective projects are built up over time; they are not one-shot affairs.
- Be willing to make mistakes in developing an outreach effort. Success with parent involvement in your science program may not come about the first, second, or third time.
- Be patient with parents. Some may be reluctant to get involved with your science program due to some kind of extenuating circumstances. Keep trying. Never give up on any parents.
- Encourage parents to actively participate in the science program through volunteering, observing, or sharing their science-related experiences (see Table 9.2). Keep this process as nonstressful as possible and provide a host of sharing opportunities throughout the school year.
- Parents must know that your outreach efforts are a natural and normal part of the science program and not an auxiliary service of the school designed for just a few.
- Get your students involved in the outreach effort; use them as "recruiters" for their parents. Solicit their ideas as much as possible.
- You must be a good role model for parents. You must be enthusiastic and committed to the idea of parent engagement. That enthusiasm will rub off on families and stimulate greater participation. The ultimate success of any outreach effort may be determined by the level of enthusiasm exhibited by the teacher.
- Parents need to be consistently informed about the existence and components of a program. Keep your "public relations" efforts current and long-range and provide parents with a constant flow of information. (See Figure 9.2.)

TABLE **9.2**

......................................................................................................................

# CAN YOU HELP US?

......................................................................................................................

Parents:                    Please complete the following survey and return it to school at your earliest convenience. Thank you.

---

Name:_____

Address:_____

_____

Phone number:_____

Do you collect any special objects that could be shared with students? These may include shells, bottles, old photographs, or scientific apparatus.
*I'd be happy to demonstrate my collection of:*

_____

_____

_____

Do you have an association with any special places we may visit as part of our science program? These may include construction sites, hospitals, television studios, industrial sites, and so on.
*Yes, I can arrange a visit to:*

_____

_____

_____

Do you have any special materials at home we could borrow as part of our science program? These may include antiques, memorabilia, special tools, gadgets, etc.
*Yes, I could loan you:*

_____

_____

_____

_____

Do you have any special skills that you can share as a part of our science program? These may include model building, electrical knowledge, fishing or hunting, cooking, and the like.
*I'd be willing to share the following:*

_____

_____

Does any part of your work or job involve scientific principles? This may include electronics, mechanics, plumbing, carpentry, machinery, architecture, etc.
*I can share the following parts about my job:*

_____

_____

_____

Do you know of other individuals in the community (friends, relatives, people at work) who have a special hobby or talent they could share with our class?
*Their name is:*_____

*Phone number:*_____

Is there any other information, materials, places, or data you can share with us that will help our science program?
*Yes, I can share:*

_____

_____

_____

---

## TEACHER TO TEACHER _____

At the beginning of the year or at any time you plan what might be considered "strange" activities, keep the people who need to know (parents, administrators, etc.) informed. A quick note home explaining why you are having the students do a task might very well save some red-faced explanation later on.

The first time I assigned my eighth-grade class to go home and inventory their garbage for a week resulted in several irate phone calls from parents, a couple of letters questioning my sanity, etc. The old saying, "An ounce of prevention is worth a pound of cure" applies here.

Ed Rezabeh
Glidden-Ralston Community Schools
Glidden, IA

- Communicate to parents the fact that their involvement in any outreach effort is ultimately intended for

the benefit of their children and not merely to satisfy the designs of school personnel.
- Recruit new parents whenever and wherever possible. Don't be satisfied with just a few participants in your science program, but continually seek the involvement of more families.
- When sending written information to parents, be careful not to use educational jargon. Keep your tone informal and to the point—don't talk down to parents and don't insult their intelligence.
- It is vital that you be friendly, down to earth, and truly interested in parents and their children. A sincere interest to work together will fuel any type of outreach effort.

What makes any outreach effort successful is the creative vision of educators and parents working together in a spirit of cooperation. It implies a partnership

A reproducible page to help parents

# *Talking to Parents*

BY ANTHONY D. FREDERICKS

# Science Home-work

Dear Parents:

Several national surveys have recently reported an alarming decline in science literacy on the part of our children. Consider the following: in a survey of 17 industrialized nations, U.S. ninth graders ranked 14th in terms of scientific knowledge; less than 50 percent of Americans know that the Earth moves around the sun and takes a year to do so; in a survey of five countries and four Canadian provinces, 13-year-old American students ranked almost dead last in science.

On a more encouraging note, however, is the fact that those same reports suggest that this trend can be turned around—particularly when science education begins early. Obviously, this is where parents come in. As desperate as our level of science awareness is now, many experts believe that the trend can be significantly altered when parents take time to demonstrate to their youngsters the magic, mystery and magnitude of science, right in their own homes.

Here are some ideas you can incorporate into your family activities to promote science awareness in your children.

**Around the house.** Take time on a regular basis to make some investigative trips around your house with your children. Examine the plumbing, the heating system, the structure of the house. Outside, look at the

Anthony D. Fredericks is an Assistant Professor of Education at York College, York, PA, and a Teaching Editor of *Teaching K-8*.

*There are many things parents can do to foster science awareness in their children. For starters, try some of these suggestions.*

leaves on the trees and discuss their shapes and patterns. Watch for any animals in your neighborhood and talk about their similarities and differences.

H. ROBERT LOOMIS

**Hobbies.** Encourage your children to investigate science-related hobbies. Building a short-wave radio, launching model rockets, observing the night sky through a telescope, collecting rocks or shells, can all be positive ventures for your children.

**Asking questions.** Encourage your children to ask questions about the world around them. Be a role model by frequently asking *them* questions—partic-

ularly questions for which there may be no single right answer: "What if leaves didn't fall off the trees?" "Why do you think some animals hibernate through the winter?" "What are some ways we can conserve energy?"

**The printed page.** When sharing books and stories with your children, include some biographies of well-known scientists—for example, Marie Curie, Louis Pasteur, Galileo and Robert Goddard. Also, there are many exciting new science books (fiction and nonfiction) by such authors as Seymour Simon, Eric Carle and Joanna Cole that can be part of your home library.

**School work.** Encourage your children to share any science work they are doing in school. Your interest now and throughout your children's schooling will have a significant impact on their future attitudes toward science.

**Miniature lab.** Obtain an inexpensive book of simple science experiments (your school or local librarian can recommend several) and set up a miniature lab in the kitchen, basement or corner of a child's room. Participate in several of the experiments. Encourage your children to keep a log of observations and discoveries made during the experiments.

By making science a regular part of your family times together, you'll be providing your children with valuable scientific experiences and attitudes that can last a lifetime. ↓

Reproduce this column and send it home to parents.

**FIGURE 9.2** Reproducible parent letter

based on common goals, common ideals, and common needs. Above all, strong projects are predicated on the desire of all individuals to work for the total science literacy of every youngster. The bond built between home and school can be one of the most powerful determinants of your effectiveness as a teacher of science—both now and well into the future. Engaging parents in the dynamics of your science curriculum is a challenging task but also one of the most rewarding. When teachers and parents join together, students are afforded educational opportunities that go far beyond the classroom.

## TEACHER TO TEACHER

One of the wonderful things about teaching science is that it invites participation by all age levels. I have routinely had "Parent Participation Science" assignments for my students.

These are simple experiments that can be done at home by students with the help of their parents. I sent a laboratory assessment sheet entitled "Which Egg Is Hard-Boiled?" home with the students and asked the parents to help the student run the experiment, record the results, and come up with some sort of conclusion. All went well until one day I had a grumpy, red-haired young lady hand me a blank paper. I asked what had happened and why she was so unhappy. She replied, "Everything started out pretty well until my Dad came home. He decided that he needed to check what I had done and added some more eggs just to make it a little more challenging. He used at least a dozen eggs, and for all I know he is still trying to find out different ways to decide which one is hard-boiled. I do know that I'm going to wait and do my home experiments over at Grandma's from now on!"

Judith I. Vandel
Laramie County School District #1
Cheyenne, WY

## LEARNING CENTERS

Learning centers provide students with valuable opportunities to use scientific knowledge in real-life independent activities. Centers are usually designed to offer a variety of materials, designs, and media through which students can work by themselves or with others to operationalize the information learned in the classroom. Centers are designed to enhance the learning of concepts, skills, themes, or topics. This learning can take place after a topic is presented to students, during the course of a presentation, or as an initial introduction to material in the text.

Learning centers are an important adjunct to the classroom science program for several reasons:

- They allow students to make independent decisions about what to learn and how that information will be learned.
- Students' curiosity is stimulated when they are engaged in activities that match their interests.
- Students can take an active role in the planning, design, and use of centers, thus stimulating their total involvement in the science program.
- Students can apply new learning in unique and practical situations that may deviate from those used by the teacher.
- Students develop a sense of responsibility when they are provided with relevant opportunities to chart the course of their own learning.
- Learning centers offer a host of instructional possibilities—enough to satisfy the needs, interests, and desires of most students.

- Teachers and students can work hand in hand in the production and implementation of learning activities.
- Learning centers can meet both the immediate and long-range goals of teachers and students.

Blackburn and Powell (1976) have outlined three different types of learning centers that can be set up in the classroom:

- *Enrichment centers.* Enrichment centers are designed to offer youngsters a variety of learning alternatives as an adjunct to a common unit of instruction. These centers are typically used after the presentation of important materials or concepts and are designed to

provide students with opportunities to enhance their appreciation and understanding of the topics through individual experiences in the center. For example, after the teacher has presented a lesson on the life cycle of plants, individual students may be assigned to a center with the following components:

Construction of a terrarium using soil, several plants, rocks, etc.

Observing several plants under the microscope

Designing an individual observation kit for use in the field

Preparation of several foods using different types of common plants

Various news articles on the applications of plants in our daily lives

Creative writing on the uses and misuses of plants in modern society

A filmstrip on the implications of acid rain on plant life

Painting a mural on the stages of plant growth

- Enrichment centers require teachers to be aware of the learning styles of their students as well as their knowledge about a topic. The enrichment center can provide individual students with varied activities or a combination of activities different from those pursued by other students. Thus the center represents an individualized approach to the promotion of science.
- *Skill centers.* Skill centers are similar to enrichment centers in that they are used after the teaching of a concept or skill. The difference lies in the fact that students are assigned particular areas in the skill center as opposed to having free choice of the topics to pursue. Thus, after introductory instruction on a particular concept, the teacher can assign students to various parts of the center to reinforce the information presented in class. The implication is that teachers must be aware of the various skill needs of their students to effectively assign individuals to the areas where the proper skills can be strengthened.
- *Interest and exploratory centers.* Interest and exploratory centers differ from enrichment centers and skill centers in that they are designed to capitalize on the interests of students. They may not match the content of the text or the science curriculum; rather, the intent is to provide students with hands-on experiences with science that they can pursue according to their own pace and level of curiosity. These centers can be set up throughout the classroom, with students engaging in their own selection of activities during free time, upon arrival in the morning, as a free-choice activity during the day, or just prior to dismissal. The advantage of these centers is that they allow students to engage in meaning-

ful discoveries that match their individual interests without requiring them to follow the sequence of concepts designed by the teacher or the curriculum.

- The success of this form of learning center is dependent on the teacher's knowledge of the interests of his or her students. Teachers may wish to design an interest inventory (see Table 9.3) to help pinpoint the specific areas that should be used in the center. Such an inventory provides important information that can promote individual access to scientific principles.

## Parts of a Learning Center

A learning center is a space set aside in the classroom that allows easy access to a variety of learning materials in an interesting and productive manner. The design of a learning center is limited only by the creativity of the individuals who put it together. Teachers should feel free to work with their students in creating a center that students will want to use. Such shared responsibility ensures that students have a sense of ownership in the center and will be more willing to engage in the activities.

The following list provides a number of options to consider for a center. It is important to understand that no two centers will be the same. Centers have ranged from elaborate displays to a card table set in the back of a room. You are encouraged to establish learning centers as formally or informally as you wish; the primary criterion is that they match student interests with curricular needs.

1. *Title.* Provide an interesting title that identifies the center as distinct from other classroom activities. The more creative center titles are, the more students' interests will be piqued. For example, labeling a center "Bugs" may not stimulate interest, but a title such as "Creepy, Crawly, Crunchy Things" may spark students' curiosity.
2. *Furniture.* Necessary furniture should be arranged in a pleasing and productive manner. Decide how chairs, tables(s), storage facilities, and other pieces will be set up. What furniture do you have in the room? What furniture will have to be obtained from other locations? Make certain furniture is of a size appropriate for the class.
3. *Storage.* Materials need to be kept in a safe place that is easily accessible to students. There should be a sufficient quantity of needed materials or a ready source of those items in the event of depletion, breakage, or loss.

TABLE 9.3

............................................................................................

# INTEREST INVENTORY

............................................................................................

Directions: Here is a list of things students like to read about and things students like to do. Circle the number after each item to show how interested you are in that particular choice

| 1. I like to read about ... | | Very much | | Some-times | | Very little |
|---|---|---|---|---|---|---|
| a. | adventures | 5 | 4 | 3 | 2 | 1 |
| b. | animals | 5 | 4 | 3 | 2 | 1 |
| c. | art/music/dance | 5 | 4 | 3 | 2 | 1 |
| d. | careers | 5 | 4 | 3 | 2 | 1 |
| e. | cars/motorcycles | 5 | 4 | 3 | 2 | 1 |
| f. | comedy | 5 | 4 | 3 | 2 | 1 |
| g. | cooking/food | 5 | 4 | 3 | 2 | 1 |
| h. | exercise/health | 5 | 4 | 3 | 2 | 1 |
| i. | famous people | 5 | 4 | 3 | 2 | 1 |
| j. | fashion | 5 | 4 | 3 | 2 | 1 |
| k. | foreign lands | 5 | 4 | 3 | 2 | 1 |
| l. | games | 5 | 4 | 3 | 2 | 1 |
| m. | history | 5 | 4 | 3 | 2 | 1 |
| n. | human body | 5 | 4 | 3 | 2 | 1 |
| o. | insects | 5 | 4 | 3 | 2 | 1 |
| p. | make-believe | 5 | 4 | 3 | 2 | 1 |
| q. | model cars/planes | 5 | 4 | 3 | 2 | 1 |
| r. | mysteries | 5 | 4 | 3 | 2 | 1 |
| s. | painting/drawing | 5 | 4 | 3 | 2 | 1 |
| t. | plants | 5 | 4 | 3 | 2 | 1 |
| u. | romance/love | 5 | 4 | 3 | 2 | 1 |
| v. | science/science fiction | 5 | 4 | 3 | 2 | 1 |
| w. | self-defense | 5 | 4 | 3 | 2 | 1 |
| x. | sewing/embroidery | 5 | 4 | 3 | 2 | 1 |
| y. | space | 5 | 4 | 3 | 2 | 1 |
| z. | sports | 5 | 4 | 3 | 2 | 1 |
| aa. | stamps | 5 | 4 | 3 | 2 | 1 |
| bb. | transportation | 5 | 4 | 3 | 2 | 1 |
| cc. | trivia | 5 | 4 | 3 | 2 | 1 |
| dd. | war/armed services | 5 | 4 | 3 | 2 | 1 |
| ee. | world events | 5 | 4 | 3 | 2 | 1 |
| ff. | other_____ | 5 | 4 | 3 | 2 | 1 |

| 2. I like to ... | | | | | | |
|---|---|---|---|---|---|---|
| a. | build model planes/cars | 5 | 4 | 3 | 2 | 1 |
| b. | collect things | 5 | 4 | 3 | 2 | 1 |
| c. | go camping | 5 | 4 | 3 | 2 | 1 |
| d. | go swimming | 5 | 4 | 3 | 2 | 1 |
| e. | go to the movies | 5 | 4 | 3 | 2 | 1 |
| f. | go to museums | 5 | 4 | 3 | 2 | 1 |
| g. | listen to music | 5 | 4 | 3 | 2 | 1 |
| h. | paint | 5 | 4 | 3 | 2 | 1 |
| i. | play a musical instrument | 5 | 4 | 3 | 2 | 1 |
| j. | play sports | 5 | 4 | 3 | 2 | 1 |
| k. | play table games | 5 | 4 | 3 | 2 | 1 |
| l. | play with animals | 5 | 4 | 3 | 2 | 1 |
| m. | read comic books | 5 | 4 | 3 | 2 | 1 |
| n. | ride bicycles/skateboards | 5 | 4 | 3 | 2 | 1 |
| o. | travel | 5 | 4 | 3 | 2 | 1 |
| p. | watch television | 5 | 4 | 3 | 2 | 1 |
| q. | other_____ | 5 | 4 | 3 | 2 | 1 |
| r. | other_____ | 5 | 4 | 3 | 2 | 1 |
| s. | other_____ | 5 | 4 | 3 | 2 | 1 |

TABLE **9.3** (*Continued*)

## INTEREST INVENTORY

**3. I like to read ...**

| | | | | | | |
|---|---|---|---|---|---|---|
| a. | comic books | 5 | 4 | 3 | 2 | 1 |
| b. | direction sheets | 5 | 4 | 3 | 2 | 1 |
| c. | encyclopedias | 5 | 4 | 3 | 2 | 1 |
| d. | funnies | 5 | 4 | 3 | 2 | 1 |
| e. | hardback books | 5 | 4 | 3 | 2 | 1 |
| f. | junk mail | 5 | 4 | 3 | 2 | 1 |
| g. | library books | 5 | 4 | 3 | 2 | 1 |
| h. | magazines | 5 | 4 | 3 | 2 | 1 |
| i. | newspapers | 5 | 4 | 3 | 2 | 1 |
| j. | novels | 5 | 4 | 3 | 2 | 1 |
| k. | paperback books | 5 | 4 | 3 | 2 | 1 |
| l. | textbooks | 5 | 4 | 3 | 2 | 1 |
| m. | television program guides | 5 | 4 | 3 | 2 | 1 |
| s. | other_____ | 5 | 4 | 3 | 2 | 1 |

4. *Space.* Consideration should be given to the use of space within the center. Where will the activities take place? Is there a need for independent study? Will large or small group instruction take place within the center?

5. *Materials.* How will materials be obtained? Is it possible to obtain materials from parents or the school? (See Figure 9.3.) You may also want to consider other sources, such as local businesses, catalog supply houses, or community agencies. It is important to go over the location and use of all materials with your students prior to initiating the center.

6. *Location.* What is the best location for a center? Should it be placed in the front of the classroom, along a wall, next to a window, or in the back adjacent to a sink? Your choice for the location of a center should also allow students to have a place in which to store their unfinished as well as completed projects.

7. *Responsibility.* An important consideration in the development of any center pertains to the responsibilities of students and teacher. For example, students need to know who is responsible for cleaning up, who will make sure that there is an adequate supply of consumable materials (paper, paint, soil, water, etc.), who is in charge of evaluation, and so on. These duties need to be established early on. The more responsibilities students are assigned within a center, the more successful that center will be. Students should have a sense of ownership in the design and functioning of a center in order to profit from that center.

8. *Learning alternatives.* There should be a variety of learning alternatives within a center. For example, a variety of tasks ranging from difficult to simple may be included. Activities relating to various student interests should also be included in the center. The use of both independent and small group activities may be part of your plan. In addition, consider the need to change the activities at frequent intervals.

9. *Instructions.* For each of the activities in a center, there should be a set of instructions indicating the specific steps or procedures students need to go through to successfully accomplish the learning tasks. Students must know what to do, where to find information, what resources are available, what to do with the results of their investigations (how to record or display the products), and what type of assessment will follow. Activity cards should be written so that students can read them independently. Are all the directions for a center written at a level comprehensible by all students in the classroom? If not, it may be possible to supplement written directions with audiotape recordings for particular activities.

10. *Sequence of activities.* Many centers appear to be nothing more than a collection of random activities, each separate from the others. It may be important to consider how activities within a center will be sequenced. Will students need to complete one or more basic activities before moving on to more complex ones? The answer to this question will allow you to select activities in keeping with the various skill levels in your classroom.

Dear Parents,

Helping your child grow in science will be an important part of our studies this year. Your child will be able to examine the wide world of science through a variety of exciting and interesting science projects.

Many of our projects will require the use of materials commonly found in the home. Could you please assist us by offering to donate some of the items on the attached list? Your child has checked those that he or she feels you may be able to contribute. Whatever else you can donate will certainly be appreciated. Please feel free to contact me if you have any questions or concerns. Thank you in advance.

Sincerely,

| | | |
|---|---|---|
| ☐ food coloring | ☐ plastic wrap—one roll | ☐ corks |
| ☐ clay | ☐ coat hangers | ☐ petroleum jelly |
| ☐ waxed paper | ☐ marbles | ☐ stockings |
| ☐ crayons | ☐ birdseed | ☐ styrofoam cups |
| ☐ scissors | ☐ paint | ☐ baby food jars |
| ☐ measuring cup | ☐ aluminum foil | ☐ teaspoons |
| ☐ knives | ☐ sponges | ☐ jar lids |
| ☐ paper cups | ☐ masking tape | ☐ baseball |
| ☐ stopwatch | ☐ colored cellophane | ☐ liquid bleach |
| ☐ string | ☐ spoons | ☐ paper bags |
| ☐ paper towels | ☐ jars | ☐ golf tees |
| ☐ seeds | ☐ magnifying glass | ☐ golf balls |
| ☐ candles | ☐ thermometer | ☐ silicon glue |
| ☐ sugar | ☐ newspaper | ☐ straws |
| ☐ cardboard | ☐ toothpicks | ☐ metal washers |
| ☐ cotton balls | ☐ copper wire | ☐ shoe boxes |
| ☐ salt | ☐ magnets | ☐ pill or film containers |
| ☐ wool | ☐ baking soda | ☐ plastic gallon milk cartons |
| ☐ bobby pins | ☐ plastic bags | ☐ yogurt containers with lids |
| ☐ pepper | ☐ coffee cans | ☐ shallow cake dish |
| ☐ wire | ☐ cigar box | ☐ cereal |

**FIGURE 9.3**   Materials request form for parents

11. *Number of centers.* You will need to decide on the number of centers to establish in your classroom. This decision will be based on your management skills as well as the needs of your students. You may wish to start with a single center and, as you and your students gain more competence in designing and using the center, develop additional centers later in the school year. You may decide to set up one or more centers for a general area of the curriculum (e.g., life science) or a variety of centers for specific areas of the curriculum.

12. *Number of students.* How many children will be able to work at a center at one time? Should students work independently, or is it possible to have them work together on the same task?

13. *Duration of centers.* You will need to decide how long a center or group of centers will remain in existence. Keeping a center in operation for several months may diminish student enthusiasm about its importance or utility. A center should be kept in operation only as long as students' interests are high and it meets the instructional goals of your program. It may be advisable to introduce new centers at fairly regular intervals throughout the year and eliminate those that have accomplished their objectives. Don't wait for students to tire of a center; rather, introduce new centers well before the others have outlived their usefulness.

14. *Home extensions.* It is valuable to plan center activities that extend learning opportunities into the home. Which of the designated activities could be pursued using materials and facilities available at home? How can parents contribute to the mastery of important concepts through simple projects? You may wish to design task cards or process sheets that allow parents and their children to investigate an area of concern together.

15. *Management system.* A good learning center provides a workable management system for both teachers and students. The management system indicates how students will use a center, which students tackle which activities, when the center is used, and how progress is charted or recorded. Center management systems can include one or more of the following features:

- Students record observations and discoveries in a personal journal.
- A pegboard is set up in the center, with students' names displayed under the activities to which they are assigned.
- A large chart is drawn on posterboard listing students' names across the top and the center's activities down the left side. Students check off activities as they are completed.

- Library pockets are mounted on a sheet of cardboard with a student's name written on each one. As a student completes an activity, the name of the activity is recorded on an index card and placed in the pocket.
- Each student is given a file folder into which he or she places skill sheets, written entries, an observation list, and similar records for teacher evaluation.
- An assignment sheet is posted for each student. Each sheet contains the name of the student, the specific activities to be accomplished within the center, dates and times when activities were started and finished, and the objectives fulfilled within the center.
- Envelopes, tin cans, shoe boxes, or other containers can be used by students to store index cards or slips of paper on which they have recorded data on their completion of center activities.

## IDEA BOX

After you and your students have constructed a learning center, be sure to take a photograph of the completed center. Keep a file of these photos, and over the years you will compile a permanent record of all your centers. Then it will be no trouble to decide what kinds of centers to set up in later years; you'll have all the data at your fingertips.

16. *Time.* An important decision concerns the amount of time students will spend at a learning center. Will all students spend the same amount of time, or will the time be adjusted according to their interests and skill levels? The ideal center allows children to proceed at their own pace within a designated time period. Your knowledge of the students in your classroom will help you decide whether extended or brief periods of time are necessary for students to accomplish center activities.

17. *Individualization.* It is not necessary for every student in your classroom to tackle every activity within a learning center. To do so defeats the purpose of a center, which is to provide youngsters with independent learning opportunities in accordance with their needs or interest. You and your students will need to decide which individuals will use which centers or which activities within a center. Such a decision is important in ensuring that centers do not become a formalized part of the science program but a comfortable and informal means of learning and practicing science.

18. *Assessment.* Decisions need to be made on the nature and form of assessment for the center(s). Will

assessment be the responsibility of the students or the teacher? How will it be accomplished—informally (discussions, observations) or formally (skills test, chapter exam)? Not all centers lend themselves to assessment, nor should they. You will need to decide what, if any, evaluation will take place and what will be done with the results.

## What Centers Are Not

Learning centers offer limitless possibilities for student explorations into a host of hands-on experiences with science. However, some important considerations must be kept in mind both prior to and during the use of centers. Cohen, Staley, and Horak (1989) have provided some important ideas on what centers should *not* become.

- Centers should not become places where students go to fill extra time for the remainder of a period. Centers should be designed as integral parts of the science curriculum, not as something done "just for fun" after other classroom assignments are completed.
- Learning centers should not serve as part of a reward system for students. Students who finish work assignments early are often allowed to use other resources in the classroom. As a result, slower children are denied the opportunity to benefit from those experiences. Learning centers must be set up to ensure equal access by all individuals. When children of all ability levels have the opportunity to work together, they can learn from each other.
- Learning centers should not be designed to match achievement groups in the classroom. In other words, one center for high-achieving youngsters, one for the middle range of students, and one for students of a lower achievement level would be an inappropriate use of the learning center concept. It is important that students have sufficient opportunities to work together in cooperative groups—sharing decisions, making investigations, designing learning outcomes, and discussing products and results.

A learning center should not be a system in which student academic differences are accentuated but one in which students work in tandem to make new discoveries and reinforce previously learned skills. It is important that students have frequent opportunities to interact not only with the center activities, but with each other as well. The creation of a mutual support system among students is at the heart of an effective learning system. Students should understand that a center is not a competitive series of activities but a means of extending a wealth of learning potentialities to each and every student in the classroom.

The most successful learning centers in science are those in which teachers and students have an equal say in their design and operation. In other words, students will benefit from center activities if they are given a voice in determining how those activities are planned and accomplished. Learning centers provide some interesting possibilities for providing youngsters with a heightened sense of responsibility for their own learning.

## Learning Center Checklist

Complete the following checklist both prior to and during the operation of a center or series of learning centers.

_____ Have I chosen a topic that will be interesting and exciting for my students?

_____ Have I chosen a topic in keeping with the design of the science curriculum?

_____ Have I designed activities that my students can read and understand?

_____ Have I designed activity cards that will hold up over a long period of time (laminated, bound in a notebook)?

_____ Have I developed activities that are sequential in nature?

_____ Have I allowed students to take an active role in the design and maintenance of the center?

_____ Have I provided opportunities for students of varying ability levels?

_____ Do the activities have a purpose or are they related to specific science objectives?

_____ Have I considered specific time limits for each activity or a group of activities?

_____ Have I considered all the consumable and non-consumable materials necessary for the center?

_____ Have I provided students with a method to record their results or observations?

_____ Have I included a variety of evaluation measures through which students can chart their progress?

_____ Have I included both individual and small group activities?

_____ Have I considered activities that can be pursued by parents and children together?

_____ Have I arranged the furniture and surrounding area in an attractive manner?

_____ Will students learn to appreciate or understand a particular area of science as a result of using this center?

_____ Were my instructions clear, concise, and easy to follow?

## Example: Geology Learning Center

### Possible Activities

1. Collect three different types of rocks from outside the school.
2. Make a scrapbook of rock pictures cut from old magazines.
3. Classify each of ten rocks into one of three categories.
4. Put a piece of pumice in water. What happens?
5. Write a story about your life as a geologist.
6. Create a cartoon about the explorations of a famous geologist.
7. Make a salt map of your neighborhood, listing the locations of various rock types.
8. Use a hand lens to observe various rocks in the box.
9. Arrange several rocks in the terrarium.
10. Put together puzzles on rock facts.
11. Classify several rocks according to Moh's scale.
12. Watch filmstrip on the creation of the Grand Canyon.

### Materials and Resources

1. Videotaped interview with professor from a local college.
2. Materials for a terrarium: soil, rocks, plants, etc.
3. Puzzle of rock types.
4. Library books on different geological formations.
5. Many examples of different types of rocks.
6. Gloves, hammers, burlap.
7. Old newspapers, magazines, scissors, glue, construction paper.
8. Filmstrips, transparencies.
9. Graph paper.
10. Boxes, tin cans, index cards.

**DID YOU KNOW?** ⎯⎯⎯⎯⎯⎯⎯⎯⎯⎯⎯⎯⎯⎯⎯

A region in the Atacama Desert in Chile known as Calama has never experienced rain—ever!

**Classroom Activity**   Have students investigate the similarities and differences among various deserts of the world. For example, what makes the Mojave Desert in California so special? What are some of the distinguishing features of the Gobi Desert in Asia? Does a desert need to have sand in order to be a desert? What kinds of animals typically live in a desert environment? ■

# SCIENCE FAIRS

Ever since the late 1920s, science fairs have been an annual event at many schools around the country. A science fair offers students a showcase for their investigations and discoveries. It has the potential to be a major, exciting school event.

An individual science fair project may be a presentation of an experiment, a demonstration, a research effort, a collection of scientific items, or a display of scientific apparatus. It represents the efforts of a student's investigation into some area of interest and provides a way for the student to demonstrate the results of the investigation. A science fair project is a unique way for students to satisfy their own curiosity about the world around them and to pose questions for which they must seek out answers. It is a venture into the world of scientific research that goes beyond lessons in the classroom or chapters in a book. Through the development of science fair projects, students gain a first-hand appreciation of the work of scientists and the value of their discoveries. Projects allow students to experiment, make decisions, form and re-form hypotheses, test and examine ideas, seek solutions, and most important, learn more about themselves and their world. Science fair projects consist of three essential components:

- *Display unit.* The display unit forms the background for the project. It should be built of sturdy materials to provide a structure for a vertical display of graphs, charts, photographs, and other printed information. Usually three-sided, it will include the name of the project as well as other information vital to observers.
- *Exhibit materials.* The exhibit materials consist of items collected or demonstrated by the student, a set of apparatus, or the experiment the student carried out during his or her investigation. Display materials give the science project a three-dimensional effect and allow others to observe the actual materials involved in the student's investigation.
- *Written report.* It is important for students to keep a written record of their investigations. This record outlines the original problem and the means and methods used to investigate it. The written report should be accurate and easy to read, and it should give a clear summary of the entire project.

## How-tos for the successful science fair

Putting on a science fair can intimidate even the most ambitious educator. The amount of time and work that

precedes a successful fair may be enormous. Nevertheless, the payoffs can be tremendous: students with an increased awareness of the importance of science in their lives who are able to investigate areas of interest to add to that knowledge base.

Following are some suggestions teachers should consider in preparing students for a science fair. These ideas should be employed in the weeks preceding a fair as well as during the fair itself. They will help to make the science fair an event that students look forward to in succeeding years.

1. *The reward is in the doing.* It should be emphasized to students that the object of the science fair is not to win first place or a blue ribbon, but simply to participate. Some students may suspect that this is not the case. Teachers can ignite student interest by announcing that everyone who enters will receive some form of recognition—whether it be a letter of appreciation or an announcement in the school newsletter. In short, everyone who enters wins.

2. *Tie the fair to other subjects.* Many science fairs are done in isolation from other areas of learning. The fair should be an integral part of the entire curriculum. For example, writing the project

report can be part of English lessons. Research for the project can be part of reading lessons. Math skills can be reinforced through the measurement or estimation of amounts and quantities involved in the project. Social studies lessons can include profiles of famous scientists and their contributions. In short, a "whole curriculum" approach to science fairs can maximize interest and participation.

3. *Involve the whole school in the team.* Teachers should work with other individuals in the school to develop a team approach to the science fair. For example, the librarian can prepare a special display of books about science experiments, famous scientists, scientific information, or fiction with science themes (see Appendix C). The principal can visit the class to talk about the importance of science fairs. The school's reading specialist can present a story or book with a science theme. Other teachers can visit to share science-related hobbies or areas of interest.

4. *Involve the community.* Students should be involved in promoting the science fair outside the school. For example, students can:

- Create a classroom or school newsletter.
- Distribute letters and notes to parents.
- Send invitations to school administrators or other district officials.
- Write news releases about the fair and send them to the local newspaper.
- Extend invitations to local scientists or college professors to visit classrooms and demonstrate scientific principles.
- Invite parents and other community members to bring in rock collections, telescopes, or vacation slides to share with the class.

Students may wish to promote the science fair throughout the school by setting up panel discussions in different classrooms (selected students can be designated experts in particular fields). In addition, pupils may want to prepare a demonstration for an all-school assembly, conduct a question-and-answer quiz show via the intercom system, or produce a special videotape for younger students.

Finally, special displays or projects set up around the school, especially if they are constructed by many different students, can go a long way toward stimulating interest and high levels of participation.

5. *Keep parents informed.* For many parents, the thought of an impending science fair is intimidating, to say the least. It is important to let parents know that the school is eager to work with them to ensure the success of the science fair for all students. Special newsletters can be prepared and sent home on a regular basis, parents can be called pe-

riodically with offers of assistance or guidance in project preparation, or after-school meetings can be scheduled to alleviate fears and uncertainties about an upcoming fair as well as to provide guidelines for project completion. It is important that parents understand that they should support their children's efforts, not construct their projects.

6. *Establish a long-range timetable and stick to it.* A major factor in unsuccessful science fair projects is lack of proper planning. A timetable should be established to ensure that students allot enough time for investigation of their areas of interest. It is important that students and parents understand that science projects must be investigated and constructed over a period of time and cannot be done in one or two evenings preceding the fair.

7. *Join forces.* Successful science fairs often are the result of a group effort. Teachers should work together, establishing partnerships and planning the event jointly. Parents and community members with science backgrounds should be located and made integral members of the planning team. These "outsiders" can be invited to visit the classroom regularly to assist the teacher and the students in designing individual projects as well as the entire science fair. There is no need to work in isolation; a joint effort may be just the ticket for a productive and successful event.

8. *Keep the principal or supervisor informed.* Good communication is essential to a successful science fair. Administrators should be involved in the dynamics of the fair and frequently solicited for their advice on how to promote students' efforts.

9. *Keep it exciting; make it fun!* Above all, teachers need to demonstrate by their own behavior that science fair projects are fun. A teacher's attitude toward the fair goes a long way toward ensuring its success. Students should experience the enthusiasm of the teacher; this enthusiasm will carry over to the event.

**TEACHER TO TEACHER** _____

In preparing my students for the science fair each year, I have found that a picture truly is worth a thousand words. Each year I photograph individual science fair projects with color slide film. Over the years I have accumulated a large collection of slides depicting a variety of excellent projects. To introduce my students to science fair project preparation, I spend a class period showing slides from previous years. As we view the slides, we discuss how to choose a topic, formulate a hypothesis, design an experiment, record data, and display the results attractively. By viewing outstanding projects from previous science fairs, my children quickly grasp the rudiments of putting together a topnotch project. To promote the science fair throughout my school, I offer my slide col-

lection to all teachers. Not surprisingly, our school has one of the best elementary science fairs in the system!

Laura Candler
Edgewood Elementary School
Fayetteville, NC

## Keys to a Successful Project

The success of a science fair project can be judged by a number of standards, but it should *not* be measured by ribbons, trophies, or other awards. If a student has selected a topic, investigated it according to a planned design, and reported the results of that investigation in the form of a display and written report, then that student has succeeded. Winning "first place" or being "grand champion" is certainly praiseworthy, but the purpose of taking part in the fair is to investigate an area of interest and discover new things about it. The satisfaction of making those discoveries will last far longer than the satisfaction of winning blue ribbons or gold medals.

Table 9.4 on page 196 presents a list of factors that can be used to help students develop and evaluate science fair projects, both during the investigation process and during the construction of the final project.

## Timetable

Successful science fair projects take planning. Trying to put a project and report together a few nights before the scheduled opening can lead to disaster. Besides submitting a hastily constructed project, the student fails to develop an appreciation for the time and effort required for a scientific investigation. Planning a project well in advance allows sufficient time for the necessary research, the construction of the display, the writing of the report, and the assembly of the final project. It also provides some leeway should difficulties arise in research or in obtaining vital materials.

The timetable presented in Table 9.5 on page 197 can be used to help students adequately plan for the science fair. It is a 12-week timetable—an amount of time sufficient to design a project, gather necessary data, develop a written report, and follow through on all components of a science fair project.

As soon as the date of the fair becomes known, the student should use a calendar to count back 12 weeks from the opening date to determine when preparations should begin. For example, if a science fair is scheduled for April 1, the 12-week preparation should begin on January 1.

TABLE   **9.4**

......................................................................................................

# GUIDELINES FOR SCIENCE FAIR PROJECTS

......................................................................................................

_____  *Does the project represent the student's own work?*

Although students may receive help in investigating their topics and designing their respective projects, the final effort must be the student's—not that of a scientist, teacher, parent, or other adult.

_____  *Is the project the result of careful planning?*

Sucessful projects cannot be accomplished overnight. They are the outcome of a systematic plan of action carried out over a period of time. A hastily constructed project undermines the value of the science fair.

_____  *Does the project demonstrate the student's creativity and resourcefulness?*

Students should be encouraged to contribute their own ideas and ingenuity to the design and development of a particular project.

_____  *Does the project indicate a thorough understanding of the chosen topic?*

Students need to investigate their chosen area as completely as possible. Doing so will take time. The project must reflect the results of investigations done over an extended period.

_____  *Does the project include a notebook, written record, or final report?*

The display should include a written summary of the investigation. Such a record provides observers with additional information on the subject and documents the student's work.

_____  *Does the project include a number of visual aids?*

Photographs, charts, diagrams, graphs, tables, drawings, or even paintings liven up any display and make it more interesting.

_____  *Is the project sturdy and well constructed?*

Using the proper materials and being careful in assembling a project are important, particularly if the display will be standing for several days. It must be within the required size limitations and should reflect a degree of permanence.

_____  *Are all signs and lettering neat and accurate?*

The quality of a display is often judged by the attractiveness of signs, titles, and written descriptions.

_____  *Does the project meet all safety requirements?*

When electrical items, specimens, or chemicals are used in a display, care must be taken to ensure the safety of observers. The display of any live organisms is discouraged.

_____  *Is the display three-dimensional?*

In addition to the background and accompanying written report, the inclusion of samples, apparatus, collections, or other items is vital to the project. These should be attractively arranged in front of the background display.

_____  *Is all information accurate?*

Data gathered from outside resources, such as printed materials or interviews with experts, and data obtained from experiments must be presented accurately. All questions about data must be resolved before the data is used in a report or on a display.

_____  *Does the display present a complete story?*

The student should illustrate the topic chosen for investigation, what was done during the investigation, the results, and a conclusion. In other words, the project should have a beginning, a middle, and an end.

---

## Helping Students Select a Topic

Choosing an appropriate topic for a science fair project is often the most difficult part of the entire process; there are so many topics to choose from and a wealth of information available on each. No wonder students are bewildered. Teachers can help provide direction and narrow down choices, but the final choice of topic should be the student's. His or her motivation will be a critical factor in the successful completion of the project. Teachers can pose the following questions to their students to help them refine their choices and decide on the most suitable area to explore.

### Interests

- What kinds of things do you enjoy doing?
- What kind of science interests you the most?
- If you could be a scientist, what would you like to do?
- What are your hobbies or free-time activities?
- What do you like to do on rainy days?
- What kinds of books do you like to read?
- Which movies or TV shows might give you ideas or information?
- What are your special skills or talents?

TABLE **9.5**

....................................................................................................

## 12-WEEK TIMETABLE
....................................................................................................

Date of the science fair_____

Date to begin working on the project (12 weeks prior to the opening date)_____

| Scheduled Completion Date | Actual Completion Date | |
|---|---|---|
| _____ | _____ | *Week 1*<br>Choose a topic or problem to investigate.<br>Make a list of resources (school library, community library, places to write, people to interview). |
| _____ | _____ | *Week 2*<br>Select your reading material.<br>Begin preliminary investigations.<br>Write for additional information from business firms, government agencies, or other pertinent sources.<br>Start a notebook for keeping records.<br>Write down or sketch preliminary designs for your display |
| _____ | _____ | *Week 3*<br>Complete initial research.<br>Interview experts for more information.<br>Decide how to set up your investigation or experiment.<br>Decide what materials you will use in the display.<br>Set up the experimental design. |
| _____ | _____ | *Week 4*<br>Begin organizing and reading the materials sent in response to your letters.<br>Decide whether you need additional material from outside sources.<br>Begin collecting or buying materials for your display.<br>Begin setting up your experiment or demonstration.<br>Add information to your project notebook as you get it.<br>Start your collection or experiment. |
| _____ | _____ | *Week 5*<br>Learn how to use any apparatus you need.<br>Continue recording notes and observations in your notebook.<br>Set up an outline for the written report. |
| _____ | _____ | *Week 6*<br>Gather preliminary information in your notebook.<br>Work on the first draft of your written report. |
| _____ | _____ | *Week 7*<br>Start assembling the unit display.<br>Continue recording notes.<br>Check books, pamphlets, and magazines for additional ideas.<br>Verify information with experts (teachers, professors, scientists, parents). |
| _____ | _____ | *Week 8*<br>Begin designing charts, graphs, or other visual aids for display.<br>Take any photographs you need.<br>Record any observations on the experiment.<br>Begin preparing signs, titles, and labels for the display unit. |
| _____ | _____ | *Week 9*<br>Have photographs developed and enlarged.<br>Talk with experts again to make sure your work is accurate and on schedule.<br>Begin writing the second draft of your report.<br>Continue recording observations in your notebook. |

TABLE **9.5** (*Continued*)

...............................................................................................................................

# 12-WEEK TIMETABLE

...............................................................................................................................

_____   _____   *Week 10*
Write text for the background of your display and plan its layout.
Complete graphs, charts, and visual aids.
Finish constructing your display.
Work on the final draft of your written report.

_____   _____   *Week 11*
Complete your experiment or collection.
Write and type the final copy of your written report.
Do the lettering of the explanations and mount them on your display.
Mount graphs, charts, drawings, and photographs.
Assemble apparatus or collection items and check them against your list.

_____   _____   *Week 12*
Proofread your written report.
Set up the display at home and check it for any flaws (leave it standing for two days).
Carefully take the display apart and transport it to the science fair site.
Set up the display.
Check and double-check everything.
Congratulate yourself!

## Difficulty Level

- How hard will this topic be for you to understand?
- What problems have you had with this subject before?
- Are you familiar with this topic, or is it brand new?
- Do you think you will need to gather a lot of outside information?
- Will you be able to work in this area for 12 weeks and still be interested?
- What special tools or apparatus do you think you'll need?

## Time

- Will you be able to spend some time on this project every week for 12 weeks?
- How long do you think you will need to gather information about this topic?
- Are you interested enough in this subject to spend a great deal of time on it?
- Will you need to set up a special schedule to complete all the things you need to do?
- Do you have enough free time at home to work on the project?

## Materials

- What special materials do you think you'll need for this project?
- Do you have those materials at home, or will you need to buy them?

- Will you need to construct anything complicated?
- Will you need help in putting the display together?
- Will you need to order any materials through the mail?
- Will you be able to buy materials in local stores?
- Will your materials be inexpensive or costly?

## Guidance

- How much help will you need with your project?
- Will you be able to do most or all of the work yourself?
- Will you need to consult any experts in your chosen field?
- How much involvement will your parents have?
- Will you be able to build the display unit on your own?

## Safety

- Will you be able to follow all safety rules in putting your project together?
- Are there any dangers from equipment or materials associated with your project?
- Will there be any dangers to observers of your project?
- Will there be any danger to you at any time during the investigation of this project?

Often students will select a topic simply because everyone else has selected it. (That's why there are so many volcanoes and solar system displays at most science fairs.) Students need to understand that the choice of an appropriate topic depends on several factors that must be discussed and agreed on before the project is begun. Of course, the primary criterion will be: Is it something the student is truly interested in pursuing? Allowing students to explore self-chosen areas of interest will be a major factor in making the fair a positive learning experience.

## DID YOU KNOW? _____

A snail has 20,000 teeth—all on its tongue.

**Classroom Activity** Students may be interested in creating a science fair project on animal teeth. For example, they could include photographs of different types of teeth in different types of animals. Which animals have the largest teeth? Which have the smallest teeth? How can we tell the age of some animals by their teeth? What are some of the diseases of teeth, particularly in humans? What animals are known for their teeth (beavers, sharks)? The answers to these queries can provide students with some exciting explorations into the animal world and a fascinating science fair display.  ■

## Types of Projects

Not only do students need to select an appropriate topic for their science fair project; they also need to select an appropriate form of presentation. The topic may be addressed and presented using one of five project categories: experiments, demonstrations, research, collections, and apparatus. Although these categories overlap to some degree, focusing on the types of projects possible helps students narrow down their selections.

> *Experiments.* The type of project most often presented at science fairs is the experiment. The students poses a problem, designs an experiment to investigate that problem, records and reports the results, and makes conclusions based on those results. The final project is a display of the steps the student took, any successes or failures, and the implications of the data.

> *Demonstrations.* Another type of project involves a student demonstration of a particular science principle or fact. The demonstration should be self-contained; that is, observers can operate or manipulate any controls, switches, or devices needed for the demonstration. Students may wish to demonstrate the way something works, a science phenomenon, or the procedure with

which something is created naturally or in the lab.

> *Research.* In a research project, the student investigates a chosen area of science by consulting primary sources. That is, students consult reading materials from libraries, museums, government agencies, and the like. In addition, they should interview experts: scientists, health care workers, county agents, shop forepersons, or other knowledgeable individuals. Encourage on-site investigations at labs, factories, a printing plant, a farm, or a fish hatchery, for example. The intent is for the student to explore a scientific area in depth and detail and to report the findings in a vivid, interesting way through the project.

> *Collections.* Collections are assemblies of items, such as seashells, birds' nests, or telephone parts, that show diversity within a chosen area of science. Usually, collection projects result from a hobby or other free-time activity. Collections need to include as many samples as possible to illustrate the magnitude of the topic.

> *Apparatus.* A fifth type of project consists of a student display of some type of scientific apparatus or instruments and a description of their use or function in detail. The project should spell out the importance of the apparatus for both scientists and the general public. A description of how each apparatus is used within or outside the scientific community would also be appropriate.

Science fairs should be designed to give students a fresh perspective on the scientific world. Students' participation in a carefully crafted science fair can be their starting point for self-initiated investigations into the world around them. More important, science fairs offer students an enjoyable look at the wonders of science that can last well beyond their projects and their school days.

## TO INVESTIGATE _____

As you visit a local school, note whether it conducts an annual science fair. Are all students required to participate, or only certain grades? What motivation or encouragement are students given prior to the fair as well as during the preparation of their projects? What is the teacher's role? The parents' role? Are students excited about the fair? Are awards given to a few individuals or to everyone who enters? Is the fair coordinated with other areas of the curriculum?  ■

# FIELD TRIPS

Field trips provide youngsters with marvelous opportunities to see how science works in the "real world." In addition, field trips can enhance and promote your science curriculum and provide students with important extensions of concepts learned in the classroom. Most important, however, students will begin to see science as something more than a subject confined to a textbook or a series of experiments that follow an established pattern. Field trips can be a dynamic part of the entire science curriculum, particularly when they are coordinated with various topics throughout the year.

There is no limit to the places and sites that should be considered for a field trip. Too often, science field trips are limited to a local museum, zoo, or arboretum. Although these sites are valuable parts of the local community, they should not be the only ones considered. The following list provides some possibilities to consider for the four major areas of the science curriculum.

### Life Science

Hospital
Forest
Lumber yard
Garden center
Pet store
Dairy farm
Natural history museum
Aquarium
Nature center
College biology department
River, stream, swamp

### Physical Science

National or regional laboratory
State department of transportation
Police crime lab
Power station
Generating station
Machine shop
Hydroelectric dam
Music store
Service station
Fix-it shop
Manufacturing plant
Precision instrument company

### Earth Science

Cave
Desert, beach, valley
Water treatment plant
Dumps
River, stream
Quarry
Tide pools
Recycling center
Hydroelectric plant

### Space Science

Planetarium
Radio station
College
Hobby store
Local astronomy club
Telecommunications center

Although many of the places listed here (as well as those listed in Table 9.6) are probably ones students are already familiar with, that should not discount them as possible sites for science field trips. The fact that most students have been in a service station doesn't mean that the one on the corner can't be considered for a field trip. Here students can learn about pneumatics (filling a tire, raising a car on the lift), simple machines (tools and other mechanical devices), ecology (disposal of oil and other wastes), and health (working around fumes). Taking students to familiar sites is just as important as taking them to places they have never visited. Children can look at a familiar place with a new perspective and can begin to appreciate how science enters every aspect of daily life.

TABLE **9.6**

························································

## ADDITIONAL FIELD TRIP SITES

························································

| | |
|---|---|
| Factory | Nature trail |
| College | Backyard of the school |
| Recreational places | Sporting event |
| Airport | Beach |
| Museum | Farm |
| Live play/theater | Aquarium |
| Zoo | Post office |
| Planetarium | Nursing home |
| Graveyard | Radio/TV station |
| Library | Fast food restaurant |
| Amusement park | Supermarket |
| Flea market | Hospital |
| Fire/police station | Power plant |
| Shipyard | Ethnic restaurant |
| Wildlife sanctuary | Greenhouse |
| Park | Hardware store |
| Drug store | Department store |
| Festival | Bank |
| Printer | Sanitation area |
| Recycling center | Cave |
| Lake | Symphony/orchestra |
| Church/synagogue | Fish hatchery |
| Mortuary | SPCA |
| Historical site | Train station |
| Airport | Newspaper |

## IDEA BOX

You can enhance any field trip by working with your students in preparing a guide book. The guide book not only should provide students with some relevant information on the site they are to visit but should also allow them to record impressions and information gathered during the trip. In addition it can become an important record of one or more field trips taken during the year. The guidebook should be prepared well in advance of the field trip and can be done individually by students or in small groups. Students can construct either a separate guide book for each field trip or a permanent guide book for all field trips taken during the year. The following items can be included in the guide book prior to the field trip:

- Brochures or other printed materials available from the site (write in advance for these)
- A capsule description of the site and the reasons for visiting it
- Student-generated questions about the site and what might be seen (provide space under the questions for responses)
- A list of safety rules and a description of the expected form of behavior during the trip
- Blank pages for students to record observations and illustrations of significant points
- A summary page for students to write a brief wrap-up of the trip (this should be done prior to boarding the bus back to school)

Any teacher who has taken a class of kids on a field trip knows that field trips are much more than loading students on a school bus, traveling to some distant site, having an "expert" dispense a variety of facts and figures, wolfing down a peanut butter and jelly sandwich, and trying to make it back to school with one's sanity still intact. Successful and effective field trips take planning and preparation. Teachers should consider the following items as important to any meaningful field trip.

## Before

What is done prior to the field trip often determines the success of the trip. Planning involves much more than sending out parental permission slips and arranging for bus transportation. Consider these activities as part of the preparation process:

- If possible, obtain some brochures or other literature about the site you are visiting or the topic(s) to be discussed. Many museums, planetariums, and similar institutions offer a variety of printed materials.
- You should visit the site before the field trip to locate rest rooms, fountains, eating places, possible hazards, and so forth.
- Discuss with students the reasons for the trip, what they can expect to discover, and any additional highlights. Let students know how the planned trip relates to information discussed in the text or in class.
- As part of your language arts or reading lessons, provide students with relevant children's literature in advance of the scheduled field trip. For example, for a class visiting a zoo, you may want to share books such as *Watching Them Grow: Inside a Zoo Nursery* by Joan Hewlett (Boston: Little, Brown, 1979), *Make Way for Ducklings* by Robert McCloskey (New York: Viking, 1941), and *Mixed-up Chameleon* by Eric Carle (New York: Crowell, 1975). On the other hand, if the field trip is to take place at a weather station, you may wish to share books such as *Cloudy with a Chance of Meatballs* by Judith Barrett (New York: Atheneum, 1978), *On Sunday the Wind Came* by Alan Elliott (New York: Morrow, 1978), and *Rain* by Robert Kalan (New York: Greenwillow, 1978). A visit to a local pond might be prefaced with one or more of the following books: *At The Frog Pond* by Tilde Michels (Philadelphia: Lippencott, 1989), *Box Turtle at Long Pond* by William George (New York: Greenwillow, 1989), and *The Complete Frog: A Guide for the Very Young Naturalist* by Elizabeth Lacey (New York: Lothrop, 1989). The use of children's literature before a field trip can provide students with the background information they need to fully appreciate what takes place dur-

ing the trip. (See Appendix C for further suggestions on relevant children's literature.)

- If possible, visit the site yourself in advance of the scheduled trip. Talk to the people in charge, pick up some literature, and ask some questions. This "dry run" can alert you to any possible problems or situations that may put a damper on the actual trip. It will also provide you with important points and observations that can be shared with students prior to the trip.

## During

To be successful, a field trip must provide students with opportunities to become actively engaged in learning new information or reinforcing previously learned material. Children should not just passively walk through an exhibit, look at displays, and file back onto the bus without having participated in the various aspects of the site. The following guidelines can be used to provide kids with opportunities to become participants rather than just observers.

- Ask students some, if not all, of the questions *they* generated before the trip. Allow students to change some of the questions they created initially.
- Make sure students understand the relevance of the exhibit or venue to what they are studying in class. Develop relationships between classroom learning and on-site learning.
- Ask several "what if" questions (see Chapter 3). Pose some imaginative and unexpected queries to students throughout the visit. Provide them with opportunities to ask you some "what if" questions, too.
- Provide opportunities for children to record their thoughts, impressions, and conclusions. It is advisable to stop periodically to review what has been seen and to allow children to make notations on new information. This data will be valuable later in summarizing the important points of the trip.
- Before boarding the bus to return to school, hold a 5- to 10-minute summary session. Go over important points with students and ask them to review the significant information they learned. Encourage students to write a summary statement or paragraph to be presented later in class.

### DID YOU KNOW? _____

In the Imperial Valley of California there is a power plant that burns approximately 900 tons of cow manure daily. This 15-megawatt plant saves about 300 barrels of oil each day.

**Classroom Activity** Your own community probably has dozens of potential field trip sites. With your students, brain-

storm for all the possibilities you can think of. Make master lists of these ideas and categorize them according to the four major science areas (life science, physical science, earth science, space science). Record the listed sites on individual index cards and keep them in a box arranged according to topics covered in the textbook. When planning lessons, you can consult this file for potential field trip destinations. ■

## After

Teachers may assume that a field trip is over when students have been returned safely to the school. Not so. Students should be given a "debriefing" session in which important points are discussed, misconceptions are cleared up, and relationships are drawn between the outside world and the world within the classroom. The following are important features of any field trip.

- Provide students with an opportunity to discuss their perceptions of the field trip, the important or unimportant points, and how specific features relate to class or textbook discussions. Be sure kids record their impressions in a scrapbook or class notebook.
- Encourage children to create drawings, models, dioramas, posters, or other artistic (and permanent) displays based on the information they learned during the trip (see Table 9.7). These should be displayed in the classroom and referred to occasionally.
- Integrate the field trip into your language arts program by encouraging students to create plays, stories, dances, poems, lyrics, and video or audio recordings of portions of the trip.
- Be sure to review the purposes for the trip and ask students to decide if those objectives were met. Ask students questions such as: "Did we accomplish what we hoped to?" "Did we learn anything new that we didn't know before the trip?" "How does the information we learned on the trip relate to what we've learned in science class?" "If we were to take the trip again, what should we do differently?"
- Provide opportunities for students to understand the relevance of the field trip to other areas of the curriculum. For example, how can the information gathered during the trip be used in social studies, reading, art, or physical education?

### IDEA BOX _____

You should consider the idea of mini–field trips. These are field trips around the school or in the immediate community. They require little planning and no money, and they provide a host of possibilities for students to integrate classroom information with the world around them.

Design several short (10 to 20 minutes each) investigations of the environment around the school. Each idea for an activity should be recorded on a separate index card

TABLE 9.7

## POST–FIELD TRIP FOLLOW-UP ACTIVITIES

1. Direct students to create a newspaper or newsletter describing the trip.
2. Have students create a bulletin board with a map showing the location of the trip. Pictures cut out of magazines can be added to the bulletin board.
3. Make sure students write thank-you notes to any people involved with the trip.
4. Have students prepare a videotape summary of the trip. This can be played for other classes.
5. Direct students to create a brochure on the activities and exhibits at the trip site. They may wish to share the brochure with students in another class.
6. Have students conduct a formal poll on the trip. They may wish to survey their classmates on favorite experiences, best exhibit, most unusual fact learned, and so on. These results can be tabulated and shared with all.
7. Have students take a popular song and rewrite it using lyrics that include facts learned during the trip.
8. Students may wish to put together a photo album of the important places they visited and information they learned.
9. Encourage youngsters to put together a lesson on the field trip. This lesson can then be taught to students in a grade lower than the one you teach.
10. Have students create a picture book (with their own illustrations) of the field trip.
11. Students may wish to create and play a game such as "Jeopardy!" using facts learned during the trip.
12. Some pupils may enjoy creating word puzzles that include facts and terminology pertinent to the area visited during the trip.
13. The field trip can be extended by having students create their own magazine about the trip. Provide them with sample magazines and ask them to develop similar sections. Their magazine can parallel the features in popular magazines.
14. You may wish to schedule a "Theme Day" in which all of the activities, lessons, and projects center on the theme of the field trip. How can the information learned during the trip be translated to the math, social studies, health, reading/language arts, and other curricular areas?
15. Direct students to create poetry based on what they learned during the trip.
16. Some students may wish to create a flip book, a series of illustrations placed in sequential order. When the book is "thumbed," the pictures tell a story.
17. Engage the students in an open discussion of what they observed and learned during the trip.
18. Have students create a skit or play about the field trip. This presentation can be shared with other classes.
19. Some students may want to assemble a news broadcast about the field trip. This broadcast can be shared with the entire school over the intercom system.
20. Have students develop a "big book" about the trip.
21. Pupils can create a "book of world records" that includes valuable information learned during the trip. For example, if a trip was taken to the zoo, students may wish to assemble information on the fastest animal, the slowest, the tallest, the smallest, and so on.
22. Have students create and write their own book.
23. Many schools have showcases, which are excellent places to collect and display artifacts gathered prior to and during the field trip.
24. Have students write a letter to the editor of the local newspaper. They may wish to include information on the helpfulness of the tour guides, how the field trip related to a unit of study, and their appreciation for being allowed to go.
25. Have some students turn the field trip into a cartoon. Provide examples of cartoons from the newspaper and ask students to create new ones or to insert their own dialogue based upon the field trip.
26. Share several trade books with students at the conclusion of the field trip. It would be appropriate to have these on hand prior to the trip and discuss their relationship to the data gathered during the trip.
27. Designate one youngster as the "field trip expert." This person is responsible for recording all the data learned during the trip and will serve as the resident expert on the trip throughout the remainder of the school year. Be sure to designate a number of students to take on this responsibility for other field trips.

kept in a card file in the classroom. The activities can be used for individuals, small or large groups, or as homework assignments. Following are some ideas for mini–field trip assignments.

*Biology:* Go outside and see how many different leaves you can collect in 10 minutes. What are some similarities? What are some differences?

*Weather:* Go outside and record the temperature, wind speed, and humidity. Do this during the day at one-hour intervals. What do you notice?

*Ecology:* Go outside and note the various forms of litter or pollution. Make a chart of the types that appear most often.

*Geology:* Go outside and collect as many types of rocks as you can in 10 minutes. What type of rock seems to occur most often around the school?

*Simple Machines:* Go home and locate examples of each of the six simple machines. Which ones are used most often? Which ones are used the least?

## TEACHER TO TEACHER

"Taking a class of 30 sixth-graders 100 miles from home? I'm not certain what our parents and school board members will say."

That was the initial reaction by my principal when I proposed a three-day field trip to Yellowstone National Park for my sixth-grade class. Having been involved with outdoor schools and oceanography trips for elementary students in another state, I had seen first-hand the educational benefits of field trips and believed in the value of such experiences.

"We'll see," was her reply.

Over the course of many weeks I began developing a plan to demonstrate that such an idea had merit. I carefully thought through each hurdle and documented them: transportation, lodging, health and release forms, parent chaperones and their responsibilities, student expectations, food preparation, daily itineraries, and equipment.

I again visited with my principal and presented my written ideas. I explained how I would teach a unit on Yellowstone Park incorporating science, social studies, language, and history. I explained how I expected each student to write a research report on an aspect of Yellowstone. The reports were to be completed before the trip, or the students would not be allowed to participate. I outlined proposed parent meetings to present the trip's itinerary and answer any questions or concerns. I presented an outline of a field study notebook that I would write for the students to record data and observations while in the park.

After examining the proposals and listening to rationale for the trip, my principal gave me the go-ahead.

That was nine years ago. I now take students to Yellowstone twice a year, three days each trip. We sleep in tents and eat food cooked over the campfire. Our ongoing studies include plant and animal relationships, water quality, hydrothermal features, and most recently, forest fires and regrowth. The original concerns over such a trip have subsided, and valuable learning experiences and enthusiasm by parents and students have taken their place.

Field trips are an essential component of any science curriculum. Hands-on, minds-on science is personified through well-planned, educational field experiences. Yet in these times of liability suits and budget crunches, field trips seem to be the first items to get the axe. However, with proper planning, creative money raising ideas, and the support of administrators, faculty, parents, and students, field trips can and should take place.

John Graves
Monforton School
Bozeman, MT

What distinguishes the successful science program from the run-of-the-mill program is the degree to which it is expanded and elaborated beyond the pages of the textbook. Your success in teaching science will be determined in large measure by the methods you use to demonstrate the universality of science. When you help children to understand how science touches everyone's life and how we experience science in a myriad of ways, they will begin to appreciate science as a "friendly," engaging, and purposeful subject.

## POINTS OF DISCUSSION

1. Collect five science-related articles from your local newspaper. Present a plan for incorporating those articles into a science unit.

2. How can current events be integrated into the science program for students who have not yet learned to read?

3. When would it be inappropriate to have a guest speaker in your classroom?

4. Draft a model letter for inviting a local person into your classroom.

5. Develop a plan of action (recruitment, activities, schedules) for a corps of "science volunteers" in your classroom.

6. Design a home packet of science activities/projects that parents and students can share at home.

7. What are some difficulties you might encounter in designing effective learning centers? How might you overcome them?

8. How would a classroom science fair differ from a schoolwide science fair?

9. Do you believe it's important for every student to take part in a science fair? Defend your position.

10. Make a list of 20 sites within a five-mile radius of your college that could be used as field trip sites for a class of third-grade students.

# REFERENCES AND SUGGESTED READINGS

Abruscato, J., and Hassard, J. (1976). *Loving and beyond: Science teaching for the humanistic classroom.* Santa Monica, CA: Goodyear.

Blackburn, J., and Powell, W. (1976). *One at a time, all at once: The creative teacher's guide to individualized instruction without anarchy.* Glenview, IL: Scott, Foresman.

Cohen, H., Staley, F., and Horak, W. (1989). *Teaching science as a decision making process.* Dubuque, IA: Kendall-Hunt.

Fredericks, A. D. (1991). Science home-work. *Teaching K–8, 21,* (5), 18.

Fredericks, A., and Asimov, I. (1990). *The complete science fair handbook.* Glenview, IL: Scott, Foresman.

Fredericks, A., Cressman, B., and Hassler, R. (1987). *The science discovery book.* Glenview, IL: Scott, Foresman.

Fredericks, A., and Rasinski, T. (1990). Whole language and parents: Natural partners. *The Reading Teacher, 43* (9), 692–694.

Iritz, M., and Iritz, F. (1987). *Science fair: Developing a successful and fun project.* Blue Ridge Summit, PA: Tab.

Jarolimek, J. (1990). *Social studies in elementary education.* New York: Macmillan.

Rasinski, T., and Fredericks, A. (1988). Sharing literacy: Guiding principles and practices for parent involvement. *The Reading Teacher, 41,* (6), 508–512.

Rathbun, D. (1987). Foolproof field trips. In Helen Hamilton (ed.), *Classroom management.* Springhouse, PA: Springhouse.

Saul, W., and Newman, A. (1986). *Science fare.* New York: Harper and Row.

Schunke, G. (1988). *Elementary social studies: Knowing, doing, caring.* New York: Macmillan.

# 10

······································································

# EVALUATING
# STUDENT PROGRESS

······································································

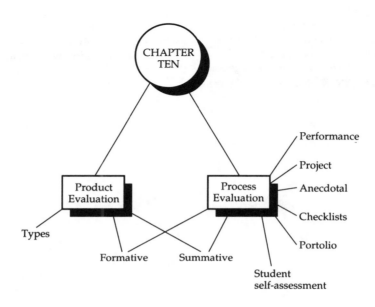

## Chapter Objectives

After reading this chapter you should be able to:

1.  Describe the importance of evaluation in the overall science program.

2.  Define both product-oriented and process-oriented evaluation.

3.  Explain the differences between formative and summative evaluation.

4.  Discuss the strengths and weaknesses of different forms of product-oriented evaluation.

5.  Describe various types of performance-based evaluative measures.

By some estimates the average student takes nearly 2,500 tests, quizzes, and exams during the school years (grades 1–12). For the most part, these measurement devices are designed to determine how much students know about a particular topic—or, perhaps more appropriately, how much they have crammed into their heads the night before an exam. Obviously, evaluation is a necessary part of the learning cycle, although not always an exciting one.

However, evaluation does not have to be the dull, dry, pedantic "monster" it's often perceived to be by students and teachers alike. It can be a useful tool in

**FIGURE 10.1** The average student will do this approximately 2,500 times

the hands of any classroom teacher seeking to promote a dynamic and engaging science program.

Evaluation is certainly not a new concept for you; however, in most situations you were the one being evaluated. As you move into your teaching position, you will assume the responsibilities of an evaluator. The *American Heritage Dictionary* defines evaluation as a way "to examine, judge, appraise, and estimate." Naturally, all teachers are required to perform these tasks, through both formal and informal approaches. You will need to evaluate the performance of your students, assess the appropriateness of the content, and determine the effectiveness of the methods and techniques utilized in your classroom.

An important point should be stated at this juncture. Effective evaluation is a continuous process. It is not simply something that is done at the conclusion of a unit of study or at the end of a demonstration or experiment. Effective evaluation is integrated into all aspects of the science curriculum and provides both teachers and students with relevant and useful data to gauge progress and determine the effectiveness of materials and procedures.

Wasserman and Ivany (1988) have delineated five criteria that should be part of all evaluation procedures within the science program:

1. Evaluation procedures must be compatible with the program's overall goals and objectives. If the program seeks to promote higher-order thinking skills, evaluation should not take the form of asking for single "correct" answers on a pencil-and-paper quiz.
2. They must serve the function of the program's learning objectives; that is, they should measure pupil progress along the learning dimensions that the program is trying to promote.
3. They must allow for diagnosing pupil weaknesses and thus point to remediative or corrective teaching.
4. They must emphasize the enablement of further pupil learning and deemphasize practices that are hurtful to the pupil's concept of self.
5. They must deemphasize practices that contribute to the pupil's losing interest in the subject.

To this list the following considerations may be added.

- Effective evaluation is an ongoing process. Much more than the practice of assessing the outcome of learning, it is a way of gauging learning over time. In other words, learning and evaluation are never completed but are always evolving and developing.
- A variety of evaluative tools are necessary to provide the most accurate assessment of students' learning and progress. Dependence on one type of tool to the exclusion of others deprives students of valuable learning opportunities and robs you of measures that help both students and the overall program grow.
- Evaluation must be a collaborative activity between teachers and students. Students must assume an active role in evaluation so that they can begin to develop individual responsibilities for development and self-monitoring in science. It is vital to supply the means for children to objectively measure their own learning and to work along with teachers in making pedagogical decisions within all aspects of the curriculum.
- Science evaluation needs to be authentic. That is, it must be based on the natural activities and processes of students both in the science classroom and in their everyday lives. For example, relying solely on formalized testing procedures may send a signal to children that science is simply a search for "right answers." If we wish to portray science as the discovery and processing of new information on a continuous basis, we need to emphasize evaluative measures appropriate to that approach. Focusing too strongly on students' knowledge of skills (through the use of multiple-choice tests, for example) may be counterproductive to students' understanding of science as process.

Evaluation is intrinsically more complex than writing a test, giving it to a group of students, scoring it, and handing it back with some sort of letter grade. It involves a combination of procedures and designs that not only judge students' work but help them grow in the process.

## TO INVESTIGATE

Visit one or more classrooms in your local area. What types of evaluation are used in those classrooms? Is the form of evaluation consistent across all curricular areas? That is, if objective tests are used exclusively in math, for example, are they also being used exclusively in science, social studies, and reading? Is the method of evaluation different in science compared to the other subject areas? How do teachers feel about the overall evaluation program? How do teachers feel about the evaluation procedures in science? How do students feel about the evaluation procedures in science? Compile your data and share it with other members of the class. What can you infer about how science is evaluated in the local school? Do you agree or disagree with those methods? Why? How will your (and your classmates') evaluation program in science match or differ from that used in the local schools? ■

## DID YOU KNOW?

The human nose can distinguish up to 10,000 different smells; the human ear can distinguish 300,000 different sounds; and the human eye can distinguish 7,000,000 different colors.

**Classroom Activity**  Students are often surprised to learn that the sense of taste is highly dependent on the sense of smell. The following activity will help demonstrate this. Blindfold one student and sit that student in front of a table or desk. Place a bowl on the table that contains equal-sized chunks of apples and potatoes (remove the skin). Have the blindfolded student select several chunks at random and eat each one separately while holding his or her nose. The student will be unable to tell which chunks are apples and which are potatoes. Next have the student repeat the activity without holding his or her nose. The apple and potato chunks will be identified quite easily. Repeat this activity with other students. ■

## KINDS OF EVALUATION

Although there are many ways of gauging student progress within the science program, we will concentrate on two broad categories: product evaluation and process evaluation.

> *Product evaluation.* Product evaluation is the form with which you are most familiar. Typically, it takes place at the conclusion of a lesson or demonstration and involves some sort of paper-and-pencil test or quiz on the material learned. Well-designed product-oriented measures are matched with the learning objectives of a lesson. That is, what was taught is what will be tested.
>
> *Process evaluation.* Process evaluation concentrates not so much on what students have learned as on how they learn. Process evaluation may include the development of teacher or student-initiated projects (i.e., science fair projects) in which students pursue a particular area of interest. It may also include performance measures in which the teacher provides materials and procedures for using those materials and then observes how students perform the specified tasks. The objective in process-oriented evaluation is not on whether students have learned a series of right answers but on how they go about learning.

The major difference between these two kinds of evaluation is that product-oriented evaluation is primarily a mental activity whereas process-oriented evaluation involves mental and physical manipulations of facts and materials.

The two forms of evaluation can be further defined according to type: formative or summative.

### Formative

Formative evaluation is utilized concurrently with instruction. It is undertaken to assess pupil progress with the material being presented, to determine student strengths and weaknesses, and to provide feedback for the pupil and teacher (Green, 1975). It is the evaluation that occurs between the introduction of a unit of work and its conclusion. Formative evaluation helps determine the effectiveness of the content through a series of questions: Is the material too difficult or too easy? Are there gaps that need to be covered before we move on? Is there a need to clarify concepts or vocabulary? Do the students have adequate referents to help them with abstract terms? Formative evaluation may also address the pacing of instruction: Are the children bored or confused? The answer to this question may indicate that you are moving too slowly or too quickly. Another purpose of formative evaluation is to uncover weak areas that require review and to identify the need to use other media and materials for the review sessions. Finally, formative evaluation may be utilized in assessing the performance level of students. How do the pupils handle scientific materials and equipment? Is there an indication of fear, lack of interest, misuse, or growth and confidence in their performance? Observations of students engaged in activities that require them to perform various functions will indicate where further instruction is needed.

## Summative

Summative evaluation is generally used at the conclusion of a unit of study. Green (1975, p. 50–55) indicates that it serves three primary functions:

1. Assessing the extent of pupils' achievement or competency at the end of instruction
2. Providing a basis on which grades or course marks can be fairly assigned
3. Providing the data from which reports to parents and transcripts can be prepared

You are probably quite familiar with summative evaluation; it is used to determine your grades and performance as a student.

One way to distinguish formative and summative evaluation is based on the utilization of the data collected through the evaluation instrument. If it is to be used to determine a final grade or assess the achievement or performance of a student or a group of students, it is summative. If the information is for planning purposes, it is formative (Woolfolk, 1990).

## TEACHER TO TEACHER

Sometime after I give an assignment, I review it and consider my grading criteria. These I write down and distribute to my students, and then explain them. We walk through the grading procedure and answers for the completed assignment as each student assesses and grades his/her own papers. I then collect these papers and examine the students' grades and corrections. Of course, I reserve the right to change any widely discrepant grade.

I also use student self-evaluation to grade their lab reports, especially when I want them to focus on a particular skill—such as providing supporting evidence in their written responses.

In order to insure that students take every assignment seriously, I use self-evaluation with discretion, and I require that their corrections be made with a different color pen or marker than their original work.

With practice, my students become capable judges of the quality of their own work, get immediate feedback, and relieve me of much of my paper correcting burden.

Inez Fugate Liftig
Fairfield Woods Middle School
Fairfield, CT

## PRODUCT-ORIENTED EVALUATION

The majority of data gathered in summative evaluation comes from teacher-prepared tests. Writing good tests is a skill that must be learned and practiced if the instruments are to yield data of any use to you or your students.

## Preparing Measuring Instruments

Construction of a good test takes careful planning. The instrument must be designed to measure the objectives you have established for a specific unit of work. The objectives may be: (1) the particular skills you wish the students to employ (e.g., designing a scientific experiment), (2) a body of knowledge you have established for the class (e.g., identifying the planets of the solar system), (3) the level of knowledge you want your students to achieve (e.g., applications of the four simple machines), or (4) the attitudes or values you want your students to acquire (e.g., using relationships

to defend answers on an essay examination). In addition to evaluating the attainment of the objectives you have established, there is a need to measure how well your students have acquired the body of facts, concepts, principles, and generalizations appropriate for the material you are presenting. The source of this body of information may be the curriculum guide you are following, the textbook you are using, or a unit you have designed. As indicated in Chapter 3, you should also consider the cognitive levels to be assessed by your evaluative instruments.

## DID YOU KNOW?

Mt. Waialeale in Hawaii averages 451 inches of rain per year (about 1¼ inches per day) making it the wettest spot on earth.

**Classroom Activity** Students may be interested in making their own rain gauge. You'll need a wide-mouthed jar, a funnel, and a small-mouthed jar such as an olive jar (about an inch in diameter). Place the large jar outside with the funnel in it to collect rainwater as it falls (the funnel will also help prevent water from evaporating before it is measured). After a rain storm, pour the water into the smaller jar and measure the amount in increments of ¼ inch. Have students keep charts and graphs of the amount of rain that falls in their area over an extended period of time. Have them compare their readings with those in the daily newspaper. ■

## TEACHER TO TEACHER

As part of my second-grade science curriculum the children in my class study whales. I explain to the children that we will be learning about animals which are in danger of becoming extinct. To help these animals, and to understand more about them, we will be adopting a humpback whale. The children do certain chores their parents assign them; and in return the children earn a dollar for our whale adoption project. Very

innocently, one of my little seven-year-olds raised her hand and asked, "But, Mrs. Lees, where will we keep him?"

Irene Lees
Parkway School
Paramus, NJ

## Types of Product-Oriented Tests

You are probably familiar with two types of examinations as a result of your college classes: objective and essay tests. However, oral examinations and performance tests are also appropriate for assessing students in science. Table 10.1 outlines some of the strengths and weaknesses of these four types of examinations.

TABLE  10.1

### STRENGTHS AND WEAKNESSES OF VARIOUS TEST FORMS

| Strengths | Weaknesses |
|---|---|
| **Oral** | |
| 1. Permits extensive measurement | 1. Is too time-consuming |
| 2. Is useful as an instructional device | 2. Provides limited sample unless pupils are tested individually |
| 3. Permits teacher to give cues to elicit desired responses | 3. Is frequently poorly planned |
| 4. Improves test rapport for pupils who fear written exams | 4. Gives poor comparative evaluation of pupils |
| | 5. Provides no written record |
| **Objective** | |
| 1. Gives an extensive test sample | 1. Frequently neglects measurement of higher thought processes |
| 2. Can be highly reliable | 2. May overemphasize rote learning |
| 3. Can be graded quickly and objectively | 3. Promotes poor study habits |
| 4. Eliminates bluffing | 4. Encourages guessing |
| 5. Can be subjected to item analysis and further refinement | 5. Is difficult to prepare |
| 6. Can be adapted to several teaching objectives | |
| 7. Can be made highly valid for some teaching objectives | |
| **Essay** | |
| 1. Is applicable to measurement of writing, organizational ability, and creativity | 1. Gives a limited test sample |
| 2. Is easy to construct | 2. Is difficult to grade objectively |
| 3. Promotes proper type of study | 3. Favors the verbally inclined |
| 4. Is adaptable to testing science concepts and generalizations, relationships, and other aspects of science | 4. Has low reliability |
| | 5. Encourages bluffing |
| **Performance** | |
| 1. Stresses application of knowledge | 1. May be difficult to construct |
| 2. Can be used as a learning device | 2. Is often difficult to grade |
| 3. May give a truer achievement picture for the verbally handicapped student | 3. Is often time-consuming |
| 4. Measures some skills and abstract abilities not measured by other conventional test forms | |

## Multiple-Choice Exams

When writing questions for multiple-choice tests, you must consider the item, stem, distractors, and problem. The item consists of the question and possible answers; it represents the entire question. The stem is the part of the item that raises the problem: it should precede the answers. Distractors are the incorrect options in the answer part of the item. The problem is the context in which the student's knowledge is being evaluated.

## True/False Tests

One of the most widely used teacher-made evaluation measures is the true/false test. Some of the advantages of this type of test are that they can be checked objectively and quickly, they are useful in evaluating knowledge level, and they can cover a wide variety of material in a short period of time. However, if not constructed carefully, a true/false test will not be a reliable instrument for measuring the achievement level of the students. A major drawback of this test is that it may be difficult to distinguish those who know the material from those who merely guessed. One way to address this problem is to have students underline the incorrect word or phrase in a statement that is false. A space may be provided at the conclusion of each question or statement for the student to insert the correct word or phrase. For example, the statement "A transformer is a device used to stop the flow of electrons when a circuit is overloaded" is incorrect. The student would underline "transformer" and insert either "fuse" or "circuit breaker" in the space provided.

## Short-Answer Tests

In another type of test students are expected to keep their answers brief, supplying in most instances a word, phrase, symbol, rule, or name. The tests are usually easy to write and grade, cover a wide range of information in a relatively short period of time, and control or eliminate guessing. A disadvantage of using this type of examination is that it requires total recall by students, which restricts them to the lower levels of Bloom's taxonomy of the cognitive domain. A problem often experienced with short-answer tests is the variety of correct responses that were not anticipated. This may cause some difficulty in scoring the test and thus make the test less reliable.

## Matching Questions

A frequently used device at the elementary school level is the matching of names, dates, quantitative data, words, rules, or ideas in one column with items in a second column. An example of matching for an elementary science examination is the following:

| | Column A | Column B |
|---|---|---|
| 1.__ | Measurement of resistance | A. Transformer |
| 2.__ | Used to alter current or voltage | B. Fuse |
| 3.__ | Measurement of current | C. Ohm |
| 4.__ | Helps to create electricity | D. Battery |
| 5.__ | Safety device to stop current when there is a short circuit | E. Armature |
| 6.__ | Energy source of direct current | F. Ampere |
| | | G. Voltage |
| | | H. Generator |
| | | I. Doorbell |

Advantages of matching questions while the reduction of guessing potential as compared with the true false and multiple-choice tests, relative objectivity and ease in checking the test, the short time required for students to read and select answers compared with other tests, and coverage of a wide variety of material if you choose to include more than one specific area of a unit of study. The primary disadvantage is that matching columns of scientific data limits students to the lower levels of the cognitive domain. It is difficult to measure analysis, synthesis, and evaluation through the matching of items.

## Essay Examinations

Although essay examinations are not used extensively at the elementary school level, they are an excellent instrument for ascertaining how well students can analyze a situation, synthesize a response to a unique problem, and make valid value judgments. Essay tests should not be used exclusively to gather specific information or data that could be acquired by using objective tests. Rather, the purpose of essay tests is to demonstrate that students know how to use the data they possess. For example, the following are two related essay questions:

1. On our windows this morning we saw moisture. The moisture is probably the result of condensation. Explain how condensation formed on the window.
2. As the day progresses, the moisture leaves the window through evaporation. Give two examples of evaporation and explain what occurs in other evaporation situations.

The disadvantages of essay examinations are related primarily to time and subjectivity. Essay examinations require more time to evaluate than objective tests. Even the relatively short tests designed for elementary science programs are time-consuming because of the volume of comments one must consider, occasional problems in reading because of poor handwriting and poor grammar, and the lack of ability of many elementary school students to organize their responses in a manner that allows one to quickly locate the key ideas. Subjectivity frequently enters into the evaluation as the "halo" effect (expecting the better students to do well) influences the evaluator. The ability of the student to use good handwriting, proper grammar, and good organizational skills can also have an influence on the teacher. A third disadvantage is the limited amount of information that can be acquired through this type of examination. The student can provide considerably more depth in answering a question, but the number of questions and the breadth of topics covered are limited because of the time factor.

**DID YOU KNOW?** _____

The amount of gold dissolved in the oceans is about 9 million tons.

**Classroom Activity**   Students may wish to determine how much salt will dissolve in a glass of fresh water. Measure a quantity of water into a glass and provide students with measuring spoons and table salt. Ask them to keep adding salt until no more salt will dissolve. How many teaspoons, for example, will dissolve in one pint of water? Challenge students to change some of the variables (heat the water to different temperatures, use soft vs. hard water, etc.) and see if more or less salt can be dissolved in the water.

Students may wish to experiment with different objects to determine in which concentration of salt water those objects float the highest. Have students repeat this activity using sugar in place of salt. What similarities or differences do they note? ∎

There is a tendency for teachers to overrely on written or summative evaluation procedures. It's important to keep in mind that evaluation, to be thorough, must occur *before, during,* and *after* instruction. A danger of some of the more formal methods of evaluation is that they often take place at the conclusion of a lesson or activity. This tends to underscore science as simply an accumulation of facts and figures to be memorized and regurgitated on various written instruments. Coupled with this danger is the fact that teachers may not recognize all the thinking processes (see Chapter 4) or manipulative processes (see Chapter 2) that are also intrinsic parts of the science curriculum. In short, an overdependence on product-oriented evaluation may be counterproductive to a process-oriented or discovery-oriented approach to learning science.

This is not to suggest that all written forms of evaluation should be eliminated. Rather, you should consider them in their proper context. You need to ask yourself some of the following questions:

1. What information do I need to know about this particular student or the class as a whole?

2. How can this form of evaluation improve my teaching competencies? How will it improve students' learning competencies?
3. How can I combine several forms of evaluation to accurately determine students' progress throughout the curriculum?
4. What do I really want to know?
5. What do I want students to know?
6. What do students want to know?
7. How can students effectively utilize the data from this evaluation to become better thinkers, doers, and scientists?

**IDEA BOX** _____

Following is a random collection of assessment ideas to consider for your science curriculum.

- Use cartoons to test concepts. Many cartoons illustrate a single concept and thus make excellent question sources.
- Put questions on 3 × 5 cards. Arrange them under a plastic sheet, photocopy them and use the copy for your test master. Cards can be rearranged for another exam.
- To make sure you cover questions at all levels of knowledge in each concept area, fill in a grid with the question numbers as you prepare your test.
- Take slides or photographs of classrooms experiments. Use these for group tests or as station items on practical tests.
- Enlarge your quizzes and make overhead transparencies so that students can examine keys immediately.
- Hand back a sample of test questions and an analysis so that students can see differences in class performance on knowledge, comprehension, and application questions.
- For higher-level questions, cut out paragraphs from *Science News* or an alternative text and use them for word problems. Use illustrations from other texts to see if students can transfer knowledge rather than relying on photographic memory.
- Tape-record five questions from your lesson at the end of the day. Write questions after class on scraps of paper. Compose tests from the accumulated questions.
- Play "Jeopardy!" with students. Tape their made-up questions and use these as answer options on multiple-choice exams. This is a good way to identify misconceptions.
- At the end of the class period, have each student write an answer to one question on a 3 × 5 card. Good questions are: "One new thing I learned today about _____ (main concept) was __." "How can __ (some principle) be used in real life?" "I'm confused about _____ (concept) because _____."
- Occasionally use collaborative exams. For example, students can work together to construct a group or whole-class instrument.

- Give students 3 × 5 cards labeled A, B, C, D, and E. Ask questions orally or put them on the overhead. Have students hold up the letter card that corresponds to the answer they think is right. Give the whole class a score.
- Exchange exams with other teachers in your district and with teachers in higher and lower grades.

(Source: Modified from undated handout obtained from NSTA Test-preparation Sub-Committee at the 1990 NSTA Annual Convention, Atlanta, GA, April 6, 1990.)

## TO INVESTIGATE

Along with several classmates, obtain a sampling of teacher-made science tests from some of the local schools. Analyze those tests in light of your knowledge of evaluation and in terms of your level of comfortableness if *you* were to take those tests as a student. What do you like about those measures? What do you dislike? How would you change those instruments? Can you suggest any alternative evaluation strategies that would provide the teacher(s) with useful information on student performance? ■

# PROCESS-ORIENTED EVALUATION

A process approach to evaluation can provide both you and your students with useful information to gauge progress and assess the effectiveness of the entire science curriculum. It can help your students assume an active role in the evaluation process and make your science program more of a collaborative effort, instead of one in which you assume all the responsibilities for teaching and evaluating.

There are many forms of process evaluation. Here we will concentrate on a few that have been proven to yield important data for teachers and students alike. You should consider these (or modifications of these) for your own classroom. You should also attempt other evaluative measures in keeping with your philosophy of teaching science and your students' abilities and interests in learning science.

## Performance Assessment

Performance assessment can be easily built into any science lesson. It is a hands-on form of evaluation that allows children the opportunity to demonstrate their understanding of important points through the manipulation of objects and concepts. In a lesson on simple machines, for example, students can be provided with inclined planes (ramps), a weight, and a spring gauge. They can demonstrate their understanding of the in-

clined plane by pulling a weight up ramps of different lengths and different heights. By choosing the ramp that involves the least amount of effort (as indicated on the spring gauge), students can show their understanding of the principle that it takes the same amount of work to pull a weight to a prescribed height up a long ramp as up a short, steep ramp. In this way students have opportunities to apply their scientific knowledge in real-life events as opposed to a paper-and-pencil test, which may measure only the factual data memorized.

Following is a performance measure that can be used to determine if students understand the concept of electrical circuits.

### Materials

Several lengths of wire
Dry cell
Light bulb (in bulb holder)
Alligator clips
Aluminum foil strips
Cardboard strip

### Teacher Setup

Attach the aluminum foil strips to the strip of cardboard as in the illustration; this will simulate a light switch. Attach a length of wire to each pole of the dry cell as shown.

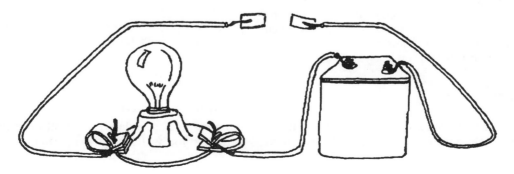

## Student Directions

"Using this setup, complete the circuit so that the bulb lights when you touch the two aluminum foil strips together".

## Project Assessment

Project assessment can be done when students are relatively independent and can work by themselves or in small groups. In this evaluative procedure, children are provided access to all sorts of materials and supplies and, using their creativity, must design or devise a project that illustrates a scientific principle. This form of assessment is long-term and allows students to formulate plans of action and carry them out to their conclusion. Science fair projects (see Chapter 9) are an excellent example of the project approach to evaluation.

If you use projects as part of your evaluative scheme, you and your students should fully discuss the objectives of the project as well as the criteria used to determine progress toward those objectives. It would be appropriate to work with your students in designing a common evaluation design consisting of checkpoints by which students are observed and provided feedback throughout the completion of a selected project. Obviously, projects allow for a great deal of leeway in terms of criteria and time for completion. But they provide students many opportunities to try many approaches in arriving at a final product—a procedure scientists use all the time.

### DID YOU KNOW? _____

During the next minute, 240 people will be born and 100 people will die.

**Classroom Activity**   Students will be amazed to discover that the world's population doubles every 30 years. How will all those people be fed? Who will grow all the necessary food? Have students keep track of all the food consumed by their individual families over the course of a day or week. Combine those totals to arrive at an approximate figure for the entire class (you may wish to have students categorize the foods into the basic food groups). Have students make projections on the number of people that will be represented by their class, their grade level, their school, the school district, and/or the local community in 30, 60, 120, and 240 years. How much food will be needed to feed all those people? Students may wish to graph their calculations on a series of charts.  ■

## Anecdotal Records

As mentioned earlier, evaluation is a process that occurs over time, one that tracks a student's development and competence over many days, weeks, or months. Anecdotal records, or narrative descriptions of students' behavior and academic performance, can be some of the most valuable evaluation tools available. Through anecdotal records you can keep a running record of each student to determine likes and dislikes, advancement or regression, and growth and development.

By their nature, anecdotal records are objective assessments of students. However, they track students over many occasions and many learning opportunities and thus serve as accurate records of performance that can be shared with administrators and parents. Note the following guidelines in using anecdotal records.

1. Don't try to write a description of each child's behavior and performance every day. Identify four or five youngsters and concentrate on them for the day.
2. Keep your comments short and to the point. It's not necessary to write long, involved sentences about what you observe. Keep the notes short; invent your own method of shorthand.
3. Maintain file folders on each student. The day's anecdotal record on a child can be placed in his or her folder at the end of the day.

### IDEA BOX _____

Purchase several sheets of adhesive mailing labels and a clipboard. Identify the students you will observe on a particular day and write their names and the day's date in the corner of several mailing labels. As you walk around the room during science lessons, jot down observational notes on each student on his or her mailing label(s). At the end of the day, remove the label or labels for a single student and place them on a sheet of paper that is divided into boxes and kept in the student's folder. In this way you can transfer your observations to students' folders quickly and easily. By having a date on each mailing label, you can easily keep track of each student's progress in a chronological fashion.

4. Record only what you see, and not your subjective ideas concerning the reasons for the behavior.
5. Plan time at the end of the day to discuss your observations and anecdotes with each identified student. Let the students know what you observed and provide them with an opportunity to react and ask pertinent questions.

## Checklists

A predesigned checklist allows you to gauge student progress against a determined set of observational criteria. As you watch students participate in a project or activity, you can check off items on the checklist according to how those students perform or behave. This data is similar in some respects to the information in anecdotal records; however, it provides a series of constants against which all students can be assessed.

One form of checklist has students' names listed down the left side of a grid and the specific behaviors or skills listed across the top. As a behavior is observed in a student, a check mark can be placed next to that student's name. Table 10.2 is a checklist that may be used to assess process skills. For each project or activity, you can check off a student's ability to use any of the process skills. Another form of checklist is shown in Table 10.3 which assesses both attitudes and skills.

## Portfolio Assessment

Most professional artists have portfolios, collections of their best work that can be shown to galleries and art dealers. A portfolio, by definition, is a coordinated assembly of past and present work that provides the viewer with a definitive and representative look at the artist's work and talent. A portfolio allows an artist to collect a variety of work that reveals not only the depth of his or her talent but the breadth as well.

Portfolios are also useful in the science program. More than a haphazard group of papers and tests, they can demonstrate the skills of individual students while demonstrating the growth record of a student over time.

A portfolio can be as simple as a single file folder for each student or as complex as a series of mailbox compartments set up in a corner of the classroom. Included in each portfolio may be the following.

1. Examples of the student's work in progress
2. Dated progress notes written by the teacher
3. Dated progress notes written by the student
4. Dated progress notes written by the parent(s)
5. Work samples selected by the teacher
6. Work samples selected by the student
7. Self-evaluation forms completed by the student
8. Anecdotal and observational records maintained by the teacher
9. Photographs/illustrations of completed projects
10. Audio- or video-tapes of selected work
11. Experiment or project logs
12. Tests, quizzes, and exams
13. Written work of any kind
14. Lists of science literature read and book projects completed

It should be obvious that the types of items that can be included in a portfolio are limitless. What is important is that the portfolio include representative samples of the student's work over time.

The advantages of portfolios are that they provide teachers, students, administrators, and parents with a vehicle to document growth, a forum to discuss that growth, and procedures and processes that might stimulate further growth. Although they are useful for parent-teacher conferences, they are more beneficial for teacher-student conferences. In a sense, portfolios personalize the evaluation process; they make it dynamic and relevant to the lives of children and useful to the planning and design of successful science programs.

## Attitudinal Assessment

Do you like science?
Do you like this course?
Has your opinion about teaching science changed as a result of taking this course?

These statements are designed to assess your feelings or attitudes about certain elements of science. Attention to the attitudes of your students is an important part of the overall evaluation process. It stands to reason that if a student enjoys science, he or she will want to learn a great deal about science. Conversely, if a student dislikes science tremendously, it is doubtful that he or she will take advantage of the learning opportunities in science.

Knowing how your students feel about science provides you with valuable data on weak areas of the curriculum or portions of your program to be revised in accordance with individual perceptions. That does not mean that all students must like science, but it does imply that we should make a conscious effort to strengthen the affective dimensions of our classroom program.

Here are Mary's tests, homework, experiment reports, and drawings.

TABLE 10.2

..................................................................................................................

# PROCESS SKILLS CHECKLIST

..................................................................................................................

Project/Activity:  Photosynthesis                                       Date:    March 19

| Name | Observing | Classifying | Inferring | Communicating | Measuring | Predicting | Experimenting |
|------|-----------|-------------|-----------|---------------|-----------|------------|---------------|
| Luke | X | | | X | | X | X |
| Helen | | | | | X | X | |
| Karen | | | X | X | X | X | |
| José | | X | | X | X | | |
| Jon | X | X | X | X | X | X | X |
| Barb | | X | | X | | | X |
| Kwan | X | | X | | | | X |

TABLE 10.3

..................................................................................................................

# ATTITUDE AND SKILLS CHECKLIST

..................................................................................................................

S = Satisfactory
U = Unsatisfactory
N = Needs improvement

1. Observation skills

| | | | |
|---|---|---|---|
| A. Notes relationship among two or three variables | S | U | N |
| B. Observes whole picture, not just specifics | S | U | N |
| C. Determines relevant, ingnores irrelevant | S | U | N |

2. Classifying materials

| | | | |
|---|---|---|---|
| A. Can classify materials using two variables (e.g., size and shape) | S | U | N |
| B. Can establish his/her own criteria for classifying | S | U | N |
| C. Can explain purpose of classification | S | U | N |

3. Using materials properly

| | | | |
|---|---|---|---|
| A. Handles materials carefully | S | U | N |
| B. Uses appropriate safety materials with equipment (e.g., protective glasses, asbestos gloves) | S | U | N |
| C. Reports dangerous and unsafe materials | S | U | N |

4. Willingness to participate in science

| | | | |
|---|---|---|---|
| A. Willing to take part in a science demonstration | S | U | N |
| B. Willing to use scientific equipment | S | U | N |
| C. Willing to change mind as a result of an observation or other experience | S | U | N |

5. Application of scientific knowledge

| | | | |
|---|---|---|---|
| A. Applies science knowledge in his/her environment outside of the classroom situation | S | U | N |
| B. When appropriate, makes decision based on scientific knowledge | S | U | N |
| C. Applies scientific method in problem-solving situation | S | U | N |

6. Communication skills

| | | | |
|---|---|---|---|
| A. Uses appropriate science vocabulary | S | U | N |
| B. Demonstrates ability to organize data | S | U | N |
| C. Uses appropriate symbols in written expressions | S | U | N |

7. Curiosity

| | | | |
|---|---|---|---|
| A. Spontaneously moves to science table or reacts to scientific elements of the environment | S | U | N |
| B. Occasionally asks "what if" questions | S | U | N |
| C. Is interested in what happens when demonstration or experiment is conducted | S | U | N |

8. Engages in the scientific process by utilizing the following:

| | | | |
|---|---|---|---|
| A. Observation: Uses observation skills effectively in making decisions | S | U | N |
| B. Measurement: Reports reflect quantitative data rather than adjectives (e.g., small, light, large, several) | S | U | N |
| C. Prediction: Makes predictions on the data available | S | U | N |

There are a number of ways to assess students' attitudes and affective perceptions of science in general and the classroom science program specifically. These include the use of an *attitude scale* (Table 10.4), *science sentences* (Table 10.5), and an *attitude continuum* (Table 10.6).

## DID YOU KNOW?

The difference between high tide and low tide in the Bay of Fundy in eastern Canada can be as much as 53 ½ feet.

**Classroom Activity** Students, particularly those who do not live near large ocean, will enjoy reading these three books: *Where the Waves Break: Life at the Edge of the Sea* by Anita Malnig (Minneapolis: Carolrhoda, 1985), *Night Dive* by Ann McGovern (New York: Macmillan, 1984), and *A Day in the Life of a Marine Biologist* by William Jaspersohn (Boston: Little, Brown, 1982).

## Student Self-Evaluation

The effective science program is one that involves youngsters in every aspect of the program—including evaluation. When students can participate in evaluating their own progress within the science curriculum, they begin to develop an internal sense of responsibility, which helps them assume some degree of control over their own learning.

### TABLE   10.4

## SCIENCE ATTITUDE SCALE

**Name:**_____ **Date: Fall   Winter   Spring**
**(circle one)**

5 = Strongly agree
4 = Agree
3 = Uncertain
2 = Disagree
1 = Strongly disagree

| | | | | | | |
|---|---|---|---|---|---|---|
| 1. | Science is for everybody. | 5 | 4 | 3 | 2 | 1 |
| 2. | Science is my favorite subject. | 5 | 4 | 3 | 2 | 1 |
| 3. | Science means memorizing lots of facts. | 5 | 4 | 3 | 2 | 1 |
| 4. | I like to read science books. | 5 | 4 | 3 | 2 | 1 |
| 5. | I'd rather play than do science. | 5 | 4 | 3 | 2 | 1 |
| 6. | Science is only for boneheads. | 5 | 4 | 3 | 2 | 1 |
| 7. | Our science textbook is fun to read. | 5 | 4 | 3 | 2 | 1 |
| 8. | I like to do science activities at home. | 5 | 4 | 3 | 2 | 1 |
| 9. | I like to do "hands-on" projects in science. | 5 | 4 | 3 | 2 | 1 |
| 10. | Science is my least favorite subject. | 5 | 4 | 3 | 2 | 1 |

### TABLE   10.5

## SCIENCE SENTENCES

Name:_____     Date:_____

*Directions:* Complete each of the following sentence stems in your own words. There are no right or wrong answers.

1. Science is . . .
2. I don't think science is . . .
3. The thing I hate most about science is . . .
4. Instead of science class I'd rather . . .
5. When it's time for science I . . .
6. I enjoy science when . . .
7. Most scientists are . . .
8. Science would be more interesting if . . .
9. Most of my friends think science . . .
10. When we do science activities I often feel . . .

Self-evaluation takes many forms. The simplest of all occurs in the context of student-teacher discussions. It is an unavoidable fact of life that one of the questions you will constantly be asked (a thousand times a day, it sometimes seems) is "How did I do?" Such a question carries a hidden message, which is that the student is overly dependent on someone else to evaluate his or her performance (i.e., a teacher-dependent student). A very effective, although frequently frustrating (for students), way of responding to that question is to re-form it and toss it back to the student:

"How do *you* think you did?"
"Do you feel you did your best work?"
"Is this representative of your best effort?"
"If you were the teacher, how would you answer your own question?"

I need to control those variables if I am to prove my answer.

TABLE **10.6**

........................................................................
## ATTITUDE CONTINUUM
........................................................................

Name:_____ Date:_____

*Directions:* Place an X somewhere along the line between each pair of words to denote how you feel about science.

### Science Is:

Easy................................Hard
Fun................................Boring
Fantastic..........................Dull
Important..........................Worthless
Clear..............................Complicated
Clean..............................Messy
Useful.............................Not useful
Great..............................Stupid
The best...........................The worst

Such responses give students an opportunity to take some responsibility for their own learning and, of course, their own evaluation. They help you promote evaluation as a collaborative effort between teacher and student.

Teacher-student conferences also allow you to pose several other types of questions that encourage students to look inward and gauge their learning. Wasserman and Ivany (1988) have provided several examples of these types of questions:

- "Tell me about the way you worked."
- "Tell me about some discoveries you have made."
- "Tell me about some of the things that did not go well for you."
- "Tell me about some of the things that gave you trouble."
- "What comments would you like to make about your behavior?"
- "What were some of the things you could do for yourself?"
- "What were some of the things you needed help with?"
- "Where do you think you need help from me?"
- "What did you discover about the materials you worked with?"
- "What were some of the decisions you made, and how did they work for you?"
- "What questions do you have about what happened?"
- "Tell me how you think the work in science is going for you."

Another format for self-evaluation is the data sheet or self-report form. There are many variations of these.

TABLE **10.7**

........................................................................
## STUDENT SELF-REPORT FORM
........................................................................

Name:_____ Date:_____

*Directions:* Please complete this report about your activities in science this week. Your comments will form the basis for a discussion with me later.

1. These are some of the things I learned in science this week:_____

2. These are some of the things that gave me trouble in science this week:_____

3. I believe I have improved in science this week. Here's why:_____

4. Here are some things I'd like to learn more about:_____

5. Here is how I would rate my performance in science this week:_____

6. This is what I'd like to do next week in science:_____

Table 10.7 illustrates one example that would be appropriate in a variety of settings and situations.

## IDEA BOX

The following ideas and activities can be used to encourage student self-evaluation within the whole science program.

- Provide opportunities for students to establish their own goals for a science activity. Afterward, encourage them to decide if those goals were attained.
- Have students design one-third of the questions for any test or quiz.
- Design a formal evaluation instrument on a unit of study. Instead of having students respond with answers, ask them to indicate (for each question) whether they:
  - a. Positively know the answer
  - b. Are mostly sure of the answer
  - c. Have some idea of the answer
  - d. Have no idea what the answer is
- Discuss and share reasons (via individual conferences) why students responded as they did.
- Ask students to evaluate the questions in the teacher's edition of the textbook. Encourage them

- to design a system that rates the questions in terms of difficulty, appropriateness, level of cognition, or any other criterion.
- Encourage students to explain their reasons for selecting answers to specific questions.
- Stimulate the development of student-generated questions throughout any activity or experiment.
- Model your own metacognitive processes as you share information with students.
- Provide opportunities for students to explain the reasons why they understood or did not understand parts of an activity.
- Allow students to state their own expectations or criteria for assignments.
- Provide opportunities for students to write lists of things they learned from a lesson as well as things they did not understand. Take time to discuss those lists.
- Permit students to rate any one of your lessons in terms of *their* level of comprehension. In other words, did your presentation promote understanding and interest? Discuss *your* reactions in terms of *their* perceptions.
- Provide a variety of self-correcting assignments within each unit of study.

Evaluation is a process that offers opportunities for growth—teacher growth, student growth, and program growth. It is one thing to assess and evaluate student performance; it is quite another to do something with that information. If you simply administer an endless bank of tests, checklists, and self-evaluative forms and do nothing with the results, your evaluation is close to worthless. The data you gather from all forms of evaluation (and, again, meaningful evaluation should be multidisciplinary in nature) should be used productively; that is, to help students develop the skills, processes, and attitudes that help make science an important part of the elementary curriculum and of their lives.

In short, evaluation is an integral part of the learning process. As such, it must be sensitive to the needs, attitudes, and abilities of individual students as well as the class as a whole. Be careful that you do not over-rely on one or more forms of evaluation just because they are easy or convenient for you. Be aware that evaluation involves some part of a student's self-esteem and that affective factors are an important ingredient in evaluation. In other words, *what* you evaluate is just as important as *how* you evaluate.

Learning to become an effective evaluator takes time. It is not easily learned or easily practiced. It is, however, an essential element of the effective science curriculum.

## DID YOU KNOW?

From the mouth of the Amazon River pours one-fifth of all the moving fresh water on earth.

**Classroom Activity**  Two videos that present the Amazon River in all its majesty are available from the National Geographic Society (Washington, DC 20036): "Amazon" (1968, catalog no. 51003) and "Amazon, Land of the Flooded Forest" (1991, catalog no. 51479). Try to obtain one or both of these films to share with your class. Afterward, have students create comparative charts on the similarities and differences between their area of the country and the Amazon rain forest. Be sure to post these in the classroom.

## TEACHER TO TEACHER

Have your students ever kept science journals? The creative possibilities are endless. My third-graders use spiral notebooks to record science happenings throughout the year. The journals accompany us on field trips. Minibeast tallies from playground excavations are totaled and then graphed. Observations while visiting and gathering specimens at tidal pools are made. Daily logging of the conditions of the fragile environment of our salt water aquarium are recorded. Creative writing flows naturally as we observe a hermit crab scurry from one shell to another. Brainstorming ideas to help our environment are shared and then recorded. These ideas become a focal point for action; i.e., currently our class is recycling all the white paper for our school. Vocabulary develops naturally and has its own section for easy referencing. Science-related sharing becomes recorded under "Touching Nature," with the date, item, and presenter noted. Each "Touching Nature" entry becomes a mini–science lesson of its own. Integration of subjects is handled with ease. When children reread their journals, memories and learning are rekindled. Former students return and often mention that their journals still provide timely referencing for learning. With educators seeking means to fairly judge process-oriented science, journals offer tangible material to assist in the evaluation.

Patricia Horan
Academy Elementary School
Madison, CT

## POINTS OF DISCUSSION

**1.** Obtain a teacher's manual for a current science series. What is that series' view of evaluation? How do they propose students be evaluated? How could you improve on their evaluation procedures?

2. Interview an elementary teacher in a local school. How does that individual evaluate the students in his or her room? Do you agree with that person's model of evaluation? Why or why not? What would you do that is similar or different?

3. Define "evaluation" in terms of the elementary science program. Define "evaluation" in terms of this particular course.

4. As a prospective teacher, with what aspects of evaluation are you most comfortable? With what aspects are you least comfortable? Explain your reasons.

5. As a student, with what aspects of evaluation are you most comfortable? With what aspects are you least comfortable? Please explain.

6. Using the information from this chapter, design a preliminary evaluation model for your first year of teaching. Will that model be significantly different from the model you may use in your tenth year of teaching? How do you account for any changes?

7. Why would evaluation be important *prior* to teaching a science lesson?

8. How do you intend to share your students' progress with parents? What data would be most helpful to parents? Interview several parents and ask them to discuss the type of information they would like to receive concerning their children's progress in science.

## REFERENCES AND SUGGESTED READINGS

AGI/NAS7A Earth Science Examination Task Force. (n.d.) *Guidelines for developing test items.* Washington, DC: National Science Teachers Association.

Bloom, Benjamin (Ed.). (1956). *Taxonomy of educational objectives. Handbook I: Cognitive domain.* New York: McKay.

Brophy, Jere E. (1986). *Educational psychology* (3rd ed.). New York: Longman.

Dembo, Myron H. (1991). *Applying educational psychology in the classroom* (4th ed.). White Plains, NY: Longman.

Green, John A. (1975). *Teacher made tests* (2nd ed.). New York: Harper & Row.

Gronlund, N. E. (1988). *How to construct achievement tests* (4th ed.). Englewood Cliffs, NJ: Prentice-Hall.

Hills, J. R. (1976). *Measurement and evaluation in the classroom.* Columbus, OH: Merrill.

LeFrancois, Guy R. (1988). *Psychology for teaching.* Belmont, CA: Wadsworth.

Pasch, Marvin, Sparks-Langer, Georgea, Gardner, Trevor G., Starko, Alane J., Moody, Christella D. (1991). *Teaching as decision making: Instructional practices for the successful teacher.* New York: Longman.

Wasserman, Selma, and Ivany, J. W. George. (1988). *Teaching elementary science: Who's afraid of spiders?* New York: Harper & Row.

Woolfolk, Anita E. (1990). *Educational psychology* (4th ed.). Englewood Cliffs, NJ: Prentice Hall.

Worthen, Blaine R., and Sanders, James R. (1987). *Educational evaluation: Alternative approaches and practical guidelines.* White Plains, NY: Longman.

# 11

# THE CURRICULA OF ELEMENTARY SCIENCE

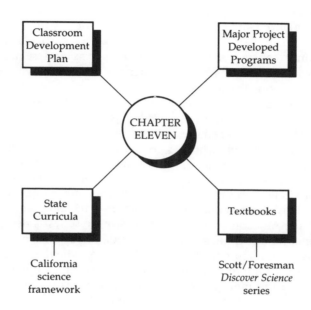

## Chapter Objectives

After reading this chapter you should be able to:

1. Define the major emphases in a selected state curriculum guide for elementary science instruction.

2. Understand the balance of life science, physical science, and earth and space science topics in a typical commercial science textbook series.

3. Compare and contrast the essential elements of three major project-developed programs in elementary science.

4. Begin to design and develop an individual classroom curriculum guide in science.

5. Elaborate on the future of science education.

The development of elementary science curricula in this country has been influenced by many things. The expansion of the space program in the 1960s and 1970s created a tidal wave of innovation, creativity, and renewed interest in what is taught in science and in how it is taught. National reports on the decline of science literacy in this country during the 1980s and 1990s stimulated the improvement of materials and teaching methods. Some instructional trends of today were prompted by the results of national achievement tests, which show that American children score significantly lower in science competencies than students in other industrialized countries. Significant too is the discovery of a plethora of procedures, processes, and practices that make science more personalized and relevant for children of all ages.

Science is a subject that is in a constant state of evolution. The facts and figures your students learn today may be out of date 10 years from now. The technological innovations of today may be commonplace in the next century. Some of the diseases and afflictions of plants, animals, and humans may be all but wiped out by the time your students graduate from high school or college. Earlier chapters have defined science not as just an accumulation of data but as a way of viewing the world and learning more about it. For example, it is far more important that your students understand the role of the tropical rain forest of the Amazon basin to the ecological balance of the planet than it is for them to memorize 50 plant names. It is more important that they understand the value of space exploration than that they simply commit to memory the nine planets in our solar system.

This places a heavy emphasis on a process approach or guided-discovery view of science. Because science facts are subject to change, redefinition, and reinterpretation, youngsters should be provided with the critical thinking and hands-on skills that will help them approach science as a true evolutionary discipline. Yes, the facts and figures of science are important, but it is far more important that youngsters evaluate and process that data than it is for them to commit it to memory. Whereas in mathematics the facts remain relatively constant over time, such is not the case with science.

**TO INVESTIGATE** _____

Obtain several textbooks or trade books about the moon, some published before 1969 and others published after 1969. Compare and contrast the information about the moon in the two sets of materials. You will note that although we had quite a bit of information about the moon prior to the start of manned moon flights in 1969, that data was enhanced and altered as a result of discoveries made by humans on the moon. In other words, memorizing only the pre-1969 information about the moon can lead to conflicts with new data learned about the moon. ∎

There is no single science curriculum, no one design that provides all the answers and information students need now will need in the future. Rather, there is a variety of curricula, each of which has a particular emphasis and sequence. Your approach to the teaching of science will be modified, redefined, and adapted many times in keeping with new discoveries (in terms of both science and your own classes). What your professor teaches you today and what you teach your students tomorrow may be different. What is presented in this book and what you see in your teacher's manual, state curriculum guide, or major funded project may be different, too. What is important is that you understand that there is no ideal science program. Each program, each curriculum guide, and each science series is designed with a particular focus in mind. To say that one is better than another may be counterproductive. The emphases, the viewpoints, and the biases may differ; it is up to you to determine how those ideas will be put into action in your own classroom.

It is vital, therefore, that you become aware of many different structures, approaches, and guides to the teaching of science. Evaluate each of them and their individual components in terms of your teaching style and philosophy. Choose elements of some, eliminate elements of others, and begin to develop a personal science curriculum that you are comfortable with and that will best meet the needs of your students.

The remainder of this chapter describes several types of science curricula as well as a plan you can use to develop your own classroom curriculum.

## CALIFORNIA SCIENCE FRAMEWORK

In the late 1980s the California Department of Education began drafting a series of documents and position statements on the teaching of science in the state. That process led to a reformulation of how science should be taught and how teachers should approach the teaching of science in their classrooms. In short, the emphasis in California schools is on a thematic approach to science education rather than the traditional life science/physical science/earth and space science continuum. This was an attempt to integrate the concepts of science so that they would not appear to be a fragmented sequence of facts and figures to be committed to rote memory.

As the American Association for the Advancement of Science noted in its book *Science for all Americans* (1988), themes should be a major emphasis of science curricula, in order to reinforce the importance of understanding ideas as opposed to the memorization of seemingly isolated facts. Themes connect facts just as the framework of a house connects its building components. This vital framework is missing from much of what is taught as science today.

Themes can be defined as the "big ideas," "overarching concepts," "unifying constructs," or "underlying metaphors." They are distinct from facts and concepts. A fact is a statement based on confirmed observation and inference, such as the number of electrons in an atom of iron, the date of the discovery of helium, or the descent of birds from dinosaurs. A concept may involve several facts. Examples of concepts are continental drift, the need for repeatable observations in constructing science, and how magnets work. Themes are larger ideas; they link the theoretical structures of the various scientific disciplines, showing how they are logically parallel and cohesive. Scientific literacy (see Appendix A) lies not only in knowing facts and concepts but in understanding the connections that make such information manageable and useful.

Themes are also distinct from theories. Theories are organized around content in particular disciplines of science, such as the theories of gravitation in physics, evolution in biology, and continental drift in geology. Themes such as "energy" or "patterns of change" cut across disciplines. By showing the interrelationships of different facts and ideas, themes primarily serve as pedagogical tools for the *presentation* of science. Themes integrate concepts and facts, provide a context through which to present content matter, and encourage better writing in science instructional materials.

Major themes (e.g., evolution, energy, patterns of change) occur again and again in the sciences, whether one studies ecology, plate tectonics, meteorology, or organic chemistry. This is not surprising; unifying constructs are a part of any philosophically united discipline. Themes also appear in the arts, for example. In the study of painting, music, or drama, essential elements of aesthetics, such as balance and symmetry, direction, form and proportion, and tension and release, give meaning to artistic expression.

A theme in science is similar to a theme in a symphony or novel. In a symphony, a theme is a repeated musical idea that gives structure and unity to the music. In a novel, a theme such as success, war and peace, love, or duty provides a conceptual background against which the plot unfolds. The plot of a novel is similar to the content or subject matter of science. A theme is a recurring idea that provides a context for explaining facts and events.

Science and technology are expanding so rapidly that a thematic approach to learning science is more than just helpful. Each branch of science has accumulated an enormous amount of detailed information, and if the basic concepts of one field can be transferred by connection or analogy to another field, students will understand that there is a purpose and a logic to the system. If curricula and instructors are successful in developing themes that enable students to connect and integrate science facts, this intellectual habit will carry over to other disciplines as well as to students' daily lives.

**DID YOU KNOW?** _____

It took approximately 30,000 years for the human species to produce 1 billion people. That same number of people is now produced in about 10 years.

**Classroom Activity**  Present this data to your students and ask them to discuss the social implications of so many people being "produced" in so short a time. What are the implications for housing, food supplies, and sanitary conditions? What are the implications if the birth rate continues to exceed the death rate in the world? Students may wish to construct brochures or minibooks with titles such as "Food," "Ecology," "Housing," "Transportation," and "Lifestyles" that detail their predictions and library research on various aspects of the worldwide population explosion. Students may wish to correspond with several national or international agencies (e.g., WHO, International Red Cross, and CARE) for additional information.  ■

## Some Major Themes of Science

The California Science Framework is organized around six basic themes: energy, evolution, patterns of change, stability, systems and interactions, and scale and structure. It should be emphasized that this is not the only possible configuration or the optimal number of themes. These six themes have been selected as *one way* of linking facts and ideas within and among scientific disciplines.

### Energy

Energy is a central concept of the physical sciences that pervades biological and geological sciences because it underlies any system of interactions. Energy can therefore be presented as a bond linking various scientific disciplines. Defined in physical terms, energy is the capacity to do work or the ability to make things move; heat, light, sound, and electricity are forms of physical energy. In chemical terms, energy provides the basis for reactions between compounds. In earth science terms, energy takes various subsurface forms (volcanoes, earthquakes, continental drift) and surface forms (wind, precipitation, chemical reactions). In the field of space science, there is solar energy and wind energy (as compared with geothermal, nuclear, water, and fossil fuel forms of energy). In biological terms, energy provides living organisms with the ability to maintain their systems, to grow, and to reproduce.

## Evolution

Evolution in a general sense can be described as "change through time" and applies to virtually all natural entities and systems. But evolution is not just the history of natural things; it is also the study of the patterns and processes that have shaped that history. These patterns and processes may be astrophysical, geological, or biological, and all contribute to the evolution of the universe as we know it. More than simple change, evolution is change with a direction; that direction is time. Evolution is not confined to life forms or to the earth and its systems; it extends throughout the entire universe. It encompasses the history of stars and planets, the formation of the planet earth, the growth and maturation of living organisms, and technological changes that have taken place in the physical sciences.

## Patterns of Change

Rates and patterns of change are essential features of the natural world. Analyses of changes help us to describe and understand what is happening in a natural system and, to some extent, to control those changes (particularly in technological applications). Understanding different kinds of changes helps us to predict what will happen next. Knowing about different patterns of change helps us to identify patterns of nature as we encounter them and to look for underlying mechanisms and connections.

Patterns of change can be divided into three types: (1) trends (such as the velocity of falling objects in acceleration, the decay of radioactive material, and the colonization of offshore islands by continental plants and animals), (2) cycles (such as life cycles, seasonal cycles, planetary cycles, tectonic cycles, and cell chemistry cycles), and (3) irregular changes (such as the predator-prey cycles of ecosystems, population cycles, and the motions of planetary bodies).

## Stability

Stability refers to constancy, that is, the ways in which systems attain an unchanging state and why. The ultimate fate of many systems is to settle into a steady state or a state of equilibrium; in such states, all forces are balanced. It is important to distinguish a state of equilibrium from a steady state. The former is analogous to a person sitting on a step of a stopped escalator, and the latter to a person walking down a moving escalator just as fast as the escalator moves upward. Equilibrium is rare in living systems, which are inherently dynamic.

Stability is related to the idea that nature is predictable. Given a set of initial experimental conditions, results are expected to be replicable. Indeed, lack of reproducibility begins search for uncontrolled variables. Science is based on observation and a testable framework of ideas. Scientific theories and laws remain fairly stable because they are based on consistent evidence.

## Systems and Interactions

Natural systems include solar systems, ecosystems, individual organisms, and chemical and physical systems. Defining the boundaries of a system allows the system and its parts and interactions to be studied. There are many kinds of interactions in systems. The components of an ecosystem (i.e., individual species) may interact through predation, competition, commensalism, mutualism, parasitism, or a number of other patterns. At

any time, a single component of a system can be interacting in various ways. A deer in an ecosystem can be a herbivore, an item of prey for a carnivore, and a living system itself with many subsystems of life functions (circulation, respiration, digestion, etc.).

To study systems, we generally focus on one or a few interactions at a time, to avoid an overload of information. These interactions are described in simplified terms using models. Models almost never simulate all the factors that are interacting or all the ways in which the factors interact, but they do provide a way of describing natural phenomena that are organized in systems.

## Scale and Structure

The kinds of structures that can be described in the natural world are many. The diversity of life, of geological forms and microstructures, and of chemical and physical structures, configurations, combinations, and interactions appears to be endless. And they can be endlessly described in instructional programs, often to the exclusion of other important themes. The point is to show how different kinds of structures are related, how they explain and illuminate each other, and how structure at different hierarchical levels (a phenomenon of scaling) shows unique properties at each level. There are component levels to the structures of most natural systems, whether one considers the hierarchy from atoms to molecules to compounds in chemistry, or the hierarchy from organelles to cells to tissues to organs in biology. It should be apparent that the theme of scale and structure is intimately tied with that of systems and interactions, because most systems are studied at some scale.

## TO INVESTIGATE _____

Visit one or more elementary classrooms in your local area. Observe several teachers during their science lessons. Determine whether those teachers present science as a series of isolated facts or as connected, interrelated themes. For example, do those teachers teach weather separate from seed plants and separate from energy? How would you gauge students' interest and understanding in those classrooms? What are some of the implications for your classroom? Discuss with your classmates any differences or similarities you discover in local schools. Is it easier or more difficult to teach science thematically? ∎

Table 11.1 illustrates how concepts in earth science can be presented to students through a thematic approach. Several themes have been combined for a particular topic so that students can see and comprehend the interactions and connections. Such an approach allows students to work with science in a global fashion, relying less on the memorization of facts and events and capitalizing on the themes that cut across artificially created boundaries to learning.

## Advantages of a Thematic Approach to Science Instruction

Science is too often presented as an endless, detailed description of natural phenomena, a parade of seemingly unconnected experiments and activities. Themes can integrate these separate pieces of information into broad, logically cohesive structures, in which demonstrated relationships among pieces of information illuminate the phenomena being described.

For example, instructional materials describing natural phenomena frequently present a series of boldface terms that are defined, often using other terms that also require definition. Science instruction thus becomes little more than an exercise in memorizing terms. Through the use of themes, such as those of scale and structure and systems and interactions, students can see how the parts fit together logically and how the information is used to describe other phenomena. A flower's parts can be named and described, but this information is more useful and more vivid to a student if these parts are described in terms of how they facilitate reproduction, how their great diversity evolved from a basic floral plan, or how they compare to reproductive systems in other kinds of plants and animals.

The integration of themes in science curricula does *not* mean that the usual divisions of earth, physical, and life sciences need be discarded; they should not be. Within the individual disciplines, themes need to be instituted and developed throughout a year's study and from one year to another. In a general science curriculum, there is even more opportunity to show how individual disciplines are connected by thematic strands.

Themes in science can also direct the design of classroom activities, providing them with a logical sequence and scope of instruction. For example, in a study of how energy flows through biological systems, students can initially monitor the flow of nutrients through a few easily kept organisms, such as houseplants, paramecia, mealworms, or mice. Later they can apply this knowledge to a study of the energy flow through ecosystems via food chains and food webs. Using the theme of energy to connect these two activities presents the basic concept in terms of a spiral effect, rather than treating the two activities as isolated.

The use of themes illuminates logical connections not only in science texts but also in review and assessment materials and in activities. Emphasis on the strict repetition of facts learned in chapters and units can be replaced by addressing the connections among those facts in the light of themes. How do these facts and concepts form cyclical patterns, show the hierarchical scale in the system, demonstrate the role of evolution, or underscore the importance of energy flow? This is

TABLE 11.1

......................................................................................

## THEMATIC APPROACH TO EARTH SCIENCE

......................................................................................

*Unifying Concept:* **The earth, within its universe, is constantly changing.**

| Theme | Grade | Grade-Level Concept and Subconcepts |
|---|---|---|
| Me in my world | K | There are observable changes on the earth.<br>* I see changes in the world around me<br>— Weather<br>— Day and night<br>— Seasons<br>* I see different landforms (mountains, valleys, plains, hills, deserts, oceans, etc.).<br>* The world of my community is made of different things, living and nonliving. (The topic of "My Community" is integrated with history/social studies.) |
| Stability<br>Energy Patterns<br>of change | 1 | Water is an important element of change on the earth.<br>* Most of the earth's water is found in the oceans and is salty. Fresh water is found in lakes, river systems, streams, creeks, and other drainage systems.<br>* Water undergoes phase changes.<br>* The sun warms the earth and the sea and drives the water cycle. Clouds can be observed and are part of the water cycle.<br>* The water cycle, in conjunction with other factors, creates the earth's weather.<br>* Weather data can be collected and reported, and the patterns can be described. |
| Patterns of change<br>Scale<br>and structure | 2 | Oceans affect or are affected by the changing earth.<br>* Forces at work in the earth create and reshape it.<br>* The earth (and its forces) work change over long periods of time. |
| Energy Evolution<br>Systems and<br>interactions | 3 | Oceans affect or are affected by the changing earth.<br>* Landforms and ocean basins can be defined.<br>* The energy of wave patterns in the ocean change landforms. Wave patterns can be studied as mechanical motions.<br>* The oceans have a profound influence on weather and climate, which in turn affect living organisms.<br>* Diverse life forms are found in the ocean habitat. |
| Systems and<br>interactions Energy | 4 | Changes in the atmosphere affect and are affected by changes in the earth.<br>* The sun warms the earth, sea, and air and drives the water cycle.<br>* Uneven heating of the earth affects air pressure and gives rise to wind patterns locally and around the globe.<br>* Moving air masses of different temperature and moisture content come in contact, resulting in precipitation and other identifiable weather phenomena.<br>* Weather data can be collected and reported.<br>* Weather has profound effects on climate and life forms. |
| Evolution<br>Patterns of<br>change Systems<br>and interactions | 5 | Forces that work on the earth cause the changes we observe.<br>* The earth is very old and has changed over geologic time.<br>* Forces arising from heat flow in the earth have caused it to change.<br>* The changing earth has had a profound effect on landforms and living organisms. |
| Evolution Systems<br>and interactions | 6 | The changing earth is part of a changing universe.<br>* Both sun and moon, objects within our solar system, have observable and identifiable effects on the earth.<br>—The sun is the source for all energy.<br>—The moon and the sun are responsible for tidal movement.<br>—Seasons are related to the earth's orientation with respect to the sun.<br>* The earth is part of the solar system. It is both similar and dissimilar to other planets.<br>* Stars provide information about the history of the universe. The earth is but a small part of the universe. |

more interesting than the typical chapter review heading "What Have We Learned?"

**IDEA BOX**

Whenever you present a new concept to your students, provide them with a way to visualize the relationships that exist between that concept and others. You may wish to draw three columns (life science, physical science, earth and space science) on the chalkboard or a large sheet of posterboard. Place the topic under discussion in one of the columns and ask students to speculate on the connections between that topic and the other two sciences. Later, students may wish to create their own theme books (for example, six homemade books using the six themes of the California Science Framework) and add information to those books throughout the school year. It would be appropriate to periodically review the books in whole class discussions.

Themes can be used to lay out basic principles of science that arise in many subfields and other disciplines. For example, the understanding of scale and structure is applicable whether one studies geological structures, biological structures, chemical structures, or what physicists call the structure of matter. The student who *expects* to find systems in which given interactions will be encountered and in which the emergent properties of each level in the structural hierarchy will be explained and related, is a student who is really being trained to understand science.

A thematic approach to science instruction can expand the expectations we have for our students. Instead of "knowing" science, students can relate science to their immediate world. This is illustrated by the program expectations of the California Science Framework in Table 11.2. Notice particularly how these expectations begin with thematic constructs and then radiate in several directions to form a broad-based science curriculum that is relational.

Of course, not all themes are for all teachers. The theme of stability, for example, may be difficult to present to kindergartners in any context. The theme of evolution may be equally inappropriate for a teacher trying to convey molecular structure and chemical reactions. However, the same materials can be presented in the context of energy or scale and structure. In teaching the elementary grades, teachers can best build the foundations for science education by (1) instilling in students the joy of science through enjoyable, expanding activities and experiences and (2) beginning to teach the processes of science, showing how they form the basis of all scientific activity.

**TEACHER TO TEACHER**

As a teacher, the greatest reward I have is when a student masters a concept covered in a science lesson. The highest level of mastery that can be demonstrated is when a student transfers knowledge from one situation to another.

**TABLE 11.2**

## SCIENCE PROGRAM EXPECTATIONS

1. The major themes underlying science, such as stability, patterns of change, evolution, systems and interactions, scale and structure, and energy, are developed and deepened through a thematic approach.
2. The three basic scientific fields of study—physical, earth, and life—are addressed, ideally each year, and the connections among theme are developed.
3. The character of science is shown to be open to inquiry and controversy, and free of dogmatism; the curriculum promotes student understanding of how we come to know what we know and how we test and revise our thinking.
4. Science is presented in connection with its applications in technology and its implications for society.
5. Science is presented in connection with students' own experiences and interests, frequently using hands-on experiences that are integral to the instructional sequence.
6. Students are given opportunities to construct the important ideas of science, which are then developed in depth, through inquiry and investigation.
7. Instructional strategies and materials allow several levels and pathways of access so that all students can experience both challenge and success.
8. Printed materials are written in an interesting and engaging style; in particular, vocabulary is used to facilitate understanding rather than as an end in itself.
9. Texts are not the sole source of the curriculum; ordinary materials and laboratory equipment, video and software, and other printed materials, such as reference books, provide a substantial part of student experience.
10. Assessment programs are aligned with the instructional program in both content and format; student performance and investigation play the same central role in assessment that they do in instruction.

Recently I was conducting a lesson on how plants can continue their life cycles in ways other than producing seeds. My third-graders were extremely excited to discover that cuttings can generate new roots. They had the opportunity to create cuttings, predict how many days it would take for roots to develop, and then plant the cuttings to create new plants.

At the end of the experience, one very enthusiastic third-grade boy came up to me, tugged excitedly on my sleeve and said, "These cuttings are just like the Gremlins in the movie." I had not seen the movie, so I did not know what he meant until he explained, "When you cut a Gremlin in half, it doesn't die—you get two!"

Transfer of knowledge? Mastery of the concept? Definitely—though never in a way that I would have imagined.

Esther B. Weiner
E.M. Baker School
Great Neck, NY

# SCOTT, FORESMAN'S DISCOVER SCIENCE TEXTBOOK SERIES (1989)

As pointed out earlier, many elementary science programs are driven by textbook series by one of several educational publishers. These series are designed to offer students a correlated and sequential series of principles and procedures for specific grade levels. Textbook series are intended to cover a great deal of material, sufficient to last the entire school year. They are not, however, intended to be the only source of science information for students.

It is important to keep in mind that science texts are a resource and a resource only. Their utility lies in the fact that they provide a plethora of possibilities and procedures for students to examine and explore within grade-appropriate guidelines. An overreliance on these prepared lessons, however, could lead to an inflexible science program—one that does not match the needs, interests, and abilities of students or the special circumstances, talents, or demographics of a particular community.

Table 11.3 illustrates is the scope and sequence chart from Scott, Foresman's *Discover Science* series, which is typical of series produced by major publishers today. As you glance over the goals and objectives for each grade level, keep in mind that this is only one possible way of sharing science knowledge with youngsters. It is not the only way or the best way. However, this "curriculum" provides teachers with a systematic procedure from which a fully functioning and engaging science program can begin. In short, this design can serve as a foundation for the fully integrated and effective classroom science program—one that also includes the special talents of the teacher and the variety of resources and materials at his or her disposal.

## TEACHER TO TEACHER

As a teacher I place an extremely high value on science teaching across the curriculum. However, there is one area in particular that links science with other curricular areas—writing.

Writing can be used in a variety of ways in science lessons. The most common, perhaps, are science lab write-ups. Other methods of utilizing writing include essay questions on exams, creative writing in science (a journey through a living cell, for example), writing research reports, writing and presenting speeches on a scientific topic, writing school newsletter articles about science class, using science-related plots in stories, journal writing for ongoing investigations; post–field trip summaries, and position papers, to name a few.

One particularly good writing exercise I use for review of materials is to have all the students write a statement or question about the material being covered. Students then exchange papers and carry on a "written conversation" about the subject. One comment/question generates another re-

sponse/answer/question. The entire activity occupies no more than 7 to 10 minutes.

In visiting with "real scientists" in industry and research, I have discovered that in order to be successful in today's technologically changing world, our students must know how to write. As educators we must provide the time and modeling for writing skills to be developed by our students.

I have also discovered a kernel of truth that seems to hold for me: "If students can write about it, they probably know about it."

Sharpen those pencils.

C. J. Graves
Monforton School
Belgrade, MT

## TEACHER TO TEACHER

Science changes so quickly that your textbooks cannot stay up to date. A scrapbook of current events in the science areas will provide a valuable reference tool as well as an incentive for the students to develop the habit of finding science in everyday life. We have a Space Technology Scrapbook and an Ecology Scrapbook going now. The students look for newspaper and magazine articles that relate to these areas. They may also submit a short write-up of something they heard on the TV news programs. They date the articles, glue them in the scrapbook, and share the main ideas with the class. (Extra credit or a piece of gum will help motivate!) I submit articles, too! We now have an up-to-date and personalized resource to use as we study these areas.

Elaine Hampton
Zia Middle School
Las Cruces, NM

## DID YOU KNOW?

The opossum has a gestation period (conception to birth) of 13 days; the alpine black salamander, on the other hand, can have a gestation period of up to 1,140 days (that's more than three years).

**Classroom Activity** If possible, have students create and produce their own video series on animals in and around the local community. Have groups of students film pets in the home as well as other animals indigenous to your area. Show the films to the class and ask them to select several animals and pursue some library research on those animals. The research can be used as narration for a video to be shown to other classes in the school. This should be planned as a long-term activity as students may need to film and refilm as well as conduct the appropriate research over an extended period of time. The result, however, will be a student-created production of immense value. (Students may wish to view several episodes of the "Wild America" series on PBS stations for ideas before initiating this activity.) ∎

TABLE   11.3

## SCOTT, FORESMAN *DISCOVER SCIENCE* SERIES SCOPE AND SEQUENCE

| | Life Science | Physical Science | Earth Science | Human Body |
|---|---|---|---|---|
| Kindergarten | Seeds and plants | Comparing and grouping matter | Seasons | Your senses |
| | Animals (growth, habitats) | Heat and cold | Helping our world | Growing and changing |
| | Living and nonliving | Sound <br> Movement | Weather <br> Earth and sky | |
| Grade 1 | Learning about plants <br> Learning about animals <br> Living and nonliving | Grouping things <br> Light, sound, and heat <br> Moving and working | The earth <br> Weather <br> The sky | Your senses <br> Growing and changing |
| Grade 2 | How plants are different <br> How animals are different <br> Life on earth long ago | Matter around you <br> Heat, light, and sound <br> Machines and electricity | Water and air <br> Changes in weather <br> The sun and other stars | How your body works <br> keeping healthy |
| Grade 3 | Plant growth <br> How animals grow and change <br> Living things need each other <br> How people affect plants and animals | Properties of matter <br> Work and machines <br> Forms of energy <br> Sound | Rocks and soil <br> Changes in the earth <br> Clouds and storms <br> The sun, moon, and planets | The body's support <br> Your body's health needs |
| Grade 4 | Flowering plants <br> Animal behavior <br> Food chains and food webs <br> Animal and plant adaptations | Measuring matter <br> Work and energy <br> Electricity and magnetism <br> Light and sound | Changes in landforms <br> Oceans <br> Measuring weather conditions <br> Movement in the solar system | Digestion and circulation <br> Your brain and your sense organs |
| Grade 5 | Plant processes <br> Invertebrates and vertebrates <br> Classifying living things <br> Populations and communities | Investigating matter <br> Heat and matter <br> Changing forms of energy <br> Energy resources | Earth's changing crust <br> Protecting the environment <br> Climate <br> Mapping the start | Body support, movement, and growth <br> Respiration and excretion |
| Grade 6 | Plant response <br> Cells and heredity <br> The fossil record <br> Change through time <br> Ecosystems and biomes | Structure of matter <br> Changes in matter <br> Electrical energy <br> Investigating light and sound | Earth's moving plates <br> Resources and conservation <br> Forecasting weather <br> Exploring space | The body's control systems <br> Growing up healthy |

.......... **MAJOR PROJECT-DEVELOPED PROGRAMS** ..........

One of the major factors influencing elementary science instruction involves several experimental projects developed in the 1950s, 1960s, and 1970s. Some of these projects were funded with government money, and others had the support of private funds. The following projects are three of the most successful:

Science—A Process Approach (SAPA)
Elementary Science Study (ESS)
Science Curriculum Improvement Study
  (SCIS)

These programs are all available from the following distributor: Delta Education, Inc. P.O. Box 950, Hudson, NH 03051.

Carin and Sund (1989) identified several features that these programs share:

1. These projects were initiated not by state departments of education or teacher education institutions, but by professional scientists who were concerned about the level of science literacy in this country.
2. Each of the projects benefited by having psychologists, science educators, elementary teachers, and other learning specialists on the team—a melding of some of the best science thinking available.
3. The projects were developed and funded before they were implemented in the schools, rather than the other way around, which was the case for most other curricular projects.
4. The projects were experimental in nature. Each was tested, retested, and evaluated through many steps to ensure that the it met all its goals before it was implemented in the schools.
5. There was a significant departure from textbook learning, which had been the norm for science teaching prior to the launching of Sputnik in 1957. Nearly all of the printed materials developed were for the purpose of recording data.

**DID YOU KNOW?** _____

On the average, men need 1,640 calories and women need 1,430 calories a day just to maintain their bodies.

**Classroom Activity**  Ask each student to record one day's diet of an adult in his or her family. Tell the student to keep track of everything the selected individual eats during a 24-hour time span. Afterward, have students calculate the approximate caloric intake of those adults. The results can be charted, and discussion can center on how many calories some adults are taking in beyond their daily requirements. Invite a dietitian to discuss the inherent dangers of high-calorie diets, particularly when they are not countered by regular exercise. What are some of the implications for students? ■

6. There was a major emphasis on the active participation of students in the learning process. The teacher was viewed less as a controller and more as a facilitator in assisting students in developing science concepts.
7. The emphasis was on teaching fewer content areas; mastery of a few was considered more important than superficial knowledge of many.
8. New theories about how children learn suggested the earlier introduction of more abstract information compared with the previous practice.
9. Many of these projects included a healthy dose of qualitative concepts, with students measuring, graphing, and charting information predicted and learned within a single lesson.
10. The projects emphasized an open-ended approach to science learning. That is, students were encouraged to ask their own questions and engage in problem-solving strategies, rather than memorize long lists of data or vocabulary words, for example.
11. Many components of these programs were "packaged"; that is, concrete materials (gauges, thermometers, flasks, wire, etc.) were included so that teachers could effectively utilize a coordinated package of items with any single activity.
12. The major emphasis dealt with the role of the teacher. *No longer was it necessary for the teacher to be a scientist to teach scientific concepts and principles.* Rather, the emphasis was on helping students investigate science and arrive at their own conclusions about the world around them.

Not only were these projects considerably different from more traditional methods of science instruction; they were also different from each other. Principally, those differences centered on the emphases on processes and content as well as the program's degree of structure. Some programs allowed teachers to assume more control in the classroom, and other projects "controlled" the content and the way it was presented to students.

Research on these funded projects in comparison to traditional text-based instruction yielded some interesting data. Shymansky, Kyle, and Alpert (1982) reported the following results:

1. The average student in an ESS, SCIS, or SAPA classroom performed better than 62 percent of the students in traditional classrooms across all performance criteria measured—a 12 percentage point gain.

2. In the three science curricula, students scored at least 18 percentage points higher than traditional-class students on measures of process skills development.

3. SCIS and SAPA students scored higher than students in comparable textbook-based classrooms on tests of reading and arithmetic skills.

Unquestionably, these programs have had a significant impact on the way science is taught in this country. Let's examine each of them in greater detail, with particular attention to the components or elements that might have the greatest significance for your future science program.

**DID YOU KNOW?** _____

With the exception of the sun, the closest star to the planet Earth is Proxima Centauri, which is 25,200,000,000,000 miles away.

**Classroom Activity** Your students will enjoy using star charts, particularly when they have opportunities to match the stars on the charts with the same stars in the night sky. Several charts are available, including "Dial the Night Sky" from Sky Publishing (49 Bay State Road, Cambridge, MA 02238), "Star Finder and Zodiac Dial" from Nasco (901 Janesville Ave., Fort Atkinson, WI 53538), and "Star and Planet Indicator" from Edmund Scientific (101 East Gloucester Pike, Barrington, NJ 08007). After students have learned some of the constellations, they may wish to "invent" some of their own—naming them after people, pets, or local landmarks and attractions, for example. ∎

## Science—A Process Approach (SAPA)

By its very name, the SAPA program of science instruction implies that the emphasis is on process skills (see Chapter 2) rather than on content. Originally developed by the American Association for the Advancement of Science (AAAS), this program now comes in two versions, SAPA and SAPA II.

In grades K–3 the emphasis is on the following eight processes:

1. Observing
2. Classifying
3. Using space/time relations
4. Using numbers
5. Communicating
6. Measuring
7. Predicting
8. Inferring

In grades 4–6 six additional processes are introduced that build on those taught in the lower grades. The intermediate-level processes include:

1. Formulating hypotheses
2. Controlling variables
3. Experimenting
4. Defining operationally
5. Formulating models
6. Interpreting data

What is critical about this process approach to science instruction is the fact that later processes depend on the mastery of preceding processes. The program is hierarchical and assumes that students who have mastered "lower-level" processes are able to handle processes that require higher levels of intellectual preparedness.

One of the major differences between SAPA and the other project developed programs is that it emphasizes behavioral objectives. A sample lesson would include the following:

1. *Statement of objectives:* The specific skills all students are expected to master at the completion of the activity.
2. *Rationale:* The necessary background information for the classroom teacher as well as the reasons why the activity is significant to students' comprehension of an area of science.
3. *Vocabulary:* Words that are necessary for understanding and that have not been presented previously.
4. *Materials:* Includes equipment and items that can be obtained from local sources or through commercial distributors.
5. *Originating problem:* A condition or scenario designed to build student enthusiasm for the activity.
6. *Instructional procedure:* A sequence of activities to be followed in a particular order that build upon skills mastered in earlier activities.
7. *Appraisal:* Procedures to determine if students have mastered the objectives stated for the lesson.

As teachers used SAPA it became apparent that some changes were necessary to make the program more responsive to the needs of individual teachers and individual students. In 1975 SAPA II was created. SAPA II has more of an environmental emphasis, and it is more humanistic; that is, rather than presenting a series of "cut and dried" activities, the new approach portrays science as a tool to solve problems and make new discoveries. The value of science as a lifelong enterprise is also promoted in the new program. The other major change is the diversity of options available to teachers within a module. Structure is deemphasized, and teachers are given choices based on their organizational plans and student needs.

**IDEA BOX** ⎯⎯⎯⎯⎯⎯⎯⎯⎯⎯⎯⎯⎯⎯⎯⎯

Create an oversized wall chart that lists all the science processes across the top. For each process, have students list
one or more activities they participate in that involves the
designated process (for example, for the process of observation students may record all the things they observe about a
tree over the nine months of school). Throughout the year
encourage students to list additional events or activities in
the columns for the various processes. Students may elect
to convert the chart to a classroom scrapbook. By the end
of the year they may be surprised to discover how many
times they use each of the science processes (and not just
in science!).

## Elementary Science Study (ESS)

The ESS program, made up of 56 units, is a nonsequen-
tial collection of science activities and explorations that
can be used at any time within the science curriculum
at the discretion of the teacher. The philosophy behind
ESS is that students learn best when they are allowed
to select the learning opportunities that best meet their
own needs and interests. The teacher acts as a facilitator, providing the environment, materials, and conditions under which students can initiate their own explorations.

There is no master plan for teachers to follow in
ESS. In fact, schools and districts are encouraged to
use as many of the units within their own science curriculum as they deem necessary. As such, ESS is not a
full curriculum but rather a series of science units that
can be integrated into other science curricula according to local conditions, teacher expertise, and material
availability. Obviously, this allows for a great deal of
flexibility in teaching science.

The program comes in the form of kits, most of
which use items and materials that are familiar to children or can be easily located in the home. Each kit
offers students an open-ended approach to science and
offers teachers a self-contained package that is easily
incorporated into the regular science curriculum.

Instruction is child centered, reflecting the natural curiosity of students, rather than teacher-directed.
Teachers using ESS are expected to introduce the units,
guide questioning, stimulate student discovery within
the experiences, and act as an overseer of individual
investigations.

Three types of units make up the ESS program:

1. Total Class Units

   Balancing
   Balloons
   Batteries and Bulbs
   Colored Solutions
   Gases and "Airs"
   Growing Seeds
   Heating and Cooling
   Ice Cubes
   Kitchen Physics
   Microgardening
   Optics
   Pendulums
   Rocks and Charts
   Sink or Float
   Slips and Slides
   Small Things

2. Individual/Small Group Units

   Animal Activity
   Attribute Games and Problems
   Balance Book
   Batteries and Bulbs II
   Drops, Streams, and Containers
   Geo Blocks
   Mirror Cards
   Mobiles
   Pattern Blocks
   Printing Press
   Sand
   Spinning Tables
   Tangrams

3. Teacher Guides (less structured units with no materials)

   Animal Book
   Bones
   Brine Shrimp
   Butterflies
   Changes
   Clay Boats
   Daytime Astronomy
   Eggs and Tadpoles
   Life of Beans and Peas
   Light and Shadows
   Mapping
   Match and Measure
   Mealworms
   Mobiles
   Mosquitoes
   Musical Instrument
   Mystery Powders
   Peas and Particles
   Pond Water
   Recipe Book
   Starting from Seeds
   Structures
   Tracks
   Where Is the Moon?

## IDEA BOX

During your student teaching experience take several photographs of other teachers' science demonstrations and experiments. Visit as many classrooms as you can, taking photos and jotting down notes about the events and presentations you see (if possible, also visit other schools within the same district). When the photos are developed, catalog them in a scrapbook or file box according to the science discipline (e.g., life science, physical science, earth and space science). Years later, when you're trying to think of some good demonstrations for a particular unit of study, you can turn to this file and replicate a demonstration observed during your student teaching days.

## Science Curriculum Improvement Study (SCIS)

SCIS is best viewed as an extension of the goals advocated in SAPA. Whereas SAPA relies almost exclusively on a process approach to science education, SCIS uses both science process skills and content in its design. Each of the 12 units is built around a major concept and is supported by subconcepts and integrated process skills.

SCIS is organized into three programs: Beginnings (kindergarten level), Physical/Earth Science Sequence (grades 1–6), and Life/Earth Science Sequence (grades 1–6). The latter two programs are subdivided into six levels each:

### Physical/Earth Science Sequence

Material Objects (grade 1)
Interactions and Systems (grade 2)
Subsystems and Variables (grade 3)
Relative Position and Motion (grade 4)
Energy Sources (grade 5)
Scientific Theories (grade 6)

### Life/Earth Science Sequence

Organisms (grade 1)
Life Cycles (grade 2)
Populations (grade 3)
Environments (grade 4)
Communities (grade 5)
Ecosystems (grade 6)

SCIS offers the classroom teacher a hierarchical approach to the teaching of elementary science. That is, the processes and content presented in early grades are reinforced and extended in later grades. Although the intention is to have a physical/earth science level taught during half of the year and a life/earth science level taught during the other half of the year, teachers are encouraged to modify this arrangement according to the specific needs and learning aptitudes of their students.

Each SCIS lesson is divided into three parts: Exploration, Invention, and Discovery. During Exploration, students are provided with an extended opportunity to manipulate equipment or observe phenomena. These explorations are open-ended discoveries on the part of youngsters but may be guided by the teacher as the need arises. After these first-hand contacts with the material under study, the lesson moves to the Invention stage, which includes a teacher explanation of the concept under study followed by additional experiences that extend the concept. The lesson concludes with the Discovery stage, in which students apply the concept to other situations or circumstances.

The emphasis in SCIS is to help students develop self-initiated discovery skills reinforced with specific content offered by the classroom teacher. The focus is on active participation in a supportive atmosphere.

SCIS is now available in three versions: the original SCIS, developed at the University of California at Berkeley, and two newer versions, SCIIS and SCIS II. Differences between the newer models and the original are minimal and include the enlargement of some levels, the introduction of newer materials, a redesign of the teacher guides, the introduction of "Extending Your Experience" (EYE) cards, evaluation procedures, title changes, management strategies, and more flexible packaging.

## YOUR CLASSROOM CURRICULUM GUIDE

As stated earlier in this chapter, there is no ideal way to teach science. The materials you use and the methods you employ will be determined by number of factors, such as availability of materials and equipment, the individual needs and abilities of your students, commercial and printed resources, your own level of comfort in teaching science, administrative support, the required science series, and in-service training. No two programs will be exactly the same.

### DID YOU KNOW?

During your lifetime, North America and Europe will separate by the average height of a person, and the Pacific Ocean will shrink by the average width of a single-family home. Next year Los Angeles will move closer to San Francisco by the length of your little finger.

**Classroom Activity** The movement of the earth's lithospheric plates (often referred to as plate tectonics) is a constant source of amazement for students. The motions of the earth's plates can be demonstrated with a sheet cake. Obtain a cake from a local bakery and cut the aluminum pan widthwise across the bottom and up the sides. Place plastic figures and houses in the frosting to simulate a community or city. Have two students grasp the ends of the pan with one student twisting the pan to the left, the other student twisting the pan to the right (this demonstrates lateral plate movement). Then, have the two students take a second cake (prepared in the same manner as the first) and push the two ends together (this demonstrates divergent plate movement). Be sure to discuss the similarities between these demonstrations and to stress that this is actually what occurs in the earth's surface. (For an excellent article that provides further ideas, see "Cakequake! An Earth-Shaking Experience" by Garry R. Hardy and Marvin N. Tolman in *Science and Children*, vol. 29, no. 1 [September 1991], pp. 18–21.)  ∎

Not all schools and school districts have the resources (financial or personnel) available for creating specialized science curricula. However, the information in this chapter should enable you to begin to develop your own unique science program. The sequence offered in Table 11.4 is but one way of approaching the design of a unique science program. No matter what

approach you take, you are the one who will need to make the important decisions about what is taught and how it is taught. Those decisions cannot be made by a curriculum guide, textbook series, or state-mandated framework or syllabus.

## Step 1

Develop a calendar for the school year. Include the weeks for each month. Consult your assigned textbook and begin filling in the calendar with the topics suggested for each week or month of the year. As you work through the calendar, make certain to include life science, earth and space sciences, and physical science topics. You should consider altering the sequence of topics suggested in the text series. For example, you may wish to present some topics when the climatic conditions are conducive to working outdoors. The unit on plant growth and development can be scheduled for spring, the study of weather forecasting can be scheduled for September or early October (typically the hurricane season along the east coast of North America), and the study of photosynthesis may be scheduled for the fall months, when the leaves are changing. In short, the textbook series is only a guide to the teaching of science; it is up to you to make decisions as to the appropriate sequence of lessons in keeping with local conditions and student interests.

## Step 2

Consult the science curriculum for your state. What objectives have been mandated for the teaching of science in your state? Are those goals commensurate with those in the science textbook series? How can you rationalize any discrepancies? What elements of the state guide can you include in your own program? The an-

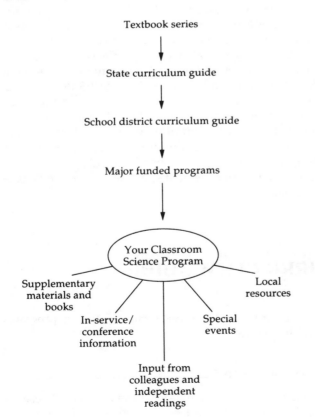

Textbook series

↓

State curriculum guide

↓

School district curriculum guide

↓

Major funded programs

↓

Your Classroom Science Program

Supplementary materials and books

In-service/ conference information

Input from colleagues and independent readings

Special events

Local resources

swers to these questions will help you tap into the expertise of the curriculum planners who developed your state's science framework.

## Step 3

Check any science curriculum guide prepared by your school district. In many cases that guide will no only reflect the philosophy of teaching science in your district, but it will be correlated to the science materials currently in use in the district. Note the elements of the guide that are similar to or different from the textbook series you will be using. You will also need to assess the support materials and personnel that have been addressed in the district's science curriculum. Another significant question is how stringently you will be expected to follow the district guide. Will you have some degree of latitude in establishing and carrying out your own classroom program, or are you expected to follow the district plan exclusively?

## Step 4

Check out the elements and components of some of the major funded projects. How can some of those procedures and plans be made part of your classroom curriculum? You may wish to contact the commercial suppliers of those materials for catalogs and sample materials. Some of the project distributors offer inservice training on their programs. Request that your school administrator ask for any necessary training (either via videos or by a trained facilitator) on the use and implementation of a specified program.

## Step 5

Are there any topics in science in which you have a special interest? Place them in your schedule, too. These topics may be influenced by the area in which you live. If there are seasonal phenomena unique to your area, utilize them. A rainy season, the aurora borealis, times when an inversion is most likely, times when birds or animals migrate or gather their food—these are all events that should be part of your science program. You may want to include any special interests or industries unique to your area, too. For example, is a keen interest in flying gliders or small planes shared by individuals in the area? A unit of study on how airplanes fly, their aerodynamics, lift, and other elements of air travel may be part of a science unit that begins with a field trip to a local small airport or with guest speakers who are pilots or work at an airport in some capacity.

## Step 6

After you are satisfied with the topics and have developed an outline of the content you will be presenting during the year, you will also need to check the availability of materials and aids at the school. Are films, filmstrips, slides, and other audiovisual materials available? If possible, preview those that appear to be appropriate for your students and content. Are there any sites in the nearby area that could be utilized for field trips? If so, list them and visit a few if possible (see Chapter 9). What industries, businesses, and government agencies (including parks) are in the area? How would they fit in with your program? Does the school maintain a speaker's list by topic? Can you utilize any of those individuals?

### IDEA BOX _____

As you read your daily newspaper, keep an eye out for experts and other potential resource people in your community. Scientists, landfill operators, electricians, botanists, plumbers, and other science-related personnel are frequently mentioned in the daily newspaper—particularly in the "Local" section. As you come across these names, record them on index cards (along with any phone numbers or addresses) and file them in a special box labeled with the topics of your science program. Then, when it is time to do a unit on electricity, for example, you will have an index card with the name of one or more electricians who can be called for a possible presentation in your classroom. Be sure to add new names to your file on a frequent basis. You will discover a host of local "experts" who can serve as guest speakers and demonstrators for your classroom science program.

## Step 7

An important aspect of your science program is to have the appropriate written material and support personnel available for you and the students. Use textbooks, encyclopedias, "how-to" books, and trade books on specific topics, such as rocks, butterflies, and birds. You may want to consult your school librarian to determine what books are available for the various topics, the procedures for borrowing significant numbers of books for your classroom library, and the availability of other printed materials, such as periodicals, bulletins, and newspapers.

## Step 8

Don't forget your needs! Your knowledge on the selected topics will grow with that of the students. What books are available that will enhance your background? Are there any resource units in the library on the topics? What other material is there for you to study as you prepare for the lessons? What types of in- service programs or special training opportunities are available? Will you be able to attend one of the state, regional, or the national conferences of the National Science Teachers Association? Remember, too, that there are other teachers in the school who may have expertise in areas in which you are weak. Ask around, especially when you are a novice. Who are the individuals that have presented interesting units in science? Be bold and ask if they would offer assistance. Don't be apprehensive about asking science teachers at the junior and senior high school level for help in developing a more extensive science background.

## Step 9

After you have acquired all this data, you will want to tentatively begin matching topics and content with the teaching techniques you deem appropriate. The key word is "tentatively"; remember, you are developing a guide and you do not want to be a slave to it. Once the methods are matched to the content, review the entire document. The curriculum guide should be a dynamic document. Leave room for comments and write notes to yourself as the year progresses. What was successful, and what was not? Can you think of reasons why? Are there obvious gaps in the guide? Would another approach have been more appropriate? What have you learned about children and science? Do you provide variety in content, topics, and procedures? You will not want to have a succession of speakers, one after the other, nor will you want several field trips in the same week. What you will want is a curriculum plan that is subject to modifications engendered by your increasing competence in science teaching and the specific needs and intellectual preparedness of each new class of students.

## Step 10

Finally, do not forget to seize the teachable moment. Something may occur that you did not include in your guide but that suddenly generates tremendous interest. It may be a weather phenomenon, a space exploration, a new report on an illness, the discovery of a new drug, the invention of a machine, or a sudden advancement in some area of technology, the eruption of a volcano, or an earthquake. Do not let the sudden interest in the

Today we are not going to cover our scheduled activity. We are going to discuss snowstorms.

occurrence pass you by; you may never have access to such extensive coverage by TV and the other media again. Seize that teachable moment and include it in your science program.

**DID YOU KNOW?** _____

Each year there are about 500,000 earthquakes around the world. Only about 1,000 of them cause any measurable damage.

**Classroom Activity**   Students are always interested in earthquakes (particularly those who live near fault lines). You can help your students understand the nature of earthquakes and their locations with a selection of trade books, including *Our Violent Earth* (Washington, DC: National Geographic Society, 1982), *The Crust of the Earth: An Armchair Traveller's Guide to the New Geology* by Chet Raymo (New York: Prentice-Hall, 1983) (an excellent teacher resource), and *How Did We Find out about Earthquakes?* by Isaac Asimov (New York: Messner, 1978). ∎

## DIRECTIONS FOR THE FUTURE

Science education today is in an evolutionary stage. We are constantly learning new things about how children learn and how science can be taught. Given your review of the curricula of science in concert with the

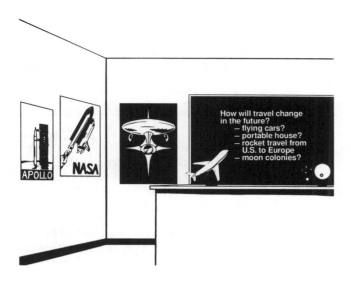

previous discussion in this book, you should consider the following guidelines as enhancers of your success as a teacher of science and as directions for the future of elementary science instruction.

1. *More emphasis on a discovery approach to science.* When students are provided with more hands-on activities, science becomes more "real" for them.
2. *Higher intellectual excitement.* Science can be promoted as a combination of "hands-on, minds-on" activities that stimulate creative and critical thinking.
3. *An emphasis on science processes.* The processes of science are just as important, if not more so, than the content of science.
4. *Encouragement of science attitudes.* How students feel about science in their daily lives continues to be a major issue in elementary science education.
5. *More emphasis on a few units rather than a collection of many isolated units.* The thematic approach to science (e.g., the California Science Framework) can have a profound effect on students' appreciation and comprehension of science principles.
6. *A more humanistic approach.* The human factor in science can help determine how well students embrace science as a personal activity.
7. *Science in social and environmental issues.* The need to portray science as a vehicle for learning about and dealing with pressing societal issues continues.
8. *Integration of science with other subjects.* The value of science lies in its relationships with the rest of the curriculum, not in its isolation from other subjects.
9. *More flexibility.* The teaching of science can be tailored to the unique talents of a classroom teacher and the special needs of students in that classroom.

10. *Teachers as facilitators.* Teachers will continue to provide the environment in which science can be enjoyed and practiced, rather than using science class as a time to memorize unrelated facts and figures.

---

### Science–Technology–Society: Excerpts from a NSTA Position Statement

The goal of science education is to develop scientifically literate individuals who understand how science, technology, and society influence one another and who are able to use this knowledge in their everyday decision making. The scientifically literate person has a substantial knowledge base of facts, concepts, conceptual networks, and process skills which enable the individual to continue to learn and think logically. This individual both appreciates the value of science and technology in society and understands their limitations.

---

### Recommendations for K–6 Grade Levels

Science should be an integral part of the elementary school program. It should be used to integrate, reinforce, and enhance the other basic curricular areas so as to make learning more meaningful for children.

A carefully planned and articulated elementary science curriculum should provide daily opportunities for the sequential development of basic physical and life science concepts, along with the development of science process and inquiry skills.

Elementary science should provide opportunities for nurturing children's natural curiosity. This helps them to develop confidence to question and seek answers based upon evidence and independent thinking. Children should be given an opportunity to explore and investigate their world using a hands-on approach, with instructional materials readily available.

The focus of the elementary science program should be on fostering in children an understanding of, an interest in, and an appreciation of the world in which they live.

*Time on Science Learning*

- Lower elementary level (grades K–3): A minimum of 1 ½ hours/week of science should be required.
- Upper elementary level (grades 4–6): A minimum 2 ½ hours/week of science should be required.

*Emphasis on Programs for All Students*

- In elementary school, science education programs should provide basic concepts for all students. Opportunities should be available for students with diverse interests and commitments, including students with exceptional interests and talents in science.

*Emphasis on Laboratory and Field Activities*

- Elementary-level laboratory and field activities should stress the development of basic inquiry skills.

*Science Instruction Matches Students' Cognitive, Physical, Social, and Emotional Development*

- Schools should provide objectives, content, and instructional strategies that are appropriate to the students's stage of mental, moral, and physical development.
- Varying strategies and materials should be provided at all grades to accommodate students with varying levels of learning skills and mental development.

*Emphasis on Science-Related Social Issues*

- Elementary level: A minimum of 5 percent of science instruction should be directed toward science-related societal issues.

The entire NSTA position statement was adopted unanimously by the board of directors in 1982. Copies of the entire statement are available; write to the National Science Teachers Association, 1742 Connecticut Ave., NW, Washington, DC 20009.

## TO INVESTIGATE

Visit a local elementary school. Interview a small group of first-grade students and, later, a small group of fifth-grade students. Ask each group what they think about science. Do they enjoy science? Why or why not? What is it they like most about science? What is it they like least? How does science rank in comparison with other subjects? What elements of the science program do they remember most? Collect your data and compare it with the data collected by your classmates. How can you account for any differences between first-graders' perceptions of science and fifth-graders' perceptions? What is being done (or not being done) in science classes that may contribute to those perceptions and attitudes? What implications do those attitudes have for your future classroom? ∎

..........................................................................................................
## POINTS OF DISCUSSION
..........................................................................................................

1. Which of the funded projects allows for the most innovation on the part of the teacher? Which allows for the least innovation? Which one would be most comfortable for you?
2. What are some of the advantages and disadvantages a thematic approach to the teaching of science (e.g., California Science Framework)? You may wish to select a sample unit in a traditional science textbook and develop a series of lessons based on themes.
3. Interview several experienced teachers (those with 10 or more years of experience). Ask them how they think science instruction has changed since they entered the profession.
4. Obtain several science series (these can be gathered from your college's curriculum library or from a local elementary school). Discuss any similarities or major differences between the series. Compare series published in different years.
5. Work with one of your classmates. Using Table 11.4, design a preliminary science curriculum for your classroom for one month of instruction.
6. Interview several parents in a local elementary school. What elements would they like to see in

their children's science program? How will you be able to provide some of those elements in your own classroom program?
7. How much input do you think students should have in their own science education or science curriculum? What may be some of the short-term or long-term effects?
8. Obtain a copy of your state's curriculum guide in science (you can write to the department of education in your state's capital, or perhaps your college library has a copy). How does your state's curriculum guide compare with the California guide presented in this chapter?
9. What kinds of decisions do you think teachers need to make to choose the best elements of other programs or projects in order to design an effective classroom curriculum? Work with a classmate to design a preliminary checklist that will help you choose the best elements of other designs.
10. Work with a classmate and design a guidebook on the "dos and don'ts" of using science textbook series exclusively. What factors need to be considered for the effective utilization of the design and materials in a textbook?

# REFERENCES AND SUGGESTED READINGS

American Association for the Advancement of Science. (1988). *Project 2061: Science for all Americans.* Washington, DC: Author.

California Department of Education, Curriculum Commission. (1989, October). *Science framework for California public schools interim edition.* Sacramento: Author.

Carin, Arthur, & Sund, Robert. *Teaching science through discovery.* Columbus, OH: Merrill.

New York State Education Department, Division of Program Department. (n.d.). *Elementary science syllabus.* Albany: Author.

Shymansky, James, Kyle, William, & Alpert, Jennifer. (1982, November/December). "How effective were the hands-on science programs of yesterday?" *Science and Children, 20* (3), pp. 14–15.

Texas Education Agency. (1987). *Science framework, kindergarten–grade 12.* Austin: Author.

# 12

# LIFE SCIENCE

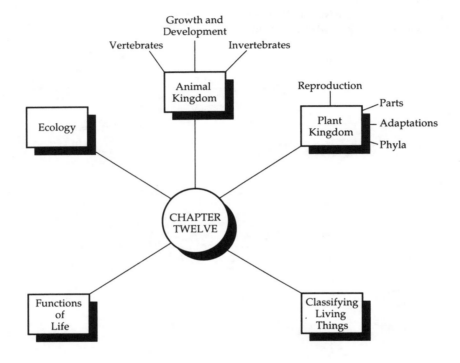

## Chapter Objectives

After reading this chapter you should be able to:

1.  Elaborate on the similarities and differences between plants and animals.

2.  Describe the life processes and characteristics of members of the plant kingdom.

3.  State the major groups and subgroups of the animal kingdom.

4.  Understand animal growth and development.

5.  Explain some of the ecological and environmental concerns of the planet Earth.

The study of life in all its forms is one of the basics of science. As students learn about patterns of growth, ecological relationships, and environmental habitats, they gain an appreciation for the majesty of the world around them. This knowledge can be used in efforts to preserve the living world for successive generations.

The life sciences are an important part of children's experiences in elementary science. Students need to be aware of the fact that life is all around them and affects them in varied and interesting ways. Following are some of the principles and concepts that drive the life sciences—those elements that define and describe the life sciences for scientist and layman alike. These elements should be components of your classroom science curriculum as much as they are components of our everyday lives.

1. Plants and animals are living things.
2. Living things are different from nonliving things.
3. Living things reproduce; nonliving things do not.
4. The basic unit of all living things is the cell.
5. Living things can be classified according to their unique characteristics.
6. Animals and plants inherit and transmit the characteristics of their ancestors.
7. Animals affect plants; plants affect animals.
8. Living things affect their environment; the environment affects living things.
9. Living things adapt to the unique conditions of the environment in which they live.
10. Living things depend upon elements of the earth, space, and physical sciences for their existence.
11. Plants are food producers; animals are food consumers.
12. The human body consists of cells, tissues, and organs that work together to perform particular functions.
13. The human body can be affected by internal and external influences.
14. Humans have an effect on the environment in which they live; the environment affects human beings.

The conditions listed will be essential ingredients of your students' explorations into the life sciences. It is important that students understand that all living things are related to all the other living things on this planet. Although we will conveniently distinguish the two major kingdoms (plants and animals) in the life sciences, students must realize that animals and plants are intimately interrelated; we are dependent on our plant neighbors and they on us. It is quite easy to have students observe, communicate, predict, classify, measure, and experiment with a classroom animal (a white mouse, for example). Yet it is also vital that youngsters realize that the existence of that creature is dependent on elements of the plant world. In short, it is critical that students be constantly exposed to the varied interdependencies that exist among living things.

## THE FUNCTIONS OF LIFE

Take a look at the two illustrations to the right. Which one is living? Which one is nonliving? How do you know? What characteristics does the living thing have that the nonliving thing does not have?

Certainly, you know the difference between a chicken and a rock. The chicken is living, and the rock is not. Now take a look at the following list of items, which all share several characteristics. Can you discern what some of those characteristics are?

| | | |
|---|---|---|
| Pine tree | Tadpole | Mold |
| Robin | Sponge | Grass |
| Newt | Lichen | Tapeworm |
| Rhinoceros | Centipede | Sunflower |
| Lima bean | Gnat | Banana |
| Aphid | Fern | Bacteria |

Obviously, the items in this list are all living things, but are you aware that they all share eight characteristics—eight basic functions that differentiate living things from nonliving things? (Before reading any further, see if you can list at least five major factors that distinguish a living thing from a nonliving thing.) These characteristics are shared by plants and animals and appear in the simplest of organisms as well as the most complex. Known as the *functions of life*, they are features scientists look for in all living organisms. Conversely, things that do not exhibit one or more of these characteristics can be classified as nonliving. The following eight functions are present in *all* living things:

1. The ability to *reproduce.*
2. The ability to *grow.*
3. The ability to *move.*
4. The ability to *respire.*
5. The ability to *respond* to changes.
6. The ability to *excrete* and *secrete* waste products.
7. The ability to *transport* materials within it.
8. The ability to *produce, acquire,* or *use* food.

All of the organisms on the preceding list exhibit these eight characteristics. The rock, on the other hand, exhibits none of these features (although some students will argue that a rock does respond to changes in its environment by cracking and splitting under extreme temperatures).

### TO INVESTIGATE

Visit several classrooms (both elementary and secondary). Ask students at various grade levels if they can identify the characteristics of living things. In other words, what features do all living things have that nonliving things do not? Classify the responses by age/grade level. Are older students able to come up with more characteristics than younger students? Which features are most often mentioned? Which features are seldom mentioned? Afterward, you may wish to ask a representative sample of adults (teachers, fellow students, professors, etc.) to identify the characteristics of living things. What implications can you draw from your research, particularly in terms of your classroom science program? What strategies or techniques can you use to help students understand the common features of living things? ∎

## CLASSIFYING LIVING THINGS

Chapter 2 defined "classifying" as the ability to assign items or things to a group. Classifying enables us to understand the characteristics and features shared by items belonging to the same group. For example, "vegetables" is the name of a group that includes carrots, celery, turnips, and lima beans. The items belonging to that group have common characteristics that allow additional items (such as radishes, lettuce, and eggplant) also to be assigned to that group and that prohibit other items (such as apples, tractors, and diamonds) from being assigned. In short, classifying allows us to recognize both similarities and differences between items.

Living things are typically classified in one of five major groupings known as *kingdoms.*[1] Kingdoms are further divided into groups known as *phyla.* Phyla are also subdivided, and groups continue to be divided until a particular living thing is in the smallest possible group of living things with identical characteristics. The following hierarchy details the groupings used for living things:

Kingdom
⇓
Phylum
⇓
Class
⇓
Order
⇓
Family
⇓
Genus
⇓
Species

As you will note, any living organism is classified into seven different categories. This classification procedure allows scientists and lay people to talk about living organisms with little or no confusion. As an example, take a look at the names of two common animals:

### Dog

| | |
|---|---|
| Kingdom | Animalia (a member of the animal kingdom) |
| Phylum | Chordata (an animal with a backbone) |
| Class | Mammalia (an animal with hair on its body) |
| Order | Carnivora (an animal that eats meat) |
| Family | Canidae (an animal with doglike features) |
| Genus | *Canis* |
| Species | *familiaris* |

[1] In your elementary science program you will probably deal only with the two most common and familiar kingdoms, animals and plants. However, you should be aware that scientists have identified three other kingdoms, too. These are the *Protista* kingdom (which includes viruses and slime molds), the *Monera* kingdom (which includes blue-green algae and bacteria), and the *Fungi* kingdom (which includes various types of fungus).

### Grasshopper

| | |
|---|---|
| Kingdom | Animalia (a member of the animal kingdom) |
| Phylum | Arthropoda (an animal with a skeleton on the outside of its body) |
| Class | Insecta (an animal that has three separate body parts) |
| Order | Orthoptera (an animal with mouthparts that chew from side to side) |
| Family | Acridiidae (an animal that tastes bad to its enemies) |
| Genus | *Schistocerca* |
| Species | *americana* |

This classification system, recognized throughout the world, allows scientists to demonstrate the relationships that exist between similar organisms and to assign each organism its own specific name, a name held by no other organism in the world.

#### IDEA BOX

To help you remember the order of the classification system, remember the following phrase:
  King Phillip came over for ginger snaps.

It is quite easy for young children to see the differences that exist between plants and animals. Outward appearances clearly differentiate an octopus from a strawberry, a mule from a sunflower, and a bumblebee from a redwood tree. What may be less apparent to children is the fact that all of these living organisms have several commonalities. Following are some of the similarities between the two kingdoms.

1. Both plants and animals have cells. Each organism has different sets of cells, each set performing specialized functions for the organism. Cells are made up of a unique substance known as protoplasm that gives cells rigidity and is involved in cell division. Examples of cells include:

| Plants | Animals |
|---|---|
| Guard cells | Bone cells |
| Root cells | Blood cells |
| Leaf cells | Brain cells |

2. Both plants and animals have tissues, groups of specialized cells that work together to perform a specific task. Examples of tissues include:

| Plants | Animals |
|---|---|
| Onion skip | Skin |
| Tree bark | Nerve |
| Stem pith | Muscle |

3. Both plants and animals have organs, groups of tissues that work and function together. Examples of organs include:

| Plants | Animals |
|---|---|
| Leaf | Liver |
| Stem | Brain |
| Root | Heart |

4. Both plants and animals have systems, groups of organs that work together to accomplish functions for the organism that are necessary for its survival. Examples of systems include:

| Plants | Animals |
|---|---|
| Vascular | Circulatory |
| Reproductive | Excretory |
| Respiratory | Nervous |

#### TEACHER TO TEACHER

Elementary age students are just naturally curious, and they love a good riddle. In order to help them learn about classification as a part of science, I pose a riddle that each child helps another child solve. As each student enters the room, I pin a tag with the name of some type of plant or animal on the back of the student's collar. The name can be as complicated or as easy as the age and experience of the student will allow. Each student takes a piece of paper and numbers from 1 to 10. He or she approaches each person in the class one by one and asks a question about the organism on his or her tag. The questions must be asked so they can be answered with a "Yes" or "No." An example question might be "Is my organism a plant?" or "Does my animal have more than four appendages?" Each clue is recorded on the numbered paper. The "bearer" of the tag does not really know what the tag says and must solve the riddle by taking down the information given by other students. As soon as the student thinks he/she has the correct answer, he/she brings the solution to me to verify.

This activity helps the students learn about questioning and how characteristics can be used to classify an organism. It also allows for critical thinking and evaluation in order to finally determine the correct identity of the organism. Besides that, it's fun!

Judith I. Vandel
Laramie County School District #1
Cheyenne, WY

## THE PLANT KINGDOM

Liz Degan was a first-grade teacher in a large school district in North Carolina. Her classroom was filled with plants of every shape, size, and color. There were plants arranged along the broad windowsill on the north side of the room, plants hanging down from the ceiling, and plants occupying almost every bookcase and shelf (other teachers in the school referred to Liz's classroom as the "Jungle Room"). Liz had obtained some of the plants from a local nursery, but many were obtained from the parents of her students as well as through the results of germination and propagation activities in her classroom.

When students arrived in the morning, several would proceed to collect an odd assortment of watering cans and devices to water all the plants. A few students were in charge of measuring the acidity or alkalinity of the soil of several plants with a compact soil-testing kit. Other students measured the height of several plants along the windowsill. Still another group of students was involved in setting up an experiment to determine the effects of too much or too little sunlight on the growth rates of geraniums. In fact, it was not unusual for all the students to be engaged in one or more plant care activities or experiments during the first 20 to 30 minutes class of each morning.

Liz had discovered some time ago that plants offer a multitude of opportunities for students to personally interact with science in a comfortable and relevant atmosphere. Liz found that most students had some kind of houseplants at home or perhaps a small garden in their backyards. Even though most of her students came from the poorer sections of town, Liz learned that plants were an element that they could all relate to and understand. So she filled her classroom with plants of all kinds and turned her students into gardeners, horticulturists, plant propagators, and agricultural experts. A majority of her science program was designed around her students' familiarity with the plants in her classroom. Even though this was first grade, students were engaged in science and science learning every day of the school year. They wrote brochures on plant care, videotaped a documentary on the varieties of outdoor plants found in their neighborhoods, took a school-wide survey of the most popular houseplants and garden plants, wrote letters requesting seed catalogs, and took a field trip to a community garden and to a private arboretum.

In addition, Liz was to relate plants and the science program to her students' lives outside the classroom. They talked about environmental concerns; the relationships between plants and animals; how we use plants as a source for food and clothing; the social, economic, and cultural benefits of plants; and the occupations and avocations associated with plants. Liz invited several community people into her classroom: the owner of the local nursery, a botanist from the local college, several amateur gardeners from a city gardening club (for a panel discussion), the county extension agent, a staff ecologist from a nearby wildlife preserve, and several parents who discussed the care of different varieties of houseplants.

As a result of these and other activities, Liz's students learned about germination rates of various seeds, the phototropism and geotropism of plants, how plants respire, the ecological balance of plants and animals in nature, the parts of plants and their functions, the nutritional needs of plants, as well as many other qualities of plants. More important, however, was the fact that this information came primarily from the direct experiences her students had with plants, and not from the pages of the science textbook.

The wide variety of indoor plants available (and outdoor ones, too, which can be maintained under "grow lights"), their ease of maintenance, and their utility in allowing students to design and follow through on self-initiated discoveries provided Liz with many important science lessons. An additional benefit was that students got to take home all the plants at the end of the school year. In short, Liz's students were surrounded by plants and certainly were surrounded by science. Making plants (and science) a daily activity helped Liz demonstrate to her students that science is much more than a collection of dry, lifeless facts assembled into textbooks. Rather, it can be a daily, hands-on, process-oriented exploration of the real world.

## Variety and Diversity in the Plant Kingdom

Plants can be found in every location throughout the world, from the tallest mountains to the deepest seas, from barren, frozen wastelands to lush, tropical rain forests. Plants can be as simple as a one-celled alga or as complex as a towering redwood tree in a northern California forest. Plant colors can range from the crimson red of a rose, to the bright yellow of a yucca, to the azure blue of a bluebonnet, to the lack of color in yeast. Leaf forms can range from those of the raffia palm tree, which may be 65 feet long and 6 feet wide,

to the thin, spiny leaves of a cactus; or there may be no leaves at all, as with a mushroom. There are plants such as the Sequoia tree that need massive amounts of water (2,500 pounds a day), and there are plants such as the saguaro cactus that can survive up to four years without water. Plants such as the redwood tree can reach heights of more than 350 feet, and plants such as molds require a microscope to be seen. There are plants

that live on other plants (mistletoe), plants that live in other plants, plants that live on animals (yeast), and plants that live in animals. There are plants that germinate, live, and die within the space of a few days, and there are other plants such as a bristlecone pine in eastern California that has been growing for nearly 4,600 years. There are plants such as the begonia, whose seeds are so small that 2 million of them weigh just 1 ounce, and plants such as the Coco de Mer coconut, whose seeds each weigh 40 pounds. Some varieties of bamboo can grow at the rate of 3 feet per day, whereas the saguaro cactus takes 30 years to grow one branch.

We eat plants (corn, lettuce, bread), wear plants (cotton, flax), sleep on plants (cotton sheets), read plants (the pulp in newspapers and magazines), build our dwellings with plants (lumber), and cure ourselves with plants (penicillin, quinine). In short, much of our daily lives depends on plants. Therefore, plants offer a plethora of opportunities for student investigation and exploration.

## Two Major Phyla

Scientists have divided the plant kingdom into two major phyla: the bryophytes and the tracheophytes. Bryophytes are very simple plants that do not produce flowers or seeds, have no true roots or stems, possess no vascular system for transporting water and other nutrients, but have chlorophyll and can make their own food.

The phylum Tracheophyta is the group of plants that have true roots and stems, have a vascular system, and can make their own food. This phylum includes ferns, horsetails, club mosses, and all the seed plants.

## The Life Processes of Plants

Plants go through several life processes in order to survive.

*Photosynthesis.* Photosynthesis is the process in which green plants make their own food. Water (along with any dissolved minerals) is taken in by a plant and passed into the leaves. Carbon dioxide from the air enters the leaves through tiny openings on the underside.

*Respiration.* Respiration may be considered the opposite of photosynthesis. Respiration is the *food-using* process of plants (vs. the *food-making* process of photosynthesis). Oxygen from the air is used to release carbon dioxide and water as well as to burn the food plants have made and stored.

*Transpiration.* Transpiration is the evaporation of excess water from the leaves of a plant. Usually, plants take in more water than they can use. Some of this water escapes through stomata in the plant's leaves and enters the atmosphere as water vapor.

*Digestion.* Digestion, the process that breaks down food so that it can be used by plant cells, takes place primarily in the leaves of a plant, although it occurs in other locations as well.

**DID YOU KNOW?** _____

More than 500 species of plants subsist partly on decomposed animal tissue.

**Classroom Activity** Most children are fascinated with carnivorous plants. Here are a few books that will provide them with everything they need to know about these unusual members of the plant kingdom: *Carnivorous Plants* by Cynthia Overbeck (New York: Lerner, 1982), *Pitcher Plants: The Elegant Insect Traps* by Carol Lerner (New York: Morrow, 1983), and *Secrets of the Venus's Fly Trap* by Jerome Wexler (New York: Dodd, 1981). ∎

*Circulation.* The movement of digested food through the vascular system of plants is known as circulation. Circulation generally involves the movement of sap, the plant fluid containing digested food.

*Assimilation.* The movement of digested food into plant cells is known as assimilation. As the food passes into the cells, it is changed into protoplasm, which is used to repair worn cells and grow new ones.

*Excretion.* The process in which plants get rid of wastes such as oxygen (through photosynthesis) and carbon dioxide (through respiration) is known as excretion.

*Reproduction.* One of the characteristics of living things is the ability to reproduce. All plants are able to produce offspring of their species.

*Tropisms.* Although young children may not believe that plants can move, plants do have several different forms of movement known as tropisms. For example, the movement of a plant toward a light source (e.g., the sun) is known as *phototropism.*

**IDEA BOX** _____

Obtain a small, healthy plant from a local garden center or nursery. Be sure to get one with a good root system and stem. Remove it from its container and place two sponges around the base (roots and soil) of the plant, securing them with some string or wire. Hang the plant upside down in a window and moisten the sponges each day. After a few days, students will notice the plant beginning to grow back up toward the light. This demonstrates the principle of phototropism, that plants always tend to grow (or move) in the direction of available sunlight.

## Requirements for Growth and Life

Plants have several requirements for their growth and survival, just as animals do. Whether perched on the windowsill of your classroom, in the arctic tundra of northern Canada, or on the edge of the Amazon River in Brazil, plants have needs that are basically the same.

*Air.* Plants need two ingredients from the air in order to survive. Plants need carbon dioxide (which is a natural waste product of animals) to make food through the process of photosynthesis. They also need oxygen to "burn" their food to create the energy needed for respiration.

**DID YOU KNOW?** _____

The typical plant or tree receives approximately 10 percent of its nutrition from the soil. The rest comes from the atmosphere.

**Classroom Activity** Have students place two small potted plants on a windowsill of the classroom. Ask them to spread petroleum jelly on the underside of the leaves of one plant. Keep the plants in sunlight and water them regularly. After several days, students will notice that the plant without petroleum jelly on its leaves will look healthier than the plant with the petroleum jelly. The reason for this is that for photosynthesis to occur, plants must take in air through the underside of their leaves.

As a further extension of this activity, students may wish to use several identical plants (half with petroleum jelly on their leaves, half without) and change some of the other growing conditions (soil composition, amount of water, amount of sunlight). How do their results compare with those of the initial activity? ∎

*Water.* To make food through photosynthesis, all plants require water. The water requirements vary according to the variety of the plant and the environmental conditions in which it lives. Dissolved minerals in the water contribute to the plant's processes of growth and cell replacement. Water is taken in by the roots of a plant and transported to the leaves through the vascular system.

*Temperature.* Each variety of plant requires a specific range of temperatures. The lichens that live near the South Pole, for example, would not be able to survive in the Sahara Desert, just as the cacti of the American Southwest would not be able to survive in the frozen tundra of northern Alaska.

*Sunlight.* Most plants, particularly green plants, need sunlight to grow. Sunlight converts food sources into usable energy. There are plants, however, that do not require sunlight in order to grow and survive (mushrooms are a good example).

*Soil.* Land plants require some type of soil in order to grow. (Note, however, that it is possible to grow many varieties of plants hydroponically, that is, without soil.) Soil is usually a combination of many organic materials (decayed animal or vegetable matter, often referred to as humus), sand, and/or clay. The minerals plants need for growth are obtained from the soil. These include potassium, phosphorus, calcium, magnesium, nitrogen, and other chemical elements.

**IDEA BOX**

Your students may be interested in growing some classroom plants hydroponically. There are several types of classroom kits available, each of which includes a pump, nutrients, trays, and an instruction booklet for a variety of classroom activities. You may wish to check out the Hydroponics Nursery Unit (catalog no. 66-6860) from Carolina Biological Supply Company (2700 York Rd., Burlington, NC 27215, 919-584-0381) and the Hydro Greenhouse®, manufactured by Uncle Milton Industries and available through major toy stores (e.g., Toys R Us, Kay Bee).

## Plant Adaptations

A plant's ability to live in a particular location is determined by its ability to adapt to that environment. The plants common to your area of the country may not be found in another area of the country or the world. For instance, northern California contains many stands of redwood trees. However, those redwoods are not found in any other region of the United States or any other area of the world. That variety of tree has adapted to the environmental conditions that exist in northern California and that do not exist in any other part of the world. The plants that grow in a particular environment have adaptations that enable them to thrive in that environment. Let's look at some other examples of adaptation:

- A cactus plant has a waxy coating to prevent excessive loss of moisture in the dry desert heat.
- The sap of a giant Sequoia tree has a high tannin content, which provides the tree with a natural healing agent if it is burned in a forest fire.
- The skunk cabbage can raise its internal temperature as much as 25 degrees so that it can melt any snow covering it in the early spring.

- Lichens can grow on the surface of barren rock, without any apparent soil whatsoever.
- In tropical rain forests, plants known as epiphytes grow on the highest branches of trees. These plants obtain water and minerals directly from the humid air.
- The goldenrod has "parachutes" on its seeds, allowing them to be dispersed over a wide area.
- The leaves of a Venus flytrap can close in less than half a second.
- Tumbleweeds die, break off at the stem, and are blown around a large area, scattering their seeds everywhere.

**IDEA BOX**

Have students locate plants in their neighborhood or community that require particular conditions and circumstances. For example, have students find plants that:

- Live where there is very little light
- Live where there is very little water
- Live where there is very little or no soil
- Live where there is a lot of light
- Live where there is a lot of water
- Live where there is a lot of soil
- Live outdoors
- Live indoors

Ask students to bring in examples of as many of these different types of plants as possible. Have them examine the physical characteristics of the plants to determine how each one has been able to adapt to its environment. Have students make a chart listing the plants across the top and the physical features down the left side. They can fill in the blank spaces on the chart with the features that help each plant adapt to its specific environment.

## Plant Parts and Their Functions

The angiosperms, or flowering plants, represent the largest number of species in the plant kingdom. The 250,000 members of this group are distinguished by several common parts. Let's take a look at those parts and their functions.

### Roots

The roots of a plant serve two basic functions. First, they serve to anchor the plant in the ground. This may be done with a *primary root* or *taproot*, the largest root in the root system, along with a jumble of other roots known as *secondary* or *fibrous roots*. The second function of roots is to take in food, water, and dissolved minerals from the soil and conduct those nutrients to the stem of the plant for delivery to the leaves. This is typically done through *root hairs*, or the fuzzy hairs that form at the ends of secondary roots. A single winter rye plant, for example, can produce nearly 380 miles of roots in two cubic feet of soil.

Roots are basic to all flowering plants. They are important to humans as well. Table 12.1 lists some of the uses humans have found for plant roots.

TABLE 12.1

## APPLICATIONS OF PLANT ROOTS

| Food | Medicine | Seasoning | Dye | Candy |
|------|----------|-----------|-----|-------|
| Carrots | Mandrake | Horseradish | Yellowwood | Licorice |
| Radish | Ginger | | Madder | Ginger |
| Beet | Sassafras | | | |
| Turnip | Licorice | | | |
| Parsnip | | | | |
| Sweet | | | | |
| potato | | | | |

## Stems

The stem is the support system and transportation system for the plant. The stem may be entirely above the level of the ground, completely below the surface of the soil, or both above and below the soil level. Through the stem flows all the plant's nutrients and water.

Plant stems are very important to humans as well, as illustrated in Table 12.2.

TABLE 12.2

## USES OF PLANT STEMS

| Food | Medicine | Industrial Products | Home Products |
|------|----------|---------------------|---------------|
| Celery | Quinine | Rubber | Lumber |
| Sugar cane | Camphor | Hemp | (furniture, |
| Asparagus | Cough syrup | Flax | heating) |
| Cinnamon | | Turpentine | Paper |
| Maple syrup | | Dyes | Witch hazel |

## Leaves

The primary function of the leaves is to make food for the plant. In this regard, the leaves are the most important part of the plant—not only for the plant itself but for life in general. All life is dependent on green

plants. Animals eat plants (and other animals who eat plants). In addition, green plants are the primary source of oxygen for all oxygen-consuming organisms (including humans). If leaves were unable to produce oxygen, life as we know it could not exist.

All green leaves contain chlorophyll, the substance that enables them to produce food. Leaves use water, transported up from the ground through the roots and stem, and carbon dioxide from the air to make food. The energy of sunlight and the chlorophyll in the leaves makes it possible for the water and carbon dioxide to combine and form glucose, a simple sugar and a usable energy source for the plant, and oxygen, a waste product for the plant but a necessary gas for animal survival.

Table 12.3 lists some ways in which humans use leaves in their daily lives.

TABLE 12.3

## HUMAN USES OF GREEN LEAVES

| Food | Flavoring | Drink | Other |
|------|-----------|-------|-------|
| Cabbage | Peppermint | Tea | Tobacco |
| Lettuce | Spearmint | | Palm leaves |
| Spinach | Thyme | | (for roofs |
| Kale | Sage | | of tropical |
| Endive | | | homes) |
| Parsley | | | |

## Flowers

The flower is the reproductive system of a flowering plant. Most flowers are composed of the following parts:

1. *Sepals* look like small green leaves and are found around the base of most flowers.
2. The *petals* are perhaps the most recognizable part of a flower. They are actually modified leaves used to attract insects to the flower.
3. *Stamens* are the male reproductive part of the flower. Stamens consist of two parts: the *filament*, which is a thin stalk or stem, and the *anther*, which is the knoblike tip of the filament.
4. The *pistil* is the female reproductive organ of the flower. The pistil is composed of three parts: the *stigma*, which is the sticky top of the pistil, the *style*, or the stalk of the pistil, and the *ovary*, the enlarged egg sac at the end of the pistil that contains the unfertilized egg cells or *ovules*.

The following illustration shows the major parts of a flower and their relative locations.

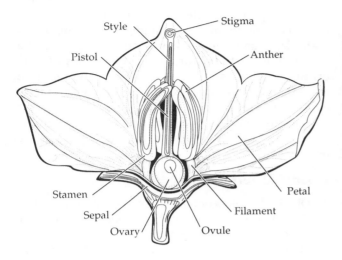

Flowers are also very useful to humans. Aside from their uses in decoration and gift giving, flowers are beneficial in other ways, as indicated in Table 12.4.

TABLE   **12.4**

### USES FOR FLOWERS

| Food | Dye | Perfume | Medicine |
|------|-----|---------|----------|
| Cauliflower Broccoli Cloves | Saffron | Rose | Cloves |

**Pollination and Fertilization.**   Pollination is the process in which the sperm cells in a pollen grain unite with the egg nucleus of the ovule. There are two types of pollination: self-pollination, in which the pollen from a flower's stamen fertilizes its own ovules, and cross-pollination, when pollen from one flower joins with the egg nuclei of another flower. Self-pollination can occur in the following ways:

- Insects can transfer pollen from the anther to the stigma.
- The pollen can fall from the anther to the stigma.
- Wind can blow the pollen from the stamens to the stigma.

Cross-pollination can occur through the action of visiting insects or birds, wind, water carrying the pollen from one flower to another, human interaction, or gravity (the pollen of one flower can fall to the stigmas of other flowers below).

### Seeds

Fertilized egg cells from the ovary divide and multiply, eventually forming seeds. Each seed consists of stored food (which provides nourishment for the developing plant until its leaves can begin producing food on their own), a seed coat (which protects the seed from extreme moisture loss), and a tiny plant called the *embryo* (which has its own tiny roots, stem, and leaves). If the seed reaches favorable growing conditions, it can duplicate or reproduce its kind. The following sketch illustrates the major components of a seed.

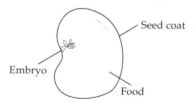

**IDEA BOX**

Get some dried lima beans from the grocery store and soak them in a pan of water overnight. Carefully cut the bean in half along its edge. Show students the tiny plant inside— the embryo. This tiny shoot is the beginning of a new plant. Let students know that the rest of the lima bean is the food that the embryo needs to grow.

**Conditions for Growth.**   Seeds need favorable conditions so that they can begin to grow. These conditions include:

- *Temperature.* Different seeds need different temperatures in order to sprout. Most seeds require a temperature between 60 and 80 degrees Fahrenheit.

- *Air.* Seeds need air to initiate the growing process. Soil that has air in it is much more favorable for the sprouting of seeds than soil that is densely packed.
- *Water.* In order to germinate, seeds need water to soften the seed coat and make the seed swell.

### IDEA BOX

Fill a glass with dried peas. Fill the glass to the brim with water and place it in a sunny location. After several hours students will notice the pile of peas rising on their own and spilling out of the glass. This process may continue for several days. This occurs because water enters the peas through the skin and dissolves the nutrients inside. As a result, the peas get larger and spill over the sides of the glass. This process of the water being absorbed by the cells of the peas is known as *osmosis.*

Contrary to what students may believe, seeds do not need sunlight to germinate. They can live off the stored food inside the seed coat and thus do not depend on sunlight to produce food. However, when the new plant emerges, it will need sunlight to begin making its own food. The following illustration shows the steps a seed takes as it develops into a new plant.

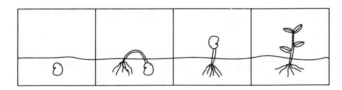

Like the other components of a plant, many seeds are beneficial to humans. Table 12.5 lists a few examples of ways in which humans use seeds.

TABLE   **12.5**

..............................................................

## HUMAN USES OF SEEDS
..............................................................

| Food | Spices | Manufactured Goods |
|------|--------|--------------------|
| Coconut | Pepper | Linseed oil |
| Wheat | Mustard | Coconut oil |
| Peanuts | Celery seed | Cotton |
| Cocoa | Nutmeg | Soybean |
| Coffee | | |
| Rice | | |
| Corn | | |
| Barley | | |

## Making a Terrarium

Making plant life part of the classroom experience of your students can be an exciting and valuable part of

your science curriculum. There are many ways to do this, one of which is to establish a classroom terrarium or series of terrariums for the display and growth of a variety of plant life. A terrarium is a miniature controlled environment containing plants, animals, or both plants and animals in an artificial situation that closely imitates the natural living conditions of those organisms. Two basic types are a woodland terrarium and a desert terrarium. Carefully set up, a terrarium can endure for a long period of time and provide students with a close-up look of a "sample" of nature. Following are directions for constructing these two types of terrariums.

### Woodland Terrarium

1. Obtain a glass container. An old aquarium (purchased at a pet store or garage sale), a large pickle jar, or even a 2-liter soda bottle can be used.
2. Thoroughly clean the container (be sure there is no soap or detergent residue left behind).
3. Cover the bottom of the container with a layer of small pebbles or rocks mixed with bits of charcoal (wood charcoal from a fire or aquarium charcoal from a local pet store work equally well). The charcoal absorbs gases and prevents the soil from turning sour.
4. Follow this with a layer of soil about twice as deep as the pebble-charcoal mixture. Outdoor soil or potting soil (obtained from any garden center) will suffice.
5. Sprinkle the soil with just enough water to make it moist (too much will stimulate the growth of molds).
6. Place several plants such as mosses, ferns, lichens, small tree seedlings, and liverworts in the soil. Grass seed may be sprinkled in one section of the terrarium.
7. Place several large rocks and decaying pieces of wood or tree branches in the terrarium.
8. You may wish to introduce small land animals such as snails, earthworms, turtles, frogs, or salamanders to the terrarium. Be sure there is sufficient food and water for the animals.
9. Place a loosely fitting sheet of glass over the top of the terrarium (to permit the humidity level to build up). Make sure that some air can enter the terrarium and keep it out of direct sunlight.

### Desert Terrarium

1. Fill the bottom of a large glass container with a layer of coarse sand or gravel. Combine one part fine sand with two parts potting soil and spread this over the top of the first layer.
2. Sprinkle this mixture lightly with water.
3. Place several varieties of cactus into the terrarium (it might be a good idea to wear gloves). Most nurs-

eries carry cacti, or they can be ordered through the mail from selected seed companies and mail-order nursery houses.

4. When planting the cacti, be sure that the roots are covered completely by the sandy mixture.
5. You and your students may decide to place several desert animals such as lizards and horned toads in the terrarium. Be sure the animals have a sufficient quantity of food and water available.
6. The desert terrarium can be left in the sun and does

not need a glass cover. It should, however, be lightly sprinkled with water about once a week.

Four books that are helpful in establishing and maintaining classroom terrariums are: *Terrariums* by John Hoke (New York: Watts, 1972), *Projects with Plants* by Seymour Simon (New York: Watts, 1973), *Making a Plant Terrarium* by D. J. Herda (New York: Simon & Schuster, 1982), and *Terrariums* by Alice Parker (New York: Watts, 1982).

# THE ANIMAL KINGDOM

Carrie Gibula was a fourth-grade teacher in a suburban school district in Florida. She was well aware of students' natural fascination with animals and sought to make her classroom one filled with opportunities for students to care for, examine, and learn about animals in every possible way. Along one wall of her classroom was an inexpensive set of shelves made from boards and concrete blocks. Nestled among the shelves were various animal cages, some of which she built herself with wire and a soldering gun and others that were purchased either with school funds or with her own money. There were cages for hamsters, mice, and lizards, and a large oversized cage used to transport animals such as cats and dogs from students' homes to the classroom for observation and temporary housing. Along the windowsill were two desert terrariums filled with desert flora and fauna (three lizards, a skink, and a horned toad). A 20-gallon aquarium occupied a space next to Carrie's desk and was populated with tropical fish of every size and color. Students were in charge of maintaining the aquarium on a rotating basis. A smaller aquarium sat on the counter next to the classroom sink. This aquarium housed several guppies and served to provide students with a first-hand look at the growth and reproductive patterns of this popular fish. On the other side of the sink was another terrarium, which housed Gus, the oldest member of the class. Gus was a turtle that had been with Carrie for nine years and had endured the handling and observing of many classes of students. In fact, Gus's movements, eating and sleeping habits, and environmental responses had been the subject of countless numbers of classroom experiments. Ever patient, Gus took it all in stride.

In the far corner of her classroom Carrie had put up two hanging cages. In one were Albert and Clarence, two parakeets she had recently obtained from a friend who was moving to Arizona. The other cage held a canary by the name of Sam, designated as the unofficial mascot for the class. Nearby was an odd assortment of student-constructed cages containing a host of invertebrates. There were several cricket cages built by students from oatmeal boxes. (Large sections were cut from each box and a nylon stocking pulled over the box. Soil and twigs were added to each box along with two or three crickets.) There was a commercial butterfly cage which had earlier housed several monarch butterflies. Students were given an opportunity to watch the metamorphosis of the butterflies, which were then released on the playground in a special ceremony. An old aquarium was the home for two large spiders, which crawled on top of large pieces of wood and sunned themselves for several hours each day.

Carrie knew that animals were an important part of her students' lives. Many of the children had pets and were encouraged to bring them to school for examination by other students. (One boy had inherited a rattlesnake from his older brother, and its arrival one day caused a great deal of excitement in the room.) Carrie also found many opportunities for students to take short field trips on the school grounds to observe the various forms of animal life that inhabited the fields around the school. A field trip to the local chapter of the SPCA and a nearby animal shelter helped students understand more about animal population control. A visit to the zoo helped students discover the variety of animals in the world. She brought in a variety of animal experts, including veterinarians, pet store owners, aquarium hobbyists, a trainer from a dog obedience school, a professor of animal husbandry, a specialist on owls from the local university, a fisherman, a hunter, and an amateur herpetologist who discussed the snakes indigenous to their region.

The many experiences provided by Carrie in her classroom enabled her students to engage in the processes of sciences through many opportunities to observe, measure, classify, infer, predict, experiment, and communicate about and with animals on a daily basis. Animals, if well cared for, can be a positive addition to any classroom. Carrie discovered (as you will) that animals are relevant to students' lives and provide an incalculable array of learning possibilities for every student.

## Variety and Diversity in the Animal Kingdom

Although it is difficult to know for sure, scientists have estimated that there are approximately 1,250,000 species of living things on the planet. Of that total, about 1 million are in the animal kingdom. Animals can be found all over the face of the earth, from the coldest polar regions to the heart of the tropical rain forest girdling the equator. Animals can be as simple as a sponge off the coast of a Grecian island or as complex as your roommate or spouse.

Animals can range in color from the bright red of a lobster, to the striking purple of a sea anemone, to the subtle green of a grasshopper, to the orange of an oriole. Some animals reach lengths of 100 feet (blue whale), and others require a micrometer to measure (fleas, gnats). There are animals that live with us (dogs, cats, birds), animals that live on us (mites, lice), and animals that live in us (tapeworms). There are animals that are born, live, and die within the span of a few days (the roundworm has a life span of just 12 days) and other animals that live for a considerably long time (lake sturgeons can live more than 150 years). There are animals that need a lot of sleep (the Finnish woodchuck sleeps 22 hours a day); animals such as the shark that almost never sleep; and animals such as the swift which can sleep while it's flying. Some animals are extremely fast (the flea can accelerate 50 times faster than the space shuttle), and other animals are extremely slow (the three-toed sloth moves at speeds of 0.068 mph to 0.098 mph. Animals such as the streaked tenrec begin to reproduce within three weeks of birth; animals such as the albatross take up to 10 years before they can reproduce; animals such as snails and oysters are hermaphroditic (having both male and female sex organs) and can reproduce with *any* other member of their species; and some animals are even born pregnant (aphids). Some animals need enormous quantities of water to survive (elephants can drink up to 50 gallons a day), and other animals, such as the kangaroo rat, can go an entire lifetime without taking a drink of water. Many animals can perform physical feats of Olympic proportions (some sea snakes can hold their breath underwater for eight hours; an ant can lift 50 times its own weight). There are animals that eat enormous amounts of food (young whales put on 2 ⅓ tons of body weight a month until they be-

come adults) and others that do not eat at all (adult mayflies do not have fully developed mouthparts; consequently they cannot eat). Some animals have physiological features that defy description (a shrimp's heart is in its head; crickets have hearing organs in their knees; starfish have no brains; ants have five different noses; snails have nearly 10,000 teeth, all on their tongues; and barnacles have their ovaries in their heads). We eat animals (beef, pork), wear animals (leather), sleep on animals (wool, silk), have contests with animals (horses, dogs), keep animals as pets (fish, hamsters), work with animals (oxen, elephants), name our children after animals (Robin, Fawn, Jay, Bunny), and cure ourselves with animal products (insulin).

In short, animals represent a great diversity of living organisms—a diversity that can be an exciting part of any classroom science program. Making the animal kingdom a daily part of the lives of your students can make science both relevant and interesting to every child.

**TEACHER TO TEACHER** _____

After observing two different insect life cycles we focused on a literary search of butterflies and moths. I made one photocopy of each of several pages from different books. Another inexpensive book I took apart. Each student chose one particular kind to study by selecting a photocopied page or book page. To show them what I wanted them to do we did an example first with the whole class. We listed descriptions of one species we had all observed as a caterpillar, pupa, and adult. I supplied the beginning line of each verse: "Once I was a caterpillar...," "Then I...," "Now I am a...." We then, as a class, wrote a poem. Finally, using the information from their reading, students wrote and illustrated their own poems.

Elaine S. Heine
Ocean Breeze Elementary School
Indian Harbour Beach, FL

## Types of Animals

As mentioned earlier, animals account for about 1 million of the more than 1,250,000 different species of living things on this planet. Of this total, insects make up approximately 800,000 species.[2]

---

[2]It is very difficult to get an accurate count of the species in the world for several reasons. First, scientists are still discovering unknown portions of the world and, consequently, unknown animal and plant species (recent discoveries on a species of tree in Panama have yielded more than 1,500 species of beetles, for example). Second, scientists cannot agree on the exact number of species in the world. Although we have accurately identified fewer than 2 million species, some sampling procedures have suggested that the actual number of plant and animal species may be closer to 30 million. Third, most scientists believe that more than 95 percent of all the plant and animal species that have ever lived on this planet are now extinct!

**DID YOU KNOW?** _____

According to some scientific estimates, we lose more than 90 plant and animal species every day!

**Classroom Activity**

1. Students may be interested in adopting an animal at a local zoo or game preserve. Contact a zoo and ask about the procedures and fees for adoption. You can also contact the American Association of Zoological Parks and Aquariums (4550 Montgomery Ave., Suite 940N, Bethesda, MD 20814) for relevant information.
2. The National Wildlife Federation will certify a backyard (or a portion of the school grounds) as an official Backyard Wildlife Habitat. There are plans to complete and forms to fill out, all of which can be obtained from the National Wildlife Federation (Backyard Wildlife Habitat Program, 1412 16th Street NW, Washington, DC 20036).
3. You and your students may be interested in writing to one or more of the following nature conservancy groups for information on their various projects and publications: Defenders of Wildlife (1244 19th Street NW, Washington, DC 20036), the Fund for Animals, Inc. (200 West 57th St., New York, NY 10019), the Nature Conservancy (1815 North Lynn St., Arlington, VA 22209), and the Sierra Club (730 Polk St., San Francisco, CA 94109). ∎

There are many different types of animals, but children need to know that animals can be put into one of two basic groups: the _vertebrates_, or those animals with backbones, and the _invertebrates_, or those animals without backbones. Within each of these groups are a number of subgroups, as illustrated in Table 12.6.

_Mammals._ Mammals are warm-blooded, which means that their body temperature is always the same no matter what the outside temperature is. All mammals are air-breathing and have lungs for that purpose. Mammals are also noted for the presence of hair. The hair may range in form from the quills of the porcupine to the short bristles of the whale to the horn of a rhinoceros.

TABLE 12.6

## CHARACTERISTICS OF VERTEBRATES AND INVERTEBRATES

| Subgroup | Characteristics | Examples |
|---|---|---|
| **Vertebrates** | | |
| Mammals | Warm-blooded, body hair, mammary glands, seven neck bones | Giraffe, gorilla, mouse, dog, antelope, cat |
| Birds | Warm-blooded, wings with feathers, scaly feet, hollow skeletons | Kiwi, crow, eagle, flamingo, robin |
| Reptiles | Cold-blooded, rough and dry skin, breathe by lungs | Crocodile, snake, turtle, alligator, lizard |
| Amphibians | Cold-blooded, breathe by gills when young and lungs when adult, smooth skin without scales | Frog, salamander, toad |
| Fish | Cold-blooded, scaly bodies, breath by gills, have air bladders | Trout, tuna, minnow, guppy, bass, perch, salmon |
| **Invertebrates** | | |
| Arthropods | Exoskeleton, segmented body, jointed legs | Shrimp, grasshopper, lobster, spider, centipede |
| Mollusks | Soft body, protective shell, muscular foot | Octopus, clam, oyster, snail, squid |
| Echinoderms | Spiny skin, radiating parts, shell-like skeleton | Starfish, sand dollar, sea urchin |
| Annelids | Segmented round body, several organ systems | Leech, earthworm, sandworm |
| Nematodes | Worms with thin round bodies, digestive system, often parasitic | Pinworm, trichinella, hookworm |
| Platyhelminths | Flattened ribbonlike worms, simple nervous and digestive systems, often parasitic | Fluke, tapeworm, planarian |
| Coelenterates | Tentacles surrounding the mouth, hollow body, opening at one end only | Coral, jellyfish, sea anemone, hydra |
| Poriferans | Hollow-tubed body with many pores, water flows in and out of tube | Sponge |
| Protozoa | Single-celled, live in fresh or salt water, parasitic | Amoeba, paramecium |

*Birds.* The most distinguishing feature of birds is their ability to fly. They are also distinguished by the presence of feathers, which are actually modified scales (in fact, many scientists believe that birds are the direct descendants of dinosaurs). The skeletons of birds contributes to their ability to fly. However, for some birds flight is impossible. These include the penguin, kiwi, and ostrich.

*Reptiles.* Reptiles are cold-blooded; this means that their body temperature is always the same as that of the water or air in which they live. Reptiles are also distinguished by their rough, thick, dry, scaly skin—a feature that makes them repulsive to many peo-

ple. All reptiles are born with lungs, which means that they must breathe air throughout their lives to survive. This feature distinguishes them from the amphibians.

*Amphibians.* Amphibians are cold-blooded and usually hibernate over the winter months by burrowing into the ground or the bottom of a lake. They are distinguished by their ability to breathe through their skin, even though they have lungs. Another important feature is that the eggs of amphibians are fertilized outside the female's body (as opposed to mammals, birds, and reptiles, in which the eggs are fertilized by the male's sperm inside the female's body). This process usually involves the laying of clumps of eggs in water by the female. The male then passes over the eggs and deposits his sperm over them.

*Fish.* Fish are distinguished from other animals by their ability to extract oxygen from water through a series of gills. Gills are feath-

ery, threadlike filaments containing tiny, thin-walled blood vessels. As a fish swims, it opens its mouth and water flows over the gills. As the water flows over the gills, dissolved oxygen passes through the thin walls of the blood vessels and is transported by the blood.

Fish are able to swim due to several characteristics. Their bodies are streamlined and can move through the water with relative ease. Most fish possess pairs of fins that not only propel the fish through the water but also help it keep its balance and steer.

## DID YOU KNOW? _____

The female anglerfish is about six times larger than the male. In fact, the male anchors himself to the top of the female's head and stays there for the rest of his life.

**Classroom Activity** If possible, set up an aquarium in your classroom and stock it with a variety of tropical fish. Provide opportunities for students to observe the fish and to discuss their similarities and differences. Have students construct large charts comparing the sizes and shapes of heads, fins, tails, eyes, body trunks, mouths, and gill covers. What features are common among various types of fish? Are there any features one type of fish has that others do not? Two excellent books to help children with their studies are *Fish Facts and Bird Brains: Animal Intelligence* by Helen Sattler (New York: Lodestar, 1984) and *What Do You Want to Know about Guppies?* by Seymour Simon (New York: Four Winds, 1982).  ■

*Arthropods.* Arthropods represent the largest phylum of the animal kingdom, having more than 900,000 species. Arthropods share the following characteristics. All of them have an outside skeleton, or exoskeleton, which provides both support and protection for the organism. Body parts, such as legs, are usually jointed and can bend. Most distinctive is the fact that most arthropods exhibit *bilateral symmetry*; that is, all parts of their bodies are paired so that one side of the body is a mirror image of the other side.

*Mollusks.* The most distinctive feature of mollusks is the foot. In the bivalves the foot is strong and muscular and is used for locomotion and digging. Bivalves are often referred to as hatchet-footed mollusks. In the univalves the foot is much larger and often makes it appear as though the organism is crawling along on its stomach—hence the name belly-footed mollusks. The third kind of mollusk is often referred to as the head-footed mollusk because the foot is actually divided into several appendages commonly known as tentacles.

*Echinoderms.* Starfish, sand dollars, sea urchins, and sea cucumbers are echinoderms. All of these animals live in the ocean and possess an exoskeleton that is usually hard and covered with spines.

*Annelids.* The most highly developed group of worms, the annelids, or segmented worms, include earthworms, leeches, and sandworms. Their most distinctive feature is the partitioning of their bodies into segments or rings. This group represents a total of 6,500 species found on land or in the water.

*Nematodes.* The nematodes, often referred to as roundworms, account for nearly 20,000 species, such as hookworms, trichinella, and pinworms. They can be found in almost any kind of environment, including fresh and salt water as well as soil. Roundworms include both parasitic and nonparasitic types.

*Platyhelminths.* Platyhelminths are also known as flatworms because their bodies are flat and ribbonlike. Examples are flukes, parasitic organisms that live in the stomach, intestines, and lungs of human beings; tapeworms, another parasitic creature that lives in the intestines of humans and is introduced through improperly cooked meat; and planarians, nonparasitic organisms found in ponds and streams.

*Coelenterates.* Coral, sea anemones, jellyfish, and hydras make up the group of animals known as Coelenterates, which includes approximately 10,000 species. All of these creatures have tentacles, which assist the animals in obtaining necessary food and nutrients from the surrounding area.

*Poriferans.* Poriferans come in an array of colors from orange, to red, to brown, to black, to purple, to yellow, to green. They live in salt water as well as in fresh water. They look like plants and even take on some of the characteristics of plants, but they're not. They're sponges.

*Protozoa.* If you took biology in high school, you have probably stared at protozoa through a microscope. These organisms, of which there are nearly 35,000 species, include amoebas and paramecia. Usually found in ponds or very moist soil, these one-celled creatures can carry out a variety of life functions. Not only can they pass water and food in and out of themselves; they can reproduce by splitting in half, with each half able to carry out the functions of the "parent."

Unquestionably, there is great variety in the animal kingdom. Helping your students understand the distinctive features of selected creatures as well as the similarities among various types of animals can be an important part of your overall science curriculum.

## Animal Growth and Development

> A tadpole changes into a leopard frog.
> A caterpillar changes into a swallowtail butterfly.
> A chick changes into a bantam rooster.
> A newborn baby changes into YOU!

Throughout the animal kingdom marvelous and wonderful changes take place in the life cycles of animals. Many of these changes are subtle and uneventful; others are rapid and quite dramatic. For some animals, the life cycle may be a series of completely different stages, each resulting in a physically different creature. For other animals, the cycle of life may simply mean the enlargement of all the parts of the anatomy. Yet no matter what the animal, it will grow (remember our definition of living things earlier in this chapter), and that growth is usually a series of predictable stages.

### Reproduction

All animals reproduce; this helps ensure the survival of the species and allows genetic characteristics to be passed along from one generation to another. In higher-order animals (mammals, birds, reptiles), reproduction is internal; that is, it takes place inside the body of the female. Lower forms of animal life use a variety of reproductive methods. Insects and mollusks rely on sexual reproduction in which males and females mate. (Mating can be extremely dangerous in the animal world. For example, the female black widow spider kills and eats the male shortly after mating.) Animals such as the starfish discharge their eggs and sperm into the water, and fertilization takes place externally. Other animals are hermaphroditic and have both male and female reproductive organs, allowing them to mate with any other nearby hermaphrodites. Simpler forms of animals reproduce simply by dividing into one or more parts and "growing up" all over again.

### Animal Behavior

Most animals behave in fairly distinctive patterns. For most animals behavior is *instinctive*: it occurs without any rational thought on the part of the animal. Just as you withdraw your hand quickly from a hot stove without taking the time to think about the actions you are performing, so do animals behave instinctively.

The behaviors of an animal are what enable it to survive and propagate. Although there is a tremendous amount of research on animal behaviors, we will look at only two kinds: protection and survival.

**Protection.** Running away from a predator, listening for an approaching enemy, and hiding from an intruder are all forms of protection employed by animals in the wild. Methods used by animals to protect themselves include *protective coloration*, a process in which an animal assumes the colors of the surrounding environment (you're undoubtedly familiar with the chameleon and the flounder, creatures that are able to change their colors to blend with the pattern or colors of their background).

Some animals are equipped with poison with which to protect themselves. Examples are the scorpion, stonefish, and rattlesnake. Other animals, such as the armadillo and sowbug, are able to curl up into a tight ball; their external armor is nearly impossible for an enemy to penetrate.

**Survival.** Some animals are able to survive through an elaborate system of behaviors. The one you are probably most familiar with is hibernation—that extended period of time, usually in the winter, in which an animal virtually "shuts down" most of its body functions and goes to sleep. Bears are probably the best-known hibernating animal, but frogs, snakes, mice, and some forms of squirrels and arctic fish may also hibernate.

When animals travel great distances in search of food or warmer temperature—what we refer to as migration—they are exhibiting a distinctive and poorly understood behavior. Butterflies, geese, salmon, and whales all migrate great distances to follow the changing seasons or to reach spawning areas (the arctic tern probably travels the greatest distance of any animal in its migration—22,000 miles per year).

### Can You Believe It?

> Female painted turtles can store sperm from a single mating and fertilize themselves with it years later.
> Ants will move up to 40 tons of dirt in constructing their underground colonies.

Although a codfish lays up to 4 million eggs at one time, only about two of them will become fish.

California's official state mollusk, the banana slug, eats poison oak.

Elephants sometimes communicate with stomach rumbles.

A frog must close its eyes in order to swallow.

Texas horned toads can squirt blood from the corners of their eyes.

The fertilized eggs of the sea catfish are carried in the mouth of the male until they hatch.

The tumbler pigeon can do backward somersaults while flying.

Elephants and humans are the only animals that can be trained to stand on their heads.

The female lobster is fertile for only six hours out of the year.

The praying mantis is the only insect that can turn its head without moving its body.

The krill, a type of shrimp that lives in the cold waters off Antarctica, jumps out of its shell when scared.

A parrot's beak can close with a force of 350 pounds per square inch.

The nine-banded armadillo always gives birth to identical quadruplets.

## Animal Adaptations

How did you feed yourself today? Did you use a can opener? Did you open a refrigerator? Did you carry a tray in the cafeteria? Did you pour some liquid into a cup or glass? Your ability to do all these things is part of your ability to adapt to your surroundings. For example, you could learn to drink coffee from a cereal bowl, although you would probably never want to. It would take the skills you learned in drinking coffee from a mug, your knowledge of the more cumbersome design of a cereal bowl, and some way to compensate for the lack of handle on the bowl in order to drink the coffee without spilling it all over yourself. In short, you have the ability to adapt to your surroundings.

Animals are able to adapt to their surroundings, too. For example, some animals must conserve water in a desert environment, so they sleep during the day and forage for food at night. Other animals have the ability to "freeze" when an enemy comes near in order to avoid detection. Still other animals have sharp teeth with which to tear flesh easily. All of these are *adaptations*, behaviors or structures that help an animal survive in its environment.

Perhaps the most common form of adaptation concerns the way in which an animal obtains food. Since most animals cannot manufacture their own food, they must be skillful in obtaining it in some other way. The shape of the head, the structure of the feet, body weight, and strong eyesight are all adaptations that help animals to obtain the food necessary for survival.

Almost every animal has one or more adaptations that help it survive. The adaptations can involve single cells, tissues, organs, or entire systems. The adaptations may be structural, behavioral, or functional. Whatever the adaptations of a particular animal are, they have evolved in response to the animal's need to survive.

# ECOLOGY

You may not realize it, but you're related to the dragonfly. You're also related to the frog and the moose. All living organisms are related to one another. We depend on members of the plant kingdom for some of our food. Our pets depend on other members of the animal kingdom for their survival. Small, seemingly insignificant creatures living on our kitchen counters and in our bathrooms are dependent on us for their very existence. We are involved in a complicated system of relationships and interdependencies with all members of the plant and animal world.

Ecology can be defined as the interaction of living things with each other and with their environment. Again, it is a system of relationships and dependencies that helps living things survive and prosper. It is very difficult to separate a living thing from its environment and completely understand it without knowing something about its relationships the with other living things in that environment.

## Ecosystems

Take a look around you. What do you see? If you are in a dorm room, you may see a bed, a table, a closet, a pile of clothes on the floor, a lamp, a soda bottle, and a half-eaten sandwich. If you are sitting outside in a grassy area on campus, you may notice a few trees, some bushes, people walking by, a cloud or two in the sky, birds flying, some scraps of litter, and a few buildings. These two settings, quite different from each other, represent *ecosystems*, or the physical elements of a particular area. Although it is easy to identify birds, bottles, and buildings in an ecosystem, we also need to consider things that are unseen, such as oxygen, pollutants, and soil. All elements within an ecosystem have an effect on the inhabitants of that ecosystem.

Although rain forests cover only about 6 percent of the earth's surface, they contain more than half of all plant and animal species.

**Classroom Activity** By some estimates, rain forests are being destroyed at the rate of about 100 acres per minute. We can only guess at the ecological implications of that devastation. Children (who will presumably inherit the earth from this generation) can take an active role in helping to preserve and defend areas of the world, from their backyards to Amazonian rain forests. To get them started, have your students write for an information packet entitled "How to Organize a Rainforest Awareness Week at Your School," available from Creating Our Future, 398 North Ferndale, Mill Valley, CA 94941, 415-381-6744. ■

## Food Chains and Food Webs

Different organisms get their food in different ways. Some organisms, known as *producers*, can manufacture their own food. However, most organisms cannot produce their own food and must consume food from another source; they are known as *consumers*. All animals are consumers, and most plants are producers (the Venus flytrap, for example, is both a producer [it undergoes photosynthesis] and a consumer [it digests insects with its specialized leaves]).

A shortage of food and food sources can adversely affect a variety of plants and animals. Witness the effect that swarms of grasshoppers have on midwestern wheat crops. Not only is a population of wheat completely eradicated; the humans and other animals who depend on that wheat are also affected by its demise. This connection occurs in nature in the form of *food chains* and *food webs*. Essentially, a food chain is a series of stages in which one organism is dependent on or consumes another organism. The following diagrams illustrate three food chains.

| Grasshopper→ | Frog→ | Snake→ | Hawk |
|---|---|---|---|
| nibbles on | eats | captures | catches |
| green grasses | grasshopper | frog | snake |

| Acorn→ | Squirrel→ | Fox |
|---|---|---|
| falls | eats | catches |
| from | acorn | and eats |
| tree | | squirrel |

| Algae→ | Fish→ | Sea lion |
|---|---|---|
| grow near | consume | catches |
| surface of | large | and eats |
| ocean | quantities | fish |
| | of algae | |

As you look at these food chains, you might expect that the consumption of one organism by another

organism, which in turn is consumed by yet another organism, might be linear in nature (as depicted in the illustrations). However, nature is never quite that simple. Indeed, several organisms may be involved at several different levels, each dependent on several others for its food supply. This type of arrangement is known as a food web. Since most organisms eat more than one type of food, most organisms belong to more than one food chain. The following diagram illustrates of one (albeit small) food web.

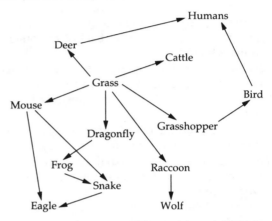

There are a number of food chains represented in this food web. Thus, when one or more elements of this food web are altered, other elements may be affected. Each part of the web depends on the other parts.

I took my kindergarten class out on the lawn to release our five beautiful Painted Lady butterflies. It was the conclusion of a particularly exciting life science unit in which we had spent a month watching five tiny caterpillars change into five magnificent adult butterflies. We formed a circle, sang our "Fly Away Little Butterfly" song, opened the box and watched in awe as one by one they fluttered up and away. Suddenly, down swooped a Black Phoebe (bird) and gobbled up one of our precious butterflies! Back it came for another, and then another! Before our horrified eyes, the bird claimed three out of five!! The children were shocked, and some of them ended up in tears. It was certainly not how we intended to culminate our unit, but it opened up a whole new discussion on food chains!

Dianne Benham
Pomerado Elementary School
Poway, CA

## Human Changes in Food Webs

For millions of years nature has been able to achieve a balance between all living organisms. Some organisms die out and are replaced by others, catastrophic events cause alterations in the organisms that inhabit an area, and new species evolve or are eliminated due to changes in climate and the availability of food sources. But what is amazing is the fact that nature is able to achieve a state of *homeostasis*, that is, balance.

Depending on your point of view, humans have been either a beneficial influence on the balance of nature or a detriment to the environment. Humans use plant products to manufacture life-saving drugs *and* to fill the air with noxious fumes and chemical pollutants. They control forest populations through selective deforestation *and* clear away vast timberlands for lumber. They drain low-lying areas to eliminate mosquitoes and other disease-bearing organisms *and* to construct homes and shopping centers. They selectively breed domesticated animals to produce better-quality foodstuffs, *and* they kill off herds of wild animals for sport or quick cash. Without a doubt, humans have had an impact on the environment unlike anything nature has experienced in the last 4½ million years.

Consider the following statistics and the effect these events might have on the food webs in your particular area of the country or on the global environment.

- In 1986 6.5 million tons of hydrocarbons and 8.5 million tons of nitrogen oxides were put into the atmosphere by motor vehicles.
- An estimated 14 billion pounds of trash are dumped into the ocean every year.
- In California alone, more than 200 million tons of pesticides are used each year.
- The average American generates about 600 times his or her body weight in garbage in a lifetime.
- Every day 74,000 acres of tropical rain forest are destroyed.

**IDEA BOX**

You can get your students involved in environmental concerns and in preserving the balance of nature. The following organizations offer materials and ideas specifically for students.

> The Environmental Defense Fund
> 1616 P St. NW, Suite 150
> Washington, DC 20036
>
> Greenpeace
> 1436 U St. NW
> Washington, DC 20009
>
> National Wildlife Federation
> 1412 16th St. NW
> Washington, DC 20036
>
> The Natural Resources Defense Council
> 40 West 20th St.
> New York, NY 10011
>
> Renew America
> 1400 16th St. NW, Suite 710
> Washington, DC 20036

It should be evident that humans can have both positive and negative effects on the environment and, consequently, on the various food webs within an ecosystem. It should be equally apparent that when we remove one portion of a food web, other portions are also affected. Although nature does have the ability to compensate for minor changes in the prevailing food webs, it is quite difficult for nature to compensate for unnatural disasters that may be both catastrophic and long-lasting.

## Endangered and Extinct Species

An unfortunate consequence of life is that some species are reduced and others fully eliminated. These events may occur as the result of natural circumstances (a food source is eliminated or the climate in an area changes dramatically) or as a result of human intervention (indiscriminate hunting or chemical defoliation of a wildlife area). Whatever the reason, the very survival of many organisms is in jeopardy or has ceased.

An *endangered* species is one whose existence is threatened. There may be very few members of a species alive, their habitat, or food source may have been eliminated, or their numbers may be so small that it is difficult to obtain an accurate count. Any of these factors is cause for concern about the species' ability to survive and prosper. Following is a list of some of the endangered species (as of this writing) in the world today.

| | |
|---|---|
| Black rhinoceros | African elephant |
| Giant panda | Bald eagle |
| American bison | Humpback whale |
| Whooping crane | California condor |
| Vicuna | Hawaiian silversword |
| Polar bear | Gorilla |
| Loggerhead turtle | Pitcher's thistle flower |
| Mexican grizzly bear | Giant otter |
| Snow leopard | Black-footed ferret |
| Woolly spider monkey | |

When a species is no longer found on the face of the earth it is said to be *extinct*. Extinction is a permanent condition, meaning that the species will never reappear on the earth. Extinction of a species can occur for the same reasons as endangerment. However, the major reasons for extinction of a species are destruction of the natural habitat and overhunting or overfishing. Following is a list of some of the species that are considered extinct.

> Passenger pigeon
> Great auk
> Labrador duck
> Dodo bird
> Heath hen
> Plains grizzly bear

**DID YOU KNOW?**

Approximately 18 percent of the total number of known bird species are currently endangered or at imminent risk of extinction.

**Classroom Activity** Write to the following organizations, each of which is dedicated to preserving wildlife around the world. Ask for information and literature for classroom use.

Defenders of Wildlife
1244 19th St. NW
Washington, DC 20036

World Wildlife Fund
1250 24th St. NW
Washington, DC 20037

The Fund for Animals, Inc.
200 West 57th St.
New York, NY 10019 ■

## TO INVESTIGATE

What are teachers in the local schools doing to introduce children to ecological concerns? Are students involved in recycling efforts, establishing nature walks around the school,

writing to city officials about waste disposal, or taking care of a plot of land on the school grounds?

With your classmates, investigate several schools and classrooms in the community. Determine what efforts teachers are using to help youngsters become activists in conservation efforts and environmental issues. Based on your survey, what would you propose as a long-term program or effort for your classroom to help students become more environmentally conscious? Can you and your classmates propose and create a schoolwide program? ■

Ecology is much more than recycling your aluminum cans or using organic fertilizers on your lawn. It is the balance of nature—a balance we can help preserve for future generations of humans, plants, and animals. Sharing those concerns with your students will be one of the most significant elements of your science curriculum.

## POINTS OF DISCUSSION

1. Define "life." Interview several different people (fellow students, children, other adults) and obtain their definitions of life. Compare your survey results with those of other members of the class. What similarities do you note? What differences? What might be some implications for teaching the life sciences in your future classroom?

2. What are some short-term activites involving plants that could be used in any classroom? What are some long-term activities? Combine your activities with those of your classmates and develop a "Plant Activity Book." Why are the selected activities appropriate for all elementary classrooms?

3. What information should all students know about plants? What information should first-grade students know about plants? What information should sixth-grade students know about plants? Is there a common body of knowledge about plants that all students should know? Why or why not?

4. What might be some difficulties in maintaining animals in the classroom? Which kinds of animals

might be most difficult to maintain? Which types of animals might be easiest to maintain? Can you and your classmates design a "guidebook" for fellow teachers on the care and maintenance of classroom animals?

5. In conducting experiments with animals, what would be some important safety procedures to keep in mind for the animal(s)? In other words, how can animals be properly "used" in the classroom without injuring or harming them in any way?

6. How important is the sudy of ecology and the environment in elementary science instruction? Do you believe it should be a small part of the science curriculum or a long-term element of the entire school year? Defend your position with your classmates.

7. What do you consider to be the single-most important environmental threat in this country? What type of activity or project can you develop that will make students aware of this threat and effectively deal with it?

ACTIVITY **12.1**

## Roots and Routes

## Introduction

For plants and animals to grow, they must take in nutrients. We know how that is done by animals, but how do plants obtain nutrients? In this activity students will learn that the root system collects and transports the water and nutrients the plant needs. A familiar root, the carrot, helps to demonstrate this process.

## Organization and Materials

This lesson is intended for small-group demonstrations. Divide the class into groups of no more than four students each.

*Per group:* A jar or glass, two carrots, water, sugar water (4 tablespoons of sugar to 1 quart of water), knife, paper towels

*Note:* Keep carrots refrigerated until ready for use.

## Procedure

1. Cut off the tops of two carrots and hollow out the centers to a depth of 1 inch.
2. Have each group fill a glass with tap water to within 2 inches of the top.

   "Why don't we fill the glass all the way to the top?" (When the carrots are put into the glass, the water will flow over the top.) (Inferring)

3. Have the groups set two carrots in each glass (cut portion on top).

   "What do you observe about the water level in the glass when the carrots are put in?" (The water level rises.) (Observing)

4. Have students fill the hollow part of one carrot with tap water and the hollow part of the other carrot with sugar water. Each should be filled halfway to the top.

   "Is it important to put the same amount of liquid in each carrot? Why?" (All the variables must be controlled.) (Inferring, experimenting)

5. Place each glass out of the sun until the following day.

   "Why is it better to place the glass away from the sun?" (Inferring)
   "Do you think any other factors in the room will affect the outcome of the experiment?" (Inferring)

6. The next day observe the carrots and note any changes.

   "How can you account for the difference in the water levels inside the two carrots?" (Refer to the conclusion.)
   "Why would this be important to the survival of carrots or any other plants?" (Observing, inferring)

7. Have the students repeat this experiment with other plants (turnips, beets, celery, potatoes, cornstalks, etc.)

   "What differences do you note between plants normally grown underground and those grown above ground?"
   "What differences do you note between plants with a high sugar content (beets, corn) and those with a low sugar content (celery)?" (Observing)

## Conclusion

The students should see that the carrot containing sugar water has more water left in its hollow the day after the project began. This is because the natural sugars found in plants are attracted by the sugar water. These sugars act as the nutrients of the plant.

## Follow-up Activities

1. Have the students repeat the experiment using other substances in place of sugar (salt, juice, gelatin) to determine whether these substances could be used as nutrients for plants.
2. Fill a clear glass halfway with water. Invert the carrot in the glass, making sure no water enters the hollow. Have students predict how the hollow will look when the carrot is immersed in various liquids.

---

ACTIVITY **12.2**

## Green Highways

## Introduction

The stem of a plant is responsible for transporting water and nutrients to the rest of the plant. Conducting tubes in the stem carry water upward to the branches, leaves, and flowers.

## Organization and Materials

Divide the class into groups of three or four.
*Per group:* One stalk of celery, two glasses of water, red food coloring, knife

*Note:* The celery stalks can be precut, except for one that is to be used as a demonstration. If possible, complete this experiment early in the day.

## Procedure

1. Have each group fill one glass with clear water and the other with water containing four drops of red food coloring.

   "Does it matter if the glasses are equally full?" (Yes.)
   "Why?" (It is important to control all variables.) (Inferring)

2. Have students cut 1 inch off the bottom of each celery stalk.

   "Why is it important to cut the bottom off the celery?" (By cutting the bottom off the plant, you remove the bacteria that would block the entry of the water.) (Inferring)

3. Ask students to cut each stalk up the middle about halfway and then put one of the celery ends in the glass containing clear water and the other end in the glass containing red food coloring.

4. Have students observe the celery every hour and note all changes.

   "Why is it important to record this information accurately?" (Careful record keeping is important in science.) (Observing)
   "Is the change in the celery sudden or gradual? Why?" (Inferring)

5. Have students record the results the next day by cutting both bottom sides every inch and noting the location of the red water.

"What causes the celery to get red?" (The flow of red water throughout the plant.) (Inferring)

## Conclusion

Nutrients dissolved in water travel from the ground up the stems of a plant in conducting tubes. In this way all parts of the plant get the water and nourishment they need to grow and develop.

## Follow-up Activities

1. Have students repeat the experiment using fresh-cut flowers (carnations work well).
2. Have students cut a large celery stalk into four parts, putting each part into a different color of water.
3. Have students experiment with other edible plants by placing them in colored water and recording the results.

ACTIVITY    12.3

........................................................................................

### Feed Me, I'm Yours

........................................................................................

## Introduction

Fresh-cut flowers brighten the day, no matter what the occasion. Unfortunately, the time of enjoyment is short-lived, as most flowers quickly turn brown and wither. If we give them proper nourishment, however, we can lengthen the time of enjoyment considerably.

## Organization and Materials

Because of the ongoing nature of this project, it is best to divide the class into three groups, each following the same steps.

   *Per group:* Several flowers (carnations are ideal), one can of lemon-lime soda, two aspirin, one can of water, two teaspoons of sugar, four quart jars, liquid bleach

## Procedure

1. With the class, list the basic needs of plants. Discuss how these needs might change when the plant is cut, leaving it without a root system.

"What will happen if we cut a flower?" (Predicting)

2. Instruct the groups to cut off the bottom of each flower at the base of the stem.

   "Why would it be beneficial to cut the stem at an angle?" (The stem's surface area is increased if it is cut at an angle.) (Inferring)

3. Have students mix the following solutions separately and add them to the jars: jar A—plain water; jar B—dissolved aspirin in water; jar C—dissolved sugar in water; jar D— one-half can of lemon-lime soda, one-half can of water, seven drops of liquid bleach (the bleach provides a deterrent to bacteria buildup at the base of the stem, allowing the soda solution to travel up the stem).

   "What reason can you offer for trying the different types of solutions?" (To see whether plants respond differently to various solutions and to identify those components necessary for plant survival.) (Inferring)

4. Tell students to put two flowers into each of the four jars. "Which group of flowers will last the longest? Why?" (Predicting, inferring)
5. Have the students draw pictures of the flowers as they appear on different date.
6. Direct students to record daily observations or notes on a chart for four weeks, noting any changes in the appearance of the flowers.

## Conclusion

Plants need water and food to survive. The types of nutrients a plant gets from its environment will deter-mine, in large measure, how well it will endure and thrive. In this activity the sugar acts as the necessary food for the flower. Plants prosper because they have adapted to those environmental conditions that facilitate their survival.

## Follow-up Activities

1. Have students repeat the activity, changing either the type of flower or the solutions.
2. Have students attempt to reproduce the soda-bleach solution in dry form by getting the ingredients off the labels.

ACTIVITY   12.4

## Hey, What's Inside? (Seeds, Part I)

## Introduction

Students will learn first-hand that within each seed is a tiny plant. They will discover how this tiny plant is able to emerge from the seed and what conditions favor or hamper seed germination. These concepts are developed in this activity and the next two. These three activities may be carried out independently or in succession. This initial project provides students with an opportunity to examine the outside and inside of a seed.

## Organization and Materials

Students can work individually or in pairs.
*Per group:* One lima bean, a magnifying glass, a collection of various kinds of seeds (flower, apple, orange, etc.), paper, container of water

## Procedure

1. Lead a discussion to determine what students know about seeds. Distribute various kinds of seeds to the class to inspect during this discussion.

   "What is a seed?"
   "Where do seeds come from?"
   "Are all seeds the same?"
   "How are they alike? How are they different?"
   "Where do new plants come from? How does this happen?"

   (Acknowledge all answers for now, but refrain from confirming or disputing any hypotheses.) (Communicating, inferring, observing)

2. Distribute a lima bean, a sheet of paper, and a magnifying glass to each student or group. Tell them to look closely at the seed and then draw what they see on their paper. (Observing, communicating)
3. Soak the seeds in water overnight.
4. The next day, distribute the lima beans to the students and have them examine them again, carefully and closely. Instruct them to look for any changes and to discuss the changes they observe. Have the students sketch how the seed appears now. (Observing, communicating)
5. Have the students gently open the seed along its natural opening (a demonstration may be necessary). Stress how gently this must be done. (Experimenting)
6. Have the students observe what they see inside the seed (they should be able to find a tiny plant). (Observing)
7. Discuss the findings.

   "What did you find?"
   "What do you think happens to this tiny plant when a seed is planted?" (It develops into a plant.)
   "What do you think all the material inside the seed is needed for?" (Food)
   "Why is the outside of the seed so hard?" (Protection)
   (Observing, communicating, inferring)

8. Have the students make sketches of the inside of their seeds. (Communicating)

## Conclusion

Within each seed, a tiny plant is found. This tiny plant, called the embryo, is the beginning of a new plant. The other materials inside the seed provide the nutrients that the new plant needs to begin growing, developing, and thriving until it can take in sustenance on its own.

## Follow-up Activities

1. See Activities 12.5 and 12.6.
2. Investigate other seeds in the same manner.
3. Have students try to open a seed without soaking it in water (this leads to Activity 12.6).

ACTIVITY 12.5

........................................................................................................

## The Soggy Seed (Seeds, Part II)

........................................................................................................

### Introduction

By performing an experiment with lima beans, students learn that water enters seeds through a tiny opening called the *microphyle*. This opening is located in the seam, or scar, of the seed and enables the seed to take up water so that it can germinate.

### Organization and Materials

Divide students into groups of two or three each.

*Per group:* Six lima beans (make sure seed coats are free of any cracks), a container of water, a candle, matches, water-resistant glue, a magnifying glass

### Procedure

1. Review the concepts developed in Activity 12.4.

   "What is inside a seed?" (Tiny plant, embryo)
   "When seeds are planted and the plants begin to grow, where do these plants come from?" (Inside the seed)
   "How were we able to look inside a seed to see the tiny plant called the embryo?" (Communicating, inferring)

2. Distribute six seeds to each group.
3. Have the students examine their seeds with and without a magnifying glass.

   "How could water get inside the seed to soften it?" (Accept all answers.)
   "Can you find a spot where the water could get into the seed?" (Observing, inferring)

4. "How could we determine whether this spot allows water to enter the seed?" (Have students formulate a test to determine whether their hypothesis is correct. Students should come to the realization that if the hole is clogged, the seed will have difficulty absorbing water.)

   "How could we clog up this hole?" (Allow students to offer suggestions.) (Inferring, communicating, predicting)

5. Have students place a drop of candle wax (or any other waterproof sealant) on the tiny spot of three of their six seeds, and tell them to mark these seeds with a water-resistant pen.
6. After the drops dry, have students place all the seeds in a container of water to soak overnight.
7. The next day, examine the seeds and discuss the findings.

   "How did the seeds change?"
   "Did all the seeds change?"
   "Which seeds changed, and which did not change?" (The seeds that were waterproofed will not have expanded and cracked as much as those not waterproofed.)
   "What do your results tell you about seeds?" (The tiny hole in the seed allows water to enter.)
   "Why is it important for water to enter a seed?" (To soften it and allow the tiny plant to emerge) (Observing, communicating, inferring)

### Conclusion

The three seeds whose holes were clogged did not change. The three plain seeds, without the clogged holes, swelled up and were easy to take apart. Water enters the seed through the microphyle and softens it so that the embryo can break through the covering and begin to grow.

## Follow-up Activities

1. Have students try the same experiment using other types of vegetable seeds.

2. Have students soak two seeds in water (one clogged, one unclogged) and plant them along with two unsoaked seeds (one clogged, one unclogged). Ask pupils to predict which seeds will germinate. Growth patterns can be charted and recorded.

---

ACTIVITY **12.6**

### Pop Goes the Plant (Seeds, PART III)

---

## Introduction

Several environmental conditions contribute to the ability of seeds to germinate. How rapidly a seed germinates and how many seeds of a given species will germinate during a given time period are determined by such factors as temperature, moisture, and oxygen. In this activity students attempt to germinate seeds to learn about conditions that favor and speed germination.

## Organization and Materials

This activity is best suited for groups of three or four students.

*Per group:* Six radish seeds (or substitute), six yogurt or milk containers, paper towels (cut to fit the containers), water, melted wax, or silicon glue (*optional*: six plastic bags to place the containers in for speeding germination)

## Procedure

1. Review the concepts presented in Activities 12.4 and 12.5.

   "What did we find out about seeds?" (They contain tiny plants, water is needed to soften the seed so the plant can emerge, water enters the seed through a tiny hole in the seed coat, and the seed contains nutrients for the tiny plant.)
   "Where does a new plant come from when a seed is planted?"
   "How does the new plant get out of the seed?"
   "What does the seed need in order for the new plant to be able to grow?" (Communicating, inferring)

2. Have the students set up the yogurt or milk containers as follows: (a) Moisten a piece of paper towel and place it in each container. (b) Put a seed in each container. (c) Vary conditions for the containers as follows:

   Container 1—paper towel, water, no light, room temperature
   Container 2—paper towel, water, light, room temperature
   Container 3—paper towel, no water, light, room temperature
   Container 4—no paper towel (seed floating in water), light, room temperature
   Container 5—paper towel, water, no light, keep in refrigerator or freezer
   Container 6—paper towel, no water, no light, room temperature, seed covered with wax (Experimenting)

3. Have students record the germination dates on the containers as they occur.
4. Discuss the results.

   "Which seeds germinated?"
   "Is light (water, temperature, growing medium) needed for a seed to germinate?" (Water and favorable temperature are necessary.)
   "What conditions hamper the germination of seeds?" (Lack of moisture, extreme temperatures, and wax covering) (Communicating, inferring, classifying)

## Conclusion

Seeds need favorable temperature, adequate moisture, and oxygen to germinate. Light is not needed for germination.

## Follow-up Activities

1. Have students perform the same experiment with a variety of other seeds.
2. Have students alter the environmental conditions (heat, light, nutrients) for selected seeds and chart the germination patterns over an extended period of time.

ACTIVITY 12.7

........................................................................................................

## Follow That Light

........................................................................................................

### Introduction

Plants need sunlight to survive. Through a process known as phototropism, plants continually seek a light source. The normal vertical growth pattern of plants will change to satisfy this need.

### Organization and Materials

This activity is best suited for groups of three or four students.

*Per group:* Two shoe boxes, one bean plant, scissors

### Procedure

1. Have students label their shoe boxes A and B. Tell them to cut off the end of box A and cut a section the same size in the middle of a long side of box B. The cut ends should be placed together to form a T.
2. Instruct students to cut a 2-inch hole at one end of box B.
3. Have students place the bean plant in box A at the end farther from box B and then place both lids on the boxes (the lids may need to be cut to size) and tape them.
4. Have students position the boxes so that the hole is facing a source of light.

   "How will the bean plant react to this situation?" (The plant will grow toward the light.) (Inferring)

5. Every two days, have students carefully remove the lids to water the plant and record any growth that has taken place. Have them draw and measure the progress of the plant.

   "Why is the plant reacting in this manner?" (The plant is seeking a light source.) (Communicating, inferring)

6. Have students continue to observe and record the rate and direction of growth for a three-week period.

   "Is the direction of growth for this plant any different from the growth observed in other normally growing plants? Why?" (Yes. Most plants, under normal growing conditions, will grow in a vertical direction.)
   "What would happen if we put a hole in both ends of box B?" (The plant would grow toward the stronger light source.) (Inferring)

### Conclusion

Plants seek out light. For plants to find light, they must make adjustments in their normal growth pattern.

### Follow-up Activities

1. Have students repeat the activity, altering either the intensity or color of the light. Compare the results.
2. Have students construct several mazes in which plants must seek a light source.

ACTIVITY 12.8

........................................................................................................

## Plants Breathe, Too

........................................................................................................

### Introduction

The needs of a green plant are best met when that plant is situated in the proper environment. These needs include water, sunlight, heat, and air. When any of these needs is not met, proper growth of the plant is not possible.

### Organization and Materials

This activity is best suited for groups of four or five students.

*Per group:* Three bean plants, petroleum jelly, drawing paper, ruler

### Procedure

1. Have students position bean plants so that each will receive equal amounts of sunlight and water. The plants should be labeled A, B, and C.
2. Have students draw a picture of each plant and measure and record its height. (Observing, measuring)
3. Direct students to rub petroleum jelly on the top side of all the leaves of plant A and on the underside of the leaves of plant B.

"Do you think that the petroleum jelly will cause a change in the leaves of these plants?"

"If there is a change in the plants, can you predict what that change will be?" (Inferring, predicting)

4. Allow the third plant to remain as it is, to act as a control.

"Why do you think a 'control' is an important part of any experiment?" (It is necessary to have a normal plant with which to compare the others.) (Communicating, inferring)

5. Every other day, have students record the height of each plant and draw pictures showing any changes that have taken place.

"Can you explain why the growth rates in the plants are different?"

"What conclusion can be drawn from observing plants A and B?" (Refer to the conclusion.) (Inferring, observing, communicating, measuring)

## Conclusion

Air is a necessary component for the chemical reaction called photosynthesis. The air enters the plants through the underside of the leaves. This explains why plant B reacted as it did.

## Follow-up Activities

1. Have students repeat this activity, but this time put petroleum jelly on both the upper and lower sides of selected leaves.

2. Have students experiment with other plants to see whether air is taken in by any other means. They may tape a plastic bag around the base of one plant, covering the soil and the container, uncovering it only for watering. Petroleum jelly could be rubbed onto the stem of another plant. Have students compare the results.

ACTIVITY   **12.9**

## Adopt a Tree

## Introduction

Trees, because of their size and abundance, are probably the most familiar of plants. Not only are they enjoyed for their beauty, but they also provide us with oxygen, food, and shelter. It is through a better understanding of trees that we can guarantee their preservation.

## Organization and Materials

This is a whole-class activity.

*Per class:* String, ruler, crayons, drawing paper, writing paper

*Note:* This activity is intended to be pursued throughout the school year. Steps 2 through 5 should be repeated during each of the four seasons (depending on your area of the country). An ongoing, cumulative display of the project will help motivate the students.

## Procedure

1. Locate a deciduous tree close to your school. (Deciduous trees are those that shed their leaves annually.)

2. Have students draw a picture of the tree's general appearance and record any peculiarities.

"What distinguishing characteristics do you notice?"

"Why would the tree have these characteristics?"

"What changes have taken place since the tree was last observed?" (Observing, inferring)

3. Measure 3 feet up from the ground and wrap the piece of string around the tree at that point. Measure the string to determine the circumference of the trunk.

"Do you believe the circumference of the tree changes with the seasons? Why?"

"Why did we put the string exactly 3 feet from the bottom?" (The string serves as a point of reference for future observations.)
(Inferring, measuring)

4. Have students take several leaves back to the classroom. Direct them to place a leaf, vein side up, on a desk. Have them lay a piece of paper on top of the leaf and rub the paper with a crayon until the outline of the leaf appears.

"What similarities or differences do you see in the vein patterns of the various leaves?" (Record these observations on the chalkboard.) (Observing)

5. Direct students to hold a piece of paper against the bark of the tree. With a crayon, have them rub the paper until the bark pattern appears.
6. Repeat steps 2 through 5 at periodic intervals throughout the year. Compare and discuss the results. (Observing, communicating)
7. (Optional) Take photographs of the tree at various times during the year. Mount them in a class scrapbook along with leaf and bark rubbings obtained at the same times the photos were taken.

## Conclusion

Each season brings about changes in plant life. These changes are necessary for the plant to adjust to the environment.

## Follow-up Activities

1. Using the fallen seeds from your adopted tree, have the class attempt to grow more trees. The seeds can be planted during an Arbor Day ceremony.
2. Have students write and distribute a brochure explaining the changes a tree goes through and describing how to properly care for it. Check with your county agricultural agent or local forestry department to obtain some sample leaflets or brochures.

## Project 12.1: Breathe Deeply

### Materials

Elodea plants (available at any aquarium store), aquarium, glass funnel, test tube, water, wooden splint, matches

### Initiating Questions

Do plants breathe?
If so, how do they breathe?
How do plants give off oxygen?
How much oxygen does a plant give off?
Why do plants need to breathe?

### Activity

Fill an aquarium almost to the top with water. Place several elodea plants in the aquarium and cover them with the glass funnel (the funnel should be placed over all the plants with its wide mouth on the bottom of the aquarium). Dip the test tube in the aquarium and make sure it is filled with water. Invert the test tube over the stem of the funnel, making sure no water escapes. Place the aquarium in a sunny location for a few days and observe what happens in the top of the test tube.

### Extending Questions

Why is there empty space in the top of the test tube?
What caused that to happen?
If we left the aquarium in the sun for one or two weeks, what do you think would happen?
What would happen if we removed the test tube and quickly put a glowing piece of wood inside it?

### Curricular Extensions

*Language arts:* Have students take photographs of the aquarium at regular intervals (twice a day, for ex-

ample). Post each photo on the bulletin board and ask students to write a brief description of what they see. Assemble the descriptions in chronological order.

*Reading:* Here are two books your students are sure to enjoy: *Gardening Without Soil* by Sarah Reidman (New York: Watts, 1983) and *Plant Fun: Ten Easy Plants to Grow Indoors* by Anita Homes (New York: Four Winds, 1981).

## Project 12.2: Pieces o' Pollen

### Materials

Microscope, water, slides, several different flowers, sugar water in three cups (cup A—water and 1 teaspoon of sugar; cup B—water and 2 teaspoons of sugar; cup C—water and 3 teaspoons of sugar), petri dishes (can be obtained from the local high school)

### Initiating Questions

What is pollen?
Where would you find it?
How is it important in the reproduction of a plant?
What does it do?

### Activity

Place a drop of water on a slide and sprinkle some pollen from a flower on the water. Have students observe the pollen grains. Repeat this with the pollen from several different flowers and have students note any similarities or differences. Put small samples of the three sugar water solutions in separate petri dishes. Sprinkle different types of pollen in the dishes and cover with the glass lids. Place the various samples in the room. Using the microscope, have students observe the drops after several hours. Ask them to write down any observations.

## Extending Questions

What differences did you note in the various pollen samples?

How can you account for those differences?

In which sugar solution did the pollen grains grow the most?

What happens when pollen settles on the anther of a flower?

Is that process similar to what you observed in the sugar water solutions?

## Curricular Extensions

*Art:* Have students prepare illustrations for each of their microscope observations. Assemble these into a scrapbook for permanent display in the classroom and for use in succeeding years.

*Science:* A terrific series of five filmstrips on plant growth is available from the National Geographic Society. Entitled "The World of Plants" (catalog no. 03785, 1976), it offers youngsters an inside look at the structure of plants, how they grow, and how they adapt to different environments.

## Project 12.3: "See Me Grow"

### Materials

Shoe box, clear acetate, scissors, masking tape, variety of plant seeds, pebbles, potting soil, water

### Initiating Questions

How do plants grow?

What is needed for seeds to germinate?

In what direction do the roots of a plant grow?

What might affect the growth of a seed?

How does the small plant emerge from the seed?

## Activity

Cut out a large section from the side of a shoe box, making sure to leave a border of about 1 inch all around. Tape a piece of clear acetate over the opening, making sure the seal is tight. Punch a few holes in the bottom of the box and sprinkle a layer of pebbles in the bottom. Fill the box with potting soil. Plants several different seeds in the soil up against the acetate sheet (the seeds should be fully visible behind the acetate). Water the seeds and observe them for several days (keep the box away from direct sunlight).

### Extending Questions

What did you notice about the seeds when we first planted them?

What happened to the seeds after several days?

How do you account for that growth?

What made the roots grow in the direction they did?

What happened to the seed coats?

How did the little plant emerge from each seed?

### Curricular Extensions

*Reading:* Two excellent books that will provide youngsters with additional information about seeds are *Eat the Fruit: Plant the Seed* by Millicent Selsam (New York: Morrow, 1980) and *Seeds: Pop, Stick, Glide* by Patricia Lauber (New York: Crown, 1981).

*Math:* Bring in several examples of different seed packets. Have students spread the seeds over a large table and arrange them into different sets, for example: a set of green seeds and a set of brown seeds; a set of large seeds, a set of medium seeds, and a set of small seeds; or a set of smooth seeds and a set of rough seeds. Invite students to establish their own sets for the seeds.

ACTIVITY  **12.10**

# Cricket Critters

## Introduction

Although many people try to rid their homes of crickets, these creatures provide students with many wonderful opportunities to observe live organisms. In this activity students will establish an appropriate environment for observing crickets for a long period of time and will, with luck, be able to see a second generation of crickets produced.

## Organization and Materials

This activity can be done in small groups of three to four students or in pairs.

*Per Group:* Two or three crickets (these can be purchased very inexpensively—15 for about $1.00—in most pet stores), oatmeal box, discarded nylon stockings, twigs, grass, water, flaked fish food, apple slices, bran or oatmeal

## Procedure

1. Students prepare cricket "houses" from discarded oatmeal boxes. Have students draw three large sections on the outside of oatmeal box. You should be the one to cut out these sections using a sharp-edged knife. After the sections have been cut and removed, cover each box with a discarded nylon

stocking and make a small hole in the top of the stocking. Replace the box top on the oatmeal box.

   "Why is the oatmeal box covered with a ny-lon stocking?" (It allows air to get into the box, but prevents the crickets from escaping.) (Inferring)

2. Assist students in "decorating" the floor of each oatmeal box with a few twigs, some dry soil, and a little grass. Place a small apple slice in each cage (these should be replaced regularly).

   "Why should the soil be dry?" (Crickets prefer a dry environment.) (Inferring)

   "Why should the cage have an apple slice in it?" (Crickets use this as a source of water.) (Inferring, observing)

3. In the bottom of each "cage" have students place a jar lid so that the top edge of the lid is flush with the level of the soil. Fill each lid with moist soil (the soil in the lid should be kept moist throughout the duration of this activity).

   "Why do we place some moist soil in each cage?" (Female crickets will lay their eggs only in moist soil.) (Inferring)

4. Assist students in transferring the crickets from the pet store container to their respective cages. Try to get a mix of male and female crickets in each cage (males are slightly smaller than females; also, males chirp, and females do not).

   "Why do we want to have both males and females in each cage?" (For breeding and reproduction) (Inferring)

   "How do crickets chirp?" (By rubbing their wings together) (Inferring, observing)

5. Have students observe their crickets over a specified period of time.

   "What changes do you observe in your crickets?" (Observing)

   "How can you account for their behavior?" (Observing, inferring)

   "What type of information do you think would be valuable to record in a science note-book?" (Communicating)

6. Have students maintain their cricket cages for several weeks. Flaked fish food can be fed to the crickets, as can oatmeal or crushed bran flakes (be careful not to overfeed). An eyedropper can be used to keep the soil in the lids moist without wetting the dry soil. If the conditions are satisfactory, the females will lay eggs which will eventually hatch into nymphs (baby crickets).

## Conclusion

The nymphs will take about eight weeks to mature into adults. If the classroom conditions (temperature, humidity) do not vary greatly, students will be able to keep their crickets for long periods of time. If the chirping of the males becomes too distracting, you may be able to arrange for the crickets to be housed in a storage closet or basement area of the school.

## Follow-up Activities

1. Students may be interested to learn that it is possible to estimate the air temperature just by listening to the chirps of crickets. Have students count the number of chirps a cricket makes in one minute (this may require several trials, since it is sometimes difficult to distinguish one chirp from another). Subtract 40 from that number and divide the answer by 4. Add 50 to that figure. The result is the approximate temperature in degrees Fahrenheit. (*Note:* This calculation works best with snowy tree crickets; other crickets are not as dependable.)

2. Have students experiment to see which conditions facilitate the chirping of crickets (many males together, one male and many females, many males and one female, temperature changes, etc.).

ACTIVITY   **12.11**

## Feathered Friends

## Introduction

Birds give us a great deal of pleasure with their beauty and song. These aren't the only benefits we gain from our feathered friends, though. By closely observing the local bird population, students can gain increased knowledge and appreciation of birds' relation to humans.

## Organization and Materials

This activity is best as a class project, with certain aspects handled by smaller groups.

*Per Class:* Construction paper, plastic milk cartons, birdseed, pine cones, crayons, peanut butter, string

## Procedure

1. Locate an outdoor area near your school that lends itself to attracting birds.
2. Have students cut a rectangular section out of the side of a plastic milk carton, leaving at least a 2-inch border of plastic around the bottom. Instruct them to fill the container with birdseed and hang it in an outdoor area.

   "How can we change the appearance of the feeder to better blend into the surroundings?" (Glue leaves on the container, paint the container, etc.)
   "Why would we want to do that?" (So that birds will be attracted to it) (Inferring)

3. Have the students mix the peanut butter with birdseed and insert the mixture into the hollow sections of the pine cones. They should tie a piece of string to each pine cone and hang them in the observation area.
4. Establish a time schedule whereby the students can observe the birds attracted to the observation area. If possible, arrange for the students to observe at the same time each day.

   "Why would it be to our advantage to observe the birds at the same time each day?" (Inferring)

5. While observing the birds at the feeding station, have students draw pictures of the various birds, record the number of birds entering the area, and note the number of different species seen.

"How do different birds obtain their food?"
"Which birds seem to prefer one food over another?"
"What advantages might humans derive from these and other birds?" (Birds provide us with beauty and song. They also help control insects.)
(Observing, inferring)

6. Maintain the feeding station throughout the year. Have students record any changes in either the number or types of birds observed. (Observing)
7. Have students develop graphs that record the number of birds seen in relation to the season of the year.

   "Why are more birds seen during one season than another?" (Inferring)

## Conclusion

Ornithology, or the study of birds, can be a fascinating subject for students. Pupils gain an appreciation for the different species of birds native to their part of the country, as well as an understanding of some of the birds' habits. The appearance and behavior of birds reflect not only climatic conditions, but also the effects of adaptation and evolution.

## Follow-up Activities

1. Have students construct a wall chart showing the various birds living in your area. They can include the information gathered from their observations.
2. Have students research the migratory patterns of birds and relate their findings to the data they have gathered.

ACTIVITY **12.12**

······································································································

### Mealworm Magic

······································································································

## Introduction

Mealworms are the larval stage of the darkling beetle. As mealworms develop, they undergo a complete metamorphosis (egg, larva, pupa, beetle). Their life cycle is influenced to a great extent by temperature, with cooler temperatures delaying their development.

Mealworms provide students with an opportunity to study animal behavior. This investigation is divided into two distinct parts, which should be performed in succession. Part 1 introduces students to the mealworm and its characteristics through the use of observation, measurement, and communication skills. Part 2 is an unstructured activity allowing students to work independently, devising experiments, collecting data, and drawing conclusions while discovering how animals react to various conditions.

## Materials

*Per student:* One mealworm (mealworms may be purchased inexpensively at most pet stores), a ruler, a magnifying glass, a toothpick, drawing paper, a mealworm home (plastic container with holes in the lid; a layer of oats, bran, or cornflakes; and a slice of apple, to provide moisture), plus various other materials as determined by student investigations in Part 2.

## Procedure: Part 1

1. Instruct students to spend time observing their mealworm using the magnifying glass, toothpick, and ruler. Have them list the characteristics they observe. Stress that the mealworms should be observed carefully so as not to harm them in any way. (Observing, measuring, communicating)
2. Discuss the students' observations.

   "What did you find out about your mealworm?" (Allow time for students to examine their mealworms as characteristics are discussed. Possible observations relate to size, feel, color, smell, and physical features—eyes, mouth, ears, antennae, legs, body structure, and so on.)
   "How does it move?" (Communicating, observing)

3. After students have had ample time to observe and discuss the characteristics of their mealworms, have each one draw a picture of his or her specimen. (Communicating, measuring)

## Procedure: Part 2

This activity deals with how mealworms react to various conditions as investigated by the students.

1. "What else would you like to learn about your mealworms?" (Accept student suggestions and discuss methods of investigating these characteristics. List 5 to 10 of the suggestions on the board. Allow students to select one of the suggested investigations.) (Communicating)
2. Possible investigations include:

   "Do the mealworms prefer light over dark, one color over another, hot over cold? Do they prefer crumbled cornflakes, bran flakes, sugar, bread, or apple as food?"
   "How do mealworms react to various substances, such as vinegar, alcohol, water, or milk?" (Drops of these substances should be placed next to each mealworm.)
   "How do they react to touch by various objects?"
   "How far does the mealworm move in one minute under varying surface conditions—smooth, rough, warm, cold, lumpy, and so on?"
   "Does the mealworm move in a straight line? Can a pattern be traced?"
   "How does the mealworm move when placed in an empty box?"

   These activities are only suggestions. Students should be allowed to formulate their own experiments as long as they do not harm the mealworms. Step-by-step procedures have been deliberately omitted, since we are striving to encourage development of problem-solving, data collection, interpretation, and evaluation skills in this activity.
3. Students perform their experiments, have them record conditions and results, which can be discussed when the experiments are concluded.

## Conclusion

In both parts of this activity, the focus is not the factual information gathered but rather the development of measuring, observing, communicating, investigating, and problem-solving skills.

## Follow-up Activities

1. Have students construct bar graphs and tables depicting mealworm reactions, sizes, and other variables.
2. Direct students to study the growth of the mealworms and their life cycle over time.

## Project 12.4: "The Ants Go Marching Two By Two..."

### Materials

Large glass (pickle) jar, loose or sandy soil, large container of water, black construction paper, sugar water, small bits of fruit

### Initiating Questions

What does an ant look like?

What do ants do underground?

What are some of the special characteristics of ants?

How are ants similar to or different from humans?

### Activity

Take the students outside and locate a rotting piece of wood or another area with lots of ants. Scoop up some of the surrounding soil into the glass jar along with a healthy collection of ants. Back in the classroom, place the jar (with soil and ants) in a larger container of water (this prevents the ants from escaping into the classroom). Cover the glass jar with black construction paper so that it is completely dark inside the jar. Establish a date to return the ants to their natural environment. Every so often students can sprinkle the top of the soil with some sugar water and small bits of fruit. The black construction paper can be removed occasionally for viewing the tunneling ants.

### Extending Questions

Why did we cover the jar with black construction paper?

Why did we sprinkle sugar water on the soil?

What did you notice when we removed the construction paper?

How is the ant colony similar to a "people colony" (i.e., a city)?

What do ants do that is similar to the behavior of other insects?

### Curricular Extensions

*Reading*: Students may enjoy reading stories about ants. The fable "The Ant and the Grasshopper" or the book *Two Bad Ants* by Chris Van Allsburg (Boston: Houghton Mifflin, 1988) would be appropriate.

*Science/art:* Have several students examine one or more ants under a microscope. Ask them to prepare enlarged illustrations of several ants, showing the three major body parts (head, abdomen, thorax). These can be displayed around the classroom.

## Project 12.5: Home Sweet Home

### Materials

Bird nests, tweezers, magnifying glass

### Initiating Questions

Why do birds build nests?

How are bird nests constructed?

What materials do birds use in building nests?

Where are bird nests found?

### Activity

During late autumn or early winter take students outdoors to locate bird nests. Carefully remove the nests from tree branches or buildings, trying to keep them as intact as possible (be sure there are no eggs in the nests). Return to the classroom and provide each of several groups with a nest. Ask each group to take their nest apart with tweezers and their fingers to determine the materials and the procedures used to construct the nest. Have the students make lists of the different types of materials used. (*Note:* Prior to taking the nests apart, students may wish to draw an illustration or take a photograph of their nests. These can be assembled into a class scrapbook.)

### Extending Questions

Were all the nests constructed in the same way?

Were the same materials used for each nest?

How are the nests similar? How are they different?

What can you infer about the lifestyles of the birds using these nests?

How did the birds obtain materials for their nests?

What material would be easiest to obtain?

Does the location or height of the nest tell you anything about the birds that used it?

### Curricular Extensions

*Language arts:* Have each student create a fictitious series of events in the life of a bird using one of the nests. Each student could write a series of journal entries as though they were recorded by the bird that actually used a particular nest. What would the bird have observed or done?

*Social studies:* Have small groups of students investigate the nesting habits of birds that live in groups (e.g., flamingos, crows) versus the nesting habits of those birds that tend to be solitary (e.g., hawks, herons).

## Project 12.6: "As Slow as a..."

### Materials

Live land snails, pieces of lettuce, black construction paper, large glass jar with damp soil, magnifying glass

### Initiating Questions

What do snails do?

How do snails travel?

What do snails eat?

What are the body parts of a snail?

How is a snail similar to or different from other animals?

Why are snails considered harmful by gardeners?

### Activity

Obtain several land snails (they can usually be found in the moist soil of gardens in the early morning). Put the snails in a large glass jar partially filled with damp soil (sprinkle the soil every so often). Keep the jar in a cool, shady place and put pieces of lettuce in it for food. Have students carefully remove one or more snails for observation. The snails can be placed on sheets of black construction paper to observe the trails they leave behind. Magnifying glasses can be used to observe the snail's body parts. Students may wish to time several snails as they move toward a piece of lettuce (how fast does a snail travel when it's hungry?). Have students place several different kinds of food (apple slice, lettuce, cereal, celery, etc.) in a circle around a snail and observe which food it heads toward.

### Extending Questions

How fast do snails travel?

Why would snails be a destructive element in a garden?

Why do snails prefer a moist environment?

How much lettuce would a snail eat in one day?

Why do snails leave a trail behind them?

Where would you expect to find snails around your house?

### Curricular Extensions

*Art:* Have students prepare a series of illustrations of different snails. Each illustration can be accompanied by a name for the snail and a brief biographical sketch. Be sure to post the illustrations on the bulletin board.

*Physical education:* Have selected students simulate the movements of a snail as they try to slide across a carpeted floor and across a tile floor. What differences do they notice?

## Project 12.7: Something's Fishy

### Materials

Large commercial mayonnaise jar (can be obtained from the school cafeteria), gravel, sand, aquatic plants, guppies or goldfish, water snails, tropical fish food (all of these can be obtained from a local pet store or tropical fish dealer), wire screening

### Initiating Questions

What do fish need to survive?

How do fish breathe?

What other organisms are helpful to the survival of fish?

What materials or elements should an aquarium have for fish to live?

### Activity

Thoroughly wash and rinse out the mayonnaise jar. Wash and rinse the gravel and sand. Place a half-inch layer of gravel and a 1-inch layer of sand on the bottom of the jar. Fill the jar almost to the top with tap water and allow the jar to sit undisturbed for 48 hours (this allows the chlorine in the water to evaporate). Place two or three aquatic plants in the bottom of the jar (make sure they are firmly rooted in the sand). Place two or three snails and two or three fish in the jar. Place some wire screening over the top of the jar. Instruct students on a proper feeding schedule for the fish.

### Extending Questions

Why were plants added to the aquarium?

Why were snails added to the aquarium?

How are the snails, fish, and plants helpful to each other?

How long will the fish be able to survive in this type of environment?

How is this aquarium different from or similar to the natural living conditions of the fish?

If we removed the (fish, plants, snails) from the aquarium, what would happen?

### Curricular Extensions

*Reading/science:* An excellent children's magazine that deals with marine biology is *Dolphin Log* (Cousteau Society, 8430 Santa Monica Blvd., Los Angeles, CA 90069).

*Art:* Provide students with old magazines, glue, and scissors. Have them plot an oversize aquarium on a bulletin board. Using pictures cut out from the magazines, students can create an enormous aquarium collage of different fish.

## Project 12.8: Worm World

### Materials

Several large glass jars, soil, gravel, dead leaves, earthworms (can be dug from someone's yard or purchased from a local bait shop).

**Initiating Questions**

In what kinds of conditions do earthworms live?
How do earthworms move through the soil?
How are earthworms important?
How do earthworms survive?

**Activity**

Wash and rinse several large glass jars. In the bottom of each place a layer of clean gravel and several inches of loose soil. Sprinkle some dead leaves over the soil and moisten with a little water. Place several earthworms in each jar. Wrap a piece of black paper around each jar (worms prefer to work in darkness and will tend to build their tunnels near the jar's sides when light is kept out). Every few days or so remove the black paper so that students can observe the tunnels made by the worms as well as their movements. The soil should be sprinkled occasionally, too. After a few weeks the worms should be let loose in a garden area.

**Extending Questions**

How do the earthworms move through the soil?
Why is that movement beneficial to the soil?

How might earthworms be helpful to farmers?
Why were dead leaves put into each jar?
How long would you expect the earthworms to survive in this environment?
How is this environment similar to the natural environment in your back yard?

**Curricular Extensions**

*Science:* Students may be interested in obtaining a commercial worm farm. One that includes worm bedding, worm food, red worms, and an instruction booklet can be purchased from Carolina Biological Supply Company (2700 York Rd., Burlington, NC 27215).

*Art:* Students may wish to create an oversize worm "mascot" for the classroom. Take several discarded nylon stockings and sew them together (after cutting off the foot sections). Have students stuff the stockings with newspapers. The outside can be painted with rings and an appropriate face. Hang the "worm" from the ceiling of the room and give it a name.

# RECOMMENDED CHILDREN'S LITERATURE

## The Plant Kingdom

Plants are a diverse and interesting group of organisms for children to explore. The following books can help students understand more about the richness of the plant world.

Brown, Marc. (1981). *Your first garden book.* Boston: Little, Brown. How children can get started in gardening with plants such as pumpkins and potatoes is engagingly told in this entertaining book.

Coldrey, Jennifer. (1989). *Strawberry.* New York: Silver Burdett. You can almost taste them as you look at the photographs and read this book about the life cycle of one of the most delicious fruits ever.

Cross, Diana Harding. (1983). *Some plants have funny names.* New York: Crown. A lively introduction to distinctively named plants such as Indian paintbrush and lady's slippers.

Crowell, Robert. (1982). *The lore and legend of flowers.* New York: Crowell. The role of 10 different flowers in the history of the world is examined.

Dowden, Anne Ophelia. (1990). *The clover and the bee: A book of pollination.* New York: HarperCollins. The various ways plants can be pollinated, including wind, water, insects, mammals, and birds, is examined in this descriptive book.

Ehlert, Lois. (1988). *Planting a rainbow.* San Diego: Harcourt, Brace. The complete growth cycle of flowering plants is wonderfully detailed in this colorful introduction to the plant kingdom.

Forsyth, Adrian. (1989). *Journey through a tropical jungle.* New York: Simon & Schuster. The varied and distinctive flora of one of the tropical rain forest areas of the world is beautifully chronicled.

George, Jean Craighead. (1983). *One day in the desert.* New York: Crowell. The lives of both plants and animals is depicted in this inside look at the desert.

Hamer, Martyn. (1983). *Trees.* New York: Watts. This is a brief yet thorough introduction to the lives of trees, including information on varieties, tree parts, fruits and flowers of trees, and their role in the environment.

Heller, Ruth. (1984). *Plants that never bloom.* New York: Grosset. Colorful drawings stand out in this examination of plants that never flower yet are just as beautiful as those that do.

Hindley, Judy. (1990). *The tree.* New York: Clarkson Potter. This insightful introduction to 12 of the most common trees is highlighted by detailed folk art drawings.

Johnson, Sylvia A. (1986). *How leaves change.* New York: Lerner. Everything a young questioner would want to know about leaves and the changes they undergo each year is richly explained.

Kuhn, Dwight. (1990). *More than just a vegetable garden*. New York: Silver Press. A vegetable garden is much more than a collection of edible plants; it is full of all kinds of life, as shown in this dramatically photographed book.

Lauber, Patricia. (1981). *Seeds: Pop, stick, glide*. New York: Crown. The "travels" of the seeds of some common plants is the subject of this delightful and insightful book.

Lerner, Carol. (1988). *Moonseed and mistletoe: A book of poisonous wild plants*. New York: Morrow. More than 30 poisonous plants from throughout North America are presented in detailed drawings and descriptive text.

Lerner, Carol. (1989). *Plant families*. New York: Morrow. The members of the 12 largest plant families are described in this book, which includes full-size drawings of their flowers, fruits, and leaves.

Lyon, George Ella. (1989). *A B Cedar: An alphabet of trees*. New York: Orchard. A wonderful first book on tree and leaf identification.

Mabey, Richard. (1983). *Oak and Co*. New York: Greenwillow. Rich illustrations and a delightful text distinguish this story about a long-lived oak tree and its many inhabitants.

McMillan, Bruce. (1988). *Growing colors*. New York: Lothrop. This delightful introduction to the colorful world of plants is ideal for the beginning reader/botanist.

Newton, James R. (1982). *A forest is reborn*. New York: Crowell. What happens to a forest after it has suffered a devastating fire? How does it begin again? Those answers and many others are contained in the pages of this well illustrated book.

Oechsli, Helen, & Oechsli, Kelly. (1985). *In my garden: A child's gardening book*. New York: Macmillan. Everything a new gardener would want to know about how to be successful with plants can be found in this comprehensive guidebook.

Overbeck, Cynthia. (1982). *Carnivorous plants*. New York: Lerner. Colorful photographs highlight this inviting look into some of the plant kingdom's most interesting species. The Venus flytrap, sundews, pitcher plants, and others are featured in this book, which students will find hard to put down.

Overbeck, Cynthia. (1982). *How seeds travel*. New York: Lerner. Students will be amazed to discover how seeds move from one place to another on the backs of animals, in the wind, or across the water.

Prime, C. T., & Klein, Aaron E. (1973). *Seedlings and soil: Botany for young experimenters*. New York: Doubleday. Full of all kinds of experiments into the structure and functions of plants, this book is ideal for the young botanist.

Rice, Karen. (1984). *Does candy grow on trees?*. New York: Walker. Students will be amazed to discover that the ingredients of some of their favorite candies originate in the plant world. The book discusses cinnamon, vanilla, sugar, chocolate, peppermint, and licorice.

Ring, Elizabeth. (1984). *Tiger lilies and other beastly plants*. New York: Walker. Plants with unusual names (skunk cabbage, snapdragon, pussy willow) are richly described and illustrated.

Robbins, Ken. (1990). *A flower grows*. New York: Dial. The complete life cycle of a flower is presented in this handsomely photographed book.

Selsam, Millicent. (1978). *Play with plants*. New York: Morrow. Students can hardly go wrong with this book, full of experiments and activities, about the habits and habitats of all kinds of plants.

Selsam, Millicent. (1980). *Eat the fruit, plant the seed*. New York: Morrow. The usual and the unusual are detailed in this book about fruits such as the avocado and the kiwi and the seeds that can be planted.

Selsam, Millicent. (1984). *Tree flowers*. New York: Morrow. A marvelous "must read" volume full of information and data on 12 flowering trees.

Selsam, Millicent. (1986). *Mushrooms*. New York: Morrow. A behind-the-scenes look at one of the denizens of the plant kingdom that doesn't produce chlorophyll and hides in the dark.

Sobel, Harriet. (1984). *A book of vegetables*. New York: Dodd. An insightful introduction to 14 vegetables, this book is particularly appropriate for those students whose only experience with vegetables is from the freezer or in the microwave.

Tarsky, Sue. (1981). *The prickly plant book*. Boston: Little, Brown. Everything the young botanist could want to know about the sharp-leaved inhabitants of the desert is in this marvelous introduction to cacti and succulents.

Titherington, Jeanne. (1986). *Pumpkin pumpkin*. New York: Greenwillow. The life cycle of a pumpkin, from seed to fruit to jack-o'-lantern and back to seed, is delightfully told in this illustrative book.

Welch, Martha McKeen. (1980). *Sunflower!* New York: Dodd. The complete life cycle of the sunflower is illustrated with black and white photographs. Readers are also stimulated to grow their own.

Wilson, Ron. (1980). *How plants grow*. New York: Larousse. Everything about plant growth and development, as well as the physiology of plants, can be found in this detailed exploration of the plant kingdom.

## The Animal Kingdom

An annotated bibliography of children's books about animals would take up this entire textbook. In fact, of all the children's books published, more deal with animals than with any other subject. The following list is a potpourri of animal books in a variety of areas by some of this country's foremost science writers. Your school's librarian or any public librarian will be able to recommend a wealth of additional books for your classroom.

Arnold, Caroline. (1980). *Five nests*. New York: Dutton. This easy-to-read book for young scientists explains different types of bird nests and how they are constructed.

Arnold, Caroline. (1982). *Animals that migrate*. Minneapolis: Carolrhoda. Animals that change their homes and habitats are the focus of this fascinating book.

Arnold, Caroline. (1989). *Cheetah.* New York: Morrow. Everything about one of the world's fastest animals and the efforts to save it from extinction is chronicled here.

Arnosky, Jim. (1990). *A kettle of hawks and other wildlife groups.* New York: Lothrop. Animals belong to some unusually named groups, and this book, filled with rich watercolor illustrations, covers many of them.

Banks, Merry. (1990). *Animals of the night.* New York: Scribner. All kinds of creatures inhabit the night and the pages of this richly illustrated book.

Bare, Colleen. (1990). *Elephants on the beach.* New York: Cobblehill. Don't let the title fool you. This text about elephant seals will open up new worlds of discovery and wonder for young readers.

Bonners, Susan. (1981). *A penguin year.* New York: Delacourt. Facts, figures, and delightful illustrations make up this book about one of nature's most interesting creatures.

Carrick, Carol. (1980). *The crocodiles still wait.* New York: Houghtin/Clarion. Young readers can discover some of the 50-foot descendants of the dinosaurs.

Cole, Joanna. (1980). *A frog's body.* New York: Morrow. This fantastically photographed book about the life cycle and physical features of frogs is sure to stimulate children's curiosity.

Cole, Joanna. (1981). *A horse's body.* New York: Morrow. If you have any horse lovers in your classroom, this book will make them appreciate horses even more.

Cole, Joanna. (1981). *A snake's body.* New York: Morrow. Incredible photographs and an informative text highlight this book about snakes.

Cole, Joanna. (1982). *A cat's body.* New York: Morrow. Clear, informative text and wonderful photography fill this book about the feline world.

Dorros, Arthur. (1987). *Ant cities.* New York: Crowell. You and your students will view ants in a whole new light after reading this engaging text.

Ehlert, Lois. (1990). *Feathers for lunch.* San Diego: Harcourt Brace Jovanovich. A cat's encounter with 12 different kinds of birds highlights this poetical introduction to our winged friends.

Florian, Douglas. (1989). *Turtle day.* New York: Crowell. A day in the life of a turtle is delightfully recounted in this book filled with full-color drawings.

Freedman, Russell. (1980). *Tooth and claw: A look at animal weapons.* New York: Holiday. How animals defend themselves is the focus of this book.

Freedman, Russell. (1981). *Farm babies.* New York: Holiday. All kinds of animal babies fill the pages of this book, which will delight readers of all ages.

George, William, & George Lindsay. (1988). *Beaver at Long Pond.* New York: Greenwillow. A story about the nighttime adventures of a beaver is beautifully told.

Goor, Ron, & Goor, Nancy. (1984). *All kinds of feet.* New York: Crowell. The diversity of feet in the animal kingdom is described and photographed.

Goor, Ron, & Goor, Nancy. (1990). *Insect metamorphosis: From egg to adult.* New York: Atheneum. The changes that insects go through during a complete life cycle are detailed in this superbly photographed book.

Henley, Karyn. (1980). *Hatch!* Minneapolis: Carolrhoda. Egg-laying animals are the subjects of this book, including birds, insects, and fish.

Hunt, Patricia. (1981). *Tigers.* New York: Dodd. Loads of black and white photographs highlight this text about some of the most powerful and beautiful creatures in the animal kingdom.

Johnson, Ginny, & Cutchins, Judy. (1988). *Scaly babies: Reptiles growing up.* New York: Morrow. Photographs fill this book about baby reptiles and their stages of growth.

Kaufman, Joe. (1981). *Wings, paws, hoofs, and flippers: A book about animals.* New York: Golden. A terrific introduction to the world of animals, filled with information and colorful illustrations.

Kerby, Mona. (1989). *Cockroaches.* New York: Watts. Yes, a book about cockroaches. Your students and you will look at these creatures in a whole new light after reading this very informative book.

Lacey, Elizabeth. (1989). *The complete frog: A Guide for the very young naturalist.* New York: Lothrop. Everything young scientists could want to know about frogs, both real and imaginary, can be found in the pages of this text.

Leinwoll, Stanley. (1980). *The book of pets.* New York, Messner. Everything young pet owners need to know is contained in the pages of this book, including costs, feeding, habitats, and other practical information.

McClung, Robert. (1984). *Gorilla.* New York: Morrow. This book details the life of a band of gorillas and the efforts of some scientists to save them.

McLaughlin, Molly. (1986). *Earthworms, dirt, and rotten leaves: An exploration in ecology.* New York: Atheneum. The earthworm may not seem like a pretty creature, but we couldn't get along without it, as this book explains in delightful detail.

Milne, Larus, & Milne, Margery. (1980). *Gadabouts and stick-at-homes: Wild animals and their habitats.* New York:Sierra/Scribner. There is a diversity of homes and habitats in the animal kingdom. This book takes a look at some common and not-so-common ones.

National Geographic Society. (1986). *The secret world of animals.* Washington, DC: Author. You can't go wrong with this book and its wonderful photographs about animals that stay mostly hidden from human view.

Overbeck, Cynthia. (1982). *Dragonflies.* New York: Lerner. You probably didn't think children could get excited about dragonflies. They will after reading this informative book.

Parsons, Alexandra. (1990). *Amazing poisonous animals.* New York: Knopf. You won't be able to wrest this book away from your students once they've discovered all the exciting and dazzling information in its pages. Part of a series.

Patent, Dorothy. (1982). *A picture book of cows.* New York: Holiday House. Everything you (or your students) ever wanted to know about cows can be found in the pages of this engaging book.

Patent, Dorothy. (1982). *Spider magic.* New York: Holiday House. A superb behind-the-scenes look at the world of spiders, their lifestyles, and their habitats.

Patent, Dorothy. (1989). *Looking at dolphins and porpoises.* New York: Holiday House. This small book filled with loads of data on porpoises and dolphins will delight young readers no matter where they live.

Peters, David. (1986). *Giants of land, sea, and air: Past and present.* New York: Sierra Club/Knopf. Seventy-one big, giant, and tall creatures fill the pages of this book, which will delight readers for hours on end.

Pope, Joyce. (1986). *Do animals dream? Children's questions about animals most often asked of the natural history museum.* New York: Viking. This book belongs on every teacher's desk, particularly if you've ever been asked if fish drink or whether animals use tools.

Powzyk, Joyce. (1990). *Animal camouflage: A closer look.* New York: Bradbury. How do animals hide from each other? How do they escape detection? The answers to these questions and many more can be found in this informative text.

Riha, Susanne. (1989). *Animals in winter.* Minneapolis: Carolrhoda. Terrific illustrations and a clear text inform readers about some of the animals of winter.

Robinson, Marlene. (1985). *What good is a tail?* New York: Dodd. All kinds of animals, all kinds of tails, and all kinds of information about how those animals use their tails can be found in this delightful book.

Ryden, Hope. (1988). *Wild animals of America ABC.* New York: Lodestar. From alligator to zone-tailed hawk, they're all here in this magnificently photographed book of familiar and not-so-familiar animals of America.

Ryden, Hope. (1989). *Wild animals of Africa ABC.* New York: Lodestar. All of the animals on the African continent, from aardvarks to zebras, are photographed in this book.

Sattler, Helen. (1986). *Sharks, the super fish.* New York: Lothrop. Any youngster with a passing interest in sharks will find this book to be an engaging introduction to these mysterious creatures of the deep.

Sattler, Helen. (1989). *The book of eagles.* New York: Lothrop. This is a complete guide to the eagles of the world, filled with illustrations.

Schlein, Miriam. (1982). *Billions of bats.* New York: Lippincott Junior. There's a lot to learn about these flying mammals, and this book has it all.

Schnieper, Claudia. (1989). *Chameleons.* Minneapolis: Carolrhoda. Children love chameleons, and they will love them even more after reading this engaging text with its full-color photographs.

Scott, Jack Denton. (1981). *The book of the pig.* New York: Putnam. This book will help dispel many of the misconceptions children have about pigs—which are, incidently, one of the smartest animals around.

Scott, Jack Denton. (1981). *Moose.* New York: Putnam. Children will be amazed at all they can learn about the largest of all antlered animals. Filled with magnificent photographs.

Selsam, Millicent. (1980). *All about eggs.* Reading, MA: Addison-Wesley. Eggs of every size, shape, and description fill this book about mammals, amphibians, birds, fish, and reptiles.

Selsam, Millicent. (1980). *Night animals.* New York: Four Winds. All kinds of nocturnal animals are wonderfully portrayed in this volume filled with large photographs.

Selsam, Millicent. (1982). *Where do they go? Insects in winter.* New York: Four Winds. Ever wonder what happens to butterflies, grasshoppers, flies, and bees during the winter? This book has all the answers.

Settle, Joanne, & Baggett, Nancy. (1986). *How do ants know when you're having a picnic? (and other questions kids ask about insects and other crawly things.)* New York: Atheneum. Although you may have difficulty remembering the title, your students will surely remember the answers to some of life's most intriguing questions.

Silverstein, Alvin, & Silverstein, Virginia. (1988). *Nature's living lights: Fireflies and other bioluminescent creatures.* Boston: Little, Brown. Wow, what a title! And what a book! Some of the strangest and most unusual creatures on land, in the sky, and in the sea are portrayed here.

Simon, Hilda. (1980). *The racers: Speed in the animal world.* New York: Lothrop. Fourteen of the fastest animals on land, in the air, and in the sea are examined in this "world records" book.

Simon, Seymour. (1981). *Poisonous snakes.* New York: Four Winds. You won't be able to get this book away from children once they've started. It will amaze and delight anyone with an interest in snakes.

Simon, Seymour. (1981). *Strange creatures.* New York: Four Winds. Twenty-two of the world's most unusual animals inhabit the pages of this book, which will delight students through many readings.

Simon, Seymour. (1985). *101 questions and answers about dangerous animals.* New York: Macmillan. This informative text will clear up any misconceptions children have about some of the more dangerous inhabitants of the animal world.

Simon, Seymour. (1989). *Whales.* New York: Crowell. The splendor and majesty of whales is presented in this book by one of America's foremost science authors for children.

Sussman, Susan, & James, Robert. (1987). *Lies (people believe) about animals.* New York: Whitman. Some misperceptions and misinformation about animals are convincingly dispelled in the pages of this very interesting book.

## The Human Body

The human body is a subject filled with mystery, awe, and surprises for the young scientist. The fact that students carry this magical machine around with them every day certainly attests to their need to explore and examine many of its facets. A knowledge of what the body looks like and how it works is basic to students' comprehension of the life sciences. Knowledge of their own bodies will help youngsters understand and appreciate other varieties of animal bodies.

Aliki. (1990). *My feet.* New York: HarperCollins. Children will be delighted by this book on human feet, including information on their parts, what they do, and their relative sizes.

Allison, Linda. (1976). *Blood and guts: A working guide to your own insides.* Boston: Little, Brown. The title lets you know that this is an imaginative and fascinating look inside the human body. Included are experiments and projects to do with one's own body.

Berger, Melvin. (1983). *Why I cough, sneeze, shiver, hiccup and yawn.* New York: Crowell. This book goes a long way toward answering kids' questions about some of the natural reflex actions of their bodies.

Branley, Franklyn. (1984). *Shivers and goose bumps: How we keep warm.* New York: Crowell. Humans have marvelous mechanisms for staying warm and dealing with heat loss. This book examines several of them.

Bruun, Ruth Dowling, & Brunn, Bertel. (1982). *The human body.* New York: Random House. The various systems and regions of the human body are colorfully presented and illustrated in this marvelous book.

Bruun, Ruth Dowling, & Brunn, Bertel. (1989). *The brain: What it is, what it does.* New York: Greenwillow. How the human brain operates, what it looks like, how it compares with animal brains, and how people think are the basis for this interesting look at "gray matter."

Caselli, Giovanni. (1987). *The human body.* New York: Grosset. Wonderfully detailed diagrams and illustrations highlight this thorough introduction to the human body, including its components and stages of growth and development.

Cole, Joanna. (1984). *How you were born.* New York: Morrow. A clear, down-to-earth text accompanied by numerous photographs helps youngsters understand conception, fetal development, labor, and birth.

Cole, Joanna. (1985). *Cuts, breaks, bruises, and burns.* New York: Crowell. The miraculous ways in which the body heals itself are presented in this fascinating book. Also included are first-aid hints for common injuries.

Crump, Donald J. (1982). *Your wonderful body.* Washington, DC: National Geographic Society. Microscopic cartoon characters who travel to all parts of the human body make this a wonderful introduction to and examination of our insides.

Kapit, Wynn, & Elson, Lawrence M. (1977). *The anatomy coloring book.* New York: Harper & Row. Designed for older readers, this is a marvelously designed book about human anatomy.

Kitzinger, Sheila. (1986). *Being born.* New York: Grosset. Filled with lots of full-color explanatory photographs, this book for both young readers and adults offers insights into conception, prenatal life, and birth.

Miller, Jonathan. (1983). *The human body.* New York: Viking. This is the best possible type of pop-up book—one that thoroughly involves the reader in manipulating tabs and learning all about basic body functions.

Ontario Science Centre. (1987). *Foodworks: Over 100 science activities and fascinating facts that explore the magic of food.* Reading: Addison-Wesley. Don't pass this book by! It is a lighthearted and totally engrossing book about food, digestion, and nutrition that will delight and amaze students of any age.

Patent, Dorothy H. (1983). *Germs!* New York: Holiday. All about germs—what they are, how they attack the body's defenses, and how the body protects itself from these silent invaders. Easy to read and filled with insightful photographs.

Settel, Joanne, & Baggett, Nancy. (1985). *Why does my nose run? And other questions kids ask about their bodies.* New York: Atheneum. Kids are naturally curious about the functions of their bodies. This book provides many of the answers.

Showers, Paul. (1982). *You can't make a move without your muscles.* New York: Crowell. How humans move and the muscles responsible for different types of movement are the focus of this simple and well-illustrated book.

Silverstein, Alvin, & Silverstein, Virginia B. (1983). *Heartbeats: Your body, your heart.* New York: Harper & Row. How the heart works and how the circulatory system operates are the focus of this engrossing and illustrative book.

Simon, Seymour. (1971). *Finding out with your senses.* New York: McGraw-Hill. This book includes a variety of activities that help students learn about their five senses and their importance in daily living.

## Dinosaurs

Ask 100 youngsters what their favorite topic is in science, and 99 will tell you "Dinosaurs!" Dinosaurs continue to be a popular topic with children (and adults) even though they have been extinct for 65 million years. The portrayal of dinosaurs in movies, the abundance of dinosaurs toys, and the popularity of books such as *Bully for Brontosaurous* by Stephen Jay Gould, *Digging for Dinosaurs* by Jack Horner, and the fictional best-seller *Jurassic Park* by Michael Crichton attest to the fascination we have with dinosaurs. Here are several selected books that can help students enjoy this topic even more.

Aliki. (1981). *Digging up dinosaurs.* New York: Crowell. The sciences of dinosaur discovery and dinosaur reconstruction are explained in an easy-to-follow text.

Aliki. (1985). *Dinosaurs are different.* New York: Crowell. The major differences among dinosaurs are discussed through an examination of their bones and skeletons. A must for any dinosaur hunter.

Aliki. (1988). *Dinosaur bones.* New York: Crowell. Paleontology is the focus of this book, which examines how dinosaur bones were preserved over millions of years and how they were eventually discovered by humans.

Aliki. (1990). *Fossils tell of long ago.* New York: HarperCollins. A great introduction to the formation and creation of fossils highlighted by easy-to-understand illustrations.

Arnold, Caroline. (1989). *Dinosaur mountain: Graveyard of the past*. New York: Clarion. The discovery of dinosaur fossils in Utah's Dinosaur National Monument is the subject of this fascinating book.

Arnold, Caroline. (1990). *Dinosaurs down under: And other fossils from Australia*. New York: Clarion. This book describes some of the evidence of dinosaurs found in Australia and how they are displayed in a museum exhibit.

Barton, Byron. (1989). *Dinosaurs, dinosaurs*. New York: Crowell. All kinds of dinosaurs, from big to small, horned to armored, long-necked, and long-tailed, are detailed in this wonderful introduction to the world of dinosaurs.

Barton, Byron. (1990). *Bones, bones, dinosaur bones*. New York: HarperCollins. An ideal book for very young readers. It offers a glimpse into the search for dinosaur bones as well as how dinosaur skeletons are constructed.

Branley, Franklyn. (1982). *Dinosaurs, asteroids, and superstars: Why the dinosaurs disappeared*. New York: Crowell. The continuing mystery of the disappearance of the dinosaurs is examined in this informative and lucid book.

Branley, Franklyn. (1989). *What happened to the dinosaurs*. New York: Crowell. The various theories and speculations about the disappearance of the dinosaurs are covered in this well-researched book.

Carroll, Susan. (1986). *How big is a brachiosaurus?* New York: Platt and Monk. Using a question-and-answer format, the author presents important information on the physical characteristics, eating habits, and living conditions of various dinosaurs.

Cobb, Vicki. (1983). *The monsters who died: A mystery about dinosaurs*. New York: Coward-McCann. A perceptive and engaging look into reasons the dinosaurs died and how fossils have helped our understanding of these creatures.

Cohen, Daniel. (1983). *Monster dinosaur*. New York: Lippincott. The emphasis in this book is on the scientists (paleontologists) who study dinosaurs and some of the concepts and misconceptions they have developed over the years.

Craig, Jean. (1989). *Discovering prehistoric animals*. Mahwah, NJ: Troll. A simple, straightforward text filled with lots of down-to-earth facts about dinosaurs.

Daeschler, T. (1990). *The dinosaur hunter's handbook: Discover the traces of a lost world*. Philadelphia: Running Press. Offers a guide and kit so that youngsters can begin excavating for their own dinosaurs.

Elting, Mary, & Goodman, Ann. (1980). *Dinosaur mysteries*. New York: Platt and Monk. Some of the mysteries surrounding 41 different dinosaurs (including their disappearance) are examined and explored in the pages of this book.

Freedman, Russell. (1983). *Dinosaurs and their young*. New York: Holiday. This book focuses on dinosaur families and dispels some of the myths about dinosaurs as solitary creatures.

Gilbert, John. (1981). *Dinosaurs discovered*. New York: Larousse. Lots of information and loads of descriptive illustrations provide older readers with a wealth of data on the world of dinosaurs.

Hopkins, Lee Bennett. (1987). *Dinosaurs*. San Diego: Harcourt Brace. Eighteen poems give students some fresh perspectives and delightful insights into the world of dinosaurs.

Jacobs, Francine. (1982). *Supersaurus*. New York: Putnam. The discoveries a paleontologist makes in Colorado leads to evidence of one of the largest dinosaurs that ever lived.

Knight, David C. (1985). *"Dinosaurs" that swam and flew*. New York: Prentice. This book takes a look at some of the relatively unknown reptiles and dinosaurs that inhabited the earth.

Lasky, Kathryn. (1990). *Dinosaur dig*. New York: Morrow. Several families are involved in the search for dinosaur fossils in this description of a dig in the Montana Badlands.

Lauber, Patricia. (1987). *Dinosaurs walked here: And other stories fossils tell*. New York: Bradbury. Everything the young scientist may want to know about fossils and their creation can be found in this enlightening book.

Lauber, Patricia. (1989). *The news about dinosaurs*. New York: Bradbury. The author looks at various theories and concepts about dinosaurs and presents solid scientific evidence about their existence.

Peters, David. (1989). *A gallery of dinosaurs and other early reptiles*. New York: Knopf. The emphasis in this book is on size, with a wonderful collection of colorful illustrations and gatefold pages to convey the enormity of these giants.

Prelutsky, Jack. (1988). *Tyrannosaurus was a beast*. New York: Greenwillow. You won't want to miss this delightful collection of dinosaur poems. A wonderful addition to the more serious studies of the "terrible lizards."

Robinson, Howard. (1984). *Ranger Rick's dinosaur book*. Washington, DC: National Wildlife Federation. Filled with lots of colorful illustrations and photos, this book offer young scientists a wealth of data about all kinds of dinosaurs.

Sattler, Helen. (1981). *Dinosaurs of North America*. New York: Lothrop. Students will be fascinated to learn that more than 80 different kinds of dinosaurs lived on the North American continent—perhaps even in their home town.

Sattler, Helen. (1983). *The illustrated dinosaur dictionary*. New York: Lothrop. An extensive and very detailed book (316 pages) covering nearly 300 known dinosaurs, where they lived, their habits, and a classification guide. A must for the sophisticated dinosaur fanatic.

Sattler, Helen. (1984). *Baby dinosaurs*. New York: Lothrop. This book takes an unusual look at dinosaur "youngsters." A delightful adventure for all dinosaur aficionados.

Sattler, Helen. (1985). *Pterosaurs, the flying reptiles*. New York: Lothrop. An engrossing look into one of the most unusual dinosaurs—one that was warm-blooded and hairy.

Sattler, Helen. (1989). *Tyrannosaurus Rex and its kin: The Mesozoic monsters*. New York: Lothrop. This book examines the most famous of all dinosaurs and takes a look at the descendants of Tyrannosaurus Rex. Colorful illustrations and a time chart highlight this book.

Sattler, Helen. (1990). *The new illustrated dinosaur dictionary*. New York: Lothrop. It's all here! Everything any dinosaur nut would want to know about over 350 dinosaurs and other related creatures.

Simon, Seymour. (1982). *The smallest dinosaurs*. New York: Crown. This book takes a close and perceptive look at small dinosaurs—which greatly outnumbered their more popular (and larger) relatives.

Simon, Seymour. (1990). *New questions and answers about dinosaurs*. New York: Morrow. Up-to-date and factual information about dinosaurs from one of the world's leading writers of nonfiction for children.

## Ecology and the Environment

The greenhouse effect, auto emissions, the razing of the Amazonian rain forest, acid rain, and chemical pollutants are all important topics for our times—perhaps even more so for the new generation of youngsters. What type of planet will your students inherit, and what will they do with that planet? These are certainly tough questions, but not impossible ones to answer. You can help make students aware of the environmental issues we face today and of their role in maintaining the balance of nature by introducing them to some of the following books.

Arnosky, Jim. (1989). *In the forest: A portfolio of paintings*. New York: Lothrop. The beauty and majesty of an important ecosystem are wonderfully illustrated in this book of paintings. This book will provoke many classroom discussions.

Baker, Jeannie. (1988). *Where the forest meets the sea*. New York: Greenwillow. You and all your students will delight in the magical and inventive illustrations used to tell the story of a disappearing Australian forest.

Ballamy, David. (1988). *The roadside*. New York: Clarkson Potter. Ecological issues may be as close as the roads we travel. This book examines one particular aspect of our environment and the responsibilities of humans to preserve it.

Bash, Barbara. (1990). *Urban roosts: Where birds nest in the city*. San Francisco: Sierra Club. The many varieties of birds that make their homes in the buildings and structures of the city are described in this most unusual book.

Baylor, Byrd. (1981). *Desert voices*. New York: Scribner. The adaptations several animals employ to live in the desert are described in this intriguing book.

Catchpole, Clive. (1984). *Grasslands*. New York: Dial. The varieties of animals that inhabit the world's grasslands are wonderfully presented in this panorama of a major ecosystem.

Cherry, Lynn. (1990). *The great kapok tree: A tale of the Amazon rain forest*. New York: Gulliver. A beautifully illustrated story of the meaning of conservation told from the perspective of the animals who inhabit a threatened ecosystem. A "must read."

Cole, Sheila. (1985). *When the tide is low*. New York: Lothrop. The wonders revealed at low tide along the seashore are enhanced by evocative watercolors and sparse text.

Cook, David. (1985). *Environment*. New York: Crown. How can we conserve our natural resources and preserve plants and animal life? This book has some answers and much more for readers to think about.

Cowcher, Helen. (1988). *Rain forest*. New York: Farrar. This books raises ecological issues through a well-told tale and wonderful illustrations.

Cowcher, Helen. (1990). *Antarctica*. New York: Farrar. The animals and ecology of this vast continent are revealed in this moving exposé of a fragile environment.

Curtis, Patricia. (1985). *All wild creatures welcome: The story of a wildlife rehabilitation center*. New York: Lodestar. How sick, injured, orphaned, and abandoned animals are cared for in a rehabilitation center and what is done with them once they are able to care for themselves is the emphasis in this delightful book.

Dekkers, Midas. (1988). *The nature book: Discovering, exploring, observing, experimenting with plants and animals at home and outdoors*. New York: Macmillan. The title says it all. This is a book that provides youngsters with active opportunities to utilize all the processes of science in learning more about the nature of nature.

Downing, Julie. (1989). *White snow, blue feather*. New York: Bradbury. Nature in winter and what one can observe during this season is the emphasis of this story.

Florian, Douglas. (1989). *Nature walk*. New York: Greenwillow. The things that one can discover in a simple walk through the forest are featured in this enlightening book.

George, Jean C. (1990). *One day in the tropical rain forest*. New York: HarperCollins. The struggle over land in the Amazon rain forest is told through the eyes of a young Indian boy. A "must read" for young environmentalists.

George, William. (1989). *Box turtle at Long Pond*. New York: Greenwillow. Delightful illustrations combine with wonderfully simple text to tell of the goings on in a pond environment.

Graham, Ada, & Graham, Frank. (1981). *The changing desert*. New York: Scribner. The American desert is far more fragile than most people think. This book presents some interesting data for young scientists to consider—and, we hope, do something about.

Herberman, Ethan. (1989). *The city kid's field guide*. New York: Simon & Schuster. A wonderfully insightful guide to the flora and fauna of an urban environment. An important book for any urban dweller.

Hirschi, Ron. (1987). *Who lives in . . . the forest?*. New York: Dodd. The varied inhabitants of a forest are the focus of this collection of marvelous photographs.

Huff, Barbara. (1990). *Greening the city streets: The story of community gardens*. New York: Clarion. Preserving our environment is not just for country dwellers; it can take place in urban areas, too. This book presents a wonderful look at some citizens' efforts.

Hughey, Pat. (1984). *Scavengers and decomposers: The cleanup crew*. New York: Atheneum. The cycle of life told in terms of the efforts of plants and animals that decompose and scavenge for the remains of others. An important viewpoint for all young scientists.

Jaspersohn, William. (1980). *How the forest grew*. New York: Greenwillow. How a forest develops and grows is the focus of this book about ecology and preservation.

Johnson, Ginny, & Cutchins, Judy. (1990). *Windows on wildlife*. New York: Morrow. An interesting examination of natural habitat exhibits (zoos without bars) from around the country.

Katz, Adrienne. (1986). *Naturewatch: Exploring nature with your children*. Reading, MA: Addison-Wesley. A collection of more than 50 activities and experiments that provide first-hand experiences with nature.

Lavies, Bianca. (1989). *Lily pad pond*. New York: Dutton. The ongoing struggle for existence among the many inhabitants of a pond is the focus of this engaging text.

Lerner, Carol. (1980). *Seasons of the tallgrass prairie*. New York: Morrow. The changing of the seasons, the varieties of plant life, and the ebb and flow of life across the prairie are carefully illustrated and described in this text.

Mabey, Richard. (1983). *Oak and company*. New York: Greenwillow. The life story of a solitary oak tree and the plants and animals that are part of that life cycle is the emphasis in this fascinating look at a tree.

Mayle, Peter. (1982). *As dead as a dodo*. Boston: Godine. Sixteen extinct species are highlighted in this book about the need to take care of those animals near extinction.

Michels, Tilde. (1989). *At the frog pond*. New York: Lippincott. The spring and summer months bring an abundance of animal life to a small pond. The importance of observing the natural interactions is effectively understated.

Miller, Christina, & Berry, Louise. (1986). *Wastes*. (New York: Watts. The disposal of wastes poses some serious questions and concerns for our environment. This book offers young readers some answers as well as some enduring issues to consider.

National Wildlife Federation Staff. (1989). *Endangered animals*. Washington, DC: Author. This book, which examines the plights of various animals throughout the world, will have an important impact on young scientists.

Newton, James. (1980). *Forest log*. New York: Crowell. How a single fir tree contributes to the cycle of life through its life and death is detailed in this book.

Newton, James. (1982). *A forest is reborn*. New York: Crowell. How a forest regenerates itself after a devastating fire is told in this portrayal of the unending cycle of life.

Parnell, Peter. (1989). *Quiet*. New York: Morrow. The wonders of nature discovered by a young boy lying in the grass are revealed in this unusual tale.

Pringle, Lawrence. (1990). *Saving our wildlife*. Hillside, NJ: Enslow. North American wildlife and our efforts at preserving many species are the emphases in this engrossing book.

Ricciuti, Edward. (1979). *Plants in danger*. New York: Harper. Although a great deal of attention is given to animals near extinction, many varieties of plants are close to extermination, too.

Ryder, Joanne. (1988). *Step into the night*. New York: Four Winds. The forms of nature at night are simply and wonderfully shared in this easy-to-read book.

Rylant, Cynthia. (1986). *Night in the country*. New York: Bradbury. A rich and wonderfully created examination of country life at night. The emphasis is on sounds and the animals that create them.

Say, Allen. (1989). *The lost lake*. Boston: Houghton Miffin. The story is about a father-and-son camping trip, but the message is about the need to preserve and appreciate our natural environment.

Schwartz, David. (1988). *The hidden life of the meadow*. New York: Crown. The interaction of animals and plants in a meadow are beautifully depicted in this ecological study.

Scott, Jack. (1980). *Window on the world*. New York: Putnam. The emphasis is on the author's observations about 12 separate animals, but the underlying theme is that anyone can become a scientist through careful observation and record keeping.

Selsam, Millicent, & Hunt, Joyce. (1989). *Keep looking!* New York: Macmillan. The emphasis is on observation skills in this book about animal life in a winter environment.

Singer, Marilyn. (1989). *Turtle in July*. New York: Macmillan. The changing of the seasons from the perspective of animals are described in this delightful book.

Skofield, James. (1984). *All wet! All wet!* New York: Harper. A rainy day, a young boy, and the animals of the forest combine to present life in both simple and complex terms.

Stuart, Gene. (1980). *Wildlife alert! The struggle to survive*. Washington, DC: National Geographic Society. Descriptions of the ecological plights of several endangered animals are reinforced with marvelous photographs.

Tafuri, Nancy. (1987). *Do not disturb*. New York: Greenwillow. The effects humans have on animal habitats is simply and colorfully told in this story of a family's camping trip.

Van Allsburg, Chris. (1990). *Just a dream*. Boston: Houghton Miffin. A young boy discovers the need to preserve trees in this wonderfully illustrated tale of recycling and renewal.

Watts, Barrie. (1990). *24 hours in a forest*. New York: Watts. The daily cycle of life is vividly portrayed in this absorbing drama of plant and animal life in a forest.

Welch, Martha. (1982). *Close looks in a spring woods*. New York: Dodd, Mead. The changing of the seasons from winter to spring and the accompanying changes in a forest community are delightfully photographed in this book.

Wiewandt, Thomas. (1990). *The hidden life of the desert*. New York: Crown. This book will dispel students' misconceptions about the desert and will introduce them to this vibrant and flourishing ecosystem.

# 13

# PHYSICAL SCIENCE

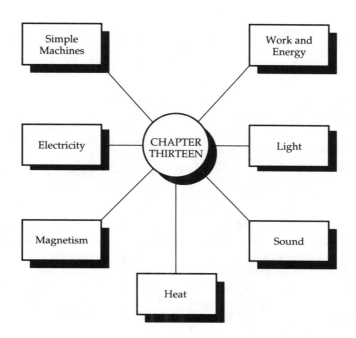

## Chapter Objectives

After reading this chapter you should be able to:

1. Describe the characteristics of heat and how it's measured and transferred.

2. Explain the origins, transmission, and characteristics of sound.

3. Understand forms of light and how it's transmitted.

4. Define work and energy.

5. Describe the functions and uses of simple machines.

6. Explain different types of electricity and its uses.

7. State the uses and functions of magnets.

As you read this chapter you are probably sitting in a warm environment (your dorm room, the library, or at home). Light is reflected off the pages of this book, allowing you to read the words. There may or may not be sounds (e.g., radio, TV) in the background as you read. You are expending some energy in turning the pages of the book, and energy was used to publish (and certainly to write) this book. There are probably a number of electrical devices assisting you in reading the book (e.g., light bulb, electric heater, stove [to heat your coffee]), and you undoubtedly used some type of machine to help you get to your present location (car, bicycle). All in all, you are using many of the elements of the physical sciences in your reading of this chapter.

A significant portion of many elementary school science curricula is devoted to the physical sciences. Although most students experience many aspects of this area of the natural sciences in their daily lives, they are frequently unaware of many of the laws and concepts that govern this part of their environment. In this chapter we will attempt to provide you with the background that will enable you to direct your students' learning in the physical sciences.

# HEAT

A topic of many daily conversations is heat. How people "feel" on a particular day, what they will wear, where they will spend their free time, and other factors are determined by their evaluation of the conditions related to comfort level. Conditions such as "comfortable," "too hot," or "too cold" are based on subjective impressions and are unrelated to objective data. During the winter months a reading of 65 degrees Fahrenheit may be considered warm or even hot, but during the summer months it may be considered as cool or cold. Obviously, our judgments of hot and cold are misleading and unreliable. To communicate an accurate indication of conditions one needs an instrument that will provide data that is consistent and free of bias related to the calendar or other factors. Although 68 degrees Fahrenheit may be considered hot to some and cold to others, it is a measurement that can be used as a reliable reference.

The thermometer is the instrument used to measure how hot or cold something is. The three most widely known temperature scales are Fahrenheit, Celsius, and Kelvin. Although thermometers are based on different scales, they utilize the same principles related to heat. For example, when nearly any material is heated, it expands. These instruments employ this concept: The higher the temperature, the more the liquid in the thermometer expands and the higher the reading; the cooler the environment, the lower the reading.

A thermometer measures the temperature of a substance, it does not measure the amount of heat in that substance. A cup of water at 95 degrees Fahrenheit and a bathtub full of water at the same temperature will both give a reading of 95 degrees Fahrenheit, yet it is obvious that the bathtub contains more heat. The quantity of heat in a substance is measured in calories. A calorie is defined as the amount of heat required to change the temperature of 1 gram of water by 1 degree Celsius.

**DID YOU KNOW?** _____

Your body loses enough heat in one hour to raise a half-gallon of water to the boiling point.

**Classroom Activity** Set up an experiment in which you pour equal quantities of boiling water into several different-sized containers. Some containers should have wide mouths, and some should be small-mouthed. Some can be made of glass, some of metal, and some of plastic. Provide students with thermometers and a stopwatch. Ask them to take readings from the containers at periodic intervals to determine which container allows the heat to dissipate most rapidly. In which container does the heat dissipate the slowest? From their data, can students make any predictions about the ideal size, shape, and materials for a coffee cup? ■

## Effects of Heat

As a substance is heated, the molecules move faster and tend to move farther apart. Thus, most substances expand as they are heated and contract when cooled. This phenomenon occurs in liquids, solids, and gases. However, water is an exception. Above 4 degrees Celsius water reacts to heat the same as other liquids; however, from 4 degrees to 0 degrees Celsius water expands, and it is less dense in its frozen state than it is as a liquid. Hence, ice floats on water because it is less dense as a result of its expansion.

There are many ways to encourage students to note the expansion of solids as they are heated. One of the most obvious is to point out the expansion joints on bridges and the sagging electrical lines in the summer. The contraction of solids can be demonstrated by pointing out the divisions between slabs of concrete on the highways, which are frequently filled with tar to occupy the openings created by the concrete contracting during the colder months. A simple demonstration of the effects of heat on a liquid is to fill a pan with water and heat it. Have students notice how the pan begins to overflow as the water expands. An example of gas expansion is to have students check the air pressure in a car's tires after it has been in a shaded area and again after it has been driven for an hour or two. It will be higher after the drive because the tires are hot, as is the air in them. The air expands, causing greater pressure.

## Heat Transfer

Unless it is prevented from doing so, heat moves from hot or warm things to cooler ones. If objects of different temperatures are in contact, they will tend to reach a common temperature. This movement of heat from one substance or area to another occurs in three ways: conduction, convection, or radiation.

## Conduction

Conduction of heat occurs when the molecules of a substance are heated and begin to move more rapidly. As they move they collide with neighboring molecules, causing them to move, with the process continuing throughout the substance. An example of this phenomenon is a pan with a metal handle that is placed on a heat source. As the base of the pan is heated and its molecules begin to move rapidly, the molecules above the base are bombarded, causing them to move rapidly also. This process continues through the pan and into the handle.

### TEACHER TO TEACHER

Molecules, molecules, molecules! They are everywhere, but invisible to the human eye. To the adult as well as the child, molecules can be a foreboding concept to grasp.

When my second-graders study the unit on water and its three states, we first do several experiments that show evaporation and condensation. Then we "act out" the experiments. Each child pretends he or she is a water molecule, and the class arranges themselves in a liquid formation. We then pretend the stove underneath us is being turned on. As each human water molecule is heated, we radiate outward to form water vapor. After we "act out" evaporation, we reverse the process by pretending the human water molecules are getting colder. As the water vapor molecules move slowly toward each other, a liquid is formed and condensation has taken place. The children love this "hot and cold" activity as well as the science experiments.

Karen Dunn
Sheckler Elementary School
Catasauqua, PA

## Convection

Heat can be transferred through currents, or the actual movement of liquids and gases. As a liquid or a gas is heated and its molecules spread outward, the substance becomes less dense and becomes lighter than the surrounding air or liquid. The lighter substance is pushed upward by the buoyant force of the heavier air or liquid. Many of our homes are heated by convection, as the heat is brought to various rooms in the form of circulating hot water or heated air. When hot air arrives in a room, it heats the air near it and the air rises, with the cooler air sinking to the floor. This air is then heated and rises, and the circulation continues with the mixing of the cold air and warm air, ultimately establishing a somewhat uniform temperature in the room.

## Radiation

The earth's greatest source of heat energy is the sun; however, the heat does not reach earth through conduction because the air is a poor conductor of heat. Nor does the heat from the sun reach the earth through currents, as there is little to generate the currents until the heat from the sun strikes the earth. How, then, does

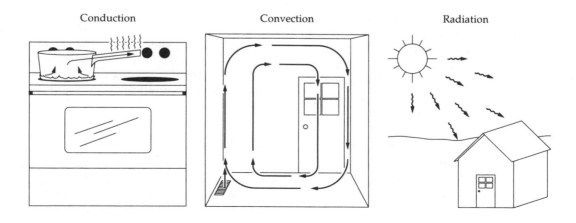

Conduction    Convection    Radiation

the heat from the sun get to the earth? It is transmitted by radiation. The sun, like all objects, radiates energy through waves. When the waves from the sun strike an object, they cause the electrons in the object to vibrate, and the temperature of the substance increases.

A fireplace is an example of heat transfer through radiation. The fire in the fireplace sends out infrared waves, and as these waves strike nearby individuals and objects, the electrons in the objects vibrate and increase the temperature.

# SOUND

Imagine a world without sound. We could not hear the song of a bird, the noise of a city, the voices of our parents, the combined music of an orchestra, the crash of thunder, the warning of a radio newscast, or any of the other sounds we encounter on a daily basis. Even though there are individuals who cannot hear because of physical disabilities, most individuals take these daily encounters for granted.

## Source of Sound

Almost all of the sounds we hear are caused by vibrating materials. The vibration may be initiated by striking an object (e.g., drums, piano), by plucking or rubbing one object over another (e.g., violin), or by creating a movement of air over an object (e.g., clarinet). The sounds reach our ears because the vibrating object pushes against a neighboring medium, usually air, causing longitudinal waves to move out in all directions.

## Transmission of Sound

For sound to originate in one place and be heard in another, there must be a medium to transmit it. Sound will not travel in a vacuum because there are no molecules to compress and expand to create a wave. Solids, liquids, and gases will all transmit sound. Most of the sounds we hear are transmitted through air, a composition of gases; however, compared with a solid or liquid medium, air is a poor conductor of sound. Sound moves more quickly through liquids and solids, primarily because the molecules in air are not as restricted and more energy is required to compress them. Sound travels at about 738 mph through air, but travels at about 11,160 mph through steel.

## DID YOU KNOW? _____

On Kauai, an island in Hawaii, there is a place where the wind blows over the sand in a particular way. The vibrations make a sound similar to that of a barking dog. The place is known as Barking Sands.

**Classroom Activity**  Provide students with several different materials such as the following: a wooden stake, a steel pole, a broken piece from a styrofoam box, a paper towel roll, and a glass rod. Turn on a portable radio and have each student put it against one end of each object with his or her ear on the other end. Have them determine which material is the best conductor of sound. Which material is the worst conductor of sound? Have students experiment to determine which material would make the best sound insulator. Have students compare notes and chart their results.  ■

## Characteristics of Sound

One individual's noise may be another's music. The difference between the two may be determined by culture or, within a culture, by generations. Rather than limit our discussion to the characteristics of musical tones, we will address the three principal characteristics of sound: pitch, intensity or loudness, and quality.

Pitch corresponds to frequency—the number of vibrations of an object in a specific amount of time. The more rapid the vibrations, the higher the pitch. Slow vibrations produce a deep, low tone.

Although the two terms are occasionally used interchangeably, intensity and loudness represent somewhat different aspects of sound. Intensity is an objective measure of the amount of sound produced; loudness is subjective and is a measure of the effect that a sound has on the listener's ears.

Although the pitch and loudness of one sound may be similar to those characteristics of another sound, we are able to distinguish the two because of the quality of the sound. A piano and a trumpet may have the same pitch and may be played with the same degree of loudness, yet the sounds are different because of the nature of the vibration occurring at the respective instruments.

## IDEA BOX _____

Provide students with several tape recorders. Ask them to record different kinds of sounds in the classroom, in the school, on the playground, in their neighborhoods, or inside their homes. Invite students to classify those sounds according to a variety of categories, such as animal sounds, people sounds, machine sounds, loud sounds, soft sounds, musical sounds, constant sounds, and one-time sounds. What similarities do students note in all the sounds? What differences can they detect? Is it possible to have an environment completely devoid of sound? Why or why not?

# LIGHT

## DID YOU KNOW?

The universe is so vast that an object traveling at the speed of light (186,000 miles per second) would take approximately 30 billion years to get from one border of the universe to the other. That same object traveling at the speed of light would take 100,000 years just to get from one side of our galaxy (the Milky Way) to the other.

**Classroom Activity**   Students will enjoy the following easy-to-read books about light: *How Did We Find out about the Speed of Light?* by Isaac Asimov (New York: Walker, 1986) and *Sight and Seeing: A World of Light and Color* by Hilda Simon (New York: Philomel, 1984).   ∎

If there were no light source, we could not see any objects. On an extremely dark night in a cabin in a forest, we do not see the chairs, tables, and other objects because they do not emit light. Objects that give off light energy are luminous and include the sun, a burning candle, burning gas, and an incandescent light bulb. Most substances that we observe reflect light, and when there is a light source present, we can observe the books, tables, chairs, and other materials around us.

When light encounters an object, it can respond in three ways. Some materials permit light to travel through them in a relatively straight line. Examples of these *transparent* objects are clear glass and plastic. *Translucent* materials permit light to travel through, but the light is scattered in many directions; consequently, one cannot see through such materials very clearly. Frosted glass, waxed paper, and an unwiped windshield are examples of translucent materials. Most objects we observe are *opaque*; no light is able to pass through them unless the material is extremely thin. We see reflected light from a tree trunk, an automobile, and other objects that do not permit light to move through them. These objects also leave a shadow if the light strikes them.

## Reflected and Refracted Light

Light travels in a straight line, but it reacts differently to various surfaces. A shiny, smooth object will reflect almost all of the light that strikes it.

## IDEA BOX

Place a stack of books on a table. Stand a medium-size mirror up against the books so that it is perpendicular to the plane of the table. Put a sheet of paper in front of the mirror. Place a piece of cardboard in front of the paper so that, when seated, a student cannot see the surface of the paper. Have each of several students sit at the table, reach around the cardboard, and attempt to write their name or some other familiar word while looking in the mirror. Have them compare their true handwriting with this sample.

If we attempt to touch a coin on the bottom of a fountain filled with water, we will usually not place our hand where we "see" it. Likewise, if we look at a spoon in a cup of water, the spoon appears to be bent. These perception difficulties are caused by refraction, or the bending of light. Light rays bend when they move from one medium to another. This is due to the light traveling at different speeds in different media. Light travels more slowly in water than in air because water is more dense than air; therefore, when light travels from air into water, the light rays bend.

Glass is more dense than water; therefore, light passing from air through glass will bend even more than light passing from air through water. This principle is utilized to help individuals with sight problems. A lens is placed between the object being seen and the eye; the degree to which the light will bend is determined by the thickness and type of the lens. Lenses fall into two categories: concave and convex. A convex lens is thicker in the middle than it is at the outer area. This causes the light rays to bend toward the center of the lens. When one observes something through a convex lens, the object is magnified. A concave lens is thin in the middle and thicker at the outer edges, causing the light ray to bend toward the outer edge. As one looks through a concave lens, an object appears smaller.

## Color

Although most individuals live in a world of color, few comprehend the reasons objects appear to be red, blue, yellow, or any other color. A red object appears red because it has the ability to reflect red light. If one were to project green light on a red rose, the rose would appear black as the frequency of red light is absent. Likewise, a red light projected on a green leaf would produce a black leaf. White light contains all of the frequencies that produce colors; therefore, when white light is projected on an object, the object will reflect the light of the spectrum that it is capable of reflecting. Hence, we see red roses, green leaves, and brown or yellow stems when a white light is projected on the flower because the various parts of it reflect their respective colors. If an object reflects all of the colors of the spectrum, it appears white. If it reflects none, it is black.

### IDEA BOX

With the following activity, you can help students understand that the color black is actually a combination of all other colors. Tear some paper towels into several strips. About one-third of the way up each strip make a mark across the width of the strip with a black magic marker. Fill several glasses with an inch or so of water. Tape the top of each strip to a pencil and place the strip in the water; the black mark should be above the level of the water, with the pencil holding the strip in a vertical position. After some time students will note the water moving up the strip to the black mark. As it moves past the black mark, it will separate the black ink into all the colors that have been combined to make black. These colors will be left on the paper towel above the original mark.

### IDEA BOX

Have students prepare notebooks or folders labeled with all the colors of the spectrum (i.e., "Red," "Orange," "Yellow," "Green," "Blue," and "Violet"). Have them brainstorm for as many synonyms for each color as they can, writing the words in the proper notebook. For example, following are some synonyms for "red":

| | | |
|---|---|---|
| Rose | Ruby | Rouge |
| Maroon | Scarlet | Burgundy |
| Vermilion | Cinnabar | Cherry |
| Magenta | Mulberry | Crimson |

Invite students to keep a running record of "color words" as they encounter them in their reading during the course of the year.

## ENERGY AND WORK

Work is not a new concept to individuals. Since the earliest times, people have had to work to supply themselves with food, shelter, protection from the elements, transportation from one place to another, and defense from a variety of enemies—including fellow humans. Most of the energy used to accomplish the work of our earliest ancestors was human energy. Today, these needs are frequently met by using other sources of energy.

### Energy

If work is to be accomplished, energy must be provided. Energy is generally defined "as the ability to do work." There are two kinds of energy: kinetic and potential. Potential energy is the energy an object has because of its position or that is stored in an object and ready to be released. A stretched rubber band, a battery, the water at the top of a waterfall, a drawn bow, fossil fuels, wound clocks, and the food we eat are all examples of potential energy. Kinetic energy is the energy that an object has because of its motion.

Energy exists in many forms, such as electrical, mechanical, heat, chemical, nuclear, and sound. Although energy cannot be created or destroyed, it may be transformed to other forms of energy. Electrical energy may be transformed to light or heat energy, for example.

### DID YOU KNOW?

If it were possible to harness it, the energy released by an average hurricane could supply the electrical needs of the United States for six months.

**Classroom Activity** Two excellent "hands-on" books for children, each filled with loads of energy-related experiments, are: *Making Things Move* by Neil Ardley (New York: Watts, 1984) and *Simple Science* by Angela Wilkes and David Mostyn (New York: Usborne/Hayes, 1983). ■

### Work

Although the word "work" has multiple meanings, for the purposes of this text it refers to the exertion of a force and the distance something has been moved. If a large amount of energy has been expended but an object has not moved, no work has been done. If the object has moved, work has been done. If you study for hours to do well in an examination, you may say that you worked hard for the examination, but your effort is not considered work in the scientific sense.

Work (*W*) is measured by combining units of force (*f*) and units of distance (*d*). For example, if a force of 15 pounds is used to move an object 20 feet, the unit of measurement is 300 foot-pounds of work:

$$W = f \times d$$
$$W = 15 \text{ lb.} \times 20 \text{ ft.}$$
$$W = 300 \text{ ft.-lb.}$$

**TEACHER TO TEACHER**

Problem solving is one of the most important skills I try to teach my students. Discovery learning has helped me to achieve this goal. We are great little writers in my second-grade class, and in an attempt to integrate writing into science and math and as an introduction to solid geometric shapes, I decided my students should write a riddle book on shapes. The class was divided into four groups, each group being given an object representing one of the four shapes

(i.e., sphere, pyramid, etc.). The children were asked to weigh and measure their objects secretly and describe the attributes of their object in riddle form. Each group was given a variety of items with which to weigh and measure their objects. As I watched the children diligently weighing, measuring, and recording their data, I came to the group with the sphere (which was an orange). They were unsuccessfully attempting to measure the orange with a ruler. As I stood watching, one frustrated child threw down the ruler and cried, "There must be a better way." They all stood puzzled for a moment until another child picked up a piece of twine that I had placed with their measurement tools. As he wrapped the twine around the orange, I could see the "light bulb" go on. With a loud "I got it!" he cut the twine and placed it against the ruler. We learned the word "circumference" that day in a way that the students will never forget.

Charlotte King
Travis Elementary School
Rosenberg, TX

## SIMPLE MACHINES

Humans have constantly searched for devices to assist them in performing their work. Machines have been developed to assist individuals in several ways: (1) to increase the amount of force being applied, (2) to change the direction of the force, (3) to transfer a force from one place to another, and (4) to increase the speed of the force. Although machines may be complex, they are all made up of one or more simple machines.

### Lever

There are three classes of levers. Each contains three basic parts, which vary in relative position. In the first-class lever the fulcrum is between the effort and the resistance. In a second-class lever the fulcrum is at one end and the effort at the other, with the resistance somewhere in between. The advantage of using this class of lever is that less effort has to be applied, but it must be applied over a greater distance. In a third-class lever the resistance is at one end, the fulcrum is at the

other, and the effort is somewhere in between. A third-class lever offers advantages in speed and distance, at the expense of increased effort. The drawings below show an example of each type of lever.

### Pulleys

There are two types of pulleys: fixed and movable. A fixed pulley does not move with the resistance. Its major advantage is that it enables one to change the direction of the effort (i.e., to pull down on a rope to raise the load). There is no advantage in terms of the amount of effort that must be applied or the speed at which it is applied.

A movable pulley moves along the rope, and two sections of the rope support the resistance. The advantage over the fixed pulley is that one-half the force must be applied, but the force must be applied over twice the distance that the resistance is being moved. The drawings on page 290 illustrate fixed and movable pulleys.

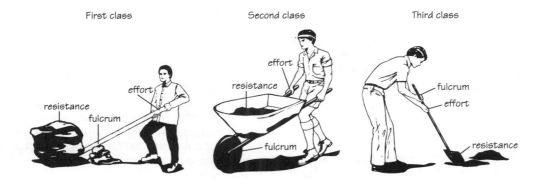

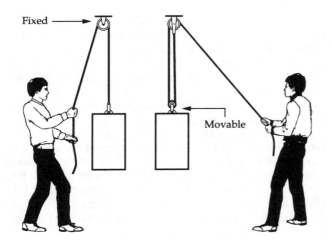

Fixed

Movable

## Wheel and Axle

The basic ingredients for a wheel and axle are two wheels—a large one connected to a smaller one. The smaller wheel is really the axle of the machine. When either wheel makes a complete turn, the other also makes one complete turn. Turning the larger wheel means that less force must be applied to turn the smaller wheel, but the force has to be applied over a greater distance. Conversely, turning the smaller wheel will move the larger wheel a greater distance, but more effort must be applied.

The advantages of a wheel-and-axle assembly are threefold: (1) it can change the direction of the force, (2) it can produce a gain in force, and (3) it can, with a loss in force, produce a gain in speed and distance. For example, when you use a hand-driven eggbeater, you are changing the direction of the force; the wheel on the side of the eggbeater is turned in an up-and-down motion to move the blades in a horizontal motion. The handle of a pencil sharpener and a doorknob are both larger wheels that turn axles. They move a greater distance but require less force to do the work.

## Inclined Plane

The inclined plane is generally a ramp that enables one to move something from one level to a higher level with less force; however, the effort must be exerted over a greater distance than the simple distance between the two levels. The longer the inclined plane or the more gradual the slope, the less force is needed. A shorter inclined plane requires more force, but it will have to be applied over a shorter distance; hence, the amount of work is about the same.

## Wedge

A wedge is really two inclined planes placed back to back. A primary application of the wedge is to split

wood. When effort is applied to the driving surface of the wedge, the force is directed both downward and outward as the wedge is driven into the piece of wood. An advantage of the wedge is that the downward effort is assisted by the force of gravity. The distance from the driving surface to the tip of the wedge determines how much effort must be applied to drive the wedge into the wood. A long wedge with a narrow driving surface will require less effort, but the wedge will have to be driven into the wood a greater distance to cause it to split. A short wedge with a broad driving area will take more effort to drive into the wood, but it will have to be driven a shorter distance. In terms of work, the longer wedge is the more efficient simple machine.

## Screw

A screw is a very effective machine that is basically an inclined plane wrapped around a base in a spiral. One revolution of the spiral is called a thread. The distance between two threads is the pitch of the screw. A major advantage of using a screw is to increase the force utilized in an application. This increase in force, however, is accompanied by an increase in the distance the screw must be moved. In other words, the screw is turned a greater distance than it is driven into the wall. The narrower the pitch, the greater the force gained by using the screw. A wider pitch increases the force required and reduces the distance the screw must be turned.

### DID YOU KNOW? _____

Scientists at the University of Utah have invented a working motor that is the width of seven human hairs.

**Classroom Activity**  Students may be amazed at the number of simple machines they use every day without thinking about them. For example, an old-fashioned can opener is an example of a wedge, an inclined plane, and a lever. Have students make up six folders for permanent display on a bulletin board. Have them collect photographs and illustrations from old magazines that show simple machines in action. For example, a picture of a girl pedaling a bicycle up a ramp would illustrate several simple machines in action. Students may wish to set up photo opportunities or collect pictures from several sources to display in each of the labeled folders. Be sure to discuss the reasons students assign certain pictures to certain folders.  ■

### TO INVESTIGATE _____

Work with a small group of classmates to explore different ways of teaching simple machines to elementary students. Visit several classrooms in your area, talk with teachers and science specialists, brainstorm among yourselves, and consult professional resources. Try to put together a compendium of activities and projects that can be used to teach simple machines. Have this compendium duplicated and distributed to all classmates.  ■

# ELECTRICITY

Most children become acquainted with the simplest facts of electrical forces during the primary grades. For example, when they run a comb through their hair and place it near pieces of paper, the paper is attracted to the comb; when they rub a balloon against their shirt and place it against the wall, it remains on the wall; and when they take clothes out of the dryer, the clothes cling together. In addition, two balloons rubbed against the same piece of cloth will repel one another.

## Static Electricity

When two different materials are rubbed together, one of the materials attracts some electrons from the other material. If a hard rubber hose is rubbed against a piece of fur, the electrons from the fur are drawn to the hose, making the hose negatively charged and the fur positively charged. When a glass rod is rubbed on the silk cloth, the electrons leave the glass rod, and it becomes positively charged while the silk cloth becomes negatively charged.

## Current Electricity

Static electricity generated is of little practical use because this type of electrical energy cannot be controlled. Although any motion of an electric charge constitutes an electric current, we usually think of an electric current as the flow of electrons through a conductor. This type of electricity is widely used to illuminate our homes, schools, streets, and other areas; to heat our homes; and to dry our clothes and cook our food.

## Electric Circuits

A circuit is the path something takes, with a starting point and an ending point. An electrical circuit is designed to control the flow of electrons so that they accomplish an established purpose (e.g., light a room, heat an oven, or cause a fan to move). For a circuit to perform its function it must be complete; that is, electrons must flow from the starting point to the end point and back.

Objects in a circuit are connected either in series or parallel. An example of a series circuit is a string of Christmas tree lights connected in such a manner that the current has to flow through one fixture to reach the other. The problem with this type of circuit is that if one light goes out, thus breaking the circuit, the other lights won't glow because the flow of electrons stops at the burned-out bulb.

In a parallel light circuit, there are individual circuits for the light bulbs. Thus, if one bulb burns out, the others will still glow because their individual circuits are complete.

**DID YOU KNOW?** _____

A power plant in Modesto, California, generates 14 megawatts of electricity per hour by burning old tires.

**Classroom Activity**    Students may be interested in discovering which metals make the best conductors of electricity. Have students put together a simple electrical circuit, as shown in the accompanying illustration. Have them collect several examples of metals (e.g, various coins, aluminum foil, metal strips, cooking implements). Clip the two alligator clips to the ends of each of the metal pieces to see which ones make the light bulb burn the brightest. Can students make predictions as to the best materials for electric wires? Which materials are least desirable? Invite a local electrician to the class to explain the materials used in wiring (as well as the materials used to insulate wires). (*Note:* Be sure to stress all safety factors when doing any type of electrical activity.)  ■

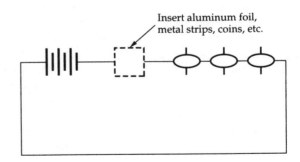

Insert aluminum foil, metal strips, coins, etc.

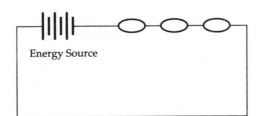

Series circuit

Energy Source

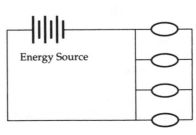

Parallel circuit

Energy Source

## Controlling Electricity

One of the biggest challenges we face with electricity is how to control it. Once we have the electrons confined to a circuit, we must find a way to use it as needed. A switch enables us to turn electricity on or off. The following illustration shows how a switch controls the flow of electricity.

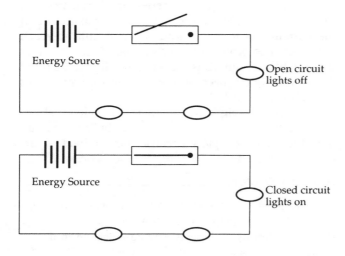

A second type of control is represented by the fuse and the circuit breaker. These devices are used to prevent wires from overheating. A short circuit or an overload leads to a demand for more electrons, and with this extra flow of electrons, the wires become hot.

To prevent this, a fuse or circuit breaker is inserted into the circuit. A fuse consists of a strip of metal that has a low melting point. When the flow of electrons (current) reaches a predetermined point, the metal strip will melt; the circuit will then be open, and the current will stop flowing. Each circuit in a home has its own fuse. In modern homes, the circuit breaker has replaced the fuse. When the circuit is overloaded, the circuit breaker trips and opens the circuit. The current will not flow again until the circuit breaker is reset.

## Types of Current

An electric current may be direct or alternating. In a circuit using direct current, the charges flow in only one direction. Batteries are a source of direct current. The terminals of the battery retain the same charge. with the current flowing from the negative terminal to the positive one. The amount of pressure pushing the charge depends on the capability and size of the battery; a single flashlight battery is 1.5 volts. Additional batteries may be connected to increase the voltage; however, the flow of the charge is still in one direction.

In a circuit using alternating current, the electrons flow first in one direction and then in the opposite direction. The alternating flow is established at the energy source (e.g., the generating plant). Alternating current is widely used in America because it can be transmitted efficiently over great distances.

## MAGNETS

Most children are familiar with magnets. They have observed them being used on refrigerator doors to hold messages, pictures, school papers, and a host of other things. Perhaps they have seen them being used to hold cupboard doors closed, or they may have noticed their use in one or more of their toys. There are three basic types of magnets: natural magnets, permanent magnets, and electromagnets. The earth is a natural magnet, and you can demonstrate this by using a compass. One end of the needle of the compass always points to the north. This end of the needle is frequently marked with an "N." This marking can confuse children if they have learned that likes repel and opposites attract magnetically. Explain to them that the "N" on a compass is a north-seeking pole, not the north pole of a magnet. The students also need to learn that magnetic north is not exactly the same as true geographical north.

A lodestone is magnetite, a common magnetic iron ore; it also is a natural magnet. It will attract metal and display a magnetic field when iron filings are placed

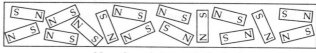

Non-aligned, unmagnetized

Aligned, magnetized

around it. If suspended, it will swing until it becomes aligned in a north–south direction.

Permanent magnets are made of magnetic materials and can take a variety of shapes, the most common being the bar, circular, "V," and horseshoe. Other materials, such as a nail, can become magnetized by being rubbed from one end to the other, always in the same direction. Not all nails, iron, and other metals are magnets, however; for them to be magnetic, their atoms must be aligned in a north–south manner. A magnet will retain the north–south alignment even if it is cut in half repeatedly.

## TO INVESTIGATE

Magnets are some of the most popular scientific apparatus available to children. Visit several schools in your area and ask a sampling of students from many different grades about their experiences with magnets in the classroom. How much time did they spend with magnets in each grade? In which grade do students tend to use magnets the most? Query students on their knowledge of magnets. Do they know the differences between poles? Do they know what a magnet does? Based on their responses, can you design a process-oriented activity that will help students discover more about magnets than is presented in the science textbook? How can you make the study of magnets exciting for children? ■

An electromagnet has a number of advantages over a permanent magnet. First, the magnetism can be controlled. A large piece of metal can be picked up by turning the current on, hauled to another place, and deposited by turning the current off. A second advantage is that the intensity of the magnetism is determined by the number of coils and the size of the iron core; therefore, if one needs a magnet that will pick up objects weighing several tons, an electromagnet can be constructed to perform the task. On the other hand, a small electromagnet can be constructed to fit inside a doorbell to draw a small hammer and release it, causing the bell to ring.

## TEACHER TO TEACHER

In order to study the Periodic Table my students research a particular element and describe it in less than 50 words. Next, they are told they must choose the most essential information and reduce their descriptions by half, and following this, they are told to reduce it again by half in order

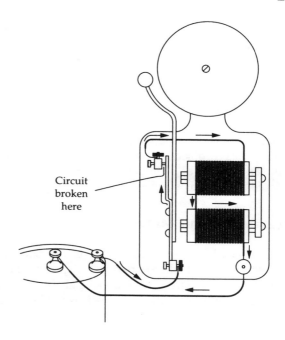

to produce a single slogan sentence of less than 12 words that captures the essence of the element they have chosen. These sentences are often very "catchy" and creative and are shared by students in small group settings and in front of the entire class.

This exercise can also be used with other topics: categories of specific animals, scientific equipment and apparatus, famous scientists, etc. This activity forces students to focus on the most important pieces of information, to separate the essential from the nonessential. It is especially useful for developing the condensing skills necessary for in-depth library research papers.

Inez Fugate Liftig
Fairfield Woods Middle School
Fairfield, CT

# POINTS OF DISCUSSION

1. How many different ways do we have to measure heat? How can you use that information to develop some classroom activities for your future students?
2. Work with a classmate to develop a semantic web (see Chapter 8) on sound. List the features, characteristics, sources, transmission, and types of sound. Compare your "web" with those of other members of the class.
3. Why should elementary students learn about color? What is the relationship between color and some of the other aspects of physical science (energy, work, simple macines, etc.)? What aspect of color will you find most difficult to teach?
4. Interview several different children at various grade levels. Ask them to define "work." How are their views different or similar? Based on the information collected, what would you need to do to rectify those preceptions (or misperceptions) of work?
5. Work with a classmate to create a list of all the simple machines in (1) your classroom, (2) a dorm room or apartment, (3) a car, and/or (4) the cafeteria. How could that informtion be used in teaching students about simple machines?
6. Create a list of classroom safety procedures for the use and demonstration of electricity in the elementary classroom. What safety rules would you want your students to be aware of whenever using or studying electricity?
7. The study of magnets is a very common topic in elementary science programs. Interview several local teachers and compile a list of the activities they use in their lessons on magnets. Can you and your classmates develop some new and original magnet activities/experiments/projects?

ACTIVITY **13.1**

..................................................................................................

## Up, Up, and Away

..................................................................................................

### Introduction

On many occasions, individuals lack pulleys to help them lift heavy objects to another level. A board or plank can be used as a simple machine that will serve the same purpose as a pulley.

### Organization and Materials

Extend a board (plank) from a table to the floor. Use a bundle of books tied together and a spring scale to demonstrate how much work is needed to move the books from the floor to the table. This is a whole-class demonstration followed by a group activity.

### Procedure

1. Have one child in the class lift the books directly from the floor to the table. Have another read how much force is required as indicated on the spring scale. Have another child measure the distance the books have been lifted. Ask the class to determine the amount of work, using the formula $W = f \times d$.
2. Ask another child to place the books at the bottom of the board and, with the spring scale attached, to pull the books up the board. Get a reading from the scale and measure the length of the board. Again ask students to estimate the work using the formula. Compare the two results and discuss what was gained or lost. (Measuring, reporting)
3. Ask if there is any difference between lifting an object through the air and pulling it over a board. Is

there a difference in friction between the air and the board. (Inferring, observing)
4. Divide the class into groups of four or five. Provide them with a board, a pile of books, and a scale. Tell them that pencils, round counting sticks, and chalk will be available if they wish to use them to overcome friction.
5. Bring the groups back to the whole-class setting. Ask for a report of what they did to move the books up the inclined plane with less effort. Did they use the pencils, chalk, and sticks as rollers and the chalk as a lubricant? (Measuring, inferring, observing, predicting)

### Conclusion

An inclined plane can be used to move objects to a higher level. There is a sacrifice of distance for less force. To reduce friction, rolling objects may be placed under the object being moved. A second factor is the use of a lubricant to reduce friction and force.

### Follow-up

1. Have children inspect their environment for examples of the inclined plane (e.g., ramps for the handicapped or in parking garages).
2. Have children experiment with longer boards. Does the length of the board have any effect on the work being done? If one has an extremely heavy object, what should he or she do to move it to a higher level using a reasonable amount of force?

ACTIVITY **13.2**

..................................................................................................

## Pull Me, Pull Me

..................................................................................................

### Introduction

Pulleys are very helpful for lifting heavy objects to a higher level.

### Organization and Materials

Divide the class into four groups and give each group a fixed pulley, a movable pulley, a spring scale, three

or four books bound together, a piece of cord that will fit the pulleys, and a board with an eyelet hook.

### Procedure

1. Tell the class to place the board on top of a bookcase and lift the books from one shelf to the next shelf. Have them lift the books directly, using no machines. What are the distance moved and the ef-

fort applied? (Observing, inferring, reporting, measuring)

2. Have them lift the books using a fixed pulley. Again measure the force and distance. (Measuring, reporting) Tell them to state any advantages of pulling down versus lifting. (Inferring)

3. Have them use a fixed pulley and a movable pulley. (You may have to help them connect the two pulleys.)

"Why is it called a fixed pulley?"
"Why is it a called a movable pulley?"
"How much force was used?"
"What was the distance the books traveled?"
"What was the total distance the rope was pulled?"
"What was gained, and what was sacrificed?" (Inferring, measuring, reporting, communicating)

## Conclusion

The advantage of using a pulley can be a change in the direction in which the force is applied and/or a gain in force with a sacrifice in distance.

## Follow-up

1. Discuss situations in which using a pulley would be an advantage (e.g., hoisting hay to the hayloft; lifting cement, bricks, or other material from the ground to a roof or higher floor).

2. Have the students add a second movable pulley. Compare the changes in force and distance. What is gained, and what is lost?

3. Ask if they could make a single pulley serve as a movable pulley. Compare it with the fixed pulley. What is the difference?

ACTIVITY   13.3

. . . . . . . . . . . . . . . . . . . . . . . . . . . . . . . . . . . . . . . . . . . . . . . . . . . . . . . . . . . . . . . . . . . . . . . . . . . . . . . . . . . . . . .

## Tote That Barge, Lift That Bale

. . . . . . . . . . . . . . . . . . . . . . . . . . . . . . . . . . . . . . . . . . . . . . . . . . . . . . . . . . . . . . . . . . . . . . . . . . . . . . . . . . . . . . .

## Introduction

Every day people use machines to help them do work. For work to be accomplished in the scientific sense, a force must be applied to an object, and the object must be moved some distance. Machines assist us by doing one or all of the following: (1) changing the direction of the force, (2) increasing the amount of the force, (3) transferring force from one place to another, and (4) increasing the speed of the force.

## Organization and Materials

Select the heaviest individual in the classroom and the lightest (probably the teacher and the smallest child, whom we will call "Sally"). Ask the children, "How can Sally lift me without hurting herself?" Materials needed include a sturdy board and a brick or other object to use as a fulcrum.

## Procedure

1. Begin by telling the class, "Sally can use a machine to lift me." Tell them that a machine need not be complicated. Begin the demonstration by placing the brick under the center of the board. Have Sally stand on one end of the board, and ask the class "What will happen when I step on the other side?" (Predicting)

2. Ask the children to close their eyes, and move the brick closer to Sally (how close will be determined by the difference in weight between you and the child). Stand on one end and ask the students to open their eyes. Have Sally stand on the other end. (Have a student on either side of Sally offer his or her support.) As Sally stands on to the board, the teacher is lifted. Ask students why Sally was able to lift the teacher. (Observing, inferring, communicating)

3. Ask the students if they noticed anything different about the "machine." (Observing)

4. Do the activity again. Ask them to observe how far Sally moved and how far you moved. Have them measure these distances. Ask if they have any ideas as to why Sally was able to move the teacher. (Inferring, calculating, reporting)

5. Discuss the application of the formula $W = f \times d$. For example:

You : 150 lb. $\times$ 1 ft. = 150 ft.-lb.

Sally : 75 lb. $\times$ 2 ft. = 150 ft.-lb.

## Conclusion

Machines help us to do work. In this activity, less force was applied, but the force had to move over a greater distance.

## Follow-up

1. Allow children to use the lever. Use children of various weights. Have some of equal weight, some close to one another in weight, and others with significantly different weights. What must be done to enable one to lift the other? (The fulcrum must be moved.)

2. Share other examples of levers (e.g., wheelbarrow, broom, seesaw, scissors, shovel, crowbar, nutcracker). Explain the three classes of levers and have them place the examples in the appropriate categories. (Classifying, reporting, inferring)

ACTIVITY **13.4**

### Just Rollin' Along

## Introduction

There are two types of energy: kinetic and potential. The former is energy of motion; the latter is the energy an object has because of its position or that is stored in an object and ready to be used.

## Organization and Materials

This activity can begin as an entire class project and then move to groups. The materials needed are a board, several balls, a wind-up toy, a battery-driven toy, and a rubber band.

## Procedure

1. Discuss work with the class. Allow them to give several examples. Then ask what it takes to do work. (Energy.) Roll a ball across the floor, and ask them if the ball has any energy. Is it moving? Can it knock something over or move something? (Yes, it has energy.) Place the ball at the top of a tilted board that is resting against an object.

   "Does the ball have any energy?" (Yes, the ball has *potential* energy.)

2. Demonstrate what happens to several clothespins standing at the bottom of the board when the ball rolls down the board. (They are knocked over.)

   "Where does the energy to knock over the balls come from?" (Inferring, observing)

Explain the two types of energy. A ball at rest at the top of the board has energy, but it needs to be released. A ball rolling down the board has kinetic energy, as it is in motion.

3. Divide the class into groups. Give each group a wind-up toy, a battery-driven toy, a rubber band, several balls, and a board. Ask them to work together to determine which are examples of kinetic energy and which illustrate potential energy. (Classifying, observing, reporting, inferring, predicting)

4. Bring the students back together and have them report their findings. (Reporting, communicating)

## Conclusion

Kinetic energy is the energy an object has because it is in motion. Potential energy is the energy an object has because of its position or stored energy that is ready for use.

## Follow-up

Ask the students to classify each of the following items as a source of either potential or kinetic energy: a wound clock, gasoline, a car parked on a hill, a dry cell battery, a hammer about to hit a nail, a moving bus. Have them add to the list. (Reporting, communicating, classifying)

ACTIVITY   **13.5**

## Bend but Not Break

### Introduction

When we look at a coin in a fountain or other container of water, it is not where we perceive it to be when we reach for it.

### Organization and Materials

Divide the class into groups of four. Provide each group with a bucket, coins, and several rulers or other straight edges.

### Procedure

1. Fill the bucket full of water and place a few coins on the bottom. Ask a student to stand to the side of the container and hold the straight edge above where he or she thinks the coin is located. Have another student hold a ruler below the first one in a straight line to the bottom of the container. Was the ruler directly over the coin? Next position the rulers in a straight line diagonally from the eye to the coin.

    "Why were they consistently off the mark?" (Observing, inferring)

2. Have students look through an aquarium filled with water to an object suspended above the aquarium. Do they see the object exactly where it is? Is the object bent away from or toward the normal? (Observing, inferring)

3. Ask the class to make several generalizations:
    a. When we observe objects in a different medium, light is bent.
    b. Light appears to bend toward the normal if the observed object is in the heavier medium.
    c. Light appears to bend away from the normal if the object is in the lighter medium. (Inferring, predicting, observing)

### Conclusion

When we observe objects in a different medium from our own, they are not where they appear to be because the light that enables us to see the object is bent when it moves from one medium to another.

### Follow-up

1. Try the activity at various depths. Is there any noticeable difference because of the depth of the water?

2. Tie a string around an object and submerge it so that it is halfway between the surface of the water and the bottom of the container. Have the students use pointers to indicate where the object appears to be. Where is it in relation to the pointer? Why? (Inferring, observing, reporting)

ACTIVITY   **13.6**

## Light Stuff

### Introduction

If we are to see an object, light must be reflected off it. Not all substances reflect light; some permit it to pass through.

### Organization and Materials

Divide the class into four groups. Provide each group with a clear piece of glass, a piece of waxed paper or frosted glass, and an object that will not permit light to pass through.

### Procedure

1. Instruct each group to work with the three materials and to record their perceptions concerning the interaction of light and the individual substances. (Inferring, observation, recording)

2. After 10–15 minutes, reassemble the class.

    "What were the characteristics you noticed about the interaction of light and each substance?" (Reporting, analyzing)

    "What generalization can we make concerning light and materials?" (Concluding, generalizing) (Light passes through transparent material, and we see a similar object. Light is diffused through translucent material, and the object is distorted. Light will not pass through an opaque material.)

"Will these three generalizations apply to all substances?" (Experimenting, observing, predicting)

"As we look at a number of objects, into which category does each one fit?" (Classifying)

## Conclusion

All objects on earth react to light in one of three ways: They are either transparent, translucent, or opaque.

## Follow-up

1. Ask students if they have seen birds fly into a picture window during the spring or summer. "Why does this happen?"

2. Have the students take a piece of glass and make a mirror by placing a piece of black paper behind it. Why will the light not pass through it? Are there any other situations where a clear piece of glass becomes a mirror? (A window of a dark room, with no light shining directly through the glass.)

3. If possible, invite a glazier in to explain how mirrors are made.

---

ACTIVITY  13.7

### Pretty Hot Stuff

## Introduction

Most substances expand when heated and contract when cooled. The exception is water, which expands and contracts like other substances until it reaches the temperature of 4 degrees C; from 4 degrees centigrade to 0 degrees centigrade, water expands.

## Organization and Materials

This activity is best suited for a whole-class or small-group activity. The follow-up may be an individual activity. Supervision is needed because a heating source is required. The materials needed are a pyrex jar, a balloon, a test tube, a cork with a tube inserted in it, and food coloring.

## Procedure

1. Put a balloon over the opening of a pyrex jar. Heat the jar, causing the balloon to become partially inflated. Remove the jar from the heating source, and the balloon will deflate. Ask the students to explain what they saw. (Observing, communicating)

    "What caused the balloon to inflate and deflate?" (Inferring)

2. Place a test tube partially filled with colored water in a clamp. Place a cork with a tube inserted in it into the test tube. Have the students report and explain what they see. (Observing, communicating, inferring)

3. Ask them to draw a generalization from what they saw. (Concluding)

4. Fill a mustard jar with water and place a lid on it. Place the jar in the freezer overnight. Take the jar out the next morning and observe what happened. (Inferring, observing, communicating)

    "Was this an exception to our generalization? Why?" (Inferring, predicting)

    "How could we have prevented the glass from breaking?" (Leave the top open.) (Predicting, inferring, concluding)

    "What usually happens when things get colder?" (They contract.) "Shouldn't we have less ice in the jar than we had water? Why didn't we?" (Water expands when it turns to ice.) (Inferring)

## Conclusion

When gases and liquid are heated, the molecules move faster and tend to move farther apart. The exception is water, which expands just prior to moving to the solid (ice) state.

## Follow-up

1. Have students look for examples in solids to justify their generalization. (Electric lines, bridges, sidewalks)

2. Ask for other examples of air and water expanding. (Hot air balloons, expansion tank in hot water lines at homes)

ACTIVITY 13.8

........................................................................................

## Too Hot to Handle

........................................................................................

### Introduction

Thermometers measure the temperature of a substance, not the amount of heat present in the substance. Two different-sized containers holding the same liquid may be the same temperature; however, one contains more heat than the other.

### Organization and Materials

This activity can be a whole-class demonstration or a supervised small-group activity. The materials required are two jars of different size but made of the same material and with comparable openings. Glass quart and pint jars or beakers would be appropriate. A thermometer and a heating source are also necessary.

### Procedure

1. Discuss safety factors when using heat. Wear asbestos gloves and safety glasses, use pyrex glass, and stand clear of the burner. (Use any other measures needed according to the age and mental ability of students.)
2. Explain that water will be placed in the pint jar, heated to 100 degrees F, and then removed from the heat source. After 10 minutes, the temperature of the water will be taken and recorded. Water will then be placed in a quart jar, heated to 100 degrees F, and then removed from the heat source. After 10 minutes, the temperature of this water will be taken and recorded.

   "Why was the temperature of the water in the pint jar lower after 10 minutes than that of the water in the quart jar?" (Observing, communicating, inferring)

"What will be the ultimate temperature of the water in both jars? (Room temperature.) (Inferring, predicting)
"Which jar of water will take longer to reach the temperature of the room?" (Inferring, predicting)
"Why does the quart jar take longer to cool?" (Inferring, observing)
"Which of the two takes longer to heat?" (Predicting, observing, inferring)
"What is the difference between heat and temperature?" (Observing, inferring, communicating)

### Conclusion

Thermometers measure the temperature of a substance, not the amount of heat.

### Follow-up

1. Have children place their hands in two different buckets of water, one at approximately 40 degrees F and the other at approximately 80 degrees F. Ask them then to place both hands in warm water. Ask them how their hands feel. (The cold hand will feel hot and the hot hand will feel cool in the warm water.)
2. If we fill a basin and bathtub with water and the temperatures are the same, which will take longer to cool? Ask the students to defend their answers.
3. Use a half-pint jar and a quart jar. Compare the time it takes the two to arrive at room temperature. Is there any relationship between size and the time? (The quart takes twice as long as the pint and four times as long as the half-pint.)

ACTIVITY 13.9

........................................................................................

## Warming Up

........................................................................................

### Introduction

Materials do not respond to heat in the same manner. Light-colored objects reflect heat; dark-colored ones absorb it.

### Organization and Material

Divide the students into three groups of five students each. The materials needed are 15 small thermometers; five large jars with lids; five medium-size jars with lids;

five small jars with lids; three sheets each of red, black, blue, green, and white construction paper; and 30 rubber bands.

## Procedure

1. Place a sheet of paper of each color partially around each size of jar. Place a thermometer in each jar, put the lids on the jars, and place all of the jars on a window ledge, preferably on the south or west side of the building. Place them in such a way that the paper faces the outside and the thermometer faces the inside of the classroom, in a position in which it can be read.
2. Have the thermometers read every hour and record the readings on a chart.
3. Do this for at least two weeks, rotating the jars and recording the temperature on sunny days, partially sunny days, and cloudy and rainy days. (Obsering, recording)

   "Why the difference in temperatures?" (Inferring)
   "What will happen if the sun is not shining?" (Inferring, predicting)

4. After all data has been collected, ask:

   "What was the effect of the colors on the outside of the jars?" (Inferring, concluding)
   "What effect did the size of the jars have on the temperature?" (Observing, inferring, communicating)
   "What caused the temperature to drop after the jars were taken out of the sun?" (Inferring)
   "How could we make the temperature in the jars drop more quickly?" (Predicting, observing)

## Conclusion

Materials react to heat differently. Dark materials absorb heat energy; white and light-colored materials reflect it. The darker the material, the more heat is absorbed.

## Follow-up

1. Have the students observe summer and winter clothing styles. Why are more white and lighter-colored clothes worn in summer?
2. Ask them to observe how some roofs are dark and some light. If they live in an area where it snows, have them notice on which roofs the snow melts more quickly.
3. After it snows, sprinkle pieces of dark paper on a section of snow and compare it with an uncovered section of equal size and in close proximity. (In an area where it doesn't snow, ice can be placed on the lawn.) In which section does the ice or snow melt more quickly?

ACTIVITY    13.10

·············································································

### Button up Your Overcoat

·············································································

## Introduction

Insulation is used to keep a cold object cold or a warm object warm. The natural tendency is for an object to take on the temperature of the environment.

## Organization and Materials

Place several coats or jackets in a cold area. Take the temperature of the air in the sleeves of the coat. Then, place the thermometer on the coat and record the temperature.

## Procedure

1. Bring the coats and jackets into the classroom.
2. Ask several children to put the coats and jackets on.

   "Will those who have coats or jackets on be warmer than the others? Why?" (Inferring)
   "If we were standing near a bonfire, would we feel more heat from the bonfire if we had on a coat or had a tee-shirt on? Why?" (Inferring, predicting, communicating)

3. Take the temperature of a jacket lying outside in a winter temperature and one in a closet at 72 degrees F.

"Why do the temperatures differ?" (Inferring, communicating)

"What is the source of heat? The room or the jacket? How do we know?" (Inferring, communicating)

## Conclusion

Material can be used to insulate us. Coats keep our body heat in and near our bodies by preventing the heat from escaping. Likewise, materials keep heat away from our bodies by preventing the heat from passing through.

## Follow-up

1. Read a story such as *Call of the Wild* by Jack London to the class. Ask students why the dogs dig holes in the snow to sleep in at night.

2. Why did the Eskimos build houses of ice to keep them warm?

3. Discuss air as a good insulator. Why are layers of clothing a good way to keep the cold air away from our bodies?

ACTIVITY **13.11**

......................................................................................................

### Sound Management

......................................................................................................

## Introduction

Sound is transmitted more efficiently through liquids and solids than it is through air.

## Organization and Materials

You will need a table 6 to 8 feet long or the chalk trough at the base of the chalkboard. Students can do this activity individually.

## Procedure

1. After a discussion of how sound travels, have students listen to sounds through various media. Have them place their ear against the table or chalk trough, and strike the other end lightly with a coin. Have them remain near the end of the table or chalk trough but with their ear removed from the object. Again lightly strike the other end.

   "In which position did you hear the noise louder? Why?" (Inferring)

   "If someone were to strike one end of the table lightly and you were at the other end, would you hear the noise more clearly if you placed your ear on the table or held your head about

   12 inches away? Why?" (Inferring, predicting, communicating)

   "If we took two cans each with a tiny hole in the bottom and tied a string from one can to the other, why would we be able to hear each other over a greater distance than if we just talked to one another over the same distance, using air as our medium?" (Inferring, reporting, communicating)

## Conclusion

Sound is transmitted through solid materials more efficiently than through air.

## Follow-up

1. Stand at one end of a hallway and tap your foot. Can it be heard at the other end more clearly through air or the floor?

2. American Indians would place their ears to the ground to determine if anyone were coming. Why?

3. Would several people near a railroad track hear the sound of a coming train sooner if they were standing above the track or had their ears on the track? Why?

ACTIVITY   13.12

## "What Light through Yonder Window Breaks..."

### Introduction

A number of situations familiar to children can be used to show that, under normal conditions, light travels faster than sound.

### Organization and Materials

1. If the school is near the flight paths of airlines and the planes fly overhead during school hours, take the class outdoors to observe the planes.
2. If the school has a large play area, place half of the class at one end of the area and the other half at the other end. Have a child clap his or her hands together while the students at the other end observe what happens. Reverse the process.
3. During an electrical storm, have the children observe the relationship between thunder and lightning.

### Procedure

1. For each of the situations listed, prepare the students by telling them to report, either orally or in a brief written report, what they observd. (Observing, communicating, inferring)
2. Ask them why they saw the plane before the sound, the clap of the hands before the sound, or the lightning before the thunder. (Inferring, communicating)

3. If possible, ask them to count between the time they saw the (plane, clapping, lightning) and then heard the sound. (Measuring)

   "What would happen if the person clapping were closer to you." (Inferring, communicating)
   "What does it mean when the lightning and thunder occur at about the same time?"

### Conclusion

Light travels at a greater speed than sound; however, if we are close to the source, the time difference is not as pronounced.

### Follow-up

1. When we are watching a band perform at a football game, do we hear the music at the same time the director directs the band to start when we are about 1000 feet away? Would someone on the field hear the music before us? Would they see the director move his hand before we did?
2. When we hear the sound of a jet airplane and we know the plane is moving in an easterly direction, would we look to the east or the west of the sound to find the plane? Why?

ACTIVITY   13.13

## Sound Off!

### Introduction

Sound may be of a high pitch or a low pitch. One can control the pitch by manipulating the number of vibrations occurring at the source of the sound.

### Organization and Materials

When an object vibrates, sounds are sent out. By controlling the number of vibrations that occur in a given

period of time, the pitch may be varied to a higher or lower range. To prepare for this exercise the teacher should have the following materials: several rubber bands of different thickness, several glasses or glass soda bottles, a crocheting needle, and several pieces of string of varying thickness.

### Procedure

1. Hold one end of a crocheting needle against the table. Press the needle down, and then release it. Ask

the children what they observe. (Needle vibrating.)

"What did you hear?"
"What happens when the needle stops vibrating?"
(Observing, inferring, reporting)

2. Lengthen and then shorten the length of the needle that extends beyond the end of the table, and repeat step 1.

"When was the pitch higher? Lower?" (Inferring, observing)
"Do you think you could make the pitch lower or higher? How?" (Predicting, reporting, observing)
"Could a similar test be performed on a piece of string? Will the thickness of the string make a difference?" (Predicting, observing, inferring)

3. Take two glasses or soda bottles and add different amounts of water. Ask students if the one with more

water will have a higher or lower pitch than the one with less water. (Predicting, inferring)

4. Use seven glasses or bottles and see if the students can make a musical scale. (Measuring, inferring, applying)

## Conclusion

The pitch of sound is determined by the vibrations which are influenced by the length of the substance and its thickness.

## Follow-up

1. We plucked the string to cause a vibration. What will happen if a bow or similar device is run over the string? How can we test that idea?

2. Using the vocal chords, how can we alter the pitch of our voice?

---

ACTIVITY  13.14

## A Good Reflection

## Introduction

Reflected light will bounce off a surface at the same angle at which it struck the surface.

## Organization and Materials

Have children work in groups of five. Give each group a long piece of string and a protractor.

## Procedure

1. Instruct two in each group to take the ends of the string. Have them stand 5 to 10 feet apart and about 15 feet from a reflecting object. Ask a third individual to take the middle of the string and place it where one of the students sees the other's reflection. Hold the string securely at that position and have the two at the ends of the string draw it taut. Have the two remaining students place a table under the "V" and draw lines to mark the direction of the string.

2. Have the student draw a line perpendicular to the base of the "V." Measure the angle between the perpendicular line and the line representing the path of light from the reflected object. It should equal the other angle—the reflected ray. (Observing, recording)

3. Have the groups change positions, and repeat the procedure with other reflected objects. Ask the students to state what they think will happen. (Predicting, observing)

4. Ask them if there could be any variable factors they would like to test, such as moving closer to the reflecting object or changing positions (i.e., using the right side as the reflected object rather than the left). What do they expect to find? (Predicting, inferring, classifying)

## Conclusion

Light travels in a straight line when it moves through a consistent medium. When it reflects off an object, the angle at which the incident ray strikes the object will be equal to the angle at which the reflected ray leaves the object.

## Follow-up

1. Open the door to the classroom and place a mirror in such a position that the class will be able to observe an object in the hallway that they could not see by looking directly out the door. Use the string method to see if the preceding conclusion holds true.

2. Have students who show an interest in reflection make periscopes by using a series of mirrors and a milk carton.

ACTIVITY    **13.15**

.................................................................................................................

## Go with the Flow

.................................................................................................................

## Introduction

Although we often treat electricity and magnetism as separate concepts, the two are related. We can help our students understand the relationship by reviewing principles related to these two phenomena, such as the attraction or repulsion of two objects, the ability of electrical power to perform work, and the need to control electricity by sending it through a circuit. This could be followed by asking if there is a way to combine electricity and magnetism.

## Organization and Materials

This activity is designed to work well with groups of four or five or as a demonstration before the entire class. If small groups are used, each group will need bell wire, a dry cell battery, a compass, a bar magnet, a galvanometer, and objects that are attracted to a magnet.

## Procedure

1. Give the materials to each group. Ask them to connect the wire to the dry cell battery and to place the compass close to the wire.

   "What happened? Why?"
   "What happens if we disconnect the wire? Why?"
   (Observing, communicating, inferring, reporting)

2. Ask each group to make a coil of a least four turns in the wire, connect the wire to a galvanometer, and then run the bar magnet through the coil.

   "What did you observe?"
   "What caused the needle to move?"

"Why did it stop?"
"What will happen if we pull the magnet out of the coil?"
(Observing, inferring, communicating, predicting)

3. Have students identify the two things they saw occur. (Magnetic field around a wire that has a current flowing through it and electrons being made to flow through a circuit by moving a magnet through the coil of wire.) (Generalizing, classifying, communicating)

4. Have students experiment with the materials to determine if they can come up with additional ideas.

   "What would you call the electric wire with a current running through it?" (Accept all answers, e.g., electricity magnet, current magnet.)
   "Can we combine the two—an electric wire with a current moving through it and a magnet?"

5. After about 5–6 minutes ask for a report from each group. (Inferring, predicting, communicating, classifying)

   "How can we make this magnet stronger? Test your theories and share them with us." (Predicting, communicating, measuring)

## Conclusion

An electric current can be generated by moving a magnet through a coil of wire. A magnetic field is found around a wire with electrons flowing through it. An electromagnet can be strengthened by increasing the number coils of wire around the magnet and by using a stronger magnetic core.

## Follow-up

1. Have students explain how gas, oil, coal, or water is used to generate electricity and how energy is converted from one type to another (e.g., heat energy to mechanical energy to electrical energy).

ACTIVITY **13.16**

................................................................................

### Stuck on You

................................................................................

## Introduction

We have all seen magnets sticking to refrigerators, stoves, some school blackboards, and other metallic objects. But why aren't all keys, which are made of metal, attracted to a magnet? In this activity, students will learn what kinds of materials are attracted to magnets.

## Organization and Materials

This activity is appropriate for individuals, pairs, or small groups, depending on the availability of materials.

*Per group:* Magnets, various materials to be tested (emery cloth, plastic, steel foil, lead foil, waxed paper, paper clips, fur, aluminum foil, paper, brass foil, sponge squares of two different colors, etc.). To prepare the sponge squares, select one of the colors and hide steel pins (with points and heads cut off) inside the sponges. Be careful that the ends are not sticking out. Test to make sure that the sponges are attracted to a magnet. Have sponges available in sufficient quantities so that half of the class receives one color and the other half receives the other color, with the steel pins. (*Note:* Foil squares and magnets are available from Delta Education, P.O. Box 950, Hudson, NH 03051, at reasonable prices and in sufficient quantity for an entire class.)

## Procedure

1. Conduct a brief discussion to determine what the students already know about magnets and magnetism.

   "Who can explain what this is?" (Magnet)
   "What do magnets do?" (They attract various objects.)
   "What kinds of objects do magnets attract?" (Accept all answers for now, and if disagreements arise, explain that students will dis-cover the answers as the activity progresses.) (Communicating)

2. Distribute materials to be tested and discuss the characteristics of each. (All materials to be tested can be stored in large envelopes to make dispersal and collection easier.) (Classifying, communicating, observing)

3. Instruct students to carefully examine the materials and predict which are magnetic. (Observing, inferring)

4. When all students have completed their predictions, class totals can be listed on the board. (This will serve to extend the recording process as well as help integrate math procedures into the experiment. For example, "If there are 25 students in the class and 19 predicted that emery cloth is magnetic, how many predicted that it is not?") (Communicating, measuring, classifying)

5. Distribute the bar magnets and allow students to test their predictions. Have the students record their findings on a worksheet as they proceed. Have them use a mark that will differentiate the actual results from their predictions. (Experimenting, observing, communicating)

6. Results can be listed on the board as in step 4, if desired. (Communicating)

7. Discuss the findings with the class.

   "Which materials were magnetic?"
   "There seem to be some different findings as to whether sponges are magnetic. Can someone explain this?" (Students may decide that color is the determining factor. If so, ask how this theory can be proven; for example, different colors of paper, plastic, cloth, or wood could be tested. This question could be left open, to be explored in the follow-up activities. The purpose of the trick sponges is to challenge the students to use higher levels of thinking and to use a scientific approach to explaining the unusual.)
   "Can you think of other objects or materials that may be magnetic?" (Communicating, classifying, inferring, predicting)

## Conclusion

Materials must contain steel in order to be magnetic.

## Follow-up Activities

1. Demonstrate a magnet picking up one pin but not another (steel versus aluminum).

   "What is the problem here?" (One pin is not made of steel.)

"What does this show about whether an object is magnetic or not?" (It must be steel.)

2. Test the ability of magnetism to pass through the objects tested.

3. If possible, allow students to keep their bar magnets at their desk or on a table to investigate other materials.

4. Have the students list some of the ways magnets are used in our everyday lives (refrigerator magnets, metallic weatherstripping for doors, cranes in junkyards, etc.).

---

ACTIVITY   **13.17**

......................................................................................

## You Shock Me!

......................................................................................

## Introduction

Your hair is uncontrollable and stands on end, your dress or slacks cling to your legs, your sweater crackles as you take it off, and the styrofoam packing pieces mysteriously fly all over as you unpack your book order. Static electricity is the cause of these unusual happenings. Students will learn that static electricity may be created by rubbing objects together, that it causes objects to attract or repel other objects, and that it may be removed from an object by rubbing it with certain other objects.

## Organization and Materials

Students can work alone or in pairs. *Note:* This activity should be conducted on cold, crisp days (low humidity). Caution students that static electricity experiments should not be tried with current electricity (outlets, lights, etc.).

*Per group:* One inflated balloon for each student, a 6-inch piece of string or yarn (attached to the inflated balloon).

## Procedure

1. Introduce this activity with a discussion on electricity.

   "What is electricity?"
   "How is electricity used?"
   "Where does electricity come from?"

   Explain that there are two kinds of electricity: current electricity (the type used in our homes for light and electrical power) and static electricity (the type experienced when we receive a shock

after walking across a carpet and touching another person). (Communicating, inferring)

2. Supply each student with an inflated balloon. Have the students stand next to some object in the room (wall, chalkboard, door, window). Ask them to hold their balloons against the object and carefully let it go.

   "What happens?" (The balloon falls to the floor.)
   "Does anyone know how we can make the balloon stick to the object?" (From past experience, students will probably suggest rubbing the balloon against something such as their hair, a sweater, a rug, and so on.)
   (Observing, communicating, experimenting)

3. Have the students rub their balloons on their hair or clothing.

   "Now hold the balloon against the wall (door, window) and let it go. What happens?" (The balloon sticks.)
   "What caused the balloon to stick to the object this time?" (An in-depth scientific explanation is not necessary; "Rubbing it against my head" is a sufficient answer.)
   "How long will your balloon stay there?" (Allow an extra balloon to remain on the wall to be observed as the activity continues.)
   (Observing, communicating, experimenting, inferring, predicting, measuring)

4. Have the students remove their balloons from the wall and rub their hands over the entire surface of each balloon a couple of times.

   "Now try to stick the balloon to the wall again. What happens?" (The balloon falls to the floor.)

"Can you explain this?" (The electrical charge was removed.)

"Does rubbing the balloon against your hands do the same thing to the balloon as rubbing it against your hair or sweater does?"

"What does this tell you?" (Not all objects cause a static charge when rubbed against each other.)

(Observing, communicating, inferring)

5. Have one student charge his or her balloon and hold it above the hair of another student.

"What happened? Is this similar to the balloon sticking to the wall?" Allow all students to perform this trick.

6. Have all the students charge their balloons again. Have two students hold their balloons by strings (tied to the balloon neck) and bring them together.

"What happened?" (The balloons moved apart.)

"Why do you think this happened? What did we do differently this time?"

(Experimenting, observing, inferring)

7. Have students cite examples of other forms of static electricity they have experienced in their lives. (Communicating)

## Conclusion

Static electricity is caused by rubbing certain types of objects together. When an object is charged, it may attract or stick to another object. When two like objects are charged, they push or repel each other. However, a static electricity charge does not last long.

## Follow-up Activities

1. Students can test materials besides balloons to see whether they can be charged to attract various objects.

2. Cut strips of newspaper and have students place one strip on top of another and rub them with a pencil. Both strips should then be held between the forefinger and thumb. Have students observe and record the results. Repeat the activity, but have students place the strips side by side when rubbing.

ACTIVITY **13.18**

......................................................................................

### Colorific

......................................................................................

## Introduction

Color is everywhere. Clothing, homes, computers, billboards—all exhibit many beautiful colors. But where do these colors come from? All colors come from the spectrum of white light. When separated, these colors include red, yellow, and blue, the primary colors. The primary colors, combined in various amounts, produce all the other colors around us.

## Organization and Materials

This project is designed as a class demonstration, followed by individual work using the information obtained during the demonstration.

*Per class:* A large piece of white construction paper, colored cellophane (red, yellow, green, blue), two light projectors, tape

## Procedure

1. Hang the piece of white paper on the wall or chalkboard. Have the students look at the white paper through individual pieces of colored cellophane and through overlapping pieces of cellophane.

"What happens to the color of the white paper as you look at it?" (The color changes.) (Observing)

2. Darken the room. With a light projector, shine a beam of light through the red cellophane onto the white paper. "What color do you see on the white paper?" (Red.) (Observing)

3. Continue this process with the other colors of cellophane. Have the students record the various colors on a chart. (Experimenting, observing)

4. Use tape to cover the lenses of two light projectors each with a different color of cellophane. Shine the two lights together on the white paper. Ask students to record the results on a chart. Repeat this process with other colors of cellophane until all possible combinations are produced.

"What combinations produce the brightest colors?"

"What combinations produce completely new colors?"

"What combinations are most like primary colors?"

"Which ones are least like primary colors?"
(Observing, experimenting)

## Conclusion

By analyzing the charts, students should conclude that when the primary colors are mixed in various combinations, the secondary colors are produced.

## Follow-up Activities

1. Provide red, blue, and yellow paint to allow students to create and experiment with the primary colors. (*Note:* Results may be somewhat different from results obtained by mixing light.)
2. Direct students to find a way, without using a prism, to separate the colors found in white light.

## Project 13.1: Follow My Trail

### Materials
A coat hanger, asbestos gloves, fireproof table, candle wax, matches, candle, fire extinguisher or pail of water

### Initiating Questions
How does heat travel through a solid material?

Will heat move from one end of a coat hanger to another?

How can we prove it without touching the material?

### Activity
Straighten a coat hanger and place three or four balls of wax at 3-inch intervals on the coat hanger. Have one student hold the coat hanger, with asbestos gloves, at one end. Have another hold a lighted candle, with the flame on the hanger or very close to it, at the opposite end.

### Extending Questions
In what direction did the heat move through the coat hanger?

How do we know?

Did it take the same amount of time for the heat to move from ball 1 to ball 2 as it did from ball 2 to ball 3 or ball 3 to ball 4?

Can you think of other examples of heat traveling from one place to another through a solid?

What safety precaution should we take as a result of learning how heat travels through a solid?

### Curricular Extensions
*Math:* Have students measure the time it takes for the heat to travel the length of the coat hanger. After it has moved through two balls, have students predict how long it will take to get through the others and to the end of the hanger.

*Art:* Have students create illustrations of other times when this process is used (standing in front of a fireplace, grabbing the handle of an iron skillet, etc.).

## Project 13.2: Don't Pressure Me!

### Materials
A tin can with a screw top, a platform, a pair of asbestos gloves, heat source (propane tank), candle, bunsen burner, bucket of ice, matches, fireproof table top

### Initiating Questions
Does air have weight, and can it exert pressure?

How can I dent the can?

Can I do it with air?

### Activity
Make certain the can is thoroughly clean on the inside and contains nothing inflammable on the inside or outside. Place the can on the platform, and then position the heat source under the platform. After a few minutes, depending on the intensity of the heat source, remove the can from the heat and screw the cap on the can. (*Use asbestos gloves.*) You can either place the can on the table or in a bucket of ice.

### Extending Questions
What caused the dents to appear in the can?

Why did they not appear before we added the heat?

Where did the air in the can go when it was heated?

Why did the dents happen more quickly when we placed the can in the ice?

Was there more air or less air in the can after it was heated?

### Curricular Extensions
*Language arts:* Have students each pretend to be a balloon (some inflated, some deflated). Have each student write an "Autobiography of My Life as a Balloon." Create a special bulletin board to display students' work.

*Art:* Using styrofoam balls, string, small baskets, and an assortment of fabric scraps, encourage students to create their own models of hot air balloons. Be sure to hang these from the ceiling for display.

## Project 13.3: A Matter of Expansion, My Friend!

### Materials

Narrow-neck beaker; candle, bunsen burner, or propane burner; platform for the beaker high enough to place the heat source under it; a balloon

### Initiating Questions

How can we inflate a balloon without blowing into it?

Where will the air come from to inflate the balloon?

### Activity

Place a deflated (and stretched) balloon over the neck of the beaker. Place the beaker on the platform. Light the heat source and place it under the platform. (Caution: Non-Pyrex containers may shatter.)

### Extending Questions

Why does heating the beaker cause the balloon to inflate?

Where does the air in the balloon go when the beaker is cooled down?

What does our demonstration prove?

Is the air in this room warmer near the ceiling or the floor? Why?

### Curricular Extensions

*Math:* Have students take the temperature of the room near the beaker just before the demonstration. Time how long it takes for the balloon to be inflated, and again take the temperature near the beaker. Keep the thermometer in the same position. How long does it take to return to the original temperature? Have students make comparisons between the time it takes to inflate the balloon and the time for the balloon to return to its original temperature.

*Music/Science:* Have students experiment to determine if bottles heated to different temperatures will cause changes in pitch of the sound of a spoon hitting each bottle. Will different amounts of water heated to different temperatures in the bottles have an effect?

## Project 13.4: Sound Off

### Materials

Eight long, thin glasses or eight soda bottles; water; a wooden implement to strike the glasses or bottles

### Initiating Questions

How can I get eight different sounds by using the materials on the table?

Could I arrange these sounds to form a musical scale?

What variable will determine the high notes, the low notes, and those in between?

### Activity

Fill the containers with varying amounts of water. Strike them and arrange them in order from the highest note to the lowest. Water may have to be added or removed to achieve a desired note. A music teacher or colleague may help to distinguish the desired notes. After the containers have been arranged, a music book with simple songs can be used to coordinate the "instrument" with a music lesson.

### Extending Questions

What other instruments can we make?

What other materials will we need?

What causes the different sounds?

Can you think of "real" instruments that one plays by striking? By blowing?

### Curricular Extensions

*Art:* Invite students to decorate their instruments using construction paper, yarn, sparkles, and colored pens. Discuss any changes in the tones of the instruments when decorations are added.

*Music:* Challenge students to create their own songs or to try to play some popular songs (e.g., "Happy Birthday," "She'll Be Comin' Round the Mountain").

## Project 13.5: Help Me Find My Way

### Materials

Bowl, water, cork (small piece), needle, magnet, liquid detergent

### Initiating Questions

How can I take a bowl of water, a piece of cork, a needle, and a bar magnet and make something that will help me find my way by locating north?

### Activity

Cut a flat piece of cork and place it in the bowl of water (to which you've added a few drops of detergent). Stroke the needle 10–15 times with the bar magnet. Make certain the needle is stroked in the same direction each time. Place the needle on the floating cork.

### Extending Questions

Why did the needle point in one direction?

If we move to another location in the room, will it point in the same direction?

In what direction is the needle pointing? What is the opposite direction?

What would happen if we dropped the needle?

What would happen if we placed the needle in the water and then back on the cork?

What would happen if we stroked the needle in the opposite direction?

What would happen if we brought the bar magnet close to the bowl?

## Curricular Extensions

*Language arts:* Have students write imaginary diary entries as if they were the needle. How do they feel? What did they notice? Would they want to do it again?

*Reading:* An excellent resource for students of all ages is *Physics* by Amanda Kent (New York: EDC, 1984). Don't let the title throw you; this is a "painless" introduction to magnetism as well as electricity, color, light, sound, and heat.

# RECOMMENDED CHILDREN'S LITERATURE

## Matter

Matter is all around us. The book you're holding, the pen you write with, and the desk you sit at are all forms of matter. Although students sometimes have difficulties with this science topic (often because it deals with abstract concepts), their understanding can be enhanced through the introduction of supplemental reading materials. The following selections offer your students some fresh perspectives and necessary data for comprehending the nature of matter.

Berger, Melvin. (1986). *Atoms, molecules, and quarks.* New York: Putnam. A well-designed introduction to the building blocks of all matter: atoms and molecules.

Bronowski, Jacob, & Selsam, Millicent. (1965). *Biography of an atom.* New York: Harper & Row. Although this is an older book, its information is current, descriptive, and insightful.

Hoban, Tana. (1985). *Is that larger? Is it smaller?* New York: Greenwillow. Another wonderful Tana Hoban book for young readers, which focuses on sizes of common objects and the comparisons one can make.

Hoban, Tana. (1986). *Shapes, shapes, shapes.* New York: Greenwillow. Using the urban environment, the author has come up with a number of common shapes in some very uncommon places.

Laithwaite, Eric. (1986). *Shape: The purpose of forms.* New York: Watts. Various intriguing shapes that appear throughout nature are the focus of this fascinating book.

Laithwaite, Eric. (1988). *Size: The measure of things.* New York: Watts. An interesting examination of size and its significance in nature and the human world.

Oliver, Stephen. (1990). *My first look at sizes.* New York: Random House. This is a wonderful introduction to size comparisons and progressions using objects familiar to most children.

Simon, Seymour. (1985). *Soap bubble magic.* New York: Lothrop. Everything a young reader would want to know about soap bubbles: how they're made, what they can do, and the various scientific principles they illustrate.

Srivastava, Jane J. (1980). *Spaces, shapes, and sizes.* New York: Crowell. An interesting variety of demonstrations and experiments help youngsters understand the concept of volume.

## Energy

How energy is produced and used is a subject filled with fascination for many youngsters. You can help stimulate that interest by introducing selected pieces of children's literature into your science curriculum. But don't just rely on readings to help students gain a better understanding of this area; make sure they have ample opportunities to use the experiments and activities described in these books.

Adkins, Jan. (1980). *Heavy equipment.* New York: Scribner. All kinds of heavy equipment, including fork lifts, tractors, graders, and loggers, are described in this book about large machines and their various uses.

Ardley, Neil. (1984). *Discovering electricity.* New York: Watts. A descriptive book appropriate for young readers, it offers a variety of electrical experiments that demonstrate basic principles of electricity.

Ardley, Neil. (1984). *How things work.* New York: Wanderer. A collection of more than 300 questions and answers about the way things work, most of them found in any youngster's home.

Ardley, Neil. (1984). *Making things move.* New York: Watts. Lots of experiments and clear explanations offer pupils many opportunities to discover the principles of movement.

Asimov, Isaac. (1984). *How did we find out about lasers?* New York: Walker. An interesting look at lasers—how they are created and their varied uses.

Asimov, Isaac. (1986). *How did we find out about the speed of light.* New York: Walker. How fast does light go? How can we measure the speed of light? What were some early experiments to measure light speed? The answers are all here.

Barton, Byron. (1987). *Machines at work.* New York: Crowell. A wonderful introduction to the various types of machines used in and around a construction site.

Berger, Melvin. (1989). *The science of music.* New York: Crowell). A thorough examination of sound—including volume, pitch, vibration, tone, and how sounds are created. Several experiments dealing with the manufacture of sound are also provided.

Berger, Melvin. (1989). *Switch on, switch off.* New York: Crowell. What is electricity? How does it work? Where does it come from? These questions and more are answered in this introductory guide to electricity, from the generator to the light switch.

Billings, Charlene. (1986). *Fiber optics: Bright new way to communicate.* New York: Dodd. How are people able to transmit information through light? A most readable text and descriptive photographs help children understand this breakthrough technology.

Burroughs, William. (1982). *Lasers.* Easthampton, MA: Warwick Press. Lots of colorful photographs highlight this very informative guide to lasers and their many uses.

Carter, Alden. (1987). *Radio: From Marconi to the space age.* New York: Watts. Radio communications from the early days of the wireless to present-day technology are the focus of this enlightening book.

Chant, Chris. (1982). *Jetliner: From takeoff to touchdown.* New York: Watts. Children are amazed at how a multiton vehicle can lift off from the ground and stay in the air. This book answers many of their questions about the forces and machinery at work.

Cole, Joanna. (1983). *Cars and how they go.* New York: Crowell. Everything about the operation of the car is delightfully detailed. Clear illustrations add to the enjoyment of this book.

Cook, Brian. (1981). *Gas.* New York: Watts. How gas resources are tapped and utilized and our need to conserve this precious fuel source are detailed in this informative book.

Coombs, Charles. (1980). *Coal in the energy crisis.* New York: Morrow. A most interesting look at how coal is mined, its advantages and disadvantages over other energy sources, and its importance as a natural resource.

Filson, Brent. (1984). *Exploring with lasers.* New York: Messner. The author has succeeded in presenting a complex subject in an interesting and very readable text. The book deals with the creation of lasers, how they operate, and what they are used for.

Gibbons, Gail. (1982). *Tool book.* New York: Holiday House. Many tools are used at home every day. This book examines their functions.

Goor, Ron, & Goor, Nancy. (1981). *Shadows: Here, there, and everywhere.* New York: Crowell. A host of activities and investigations on the nature of shadows and light are shared in this book.

Graf, Rudolf. (1973). *Safe and simple electrical experiments.* New York: Dover. Nearly 100 experiments on magnetism and electromagnetism, currents, and static electricity offer young scientists an easy-to-follow introduction to the subject of electricity.

Irvine, Max. (1984). *TV and video.* New York: Watts. An inviting look at the variety of uses for an object most children take for granted. How TV is used in industry, medicine, and space exploration is highlighted.

Kramer, Anthony. (1982). *The magic of sound.* New York: Morrow. Lots of experiments help youngsters understand the principle of sound—how it is created, used, and controlled.

Laithwaite, Eric. (1986). *Force: The power behind movement.* New York: Watts. An interesting and enlightening look into the principles of gravity, inertia, and friction. Also covered are simple machines and the various forces that help us survive.

Lauber, Patricia. (1987). *Get ready for robots.* New York: Crowell. What robots are and the tasks they can do are the focus of this delightful book for young scientists.

Macaulay, David. (1988). *The way things work.* Boston: Houghton Mifflin. A unique and insightful inspection of the way everyday objects work. Scientific principles are highlighted and discussed in language youngsters can understand.

Math, Irwin. (1981). *Wires and watts.* New York: Scribner. A variety of experiments and demostrations help students understand the principles of electricity.

McGowen, Tom. (1986). *Radioactivity: From the Curies to the atomic age.* New York: Watts. Descriptive photographs and illustrations highlight this very readable text about atomic energy.

Milton, Joyce. (1981). *Here come the robots.* London: Hastings. The versatility and functions of robots throughout the world are imaginatively described in the pages of this book.

National Geographic Society. (1983). *How things work.* Washington, DC: Author. Lots of photographs and decriptive illustrations describe the workings of everyday items such as alarm clocks, cameras, and bicycles.

Olney, Ross. (1982). *The internal combustion engine.* New York: Lippincott. How automobile engines work and their various components are the subject of this inviting book.

Roth, Harold. (1985). *Bike factory.* New York: Pantheon. The most basic machine of all, the bicycle, is shown during its manufacture—from 400 separate parts to the finished product.

Simon, Seymour. (1980). *Mirror magic.* New York: Lothrop. Descriptions of the variety of ways in which mirrors are used and how they work will delight any reader of this book.

Weiss, Harvey. (1983). *Machines and how they work.* New York: Crowell. This book describes how the six simple machines (pulley, inclined plane, screw, wedge, lever, and wheel and axle) are used in everyday life. Readers are provided with instructions for creating their own simple machines.

White, Lawrence, & Broekel, Ray. (1986). *Optical illusions.* New York: Watts. The tricks our eyes play on us and several familiar optical illusions are the focus of this fascinating book.

Zubrowski, Bernie. (1981). *Messing around with water pumps and siphons.* Boston: Little, Brown. An intriguing and delightful look into water pumps and their uses. A variety of experiments and contraptions are provided for youngsters to explore.

Zubrowski, Bernie. (1985). *Raceways: Having fun with balls and tracks.* New York: Morrow. No youngster will want to pass up this book. The author demonstrates how homemade raceways illustrate the principles of velocity and acceleration.

Zubrowski, Bernie. (1986). *Wheels at work: Building and experimenting with models of machines.* New York: Morrow. This book is a marvelous addition to youngsters' study of machines and their construction. Provides many opportunities (with directions) for readers to create their own machines.

CHAPTER
# 14

# EARTH SCIENCE

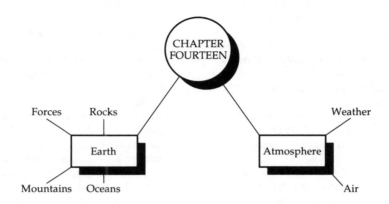

## Chapter Objectives

After reading this chapter you should be able to:

1.  Describe the surface of the earth, including its composition and different rock types.

2.  Elaborate on the constructive and destructive forces that shape and change the earth's surface.

3.  State the characteristics of oceans, including currents, tides, and waves.

4.  Describe the earth's atmosphere, including its layers, air movement (wind), and weather types.

5.  Provide students with a variety of process and discovery activities in the earth sciences.

Four and a half billion is a number almost too large to comprehend. Yet that's how many years the earth has been in existence. During that time it has undergone some remarkable changes. Rocks formed, primeval seas ebbed and flowed across vast continents, and dramatic weather conditions contributed to the geography and structure of the planet. Still, it's amazing to realize that this planet is only a speck in the vastness of the universe. It is but one particle in a galaxy of stars, satellites, and other celestial bodies. Yet the majesty of our

world is an area ripe for exploration and discovery. For knowledge of our world contributes not only to an appreciation of its many wonders, but to an initiative to preserve it as well.

The decade of the 1960s was extremely important because it led many individuals to develop a greater awareness of the planet we call home. The astronauts and cosmonauts who journeyed into space were able to send back photographs of earth, generating greater interest in our planet. For the first time we could actually see the earth as a sphere, with its oceans, landforms, and atmosphere. Other photographs drew attention to our environment and how we have polluted our land, water, and air.

One of your major responsibilities as an elementary school teacher is to help your students understand the importance of our global home, its position in the solar system, and its composition. This chapter focuses on the study of planet Earth and its composition. Just as our individual homes have various components and functions, so does our planet.

# THE SOLID EARTH

The solid section of the earth consists of four major layers: (1) the inner core, which is basically a solid metallic substance approximately 750 miles in radius; (2) the outer core, a thick but mobile liquid about 1,400 miles in radius; (3) the mantle, which basically consists of rocks and is about 1,800 miles in radius; and (4) the crust, the thin outer layer on which we live and on which all forms of life depend for their existence. Its thickness varies from 3 miles in the ocean basins to 30 miles beneath mountains.

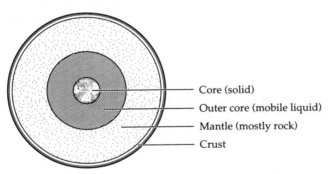

Core (solid)
Outer core (mobile liquid)
Mantle (mostly rock)
Crust

## Classification of Rocks

There are three basic types of rocks found on earth: igneous, sedimentary, and metamorphic. The initial stage for all rocks is igneous, followed by either the sedimentary or metamorphic stage. The rock cycle is demonstrated in Figure 14.1. All rocks are composed of one or more minerals. Minerals are naturally occurring inorganic solids distinguished by physical properties such as crystal form, color, the streak it makes when rubbed across another substance, luster, hardness, cleavage, fracture, and specific gravity.

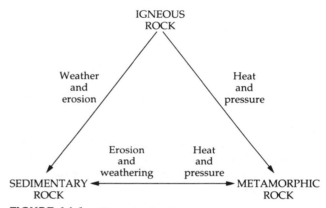

**FIGURE 14.1**  The cycle of rocks

## Igneous Rock

Igneous, or fire-formed rock, has its origin in the earth's interior (mantle). It begins as magma, a hot molten substance, and the rock forms as the magma cools and crystallizes. If the magma reaches the earth's surface and loses most of its gaseous component, it becomes lava. Obsidian rock is formed by rapidly cooling lava; it is very black, with a glassy appearance and no orderly crystalline structure. Granite, perhaps the best-known igneous rock, solidifies below the earth's surface and has large crystals, the result of a slow cooling process.

## Sedimentary Rock

Sedimentary rock is formed on the earth's surface by the weathering of bedrock and the movement of the weathered products by water, gravity, and wind. Tiny particles of rock are transported by wind, gravity and water and are eventually deposited. As piles of these sediments accumulate, the particles at the bottom are compacted by the weight of the upper layers. After a considerable amount of time the sediments are ce-

Sandstone

mented together by minerals deposited in the spaces between the pieces of weathered rock.

## Metamorphic Rock

A rock that has been transformed from another kind of rock is a metamorphic rock. This type of rock can be formed from an igneous, sedimentary, or even another metamorphic rock. The change in classification is caused by extensive heat, pressure, and chemically active fluids—mostly water. The change in rock form occurs in the earth's crust. Examples of metamorphic rocks are marble (previously limestone, a sedimentary rock), slate (previously shale, a sedimentary rock), and gneiss (previously granite, an igneous rock).

## The Earth's Changing Surface

Although in our lifetimes we may not observe a mountain being eroded or a lake being filled with sediment, the surface of the earth is changing; it is a dynamic planet. Volcanic and earthquake activities are causing the surface to rise in some places, and weathering and erosion are causing some areas to be lowered.

## Weathering

Weathering, in geologic terms, is the breaking of rock at or near the earth's surface. Two of the most common ways in which rocks are broken are mechanical and chemical weathering.

Through mechanical weathering, little pieces of rock are made out of larger pieces with no change to the composition of the rock. Examples of mechanical weathering are frost, thermal expansion, and organic influences.

Chemical weathering alters the composition of the rock, making new materials (i.e., the chemical makeup of the rock changes). Chemical weathering is caused by water and air, mixed with a small amount of dissolved material, interacting with the rocks and causing the internal structure of certain minerals to be altered.

## Erosion

The ultimate destination for a considerable amount of rock material is the sea. Although some particles of rock are carried from one place to another by wind and glaciers, by far the primary agent of erosion is the water in streams and rivers. Streams remove loosened materials from their banks and beds and transport them to a lower destination. Deltas, deposited particles from upstream, may form where a river meets another river, the ocean, or a lake.

## Constructive Forces

If weathering and erosion were the only forces involved in the ever-changing world, the earth's surface would be close to a level plane today. However, there are other forces causing changes in its appearance. One is plate tectonics; the other is mountain building.

**Plate Tectonics.**   Many scientists hold to the theory that the crust of the earth is divided into approximately 20 large, rigid, and mobile platelike regions. One of the largest, the Pacific plate, is located primarily within the Pacific Ocean but includes southwestern California and the Baja Peninsula. Scientists believe plate tectonics have been active for at least millions of years and have been a strong influence on the formation of the surface of the earth as we know it. The plates move in different directions, causing some of them to collide and others to pull apart. The Pacific plate, for example, is thought to be moving in a northwest direction, and the North American plate in that region is moving southeast. The point at which these plates slide past each other in opposite directions is the San Andreas fault.

### DID YOU KNOW? _____

Hawaii and Australia are moving closer to each other by about 2½ inches a year. At the same time, both are moving away from the South American continent.

**Classroom Activity**   Students may be interested in obtaining several different types of maps about various regions of the world. They will be startled to discover the various ways humans have devised to map the planet Earth. The National Cartographic Information Center of the U.S. Geological Survey (907 National Center, Reston, VA 22092) offers a variety of maps, including aeronautical, nautical, geologic, land use, soil, and topographic maps, as well as gazetteers, atlases, and other cartographic materials. Write to them and ask for specific information on a specific area of the earth. The information your students receive will be mind-boggling!   ■

**Mountains.**   Although mountain ranges vary, they all have the same basic structure: parallel ridges that consist of a combination of sedimentary, volcanic, and geologically recent igneous rock. There is also some evidence of metamorphosed rock. The sedimentary rock is usually considerably older than the mountain itself. Sometimes there is fossil evidence suggesting that the mountain was once the bed of a lake or other body of water. There are four different types of mountains: fault-blocked, folded, domed, and volcanic.

Fault-blocked mountains are formed by the stress placed on one plate by another. This stress causes the earth's crust to fracture and sections of the crust to rise in nearly parallel mountain ranges.

Folded mountains are formed by great pressure within the earth exerting tremendous sideways force against layers of rocks. This causes a wavelike development, with some of the earth's surface becoming peaks and other areas becoming troughs.

Domed mountains are the result of a broad arching of the earth's crust. This occurs because of folding or when magma flows up between two layers of rock. As the magma accumulates, it causes the layers of rock to move upward and form a large dome.

Volcanic mountains are formed by the buildup of lava when volcanoes erupt.

## DID YOU KNOW? _____

Mt. Saint Helens in Washington lost 1,311 feet in height when it erupted in 1980.

**Classroom Activity** Students will be interested to learn that Mt. Saint Helens is located along the infamous Ring of Fire, a band of highly volcanic activity that extends from Indonesia up the western shore of China, through Japan, across the Aleutian Islands, and down the western side of Canada and the United States. It is here that most of the volcanic activity in the world takes place. Have students do some library research on the Ring of Fire and construct a salt map of the Pacific Ocean and the major volcanoes or volcanic eruptions that have occurred along the Ring. Have them speculate on the reasons so many volcanoes are located along this band. ■

## Oceans

From a globe, it is readily apparent that there is more water on the surface of the earth than land. It should also be noticed that more water covers the Southern Hemisphere than the Northern Hemisphere. In all, about 71 percent of the earth's surface is covered by water. The major areas of water are the five oceans: Pacific, Atlantic, Indian, Arctic, and Antarctic. Smaller bodies containing salt water are usually called seas. Deep seas such as the Mediterranean and the Gulf of Mexico are found between continents, and shallow bodies of salt water such as the North Sea, Hudson Bay, and Chesapeake Bay occur in depressed areas of a continent.

## Tides

A large number of children experience tides during beach vacations. Children may experience both the incoming (high) tide and the outgoing (low) tide during a day at the seashore. Tides are the result of the gravitational attraction upon the earth by the moon and, to some extent, the sun.

## Waves

Waves derive their energy and motion from the wind. The top of a wave is the crest, and the bottom, or the area that separates one wave from another, is the trough. Some waves are small and rolling, whereas others are very steep and close to one another. The height, length, and distance between waves are determined by wind speed, how long the wind has blown, and the distance the wind has traveled across the body of water.

## IDEA BOX _____

Some children, particularly those who live inland or those who have never visited the beach, may have difficulty understanding the nature of currents, tides, and waves. The National Geographic Society (Educational Services, Washington, DC 20036) produces an excellent filmstrip series entitled "The Oceans: Earth's Last Frontier" (catalog no. 30145), which details tides and currents, mountains and canyons on the sea floor, creatures and plants, and ocean resources and their uses. It is well worth the effort to obtain a copy for your classroom.

Although we have so far discussed the liquid portion of the earth by addressing the actions of salt water, our existence depends almost exclusively on fresh water. We rely on fresh water to satisfy our thirst and hygienic needs, to water our plants and crops, and to meet other requirements.

## DID YOU KNOW? _____

Only about 1.6 percent of all the water on the earth is fresh water.

**Classroom Activity** Ask students to each keep a daily diary (over a period of three days) of all the water they consume or use in a 24-hour period. Be sure they include toilet water, water used for taking a shower, water needed for brushing teeth, drinking water, and cooking water. Have students add up the totals for all three days and take an average. This data can be charted on a graph in the front of the classroom. Have students calculate how much water is used each day by the entire class or by an entire grade level. Ask students to discuss conservation measures that would reduce each individual's daily consumption of fresh water. ■

# THE EARTH'S ATMOSPHERE

The earth's atmosphere is divided into several layers.

The troposphere is the lowest region of the atmosphere; it extends to a height of approximately 18 kilometers (11 miles) over the equator and 8 kilometers (5 miles) over the polar region. It is here that we live, play, and work. It is here that our weather develops. The air we breathe is primarily limited to this area, consisting of approximately 78 percent nitrogen, 21 percent oxygen, and 1 percent other gases, including carbon dioxide, helium, and hydrogen.

## TEACHER TO TEACHER

When we study weather, students learn about the water cycle. Our school district is emphasizing composition writing, so an excellent opportunity to write essays was in illustrating the water cycle. The assignment was to write about the water cycle from the point of view of the raindrop. We did this in the form of a picture story with additional illustrations. Here's an example of one of the essays:

*Autobiography of a Raindrop*
by
Katie Huddleston

I am a rain drop. I am sitting in a small puddle in the road. It is dawn. As soon as the sun comes up I will begin the water cycle. Here comes the sun. I will evaporate, or change from a liquid to a gas, soon. All the puddles around me turn into water vapor (a gas). Now I am going up into the troposphere to form a big, white, fluffy cumulus cloud. My friends turn into cirrus clouds, which are very high and made of ice crystals. Others turn into stratus clouds. They are low and look like blankets. Some others turn into cumulo-nimbus clouds. They are like cumulus clouds but make rain storms, thunder, and lightning. The wind blows the clouds all over the U.S.A. I can't wait to see where I land! Suddenly I stop. It looks as if I'm over Tennessee. I start condensing. My friends and I start to precipitate or fall from the sky. Some are snow, some are hail, and others are rain drops. I am sleet. 'Ouch!' I land on rocky ground and roll into the muddy water of the Mississippi River. I float along until I see the Gulf of Mexico, which will be my water storage. I will wait a little longer, and when the sun comes up again maybe I will land in Italy!

Obviously, this has proven to be a very popular activity for all my fifth-grade students.

Bettie L. McCord
Wimbish Elementary School
Arlington, TX

The second layer of the atmosphere extends from approximately 11 kilometers (7 miles) to 50 kilometers (31 miles) above the earth's surface. This is the region of the ozone layer. The ozone has a significant role in sustaining life on our planet, for it absorbs a consider-

able amount of the earth's ultraviolet radiation. If this radiation were not filtered, many forms of life would cease to exist or be significantly threatened.

The ionosphere is an extensive area from about 50 kilometers (31 miles) to thousands of kilometers (more than 600 miles) above the earth's surface. In this area is a large concentration of electrons and ions that are formed by the absorption of the sun's ultraviolet radiation and the collision with cosmic rays. This region is very important for radio transmission. Radio waves travel in straight lines in all directions. However, because of the earth's curvature, they would only cover a short distance on the earth's surface. The waves that are sent out into the earth's atmosphere are deflected back when they strike the electrically charged region of the ionosphere.

The exosphere extends from an average of 500 kilometers (310 miles) above the earth's surface to the outermost area of the atmosphere. Through the utilization of artificial satellites, scientists have discovered a large region of radiation around the earth. This area is referred to as the Van Allen belt.

## Air

Most of the gases that are found in the air are colorless, tasteless, and odorless. When we experience an odor, it is due to the molecules of another substance that has entered the air. Likewise, if the air appears "blue" or has a haze, this is due to molecules of smoke or water vapor.

Although air is invisible and we move in it unencumbered, it does occupy space. We observe this when we inflate a balloon, inner tube, or tire.

Air-related activities

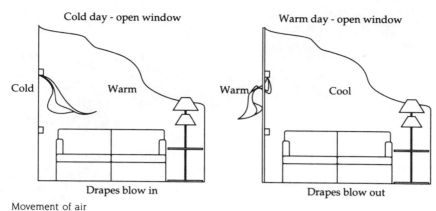

Cold day - open window

Warm day - open window

Cold      Warm

Warm      Cool

Drapes blow in

Drapes blow out

Movement of air

## Wind

Wind is air in motion. The faster the wind blows, the more pressure it exerts.

Wind is caused by the unequal heating and cooling of the earth's surface. When air is heated, it expands and becomes less dense, or lighter. This causes it to rise, and cooler, more dense air moves in to replace it. This movement of air may be a breeze or a strong wind. An excellent example of this occurs at the seashore, where one frequently experiences a sea breeze during the day and a land breeze at night. During the day the land heats much more quickly than the water. The warm air over the land rises, and the cool air over the water moves in, creating a sea breeze. At night, the land cools more quickly than the water, and the reverse occurs; the warmer air over the water rises, and the cooler air from the land area moves in to replace it. This happens all over the world as a result of the uneven heating of the earth. If the earth did not rotate on its axis, warm air would rise and move toward the poles, and the cold air from the poles would rush in to replace the less dense air. Air movement would therefore be a north–south occurrence.

**DID YOU KNOW?** _____

The strongest wind ever recorded occurred on Mt. Washington, New Hampshire, on April 12, 1934. It was measured at 231 mph.

**Classroom Activity** Put students in charge of setting up their own weather station. An inexpensive weather kit, "Weather Check," can be obtained from Nasco (901 Janesville Ave., Fort Atkinson, WI 53538, 800-558-9595). The "Daily Weather Log" is available from Edmund Scientific (101 East Gloucester Pike, Barrington, NJ 08007, 800-257-6173). Both kits allow students to record temperature, humidity, wind direction, wind speed, and rainfall. This data can be taken on a daily basis and logged throughout the school year. Have students discuss the daily, weekly, and monthly changes that take place in their local area. What kind of trends do they notice? How much variation is there from one month to another? Based on their recordings, can they predict the weather for the same time period in the following year? ∎

Boundaries between air masses are called fronts. Warm air that moves into an area previously covered by cold air is a warm front. As the air associated with the warm front reaches the colder air, it moves over it, producing clouds and frequently rain. Cold air that advances toward an area of warmer air is labeled a cold front.

## Severe Weather: Thunderstorms, Tornadoes, Hurricanes

Most children have seen the results of severe weather: trees down, homes damaged, highways eroded, and, in some occasions, lives lost. The most common type of severe weather is a thunderstorm. They are usually associated with cumulonimbus clouds. Most of these storms occur for a brief period of time and do not cover a large area. Severe storms are accompanied by heavy rain, lightning and thunder, high winds, and occasionally hail.

**DID YOU KNOW?** _____

At any given moment there are about 1,800 thunderstorms taking place around the world.

**Classroom Activity** Students will enjoy reading about the nature of thunderstorms. Two books to get them started are *Flash, Crash, Rumble and Roll* by Franklyn Branley (New York: Crowell, 1985) and *Thunderstorm* by Mary Szilagyi (New York: Bradbury, 1985). You may be interested in a magazine specifically designed for amateur meteorologists, *Weatherwise* (4000 Albermarle St. NW, Washington, DC 20016). It reviews weather data, contains numerous weather experiments, and carries articles of current interest. ∎

One of the most destructive acts of nature is of short duration. Tornadoes may occur during any month of the year, with April through June the high-frequency period in the United States. They are associated with thunderstorms; however, less than 1 percent of all thunderstorms produce tornadoes.

Hurricanes have become known as the greatest storms on earth because their size, destruction, and

Cumulus clouds

Nimbus clouds

harm to people exceeds the damage associated with thunderstorms and tornadoes. These storms form in tropical waters and have various names: "hurricanes" in the Atlantic Ocean, "typhoons" in the Pacific Ocean, and "cyclones" in the Indian Ocean. A tropical storm becomes a hurricane when its winds reach 75 miles per hour and it has a rotary circulation. Hurricanes average 375 miles in diameter and often extend about 40,000 feet above the ocean. A unique area of the hurricane is the eye, a zone of calm and scattered clouds that averages 12 miles in diameter.

## Precipitation and Clouds

### Clouds

One usually associates precipitation with clouds. Clouds are an accumulation of minute droplets of water and/or small ice crystals. They are classified by their appearance and height. The three basic forms of clouds are cirrus, cumulus, and stratus. All other clouds

Cirrus clouds

are combinations or modifications of these three. The high clouds, found between 18,000 and 45,000 feet, are the cirrus, cirrostratus, and cirrocumulus. They appear wispy and feathery if they are cirrus, as a halo around the moon or sun if they are cirrostratus, and as mackerel-type clouds if they are cirrocumulus. The middle clouds are found between 6,500 and 18,000 feet. Altocumulus clouds look like puffy cotton balls or cauliflower, and altostratus clouds are characterized by a thick to thin overcast. The lower-level clouds are found from sea level to about 6,500 feet. The stratocumulus are soft, gray clouds that may be joined to produce one continuous cloud. Stratus clouds may give the appearance of fog, but high off the ground. Rain clouds are nimbostratus. They are low and dark gray and are usually associated with a period of continuous rain.

## Precipitation

One of the ingredients found in air is water vapor. It is rather constant because of the rate of evaporation and condensation that occurs as part of the hydrological cycle. Moisture in the air is lost through precipitation and replaced by evaporation from oceans, lakes, rivers, streams, and moist soil. Water vapor condenses to liquid water when the air reaches its capacity to hold the vapor. Temperature is an important factor in determining when air has reached its capacity to hold moisture. Warm air, per volume, can hold more water vapor than cold air. The temperature at which the air becomes saturated is called the dew point. At or below the dew point, water vapor condenses to liquid water. Precipitation in the form of rain, snow, hail, sleet, or drizzle occurs when a mass of air is cooled below its dew point and the form of precipitation is large enough to reach the earth without evaporating.

**TEACHER TO TEACHER** _____

Making a rain gauge as part of a study of weather is a common activity in many texts. This activity offers a practical application of Piaget's work. Some elementary students will think that the higher the level of water, the more water there is, without regard to the diameter of the container. Pouring a set quantity of water (e.g., 50 ml) into a number of jars (baby food, peanut butter, olive, pickle, mayonnaise) and asking students to say which has more is an important step prior to making a rain gauge. I have found that fourth-grade students need to watch or pour the water back and forth several times before they realize the volume doesn't change. Unlike younger students, they are ready for the change in concept and with experience will make the leap. Then a rain gauge makes sense to them.

Elaine S. Heine
Ocean Breeze Elementary School
Indian Harbour Beach, FL

**DID YOU KNOW?** _____

On an average day, 4,200 billion gallons of rain fall on the continental United States.

**Classroom Activity** Students will enjoy watching how rain is created. (*Note:* Please do this activity as a teacher demonstration.) Heat a teakettle on a stove or hotplate. Fill a pot with ice cubes and, as soon as the teakettle begins to boil, hold the pot over the rising steam. After a few moments students will notice "raindrops" appearing on the bottom of the pot. Have students describe what they are seeing and the reasons why the "rain" is forming. How is this demonstration similar to what happens in nature? What does the teakettle represent? What does the pot with ice cubes represent? How are these part of the water cycle? ∎

**TEACHER TO TEACHER** _____

At our school, the kindergarten curriculum evolves around our phonics program. Everything during the week correlates with our "Letter for the Week." During the week of "oi," I included a moisture unit. We discovered about clouds, types of moisture, and how it rains. I told my children it would rain in our classroom tomorrow. As I started our experiment, one little girl quietly got up and walked to her locker. She pulled out her umbrella and sat down holding her umbrella opened so she would not get wet.

Linda Lewis Cundiff
R. F. Bayless Elementary School
Lubbock, TX

··············· ············· ··············

# POINTS OF DISCUSSION

··············· ············· ··············

1. Check out the weather reports in several different newspapers. What information is traditionally reported? How can that data be useful to you in your classroom?
2. There is a great deal of controversy about the depletion of the earth's ozone layer. Assemble some articles and newspaper clippings on the two sides of this issue. Which side do you take? Why?
3. Work with a classmate and take a survey of the weathering and erosion taking place in a section of your local community. How can that data be useful in your future classroom? What type of demonstration or activity could you set up for students?
4. Students who live a great distance from an ocean may argue that they do not need any or lessons on the world's oceans. What argument can you offer these students on the advantages of knowing about oceans and their characteristics?
5. How much of our daily lives is influenced by the weather? Work with a classmate and list all the activities you participated in during the past 48 hours. How many of those were determined or influenced by the weather? How can this activity be part of your students' study of the weather?
6. Work with a friend to record and chart the cloud formations that occur in your area over a period of several weeks. What patterns do you note? What type of cloud seems to predominate? What does each cloud indicate?
7. What short-term or long-term activities can you develop that focus on the changes taking place in and on the earth's surface? How can those activities be made part of your classroom science program?

ACTIVITY 14.1

......................................................................................

## ...It's the Humidity.

......................................................................................

## Introduction

In many weather reports, the relative humidity is reported. Humidity is the amount of water vapor in the air. Relative humidity is reported as a percentage, as it indicates the amount of moisture in the air relative to the amount of moisture the air could hold. Warm air can hold more moisture than cold air.

## Organization and Materials

The class can work in groups of four. Each individual will have an opportunity to read the relative humidity chart, organize the sling psychrometer, and record his or her findings.

*Materials:* Sling psychrometer, two thermometers, piece of cloth, rubber band, shoestring or cord, paper, pencil, relative humidity chart

## Procedure

1. Discuss the kinds of days when we feel most uncomfortable. One major element is high humidity.

   "What is humidity?"
   "How do we know there is moisture in the air?"

2. Discuss how we can measure relative humidity. Construct the sling psychrometers and have the students use them.
   a. Tie two thermometers back to back. Place a wet cloth around the bulb of one.
   b. Gently spin the instrument for one minute.
   c. Read both thermometers.

   d. Subtract the wet-bulb reading from the dry-bulb reading.
   e. Read the scale to determine the relative humidity.

3. Have students continue this for several weeks. Keep a chart indicating the comfort level and the relative humidity.

   "What were the weather conditions when the humidity went up?"
   "Where did the weather come from? The north? Northwest? South? Southeast?"
   "What type of air mass was it?"
   "Is there any relationship between the air mass and the relative humidity?"
   (Observing, reference, predicting)

## Conclusion

Relative humidity is related to the air mass moving into an area. It can be measured, and there is a relationship between the amount of water vapor in the air and the comfort level.

## Follow-up Activities

1. On a daily basis, have students predict if humidity is high or low using their own feelings. Afterward, have them check the humidity using a sling psychrometer.

2. Have students research newspaper weather reports. Is high/low relative humidity seasonal? Can it be predicted according to the air masses moving into an area? Students may wish to construct a chart that records humidity levels over a period of several months.

ACTIVITY 14.2

......................................................................................

## Oh, Just Dry Up!

......................................................................................

## Introduction

The water cycle is maintained by three processes: evaporation, condensation, and precipitation. In the condensation process, a gas (water vapor) is changed into a liquid. In evaporation, a liquid is changed into a gas.

## Organization and Materials

Form groups of four or five students.

Per group: Ice cubes, glass container, water or other liquid (e.g., lemonade, ice tea, or soda), notebook

## Procedure

1. Give each group a glass container and five or six ice cubes. Place the ice cubes in the container and pour lemonade, water, or some other liquid over them. Observe the container for approximately five minutes.

   "What is forming on the outside of the glass?"
   "Where did the water on the outside of the glass container come from?" (Inferring)

2. Empty all glasses and thoroughly dry them. Divide the class into three groups and again distribute the ice cubes and glasses. Have group 1 do the same experiment. For group 2, have a fan running, moving the air around the container. For group 3, have a teapot of boiling water placed about a foot away. Discuss the necessity of safety. Place each glass on a paper towel. Have each group record when the paper towel initially showed an indication of water at the base of the glass.

   "What was the time differential; what was the sequence?"
   "What effect did the fan have on the water vapor condensing? Why?"

3. Have each group continue to observe the glasses until the ice cubes are melted and the water assumes room temperature.

   "What was the sequence in the water drying on the outside of the glass?"
   "What are some of the reasons why the glass with the fan blowing on it dried first?" (Observing, inferring)
   "What will happen if we wet our chalkboard and have the fan blowing on one half and not the other half of the board?" (Predicting)
   "Why is there no moisture on the outside of the glass now that the water is at room temperature (the temperature of the air in the room)?" (Inferring)

## Conclusion

Condensation occurs when there is water vapor in the air and there is a difference in temperature between an object and the air surrounding it. Moving air removes the saturated air and permits evaporation to occur at a faster rate.

## Follow-up Activities

1. Discuss the clothes dryer, an appliance many children have in their homes. Why is there a vent? Does the air come out as though it is being blown? Why? Why must the air in the dryer be removed?
2. Have students look at the windows in their homes. Is there any condensation occurring? Why?
3. Ask students why, on a cold day, we see water vapor coming out of our mouths when we breathe.

ACTIVITY 14.3

## Blow Hards

## Introduction

Wind is air in motion. Air moves from a cold area to a warm one. One can observe this at the seashore, where the air blows from the ocean toward the land during the day and from the land to the ocean during the evening.

## Organization and Materials

The entire class can observe this demonstration from their seats. There should be a substantial difference in temperature between the inside of the classroom and the outside. If possible, perform this activity on a calm day.

*Material:* A piece of paper or light cloth

## Procedure

1. Have a student stand by an outside door or window and hold a piece of cloth or paper at the end of his or her outstretched arm. Have the student do this inside, first with the door or window open and then with the door or window closed.

   "What do you notice about the cloth?"
   "Why isn't it moving?" (Observing, inferring)

2. Open the door or window and have the student stand in the same position.

   "What do you now observe about the cloth?"
   "In which direction is it blowing?"
   "Why is it blowing in this direction?"
   (Observing, inferring)

3. If there is a temperature differential between the hall and the classroom, repeat the same procedure at the classroom door.

   "What do you notice about the cloth?"
   "Why isn't the cloth being blown as much in the classroom doorway?"
   "If Beth were to stand in the hall and hold the cloth in the same area and position as she is now holding it, would the cloth be affected?"

4. Have students form groups of five and discuss what they observed. Ask them to determine and report to the class answers to the following questions:

   "Is there any relationship between temperature and the force of the wind?"
   "What is the relationship between temperature and the direction of the wind?"
   "What would happen if it were cold in the classroom and warm outside?"
   (Predicting, inferring, reporting)

## Conclusion

Air moving from a cold area to a warmer one causes wind. The greater the temperature difference, the more force there is to the wind.

## Follow-up Activity

When one opens the refrigerator, does the air from the room move into the refrigerator or does the colder air move out? How can we find out? Have the students report their findings.

ACTIVITY   **14.4**

....................................................................................................

# All Filled Up

....................................................................................................

## Introduction

People say that a room is empty when it has no objects in it. However, it does have something—air. Air occupies space just as other objects do.

## Organization and Materials

Group 5 to 10 children around a water table, sink, or demonstration table.
   *Materials:* Clear glasses, paper towels

## Procedure

1. Place an empty glass, with the open end down, into a container of water. Make certain the glass is placed into the container at a 90-degree angle.

   "What is in the glass?" (Observing, inferring)

2. Remove the glass at the same angle.

   "What did we notice?"
   "Was the water dripping from the outside or the inside of the glass?"
   (Observing)

3. Have students place the glass into the container in a random fashion.

   "What did we notice when John put the glass in at a 45-degree angle?" (Observing)
   "What effect do we notice as we insert the glass at different angles?"
   "What causes the bubbles at one angle (45 degrees) and not the other (90 degrees)?"
   "What are the bubbles?"
   (Observing, inferring)

4. Place a dry paper towel in a dry glass and insert the glass into the container at a 90-degree angle.

   "Can you see the paper in the glass? Is it getting wet? Why?" (Observing)

5. Remove the glass and examine the paper.

   "What prevented the paper from getting wet?" (Inferring, communicating)

6. "How much air is removed when we tilt the glass?" (Measuring)

## Conclusion

Air occupies space, and if it remains in a container, it will prevent other substances from getting into the container.

## Follow-up Activities

1. Have the students insert the glass at a 90-degree angle. Once it is totally immersed, have them move it to other angles to determine if the air will "spill" out.
2. Mix other ingredients with water (e.g., liquid soap, oil, soda). Do these ingredients alter the results?

ACTIVITY 14.5

# Plates and Patterns

## Introduction

One of the forces behind the ever-changing earth surface is plate tectonics. The theory is based on the concept that the surface of the earth rests on approximately 20 moving plates, not all of which move in the same direction. The San Andreas fault on the West Coast is believed to be the result of two plates, the Pacific plate and the North American plate, moving in different directions at that location.

## Organization and Materials

Gather groups of 10 students around a water table.

*Materials:* Water table, aluminum plates, two plywood tops—one with the Pacific Ocean and part of California and the Baja Peninsula on it and the other with North America (make certain the two plates fit together like a puzzle)

## Procedure

1. Have students look at the globe or a world map.

   "Do you see any similarities in the coastlines of the continents? What can you conclude from this?" (Observing, inferring)
   "What continents seem, with a little allowance, to fit together?" (Inferring)

   "What could scientists conclude from this observation of the world map or globe?"
   "How do you think the various areas of the earth drifted apart?" (Predicting)

2. Gather the students around the water table and have the Pacific plate and the North American plate joined together.

   "Suppose these two were drifting in similar directions. What would happen?" (Predicting)
   "Now suppose they were moving away from one another. What would happen?" (Observing, predicting)

## Conclusion

The surface of the earth is on a number of plates. At one time the earth contained a solid land mass surrounded by water. As time went on, the plates moved in different directions, causing continents to form as the solid mass divided.

## Follow-up Activity

Research the San Andreas fault—where it is located and what the predictions are for its movement and its effect on Los Angeles. Where will Los Angeles be located in 1,000 years?

ACTIVITY **14.6**

.............................................................................................................

## Heavy Air

.............................................................................................................

### Introduction

Air weighs 14.7 pounds per square inch at sea level. We are not aware of its weight because the pressure of the air is in all directions and the body adjusts to it. Ask the students what happens to their ears when they are in a car going up a mountain. This is an example of the body adjusting to a change in air pressure. We use the weight of air when we use a straw to draw liquid from a container. We can also demonstrate this scientific principle by filling a balloon with air and comparing it with a similar balloon without air. Several other demonstrations will support the concept.

### Organization and Materials

Arrange the entire class around the sink or a science table. Later have them work in groups of five to perform the demonstration.

*Materials*: Suction cups, six glasses, six 3 × 5 cards, 30 straws, glass beaker

### Procedure

1. Demonstrate the suction process by getting a liquid from a bowl or beaker into the straw. Hold your finger at the upper end of the straw so that the liquid will not drain out.

"Why does the water remain in the straw?"
"What is holding it there?"
"What happens if I remove my finger? Why?" (Observing, inferring)

2. Take two suction cups and bring them together, driving all of the air out. Have a child try to pull them apart.

"Why can't you pull them apart?"
"Why are they stuck without glue or paste?"
"What will happen if I let a little air in between the two cups?" (Observing, predicting, drawing conclusions, inferring)

3. Fill a glass approximately three-quarters full of water. Place a 3 × 5 card over the entire mouth of the glass. Invert the glass, making certain to hold the card firmly to the mouth of the glass; do not allow any air to seep in or water to get out. Do this over the sink. Remove your hand holding the card and ask:

"What is holding the water in the glass?"
"What is making the card adhere to the glass?"
"How can we break the seal?" (Observing, predicting, communicating, inferring)

### Conclusion

Air has weight that we do not feel because it is exerted in all directions. We sometimes refer to the weight of air as air pressure.

### Follow-up Activities

1. Have students demonstrate the weight of air by placing two balloons, blown up to different levels, on the ends of a ruler or yardstick. Balance the ruler on a beam equidistant from the two ends. Let go and ask the students to decide on the reasons one end seemed heavier than the other end.

2. Have students do research to determine if water boils at different temperatures at different altitudes. They may wish to write to friends or relatives around the country and ask them to determine the exact temperature at which water boils in their respective areas. The results can be charted.

ACTIVITY   **14.7**

..........................................................................................................

## Dirty, Dirty, Dirty

..........................................................................................................

### Introduction

As an introduction to earth science, students will be asked to take paper cups and walk around the school grounds gathering rocks and soil. When they return, they will look at the soil under a hand lens and a microscope. They will notice differences in the texture of the soil, different types of rocks, and other aspects, such as how the soil clings to the roots of plants.

### Organization and Materials

Children will be divided into groups of five and instructed to share a digging tool but to gather their soil samples individually.

*Materials:* Paper cups, one digging tool for every five students, a hand lens for each student, one microscope for every five students, one glass beaker for every five students, glass jars

### Procedure

1. Establish some guidelines for observing the soil. Students need to understand the required behavior, safety factors, and the need to share data with other students.

2. When students return to class, have them spread soil and rocks on paper towels at their seats.

   "What do you notice about the soil and rocks?" (Observing)

3. Have them use the hand lenses.

   "What do you now notice about the soil and rocks?" (Children in the early grades may indicate color, texture, dampness, specks on rocks, etc.) (Observing, reporting)

4. Ask the students if they think there is any air in the soil. Have them, in groups of five, place approx-

imately 3 inches of soil in a beaker containing 5 inches of water.

   "What are the bubbles?"
   "Where did the bubbles come from?" (Predicting, observing, drawing conclusions)

5. Pour the soil and water into a glass jar with a lid and shake it.

   "What do you think will happen?" (Predicting)
   "Why did the water get cloudy?" (Inferring)
   "What will happen if we let the jar sit on the shelf for 15 minutes?" (Predicting)
   "Why?" (Drawing conclusions)

### Conclusion

Soil has a variety of textures, colors, and densities. Rocks are not all alike: they vary in texture, color, hardness, density, crystals, and cleavage. Soil contains air. Soil will mix with water to give the water a cloudy appearance; however, the tiny particles will, when the water is kept still, fall to the bottom of the jar and not mix as a solution.

### Follow-up Activities

1. Have students collect soil at other areas around their homes or in the community and compare it with the soil at school.

2. Have students dig to different depths. Does the soil change appreciably?

3. Have students examine soil from different areas immediately after a rain. What do they notice? Are there any similarities? Any differences?

4. Have students place soil samples on a paper towel to determine which soil retains moisture best.

ACTIVITY   **14.8**

..........................................................................................................

## Clouds Above

..........................................................................................................

### Introduction

As water evaporates from streams, ponds, oceans, and soil, it rises into the upper atmosphere. Upon reaching

the cooler air currents, the water vapor gathers onto small dustlike particles, forming clouds. Each cloud is capable of releasing its moisture onto the earth again, setting the stage for the process to repeat itself.

## Organization and Materials

This activity is best suited for groups of three to four students.

*Per group:* Three large jars, two small jars, water, soil, ice, one cut plant (flower, apple, celery, etc.)

## Procedure

1. Have students fill one small jar with moist soil and the other with water.

2. Direct students to cover each small jar with a large jar and to cover the plant with a large jar.

   "What do you think will happen to the materials inside the jars or to the jars themselves?" (Predicting)

3. Have students lay several ice cubes on top of the large jars. Allow the jars to stand for several hours, and observe the results.

   "What changes have taken place inside the jars?"
   "Where did the water on the inside of the large jars come from?" (Observing, inferring, experimenting)

4. Have the students remove the ice and dry the inside of the large jars completely. Have them repeat the procedure by placing the jars on a shelf overnight (do not include ice in the procedure this time).

   "What do you think will happen to the inside of the containers this time?"
   "By not using ice, will the results be different?" (Predicting)

5. Have students examine the jars the following day, recording all similarities and differences between the trial using ice and the trial without ice.

   "How can you explain the results observed in the two trials?" (Communicating)

## Conclusion

Evaporation is the physical change that takes place as water is transformed from a liquid to a gas. This gas, upon striking the cool outer jar, condenses, reversing the process and forming a liquid. This is analogous to the process that occurs during cloud formation.

## Follow-up Activities

1. Have students construct a diagram of the water cycle using the concepts of evaporation and condensation.
2. Direct pupils to complete a research project classifying clouds according to their types and functions.

ACTIVITY   14.9

......................................................................

# Leaky Soil

......................................................................

## Introduction

Many types of materials cover the surface of the earth. Each material has characteristics and qualities that can be either advantageous or disadvantageous to the animals and plants that inhabit the surroundings. This project examines the ability of water to pass through various types of soil—an important consideration for farmers and home gardeners.

## Organization and Materials

This project is best suited for groups of two or three students.

*Per group:* One-half metric cup each of various soil samples to be studied (peat moss, potting soil, sand, pebbles, clay soil, etc.), paper cups, plastic cups, pencils, two popsicle sticks per cup, one paper towel, water, a clock or watch with a second hand

## Procedure

1. Have students examine each sample and list its characteristics. (Observing, communicating)
2. Direct pupils to use a pencil to poke 10 or 12 holes in the bottom of each paper cup.
3. Have students place a piece of paper towel in the bottom of each paper cup to prevent the granules of each sample from falling out.
4. Ask students to fill each of the paper cups exactly half full with the various samples and label each container with the name of its contents.

5. Instruct students to place two popsicle sticks across the tops of the plastic cups to form a bridge and to set the paper cups on top of the sticks (this allows water to flow into the plastic cups).
6. Tell students to fill each paper cup (one by one) with water and time how long it takes before water begins to seep through into the plastic cups. Have them record the results. (Measuring, communicating)
7. Discuss the findings.

   "Which sample permitted water to seep through first?"
   "Which sample was the slowest in allowing water to seep through?"
   "Did each sample allow the same amount of water to seep through? Can you explain why?"
   "Where is the remainder of the water?" (Communicating, classifying, measuring, inferring)
   "What advantages or disadvantages would each of the samples have if it covered the earth in a particular area?"

   "How would the plants and animals have to adapt to each area?" (Inferring, communicating)

## Conclusion

Results will depend on the samples used. Some samples, such peat moss and potting soil, allow water to pass through very quickly compared with others, such as sand. However, those samples retain more water than sand does.

## Follow-up Activities

1. Have students measure the amount of water retained by each sample (amount poured in minus the amount collected in the plastic cup).
2. Ask students to predict which samples would be most conducive to the growth of various kinds of plant life (e.g., sand for cactus, peat moss for ferns). Provide opportunities for pupils to grow various varieties of plants in different soil samples and record their results.

ACTIVITY 14.10

## Dirt Cheap

## Introduction

Depending on the geographical location, the surrounding environment, climatic conditions, and other factors, soil can be composed of many different materials. Soil composition in turn affects the plant life—and consequently the animal life—that inhibits the particular area.

## Organization and Materials

Individuals or pairs of students can complete this activity.

*Per group:* Newspaper to cover desk, a plastic bag of soil, a piece of white construction paper (12 × 17 inches), one large toothpick, magnifying glass, sheet of paper to record data

*Note:* Prior to beginning this activity, direct students to cover their desks with newspaper. Upon completion of the activity, have students work in pairs to carefully fold the white paper and funnel the soil back into the bags.

## Procedure

1. Begin the activity with a brief discussion of what covers the earth.

   "What is the composition of the Earth?" (Rock, soil, sand, water, etc.)
   "What covers the earth?" (Soil, plants, etc.)
   (Communicating, observing)

2. "Today we are going to look at one of the materials that covers the earth—soil. Does anyone know what soil is?" (Accept answers that students can support with evidence.) (Communicating, inferring)
3. Distribute the soil samples, white construction paper, toothpicks, and magnifying glasses.
4. Instruct the students to empty the bag of soil onto the white paper. Students should be encouraged to keep the soil on the white paper throughout the activity. After the bags have been emptied, have the students observe their samples by separating into groups the various kinds of substances they find (using the toothpick) and making a list of various substances discovered. (Observing, classifying, communicating)

**5.** After 5 to 10 minutes, discuss the findings with the class.

> "What types of substances did you find in the soil?" (Roots, leaves, small stones, possibly dead insects, etc.)
> "Where do we usually find these kinds of substances?" (Growing or living near or in the soil.)
> "How do you think these substances got into the soil?"
> "What did you find the most?"
> "Describe (or list) the characteristics of each substance."
> "Where does soil originate?"
> (Observing, classifying, communicating, inferring, predicting)

## Conclusion

Soil is composed of bits of wood, leaves, roots, insects, plants, and small stones. As the organic substances die and decay, they turn into soil.

## Follow-up Activities

**1.** Ask students whether there is anything in the soil that they were unable to see with their eyes or the magnifying glass. If students say "water" or "air," ask them how they can prove this. (To check for water, soil can be heated to detect steam. To check for air, water can be added to a small soil sample and observed for the appearance of bubbles.)
**2.** Have students collect and examine soil from various outdoor areas (woods, stream bank, open field) and discuss and chart their findings.

ACTIVITY   **14.11**

## Soil Shake

## Introduction

As we dig in our gardens or yards we may notice that the composition of the soil changes as we dig deeper. The many different materials that make up soil form layers, depending on their composition or relative weight. In this project various soil samples are mixed with water to demonstrate how sediment layers are formed.

## Organization and Materials

Divide the class into groups of three or four.
*Per group:* Soil samples (approximately one-half metric cup each of humus, garden soil, peat moss, clay, etc.), a jar and lid for each sample, water, magnifying glass

## Procedure

**1.** Have the students place approximately 6 centimeters of each soil sample in a clean jar and label the jar. (Communicating)
**2.** Instruct the students to examine the soil sample in jar 1 and list its characteristics. (Observing, communicating)
**3.** Have students fill the rest of the jar with water and put the lid on.
**4.** Instruct students to shake the jar for 30 seconds and observe and describe the results.

> "Has the water changed?"
> "How would you describe the soil at the bottom?" (Bigger particles.)
> (Observing, communicating)

**5.** Have the students observe the soil and water in the jar for one or two minutes and list their observations. (Observing, communicating)
**6.** Have students repeat steps 2 through 5 for each sample. (Observing, communicating)
**7.** Have students compare the findings for the various samples.

> "How does the water of one sample compare to that of another?"
> "Are the layers of sediment the same or different between samples?"
> "How do the layers differ between samples?"

## Conclusion

Soil is composed of numerous particles, ranging from minute sandlike pieces to larger pieces of gravel or wood. When soil is mixed with water and allowed to

higher layers containing smaller and smaller particles. The lightest particles float on the surface of the water.

(a)　　　　　　　　　(b)

Soil shake

settle, layers are formed. The bottom layer contains the largest and heaviest particles, with successively

## Follow-up Activities

1. Have students pour the samples into paper cups and place them in the sun. Allow the water to evaporate (it can be removed with an eyedropper for faster results). When the soil samples dry, have students peel off the paper cups and examine the sediments formed.
2. Have students measure and record the daily evaporation of water from each sample.

   "Does the composition of the soil affect the evaporation rate of the water?"
   "What soil characteristics lead to slower evaporation rates?"
   "Would this information be helpful to know? Why?"

ACTIVITY **14.12**

## Splish Splash

## Introduction

Erosion is responsible for the loss of a great deal of land and coastal property. Such loss can be reduced, however, by the use of careful planning and corrective measures.

## Organization and Materials

This activity is best completed in groups of six to seven students. Each group should use a different soil medium.

*Per group:* One 12" × 18" container (cake dish), soil sample, modeling clay, marble, golfball, baseball, rulers

## Procedure

1. Tell students to place soil at one end of the container, making certain that the soil is at least as high as the container's side.
2. Have pupils fill the remainder of the container with water (the water level should be no more than halfway up the medium).

3. Direct students to drop each of the following into the water several times and observe the medium's reaction to the waves as they strike it: marble, golfball, baseball.

   "What conclusion can be drawn about the larger objects dropped into the water?" (The larger the object, the larger the wave.) (Observing, inferring)

4. Have students alter the frequency of the object dropping (every four seconds, then every three seconds, etc.). Observe and record the changes that take place.

   "What happens to both the water and the medium as the frequency of dropping is increased?" (Observing)

5. "Which of the media seems to erode the quickest? The least? Why?" (Experimenting, observing, inferring)
6. Discuss with students how constant wave action affects the shoreline of an ocean or lake.

   "How would waves affect the erosion of a shoreline?" (They would increase the rate of erosion.)

"What measures should be used to retard this erosion?" (Shoreline plantings or rocks should be placed along the shore.) (Inferring, communicating)

7. Have students use rulers or clay to construct breakwaters or jetties in their containers to slow down or prevent wave damage. Pictures of harbors may be shown to illustrate this principle.

   "Why are these jetties important?" (They stop the waves and thereby reduce the amount of erosion.)
   "Should humans interfere with the natural course of nature?" (Inferring)

## Conclusion

The more compact the soil, the less likely it is to be influenced by the forces responsible for erosion. When soil is protected by other barriers, its erosion can be greatly reduced or even eliminated.

## Follow-up Activities

1. Have students repeat this activity, altering the direction and force of the waves by holding a ruler on the surface of the water.
2. Have students plant grass seed on the soil and compare the results of wave action on planted and unplanted surfaces.

## Project 14.1: All Cracked Up

### Materials
Pieces of limestone or sandstone, water, large plastic freezer bags, freezer

### Initiating Questions
In what ways can water affect the breakup of rocks?
   Is water a powerful force in breaking down rocks?
   How do big rocks become smaller rocks?
   What happens if water gets into the holes or cracks in rocks?

### Activity
Soak several large pieces of limestone or sandstone in a pan of water for several hours. Place the saturated rocks in a plastic freezer bag. Place another group of rocks (that have not been saturated) into another freezer bag. Seal both bags and leave them in a freezer overnight. Remove the bags the next day.

### Extending Questions
What happened to the saturated rocks?
   What happened to the water that was trapped inside the saturated rocks? Why did that occur?
   What happened to the rocks that were not saturated in water? Why?
   What do you think would happen to large rocks outdoors that got water into their cracks and froze?
   Is there another way we could duplicate this demonstration?

### Curricular Extensions
*Language arts:* Have students put together a small booklet or leaflet describing the various steps rocks go through as they break up from larger to smaller pieces. Illustrations for each step would be appropriate.
   *Reading:* Students may be interested in reading *I Can Be a Geologist* by Paul Sipier (Chicago: Children's Press, 1986).

## Project 14.2: Slippin' and Slidin'

### Materials
Sand and small rocks or pebbles, water, two pie tins, sandpaper (coarse and fine-grain), two boards (about 3' each), glue

### Initiating Questions:
How do glaciers affect the surface of the earth?
   What is a glacier?
   Where are glaciers found?
   What do glaciers do?

### Activity
Mix some sand and pebbles in each of the two pie tins, fill each with water, and freeze overnight. Glue coarse sandpaper along the entire length of one board and fine sandpaper along the length of the other board. Prop both boards at about a 45-degree angle over a sink or water table. Remove the "glaciers" from the pie tins and place one at the top of each board. Allow each "glacier" to move down the board over a period of several hours.

### Extending Questions
What happened to each board as a result of the "glacier" action?
   Which board showed the most wear? To what can you attribute that?
   What would happen if we changed the composition of each "glacier" (add more sand, add larger pebbles, etc.)?
   How do glaciers affect the land they move across?
   How does the angle of the earth's surface affect the action of glaciers?

### Curricular Extensions
*Social studies:* Have students investigate some of the glacial areas of the United States, for example, the Great Lakes region of the Midwest or the Finger Lakes region of New York. Small groups of students can pre-

pare reports on the land use (agriculture, industry, settlements) in those areas.

*Math:* Students may wish to make a comparative chart on the world's five largest glaciers (in terms of relative size) or the average speed of a glacier—how far does a typical glacier travel in one month, one year, or one decade?

## Project 14.3: Float Away

### Materials

Several new pencils, water, table salt, graduates or tall olive jars

### Initiating Questions

Why do objects float in water?

Do objects float better in salt water or in fresh water?

Does the amount of salt in the water affect the ability of things to float?

Will a ship of a given weight float higher in the Great Salt Lake, the Atlantic Ocean, or Lake Michigan?

### Activity

Take several graduates or tall olive jars. In one pour a quantity of fresh water. In another pour an equal quantity of water that has been mixed with 3 tablespoons of salt. In another vessel pour an equal quantity of water that has been mixed with 6 tablespoons of salt. In a fourth graduate pour an equal quantity of water that has been mixed with the largest concentration of salt possible (to the point at which the salt no longer dissolves). In each container place a pencil. Ask students to observe how much of the pencil is above the level of the water in its respective vessel.

### Extending Questions

How do you account for the differences in the floating pencils?

Which pencil floats the highest? Why?

Which pencil floats lowest? Why?

How do you think the salinity of the water affects the ability of objects to float?

If you had to float in water for a very long time, what kind of water would you rather be in?

Why do some bodies of water have more salt in them than others?

### Curricular Extensions

*Language arts/science:* Ask students to write letters to several salt companies around the country and ask for information on extracting salt from salt water. What processes are used? How does the salt compare with salt extracted from underground?

*Science:* An excellent filmstrip entitled "Life in the Sea" (catalog no. 03988) is available from the National Geographic Society (Washington, DC).

## Project 14.4: Pressure Points

### Materials

Widemouthed bottle, long-necked bottle, wax pencil, water, wire coat hanger, food coloring

### Initiating Questions

What is meant by air pressure?

What do we mean when we talk about high air pressure or low air pressure?

What is meant when a TV weatherperson says the air pressure is falling? What is meant when he or she says the air pressure is rising?

How is air pressure measured?

### Activity

Fill the widemouthed jar about halfway with water. Put several drops of food coloring in the jar for effect. Invert the long-necked bottle into the jar and, using the wax pencil, mark a graduated scale up the neck of the bottle (the marks should be in equal increments—¼", for example). Create a holding apparatus from the wire coat hanger so that the long-necked bottle can be held upside down in the jar. Place the bottle in the apparatus and in the jar, and have students record the level (as indicated on the graduated scale) of the water at various intervals throughout the day over a period of one or two weeks. Students may wish to compare their high and low air pressure readings with those recorded in the daily newspaper.

### Extending Questions

Why was the water level higher in the bottle on clear, sunny days than on cloudy rainy days?

What can we infer from the level of the water and the weather outside?

How would an instrument like this be useful to meteorologists (weather scientists)?

### Curricular Extensions

*Reading:* Two weather-related books your students will want to read are are *What Does a Meteorologist Do?* by Grant Compton (New York: Dodd, Mead, 1981) and *Nature's Weather Forecasters* by Helen Sattler (New York: Lodestar, 1978).

*Language arts/science:* Have students write letters to a local TV weatherperson inviting him or her to visit the class and explain the tools used in the forecasting of daily weather.

## Project 14.5: Wash 'n Wear

### Materials

Sand, white glue, spoons, small containers with lids (e.g., yogurt containers), small pebbles, water

### Initiating Questions

How can water wear away solid objects such as rocks?

How long does it take for a rock to be worn away?

What happens when water runs over rocks for a long period of time?

Is water a major factor in erosion?

What are some examples of erosion in nature?

### Activity

Divide the class into several groups. Have each group mix about eight spoonfuls of sand with a large amount of white glue. Have the students shape the mixture into cubes and allow each cube to dry for one or two days. Put each cube in a small container with a lid, along with some small pebbles and water. Have students shake each container for about five minutes. Ask them to remove what is left of each cube and observe the changes that have taken place.

### Extending Questions

Why is the cube smaller?

How are these results similar to events in nature?

What was the overall effect of the water and pebbles on the cubes?

How might these actions be similar to those that take place in a river or stream?

How could this type of erosion be prevented or reduced?

What are the long-term effects of this type of erosion (after several years, decades, or centuries)?

Do you know of any examples in nature that illustrate this process?

### Curricular Extensions

*Art:* Have students put together a scrapbook of illustrations that depict eroded areas of the United States (e.g., Grand Canyon, Snake River). Ask them to add to the scrapbook photos of sites in their local area that depict various forms of erosion.

*Science:* Produced by the National Geographic Society (Washington, DC), "The Earth Beneath Your Feet" (catalog no. 30352) is a fascinating filmstrip that looks at weathering, erosion, and other natural changes in the earth's surface.

## Project 14.6: Warm Me Up!

### Materials

Paper cups, soil, water, thermometers

### Initiating Questions

How can we measure the temperature of the soil? Of the water?

Which do you think absorbs heat faster, soil or water?

Which do you think will hold heat longer, soil or water?

### Activity

Have students fill several paper cups halfway with soil. Have them fill another set of paper cups halfway with water. Insert a thermometer in each of the cups and place them all on a shelf in the sunlight. After a few minutes have students record the temperature in each cup. After half an hour, compare the results. After an hour, again compare the results. Remove all cups from the sunlight and place them in a cool place in the classroom. Have students record the temperatures after half an hour and after one hour.

### Extending Questions

After half an hour, was the temperature in each cup the same? Why?

After one hour, was the temperature in each cup the same? Why?

When we took the cups out of the sunlight and put them in a cool spot, was the temperature in each cup the same after half an hour? Was it the same after an hour?

Do you think soil absorbs heat faster than water? Why?

Do you think soil holds heat longer than water? Why?

Why would this information be important to people who live along the seashore?

### Curricular Extensions

*Math:* In many areas near the coast TV stations will report the ocean temperatures (this data is also carried in the weather section of many newspapers). Ask students to graph the water temperature of a selected seaside area over a long period of time (two to four months). What fluctuations do they note in the temperature?

*Science:* Have students replicate this activity with different types of soil (soil with high clay content, sandy soil, soil with lots of organic matter). What differences do they note?

## RECOMMENDED CHILDREN'S LITERATURE

### Earth Science

Children are fascinated to discover the things that are going on beneath their feet. The earth is in a constant state of flux—changing and shifting, wearing down and building up, shaking and erupting. The tremendous forces that alter the face of the earth have always intrigued youngsters. Volcanoes, earthquakes, and other natural happenings demonstrate the powers of nature and offer an area ripe for exploration. The following books will help students appreciate the planet they live on and the forces that influence it.

Arnold, Caroline. (1988). *A walk on the Great Barrier Reef.* Minneapolis: Carolrhoda. An examination of a coral reef at low tide, this book is highlighted with wonderful photographs.

Aylesworth, Thomas, & Aylesworth, Virginia. (1983). *The Mount St. Helens disaster: What we've learned.* New York: Watts. This book describes the effects of a violent volcanic eruption on the surrounding area. Also included is information on how eruptions may be predicted in the future.

Bain, Iain. (1984). *Mountains and earth movements.* New York: Watts. What are the effects of erosion, weathering, faulting, folding, and continental drift on the creation of mountains? This book describes all of them in detail and includes colorful photographs.

Bannan, Jan G. (1989). *Sand dunes.* Minneapolis: Carolrhoda. A wonderfully detailed examination of the creation and movement of sand dunes along the Oregon coastline.

Bramwell, Martyn. (1983). *Understanding and collecting rocks and fossils.* London: Usborne. Everything the young rock hound needs to identify, sort, and collect some of the more common rocks, fossils, and minerals.

Brownstone, David M., & Franck, Irene M. (1989). *Natural wonders of America.* New York: Atheneum. Photographs and descriptions of 42 wonders of nature from throughout the United States.

Cowing, Sheila. (1980). *Our wild wetlands.* New York: Messner. This book illustrates some of the dangers facing this country's wetlands and why wetlands are worth preserving.

De Paola, Tomie. (1977.) *The quicksand book.* New York: Holiday. Children are fascinated by quicksand and how it's formed. Not only will they learn some interesting information about this substance, but they'll also learn how to make their own.

Fichter, George. (1982). *Rocks and minerals.* New York: Random House. A quick and easy reference guide to more than 75 different rocks and minerals.

Fodor, R. V. (1981). *Earth afire! Volcanoes and their activity.* New York: Morrow. This engaging book goes into some detail about the birth of volcanoes, the different varieties, and how they can be helpful to humans and the earth in general.

Fodor, R. V. (1983). *Chiseling the earth: How erosion shapes the land.* Hillside, NJ: Enslow. This book addresses the effects of erosion on the earth's surface and the efforts used to curb this natural phenomenon in various areas of the United States.

Goldin, Augusta. (1981). *Geothermal energy: A hot prospect.* San Diego: Harcourt Brace. This book provides an intriguing look into an alternative energy source and how it is utilized around the world.

Hargrove, Jim, & Johnson, S. M. (1983). *Mountain climbing.* New York: Lerner. The authors detail the special training and procedures used by mountain climbers in their quest to scale lofty peaks.

Hiscock, Bruce. (1988). *The big rock.* New York: Atheneum. The story of a single rock in the Adirondack Mountains and the natural forces that created it.

Hyden, Tom, & Anderson, Tim. (1984). *Rock climbing is for me.* New York: Lerner. This book explains how one person learned to climb a 60-foot cliff, including mastery of special equipment and safety procedures.

Jacobs, Francine. (1980). *Coral.* New York: Putnam. This book provides an interesting look into the life cycle of coral and how coral reefs are formed throughout the oceans of the world.

Lauber, Patricia. (1986). *Volcano: The eruption and healing of Mount St. Helens.* New York: Bradbury. The cycle of life is beautifully told in this story of Mt. Saint Helens prior to and immediately after its violent eruption.

Malnig, Anita. (1985). *Where the waves break: Life at the edge of the sea.* Minneapolis: Carolrhoda. Vivid color photographs highlight this exploration of life along the edge of the ocean. Various creatures and their habitats are described in detail.

McFall, Christie. (1980). *Wonders of dust.* New York: Dodd. Most readers will get a new perspective on dust after reading this book. The composition of dust, its effects on the environment, and efforts to control it are all detailed.

McGovern, Tom. (1981). *Album of rocks and minerals.* Chicago: Rand. This book is a marvelous introduction to geology and how various kinds of rocks were formed.

McNulty, Faith. (1979). *How to dig a hole to the other side of the world.* New York: Harper. The title just about says it all. The book describes everything one would find if a hole were dug 4,000 miles into the center of the earth.

Navarra, John. (1980). *Earthquake!* New York: Doubleday. The author gives readers an inside look into the causes, location, and prediction possibilities of one of nature's most devastating forces.

Nixon, Hershell H., & Nixon, Joan L. (1980). *Glaciers: Nature's frozen rivers.* New York: Dodd. An inviting and perceptive look at glaciers, including how they move, where they're found, and their uses in the future.

Nixon, Hershell H., & Nixon, Joan L. (1981). *Earthquakes: Nature in motion.* New York: Dodd. This book is designed to answer all the questions students may have about earthquakes, including how they occur, where they occur, how they are measured, and the kinds of damage they do.

Peters, Lisa W. (1988). *The sun, the wind, and the rain.* New York: Holt. The author describes the geological processes that affect a mountain in Washington in comparison to one created by a young girl on a beach.

Poynter, Margaret. (1980). *Volcanoes: The fiery mountains.* New York: Messner. A tremendously interesting text that explains how volcanoes are formed, their impact on the surface of the earth, and some of the major volcanic sites in the United States.

Poynter, Margaret, & Collins, Donald. (1983). *Under the high seas: New frontiers in oceanography.* New York: Atheneum. This book goes into great detail about the science of oceanography and what scientists are learning from their studies of the world's seas.

Pringle, Lawrence. (1987). *Restoring our earth.* Hillside, NJ: Enslow. This book focuses on efforts to revitalize and restore North American land and water. It provides much food for thought for young readers.

Radin, Ruth Yaffe. (1989). *High in the mountains.* New York: Macmillan. A young child experiences the sights and sounds of mountain life. Rich illustrations highlight the text.

Rinkoff, Barbara. (1975). *Guess what rocks do.* New York: Lothrop, Lee & Shepard. Rocks are used in many different ways throughout the world. This book describes some of those ways, as well as how one can become a rock collector.

Robin, Gordon. (1984). *Glaciers and ice sheets.* San Diego: Harcourt Brace. The author describes the history, movements, patterns, and locations of glaciers and ice sheets, as well as how scientists study these enormous "ice cubes."

Ryder, Joanne. (1990). *Under your feet.* New York: Four Winds. The organisms that live underground are beautifully detailed in this story about a young boy's walk through the changing seasons.

Selsam, Millicent. (1984). *First look at rocks.* New York: Walker. For youngsters who need an easy-to-follow guide to rock collecting, this book fits the bill.

Simon, Seymour. (1977). *Beneath your feet.* New York: Walker. A perceptive and fascinating look into soil, its composition, and some experiments that can be done with it at home or in the classroom.

Simon, Seymour. (1987). *Icebergs and glaciers.* New York: Morrow. Once again, Mr. Simon takes the reader into a marvelous exploration of one of nature's great mysteries. Colorful photographs and engaging text highlight this book.

Simon, Seymour. (1988). *How to be an ocean scientist in your own home.* New York: Lippincott. This book describes 24 ocean-related experiments that any child can do at home. Included are activities with waves, brine shrimp, and seawater.

Simon, Seymour. (1988). *Volcanoes.* New York: Morrow. A wonderfully detailed and illustrated description of volcanoes and their effects around the world.

Smith, Henry. (1983). *Amazing air.* New York: Lothrop. The author provides a wide variety of experiments to help students learn about oxygen, carbon dioxide, relative humidity, water vapor, air pressure, and wind.

Srogi, LeeAnn. (1989). *Start collecting rocks and minerals.* Philadelphia: Running Press. This book describes the collection, identification, qualities, and location of rocks, minerals, and crystals.

Taylor, G. Jeffrey. (1983). *Volcanoes in our solar system.* New York: Dodd. This book goes into great detail about the causes and effects of volcanoes on the planet Earth as well as on other celestial bodies.

## Weather

Mark Twain said, "Everybody talks about the weather, but nobody does anything about it." Children, too, are fascinated by the weather and its forces. The power of weather in the form of hurricanes, tornadoes, and thunderstorms; and the common patterns of weather, such as rain, snow, and fog are exciting areas for discovery and investigation. The following books provide opportunities for youngsters to comprehend weather by reading about it and experimenting with it.

Alth, Max, & Alth, Charlotte. (1981). *Disastrous hurricanes and tornadoes.* New York: Watts. This book describes various kinds of devastating weather patterns, including how they develop and are forecast. Information on safety procedures is also provided.

Branley, Franklyn. (1983). *Rain and hail.* New York: Crowell. In an easy-to-read text the author explains how precipitation forms and falls to the earth as rain or hail.

Branley, Franklyn. (1983). *Shivers and goose bumps: How we keep warm.* New York: Crowell. This book describes the protective covering animals use to keep warm in winter.

Branley, Franklyn. (1985). *Flash, crash, rumble and roll.* New York: Crowell. A wonderful and inviting description of thunderstorms provides answers to many of the questions children have.

Briggs, Carole. (1987). *Research balloons: Exploring hidden worlds.* New York: Lerner. The author traces the history of research balloons and how they have added to our understanding of the atmosphere.

Compton, Grant. (1981). *What does a meteorologist do?* New York: Dodd, Mead. This book describes the various jobs of a meteorologist and the instruments used.

De Paola, Tomie. (1975). *The cloud book.* New York: Holiday House. The author describes 10 different cloud patterns and how they are used to forecast weather.

Dorros, Arthur. (1988). *Feel the wind.* New York: Crowell. This book describes how wind is created as well as its power, its effects, and its influence on our everyday lives.

Ford, Adam. (1982). *Weather watch.* New York: Lothrop, Lee & Shepard. The author discusses the atmosphere, moving air, and temperature, along with forecasting, pollution, and possible future weather conditions.

Gay, Kathlyn. (1983). *Acid rain.* New York: Watts. A discussion of the causes and effects of acid rain as well as what can be done to reduce or eliminate this problem.

Gibbons, Gail. (1986). *Weather forecasting.* New York: Four Winds. The author describes the changes that occur regularly in the weather and the instruments used to measure the weather.

Ludlum, David. (1984). *The weather factor.* Boston: Houghton Mifflin. A fascinating description of how weather has influenced some of the events in this country's history.

Markle, Sandra. (1983). *Exploring winter.* New York: Atheneum. This book is a potpourri of information on the creation of weather instruments, how animals survive winter, and winter home gardening.

McNulty, Faith. (1983). *Hurricane.* New York: Harper. Told from the perspective of a child, this book describes the coming of a hurricane and its devastating effects.

Pringle, Lawrence. (1989). *Global warming.* New York: Arcade. The nature and causes of the greenhouse effect and its impact on humans around the world are presented.

Rahn, Joan Elma. (1983). *Keeping warm, keeping cool.* New York: Atheneum. This book tells how animals stay cool in the summer and warm in the winter. The focus is on environmental adaptations.

Sattler, Helen R. (1978). *Nature's weather forecasters.* New York: Lodestar. Nature has some marvelous ways of indicating changes in the weather. This book describes many of them.

Simon, Seymour. (1989). *Storms.* New York: Morrow. An exciting look into tornadoes, storm clouds, and lightning—how they're created and what they do.

Webster, Vera. (1982). *Weather experiments.* Chicago: Children's Press. A collection of easy-to-do weather experiments for both home and school.

# 15

# SPACE SCIENCE

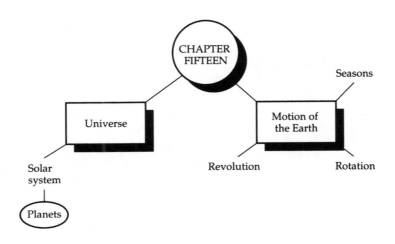

## Chapter Objectives

After reading this chapter you should be able to:

1. Identify one theory about the origin of the universe.

2. Locate and identify the nine planets of our solar system.

3. Provide an explanation on why day and night occur.

4. Demonstrate the different phases of the moon and why they occur.

5. Describe the four seasons and the reason for their occurrence.

6. State the differences between comets, meteorites, and planets.

7. Provide students with a variety of process and discovery activities in space science.

Billions and billions of stars. Billions and billions of miles. The objects in our universe and the distances between them are almost beyond our comprehension.

Although we know a great deal about the planet we live on, much of what lies beyond our planet remains unknown. How the planets were created, their composition, and the nature of the other celestial bodies that appear as distant glimmers on earthbound telescopes are a continuing source of intrigue and mystery. Although we are learning more and more about the universe we inhabit, there is still much more to discover; much more to investigate.

# THE UNIVERSE

How did it all begin? There are a number of theories, some scientific and others religious, each with its dedicated supporters. The most widely accepted scientific theory is that the universe began billions of years ago with an explosion of gigantic proportions. This "big bang" released energy and matter that is still in motion and constantly expanding.

Our view of the universe has been greatly enhanced by new scientific discoveries made with the aid of telescopes in space, greater capabilities for evaluating data through computers, and through data collected on spacecrafts such as Voyager and Mariner.

### DID YOU KNOW?

All things considered, 99 percent of the entire universe is actually *nothing*.

**Classroom Activity**  An excellent magazine on outer space and astronomy for elementary students is *Odyssey* (AstroMedia Corporation, 625 E. St. Paul Ave., P.O. Box 92788, Milwaukee, WI 53202). For older students and adults just beginning to explore the heavens, there's *Astronomy* (also available from AstroMedia Corporation). The premier magazine for amateur astronomers is *Sky & Telescope* (Sky Publishing Corp., 49 Bay State Road, Cambridge, MA 02238). You should consider obtaining back issues (or your own subscription) of one or more of these magazines to share with your students on a regular basis. ∎

## Galaxies

The number of galaxies in the universe is estimated to be in the billions. Like stars, galaxies are not evenly spaced in the universe; rather, they are grouped in clusters spread randomly throughout the universe. Galaxies were probably formed from a huge hydrogen cloud released during the big bang. As the cloud began to condense about 10 billion years ago, its density increased and stars formed. Our sun is but one of at least 200 million stars in our galaxy, the Milky Way. All of the materials in a galaxy are bound together by gravitational force and rotate around the nucleus of the galaxy. Our sun is about two-thirds of the way out from the galaxy's center, and its orbit in the galaxy

takes 200 million years. The distance across our galaxy is immense—about 100,000 light-years.[1]

### IDEA BOX

A most interesting sky map known as the "Sky Challenger" can be obtained from Discovery Center (Lawrence Hall of Science, University of California, Berkeley, CA 94720 [write for a catalog]). This instrument, with several interchangeable wheels, provides many different views of the night sky. After students have had an opportunity to use this instrument or a similar one, they may want to create their own star map. Provide students with black construction paper and ask each one to copy the location of a cluster of stars or a constellation onto the paper (locations can be marked with white chalk). Prick the paper at each "star" with a needle (enough to let light through). Cut out the end of a shoe box and cover the end of the box with the construction paper (each piece can be temporarily held on with masking tape). Cut a small hole in the opposite end of the box and ask each student to stand in front of a light source and look through the hole. Each of the constellations can then be placed at the end of the box for student viewing. Have students compare what they see in their "star box" with the actual constellations in the night sky.

## The Solar System

The solar system, located in the Milky Way galaxy, is believed to have originated approximately 5 billion

---

[1] A light-year is the distance light travels in one year:

| 186,000 | miles/second |
|---|---|
| x 60 | |
| 11,160,000 | miles/minute |
| x 60 | |
| 669,600,000 | miles/hour |
| x 24 | |
| 16,070,400,000 | miles/day |
| x 365 1/4 | |
| 5,869,713,600,000 | miles/year |

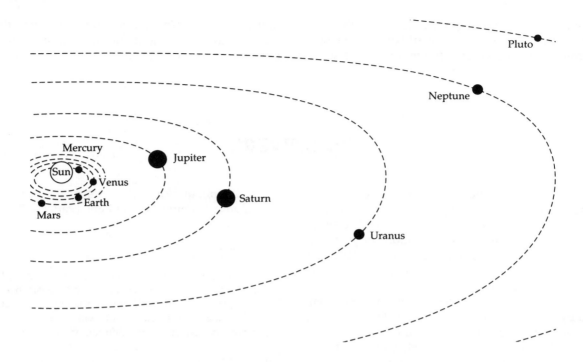

years ago as a large, nebulous cloud, part of the matter and energy expended in the original explosion. The particles of the clouds were drawn to one another because of gravity; as a result, the cloud began to contract toward its center. During this process the entire cloud rotated in a whirlpool manner, drawing material toward the center and building up small concentrations at various distances from the center. These smaller collections of matter eventually became the planets and their moons.

The earth's nearest neighbors in the universe are the sun, the nine known planets and their satellites, and a large number of asteroids, meteoroids, and comets. Let's take a brief look at some of our neighbors in space.

## The Sun

The sun is the dominant feature of the solar system, not only because all other bodies of the system revolve around it, but also because of its brilliant light, energy, and tremendous size. It possesses over 99 percent of the entire mass of the solar system. Its diameter of 861,800 miles is considered huge by earth standards; however, it is a dwarf compared with other stars. The sun is extremely hot, with an interior temperature thought to be between 15 million and 20 million degrees Celsius (59–68 million degrees Fahrenheit).

### DID YOU KNOW? _____

The earth receives only one-half of one-billionth of the sun's radiant energy.

**Classroom Activity** Students may enjoy creating some "sun pictures." Have each student cut shapes or letters from a piece of paper. Place one or more small pieces of tape on the back of each picture or letter and affix them to individual sheets of construction paper (large 12″ × 18″ sheets are recommended). Place each sheet outside or in a sunny window. Have students note the amount of fading that occurs over a period of several days. After one or two weeks, have the students remove the shapes or letters from the construction paper and note the contrast between the faded portion of the paper and the portion that was covered. The resulting sun pictures can be displayed in the classroom. ■

## The Planets

There are nine known planets; the four closest to the sun are called the inner planets, and those farthest away are known as the outer planets. The inner planets—Mercury, Venus, Earth, and Mars—are relatively small and dense. The order of the planets from the sun outward is: Mercury, Venus, Earth, Mars, Jupiter, Saturn, Uranus, Neptune, and Pluto.

### TO INVESTIGATE _____

Aside from volcanoes, models of the solar system are one of the most frequent entries at school science fairs. A common problem with these models is that the planets (usually constructed from styrofoam balls) are entirely out of proportion with each other in size, and the distances between planets are also misrepresented (a football field would be needed to accurately represent the distances). If you have an opportunity to visit a local school science fair, observe the number of solar system models on display. What can you infer about students' knowledge of the relative sizes of and distances between the planets? How would you correct this misrepresentation? What kind of science fair display would more accurately present the sizes of the planets and their distances from each other? Can you and your classmates construct such a model for permanent display in your college classroom? ■

## IDEA BOX

Perhaps the best and most informative set of children's books on the planets have been written by Seymour Simon. Books such as *Mars, Jupiter, Saturn, Uranus*, and *Neptune* are not only accurate and up to date, but they are also filled with mind-boggling photographs and illustrations that will simulate any reader's curiosity. All of these books are published by William Morrow & Co. (105 Madison Ave., New York, NY 10016) and should be available in any public school or community library.

**Mercury.** Mercury is closest to the sun and moves around the sun at a higher speed than the other planets. It is the second smallest planet in the solar system and is about one-third larger than the earth's moon, with a diameter of 4,878 kilometers (3,024 miles). Mercury revolves around the sun in about 88 earth days and makes one rotation on its axis every 59 days. It, like Venus, has no known moon.

**Venus.** Venus has occasionally been referred to as our sister planet. Venus is seen as a bright object in the night sky, second in brilliance to the moon. It differs from the earth in its clockwise rotation pattern, which indicates that the sun would rise in the west and set in the east on Venus.

**Mars.** Mars, like Venus, is visible to the naked eye and has probably received more attention than any other planet. The atmosphere of Mars is very thin, about 1–2 percent as dense as that of the earth, with its primary gas being carbon dioxide. It does contain a small amount of water vapor.

**Jupiter.** The largest planet in the solar system is Jupiter, with a mass about 318 times the mass of the earth. Like Venus, it glows brightly in the night sky and is brightest when it is directly opposite the sun as viewed from the earth. One of the most noticeable features on Jupiter is the great red spot, which varies in size.

## DID YOU KNOW?

Jupiter is more than 2 ½ times larger than all the other planets of our solar system *combined.*

**Classroom Activity**  To demonstrate the comparative sizes of our planet and the planet Jupiter, have a student cut out a

paper disk about 1″ in diameter (this represents the earth). Have the student cut out another paper disk 114″ in diameter (this represents Jupiter). Have the student place the "Earth" disk on the "Jupiter" disk and discuss the difference in size between the two disks. If you wish, you may want to challenge students to determine the number of "Earth" disks necessary to cover one "Jupiter" disk. ■

**Saturn.**  The rings of Saturn are very thin, perhaps no more than several miles thick, and are made up of small, ice-coated rock particles that may be left over from the formation of the planet itself.

Beyond the outermost ring Saturn has 17 known moons, the largest—Titan—being larger than Mercury. Titan is unique in that it is the only satellite in the solar system with a substantial atmosphere.

## DID YOU KNOW?

Saturn, with a density of less than half an ounce per cubic inch, would float like a bar of soap if you could find a bathtub big enough.

**Classroom Activity**  You may wish to obtain some astronomical posters and charts of the solar system and other celestial objects for your classroom. Most are inexpensive and provide wonderful views of various parts of the universe. The following companies offer posters; write to them and request catalogs:

Celestial Arts (231 Adrian Rd., Millbrae, CA 94030)
Nature Company (P.O. Box 7137, Berkeley, CA 94707)
Sky Publishing Company (49 Bay State Rd., Cambridge, MA 02238)
Edmund Scientific (101 East Gloucester Pike, Barrington, NJ 08007)
Astronomical Society of the Pacific (1290 24th Ave., San Francisco, CA 94122) ■

**Uranus.**    Perhaps the most unique feature of Uranus is its tilt. If one compares each planet to a top spinning on its axis, Mercury and Jupiter would be vertical; Venus, Earth, Mars, Neptune, and Pluto would be tilted at various angles between 23 and 29 degrees; and Uranus would be tilted at about 92 degrees. It seems to roll along rather than spin in its orbital journey. As a result of this severe tilt, one Uranian pole faces the sun, or total daylight, for one-half of its rotation, and it spends the other half in total darkness.

**Neptune.**    Neptune was discovered primarily because of the deviating behavior of Uranus from its calculated orbit. Astronomers have determined that Neptune contains a dynamic atmosphere similar to those of Jupiter and Saturn, and winds exceeding 600 mph encircle the planet. There are two moons orbiting Neptune. This planet is frequently referred to as Uranus's twin because of their similarity in size, color, and composition.

**Pluto.**    Pluto, considerably smaller than the earth's moon, and is the outermost planet of the solar system, and its orbit around the sun is the most eccentric. There is no atmosphere on Pluto because of the extreme temperature, so cold that any gas would solidify.

**IDEA BOX** _____

You can help students understand the relative distances between the planets with the following activity. Take the students to the high school football field. Have one student (the "sun") stand on the end zone line at one end of the field. Ask nine other students to take on the roles of the nine planets and to place themselves at the following distances from the "sun":

| Planet | Distance from Sun |
|--------|-------------------|
| Mercury | 2 ½ ft. |
| Venus | 4 ½ ft. |
| Earth | 6 ½ ft. |
| Mars | 10 ft. |
| Jupiter | 11 ⅓ yds. |
| Saturn | 20 ½ yds. |
| Uranus | 41 ½ yds. |
| Neptune | 65 yds. |
| Pluto | 86 yds. |

Make sure you emphasize to students that the sun is the center of our solar system. Therefore, the planets are not strung out in a straight line as in this re-creation. If the school has a very large, open field, you can set up this demonstration with the "planets" arranged in many different directions.

### Asteroids

The asteroids are sometimes referred to as the minor planets. They are found orbiting the sun between Mars and Jupiter. They are considerably smaller than the smallest planets, ranging from less than 1 mile to approximately 500 miles in diameter.

### Comets

Comets consist of frozen gases and small pieces of rocky and metallic materials. A comet is sometimes referred to as a dirty snowball. A comet moves around the sun in a huge orbit; some require hundreds of years to complete one orbit. When a comet is a great distance from the sun, it is primarily made up of frozen water, ammonia, methane, and rocklike particles. As it approaches the sun, the frozen material melts and vaporizes, and the comet may form a tail that points away from the sun. As the comet continues its orbit and moves away from the sun, it returns to its frozen state, losing much of the material that formed the tail.

### Meteoroids

Almost everyone who has observed the night sky has seen "shooting stars." They move across the sky very quickly, glowing and leaving a dim streak. This streak of light is a meteor, a solid particle that enters the earth's atmosphere and, because of friction with the particles of air, produces heat and light. These particles are from within our solar system; they are thought to be the remnants of comet tails. Most meteoroids are small and burn out in the earth's atmosphere; however, some do strike the surface of the earth. When they are found on the earth, they are called meteorites. A large crater in Arizona is the result of a meteoroid striking the planet's surface.

## MOTION OF THE EARTH

Many early astronomers believed the earth was a stationary planet, with the other bodies of the universe moving around it. As scientists continued their studies of objects in space, they realized that the earth had two movements—rotation and revolution.

### Rotation: Night and Day

**DID YOU KNOW?** _____

Due to the rotational velocity of the earth, a person standing on the equator is moving at a speed of 1,040 mph.

**Classroom Activity** Provide students with several flower pots with holes in the bottoms. Tape paper around the inside of each pot. Have students stick a pencil vertically in each flower pot hole and place each pot in a sunny location. At each hour of the day, have the students mark the location of the pencil's shadow on the inside of each pot. Point out that the markings move from one side to the other. Those markings indicate the direction of the rotation of the earth. In what direction is the earth rotating? ■

The earth rotates on its axis and revolves around the sun. It is the rotation that causes night and day to occur.

The earth's rotation is the standard on which the concept of a day (24 hours) is based. The earth is basically circular, and all circles have 360 degrees. As the earth rotates on its axis, at a particular location the sun appears at its zenith, or highest point, once every day.

Scientists have decided to call this 12:00 P.M., or noon. Of course, this is a constantly changing phenomenon because of the earth's rotation. The sun's zenith is observed at a different time every few miles toward the west. It would be impractical to have time changes every 5 or 10 miles, so it was decided to change time zones every 15 degrees of longitude. If you divide 15 degrees into 360 degrees, the number of degrees in a circle, you arrive at 24—the number of hours in a day.

## Revolution: A Year

Although we do not sense it, we are on a fast-moving spaceship. As the earth revolves around the sun, it moves at about 66,000 miles (107,000 kilometers) per hour. The revolution is elliptical; the earth is closest to the sun in January, when it is about 91 million miles away, and farthest from the sun in July, when it is approximately 94 million miles from the sun, with the average distance between the sun and the earth being 93 million miles. It requires 365¼ days for the earth to make one elliptical revolution around the sun; hence, a year is 365 days long, with every fourth year being a leap year, or a 366-day year.

## Seasons of the Year

As the earth continues its journey around the sun, we experience changes in the duration of sunlight, in temperature, and in other phenomena. These changes occur primarily because the earth is tilted 23½ degrees from a line perpendicular to the plane of its orbit. This tilt causes individuals living in the Northern Hemisphere to experience less sunlight during a certain time each year, which they experience as winter. While the Northern Hemisphere is experiencing winter, the Southern Hemisphere is having summer. This situation is reversed six months later.

Because of the earth's orbit, the sun appears at different positions in the sky at a designated time of the day. At noon, for example, the sun is much higher in the sky on June 21 in the Northern Hemisphere than it is on December 21. Thus, the rays of the sun are striking the Northern Hemisphere more directly and for a longer time on June 21 than on December 21; hence, it warms the earth more, and there are fewer hours for the earth to cool. When the sun is at its zenith over the equator, areas at equal degrees of latitude north and south of the equator are receiving the same amount of sunlight. This is the beginning of spring in one of the hemispheres and of fall in the other. The determining factor is the direction of the earth's rotation. The beginning of each season is determined not by the weather in a particular location, but according to where the sun is directly overhead at noon at a particular location on earth.

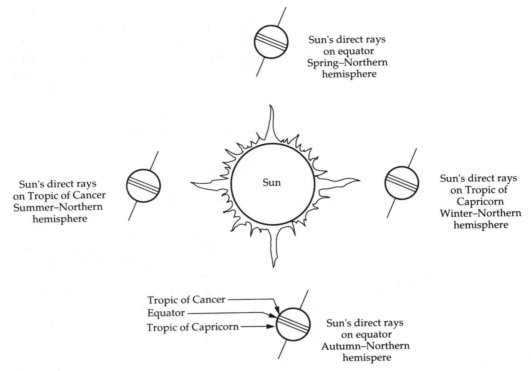

Seasons of the year

## TO INVESTIGATE ────────────────

One recent study on the level of science literacy in this country reported that less than half of all Americans know that the earth moves around the sun and that it takes a year to do so—facts established several centuries ago. You and your classmates may wish to interview several individuals in your college and local community concerning this fact. Ask a sampling of adults, a sampling of educators, and a sampling of students (in elementary school, secondary school, and college). You may wish to devise questions such as: "How long does it take for the earth to make one rotation?" "How long does it take for the earth to make one revolution?" "Around what celestial body does the earth revolve?" What are some of the implications of your findings in terms of the instructional plans for your classroom? ■

## Moon

Compared with other satellites in the solar system, the earth's moon is unusually large relative to its parent planet. The diameter of the moon is 2,150 miles, and its

density is similar to that of crushed rock on earth. The gravitational pull on the moon is one-sixth of that on earth.

## DID YOU KNOW? ────────────────

The moon is approximately 240,000 miles from the earth. However, during the primal stages of the earth, the moon was only 12,000 miles away.

**Classroom Activity**   Students will enjoy reading books about the moon. The following are possibilities for sharing with your class: *The Moon* by Seymour Simon (New York: Four Winds, 1984), *Flying to the Moon and Other Strange Places* by Michael Collins (New York: Farrar, 1976), and *First Travel Guide to the Moon: What to Pack, How to Go, and What to See When You Get There* by Rhoda Blumberg (New York: Four Winds, 1980).                                        ■

The moon rotates on its axis, but not nearly as rapidly as the earth. It makes one complete rotation at the same rate as it revolves around the earth—approximately 27⅓ days. We, on earth, therefore see

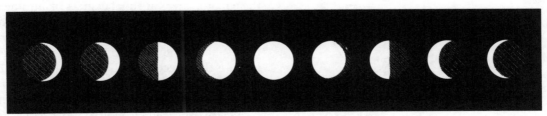

Phases of the moon

only one side of the moon. The moon appears to us in a variety of shapes during each month. On a monthly basis we note the changes that occur as the moon moves through the different phases in a systematic and predictable fashion. Since the moon emits no light of its own, we see the moon as a result of reflected light from the sun. We also see various images of the moon because of the relative positions of the moon, sun, and earth. The phases of the moon are shown in the following diagram. Notice the positions of the sun, earth, and moon as they relate to the various phases.

Although half of the moon is illuminated at all times, individuals on earth see only a percentage of the reflected area because of the location of the moon and its relative position to earth.

### Eclipses: Solar and Lunar

Periodically we observe the sun, or a portion of it, being blotted out during normal daylight hours. Similarly, we experience, on occasion, a lunar eclipse. During a lunar eclipse, the earth moves between the sun and moon and casts a shadow on the moon, preventing it from reflecting the sun's light. If the earth's orbit and the moon's orbit were the same, we could expect a lunar eclipse about every month. However, the plane of the moon's orbit is 5 degrees off from that of the earth's orbit, and we witness a lunar eclipse only when the two planes intersect and when the three heavenly bodies are in the order: sun, earth, moon. This situation occurs twice a year.

When we experience a solar eclipse, the alignment is: sun, moon, earth. During this phenomenon, the moon moves between the sun and the earth, blotting out the sun for a brief period. In a total solar eclipse, street lights go on, and many animals behave as though it were night. Not all of the areas of the earth observe a total solar eclipse, and varying amounts of light are experienced depending on the extent of the eclipse.

### TEACHER TO TEACHER

It's been five years. However, I will never forget the first time that I taught model rocketry to second-graders. I wanted to challenge my class. I told them I would put a trash can about 50 feet from the launching pad. Any group that got their rocket to land in the trash can would win the entire class an ice cream party. I personally was trying to teach the class about cooperation and about paying attention to details. Knowing about the effect of wind on model rockets was to be my surprise. Our next science unit was wind and weather. So the model rocket experiment and failure would be the perfect introduction. I had figured that there were very few who would be able to land a model rocket within a 36-inch circle.

The day of the contest brought light winds from the west. This would have them blowing right at the launching pad. I figured that the kids would feel like they could aim right at the trash can. With no accounting for drift or the aerodynamics of the rockets, I was safe. The contest began with all of the groups, except one, telling me how good their ice cream was going to taste. Each group was to get three chances to hit the mark. The class watched as group after group tried and failed. All but the quiet group had gone. They stepped up to the launching pad. We counted down. Then, by a quirk of fate, the rocket blew its charge early. The engine and rocket went in different directions. Wouldn't you know it. Ninety percent of their rocket landed right in the trash can. I was out 24 ice cream sandwiches!

Scott O. Anderson
Clear Creek Elementary School
Bloomington, IN

## POINTS OF DISCUSSION

1. The terms "revolution" and "rotation" are difficult for many students to understand. What types of hands-on activities can you suggest that would help youngsters understand these concepts?
2. How much of our daily life is influenced by the rotation of the earth? How much of our daily life is influenced by the revolution of the earth? What about our month-to-month life? Our yearly life?
3. Given the opportunity, which of the planets would you find most interesting to explore? Why? What would you like to discover?
4. Which of the planets is most similar to the earth? Which planet is most dissimilar? How do you account for those similarities and differences?
5. As mentioned in the chapter, most youngsters have a distorted view of the sizes of the planets and their relative distances from each other. What other kinds of hands-on, minds-on activities can you and your classmates devise that would help students understand these concepts?
6. Do you believe we should accelerate our exploration of outer space or deemphasize space exploration? Why? Can you and your classmates set up a panel discussion to argue differing points of view?
7. Work with a group of fellow students to create a scrapbook of articles and clippings about space exploration, which could be used as a supplement to a classroom unit on space. What types of articles would be most useful? How could the scrapbook become an important feature of space exploration studies?

ACTIVITY 15.1

......................................................................

# Like a Top

......................................................................

## Introduction

How do we know the earth is spinning, and in what direction does it move? We instruct our students that the earth rotates on its axis and is moving at about 1,000 mph at the equator. Teachers need to demonstrate this concept and help students conclude that the earth does indeed spin by using their observational skills, their ability to draw inferences, and their ability to analyze information.

## Organization and Material

To help students realize that the earth moves from west to east, a globe and a model of the sun are required. Place cutout models of children at several places on the globe (e.g., Philadelphia, San Francisco, Peking, London). To further demonstrate that the earth does indeed rotate, and in a particular direction (west to east), use a pendulum suspended from the ceiling. Move the seats away from the center of the room, affix a strong string to the ceiling, and attach a weight to it so that it hangs about an inch over a table placed in the center of the room. Place small blocks of balsam wood (of the same size and shape) in a circle on a piece of posterboard on the center of the table.

## Procedure

1. Discuss cardinal directions with the students. With a compass, show them where north, south, east, and west are located. You may do this on the playground, in the classroom, or in the multipurpose room. Then move to the front of the school and do the same, but this time have the students use a compass and point to the respective directions. Ask them why it is important to know directions. (Inferring, communicating)
2. If possible, allow each child in the room to take a compass home and report the next day where the directions are in reference to his or her home. (Applying, analyzing, reporting)
3. For homework (this may require several days if it is cloudy and there is no sun) ask the students where

the sun was located when they got up. (Observation)
4. Discuss the sun rising in the east.

 "What does that mean?" (Observing, inferring)
 "Where will it set?" (Predicting, observing)

5. "Who will see the sun first—Joe in London, Mary in Philadelphia or Susan in San Francisco? Why?" (Inferring, predicting, analyzing, applying)
6. Using the pendulum, demonstrate how Foucault proved the earth is indeed spinning. After placing the blocks on the table, start the pendulum. Assign two students to verify that the pendulum is swinging in a constant plane. Explain that you will move the blocks to demonstrate the earth rotating.

 "Should the blocks be knocked down in a clockwise or counterclockwise manner?" (Counterclockwise.) "Why?" (Earth spins west to east.) (Inferring, predicting, applying, communicating)

## Conclusion

The earth rotates on its axis in a counterclockwise motion. Individuals on the East Coast of North America see the sun before those on the West Coast; likewise, the sun sets in the west, and those in the West Coast experience daylight after the East Coast is in darkness.

## Follow-up Activities

1. Ask the students to look at the Atlantic Ocean and Pacific Ocean from the shores of America. Over which ocean would one see the sun rise in the morning? Set in the evening? Why? What would happen if the earth rotated east to west?
2. If possible, take a trip to a museum or similar institution where there is a functioning model of the Foucault pendulum (e.g., the Smithsonian in Washington, DC). After viewing it, ask the students which blocks were knocked down and which remained upright. Why?

ACTIVITY 15.2

......................................................................

# Just a Matter of Time

......................................................................

## Introduction

Many individuals take aspects of our society for granted. Time is an important element in most of our

lives, and we assume people have always had a way of measuring various segments of their lives. Children need to be aware of the numerous measurements of time and how time controls many of our activities.

## Organization and Materials

Initially, the entire class should work as an group. Discuss time and the various ways we measure it: century, decade, year, month, day, hour, minute, second. Divide the class randomly into four or five groups and have them discuss the importance of time in their lives. Have calendars, clocks, time lines of historical significance, and newspapers available to stimulate thinking.

## Procedure

1. Discuss how the class will utilize time as a measuring device to divide the day and organize their lives during the next 24 hours (lunch, dismissal, class times, dental appointments, etc.).
2. Divide the class into groups and have them list the ways we use time. You may want to establish columns to help organize their ideas, for example:

**Appointments**
Dentist 2:36

**Age of Something**
Furniture 250 years old

**Something Happened**
Oct. 12, 1492

**When We Do Certain Things**
School begins 8:45

**Present**
Sunday, Oct. 1, 1992

**Classify**
Baby
Adolescent

3. After approximately 30 minutes, have each group present its list and compile them into a master list for the entire class.
4. Discuss how our lives are controlled by time. (Communicating, drawing conclusions)

   "What would it be like if we had no time reference?" (Predicting, communicating, inferring)

## Conclusion

Modern societies could not function efficiently without utilizing time. We classify many things by their age, we arrange our lives to meet time commitments, and we identify where we were, are now, and will be in the future according to our concept of time.

## Follow-up Activities

1. Take the local newspaper and divide it among the groups. Have students count or circle the references to time.
2. Discuss some uncommonly used measures of time (e.g., light-year). Why do we have to use minute measurements, such as fractions of a second, as well as extremely large units of time?

ACTIVITY **15.3**

## Day and Night, Night and Day

## Introduction

All children are aware of the changes that occur in a 24-hour period with regard to daylight and darkness. However, they may not be aware of the principle that causes this phenomenon: the rotation of the earth on its axis. As a result of this activity, students will be able to demonstrate why we experience day and night every 24 hours.

## Organization and Materials

The class should be divided into groups of three individuals. Each group should have a model of the earth, a small globe, and a flashlight.

## Procedure

1. Review the concept of the earth spinning on its axis. Place a small ball of clay with a banner in it on the area of the globe where the students live. (Observing, classifying)
2. Turn off all artificial light and draw drapes or blinds. Make the room as dark as possible within safety considerations.
3. Have one child hold the globe while the other shines the flashlight directly on it.

   "What do you see?" (Observing, communicating)

4. Have the third child draw a line with his or her finger where the globe is separated by darkness and light. (Observing) Do the others in the group agree?
5. Spin the globe—west to east—until the light is shining directly on the clay and banner.

   "What are they experiencing?" (Day.) "What time of day?" (Noon.)
   Continue spinning the globe until the clay is out of the rays of flashlight. "Now what are they experiencing?" (Night.)
   (Observing, drawing conclusions)

6. Ask how long it takes for the clay and banner to get back to the direct rays. (Inferring, observing, measuring)
7. Move the globe to different positions.

"Why does the amount of daylight and night change?" (Inferring, predicting, communicating)

## Conclusion

As a result of the earth spinning on its axis, the individuals living on this planet experience a period of daylight and a period of night every 24 hours. The length of daylight is not the same throughout the year. The amount of daylight is determined by the area of the earth that is receiving the direct rays of the sun. This varies as the earth rotates around the sun, with the Northern Hemisphere receiving the most direct rays on approximately June 21 and the least direct rays on December 21.

## Follow-up Activities

1. Have the class observe where the sun rises and sets each day. You may want to take them outside and point to where it appears in the morning and leaves in the evening. With a compass, show the direction (Northern Hemisphere, southeast and southwest).
2. Have the class record when the sun rises and sets each day for a month; this information can be acquired from the paper or television. Ask them for an explanation. This leads to the next activity, which is an explanation of the seasons.

ACTIVITY  15.4

## The Proper Season-ing

## Introduction

In a large area of the United States, individuals experience four seasons: winter, spring, summer, and fall. They experience changes in weather, temperature, and daylight hours. This is due to the earth's rotation, its tilt of 23 ½ degrees, and its revolution around the sun. In an attempt to better understand certain phenomena, human beings have created models. One model is the globe, with its 23 ½ degree tilt, equator, Tropic of Cancer, and Tropic of Capricorn. This model will be used to demonstrate the seasons of the year.

## Organization and Material

A large object is needed to represent the sun. This may be a large beach ball or a large circle cut out of construction paper or posterboard. The "sun" will be placed in the center of the room, and the individual carrying the globe will move in an elliptical fashion around the sun. As the globe is moved around the sun, the north pole should always point toward the north star. A flashlight may be inserted in the center of the sun to show where the direct rays of the sun strike the earth at various times.

The labels "winter," "spring," "summer," and "fall" should be placed in the areas of the classroom corresponding to the seasons being demonstrated.

## Procedure

1. Use a compass to orient the class to the directions. Place a star in the ceiling above the north wall. Explain that the north pole of the globe must point in the direction of the north star as it revolves around the sun.
2. Place the sun in the center of the room. Have a student hold the sun with a flashlight, if possible, in its center. Review the rotation of the earth and the concept of day and night.
3. Have a second student hold the globe. If it is not fixed with a 23 ½-degree tilt, explain the necessity of holding it at a tilt and pointed in the northerly direction.
4. Ask the student to walk the globe around the sun, making one complete revolution. Ask the students to explain what they observed. (Observing, inferring, reporting, communicating)
5. After the discussion, have students place, at the appropriate locations, the labels "winter," "spring," "summer," and "fall." Have the student make the revolution of the earth a second time, with the other students noticing where the sun shines directly. (Observing, reporting, inferring) Ask students why there are lines on the globe at the equator, Tropic of Cancer, and Tropic of Capricorn. (Inferring, concluding, reporting, communicating)

"What degrees of latitude correspond to these respective markings? Why there?" (Inferring, drawing conclusions, communicating)

## Conclusion

Many individuals living on the earth experience four different seasons every year. With the changes in seasons, there are noticeable changes in weather, duration of daylight, and other features. The reasons for these changes is because the earth is tilted 23½ degrees from perpendicular. As the earth revolves around the sun, the area of the earth where the sun shines directly overhead changes. On approximately September 21 and March 21 it is shining directly on the equator, on June 21 it is directly overhead at the Tropic of Cancer, and on December 21 it is directly overhead at the Tropic of Capricorn.

## Follow-up Activities

1. Discuss the concept of how the seasons are related to the hemisphere in which one lives. Ask the class to explain what season the people living in the southern hemisphere are moving into on December 21. (Inferring, observing, predicting)
2. Discuss what the climate of the earth would be if it were not tilted. Would the direction of the winds be affected? (Predicting, inferring)
3. Have a discussion on the equator, Tropic of Cancer, and Tropic of Capricorn. If one were at these locations on earth, would they find circles or natural markings? Why do we have them? How do they help us? (Inferring, predicting, communicating, organizing answers)

---

ACTIVITY  **15.5**

................................................................................

### 'Round and 'Round We Go

................................................................................

## Introduction

Many children at the elementary school level know that January 1 begins a new year. However, how many realize that our year is approximately 365¼ days long? How many know why we have a leap year every four years? This activity will demonstrate one method utilized to determine when the earth has completed one complete revolution around the sun.

## Organization and Material

Have the entire class sit at tables at the edge of the cafeteria. Cut out a large circle to represent the sun and place it in the center of the cafeteria. Give a globe to one student and ask the student to move around the sun in an elliptical orbit.

## Procedure

1. Ask the class what the student needs to do with the globe as it is being moved around the sun. (Rotate it.)

   "How many times will it rotate as it completes one revolution?" (Predicting, drawing conclusions)
   "How will we know when the earth has made one complete revolution around the sun?"

(Predicting, inferring, explaining, communicating)

2. Ask the students to leave their tables and randomly take up positions in the cafeteria along imaginary circles 10 feet away from the sun and 20 feet away from the sun. Tell the students they are representing the stars in the sky.

   Now have a student take the globe and find a position 5 feet away from the sun in which two students in the outer circle are lined up, or one blocks the view of the other. Mark that position with a piece of posterboard 1 foot square. Have the student move around the sun, rotating the globe and looking at the outer circles, until he or she gets back to the piece of posterboard. Ask the students how long they think it took. (Predicting, inferring)
3. Tell the students that the time it takes for the earth to return to its starting position is 365¼ days. Discuss the reasons for the leap year and why we begin our year on January 1. (Inferring, drawing conclusions, measuring)

## Conclusion

Although we tend to accept a number of ways of measuring time, there is a reason for each of the units (day, year, etc.) that we use. A year, for example, is the time it takes the earth to make one revolution around the sun. One way of measuring a year is by using stellar parallax, which this demonstration simulates.

## Follow-up Activities

1. Discuss what would happen if we did not observe leap years for 200 years.

2. Have students who show an interest in time research encyclopedias, science books, and other sources to determine if there are other ways to determine when the earth has made a complete revolution.

ACTIVITY 15.6

## Planet Probe

### Introduction

Our solar system consists of a star, planets, asteroids, and comets, with a backdrop of millions of stars and other heavenly bodies. Although we cannot step into outer space and observe the solar system in this setting, we can make a model and fix it to the ceiling of the classroom.

### Organization and Materials

Divide the class into committees representing planets (three for one group), asteroids, comets, constellations, and the sun. Have each group research their special area and, by using construction paper, pins, paints, crayons, and other materials and instruments, design their objects in space. Assign a layout committee to decide on how the solar system will be displayed.

### Procedure

1. Place the words "planets," "asteroids," "comets," "sun," and "constellations" on the board and ask each child which group he or she would like to work with.
2. After groups are assigned, direct students to resources that relate to the respective concepts or objects (books, encyclopedias, filmstrips, pictures, resource people, if any, etc.).
3. Work with the layout committee to decide how the solar system will be displayed. The committee will consult resources and then draw a "map." (Organizing, communicating)

4. As a class, place the objects on the ceiling, using pins or whatever is permissible. Utilize the utmost caution and discuss safety in placing the objects. If one cannot place pins in the ceiling, bed sheets can be fixed to the ceiling of the classroom.
5. Although an exact scale for distance and size may be impractical, an attempt should be made to demonstrate the differences in size of the various objects and their distances from one another and the sun. (Reporting, recording, communicating)

### Conclusion

The center of our solar system is the sun, and the nine planets move around it in elliptical orbits. The constellations are stars that form imaginary objects in the sky. There is an asteroid belt located between Mars and Jupiter.

### Follow-up Activities

1. Have students draw the night sky and divide it into hemispheres. Place several easily identified objects in the drawing (e.g., Big Dipper, Little Dipper, Venus, Orion, Polaris).
2. Have students observe the sky at three different times during the same night. This will work best during the winter because of the longer periods of darkness. In the drawing from the preceding activity, have the students indicate where the objects are at the various time—5 o'clock, 7 o'clock, and 9 o'clock, for example.

ACTIVITY 15.7

## Moon Watchers

### Introduction

The two bodies in the universe that are observed most by children are the sun and the moon. The sun, although it may appear in different locations of the sky and may seem larger at times, remains relatively the same in appearance; however, the moon is a changing object in the sky. If the students are not aware of the changing appearance of the moon, have them become "moon watchers" for a month or two.

## Organization and Materials

For a brief period of time each day, discuss the observations of the students. What did the moon look like? Where was it in the sky? When did they see it? As the observations are presented, place the information on a bulletin board.

## Procedure

1. It may be best to begin the project when there is a full moon. The full moon appears in the east at approximately the same time the sun is setting in the west. Have the students note when the moon appears, where it is, and how it looks. (Observing, reporting)
2. Have the students observe the moon the next night. Have them use the same procedure. (Observing, measuring, communicating)
3. The third night, have them use the same procedure, but ask them if they noticed any difference in when the moon appeared. Ask them when they expect to see the moon on the fourth night. (Observing, reporting, inferring, predicting)
4. Have students continue observing the sky for the moon—for example, they may see the first quarter during the daylight hours, as it is visible from noon until about midnight. Ask the students to express an opinion as to why it can be seen during the daytime. (Observing, predicting, inferring, reporting)
5. After the students have observed the various phases of the moon for a month, demonstrate the concept

by using a white ball, a flashlight, and a globe. Ask the students to indicate the phase they are witnessing and what phase they expect will follow. (Observing, predicting, inferring, drawing conclusions)

## Conclusion

As the moon revolves around the earth, the illuminated area of the moon changes in a systematic manner. The moon appears in predictable phases. The phases are: new moon, crescent, first quarter, gibbous, full moon, gibbous, third quarter, crescent. The children should also be shown that the moon rotates only once as it makes a revolution around the earth. Students should conclude from their study of the moon that the moon has no light energy of its own; it reflects sunlight.

## Follow-up Activities

1. The class should observe the phases of the moon for a second or third month to ascertain if their conclusions are accurate. They should record phase, time of day, and position in sky.
2. If a telescope or a set of field glasses is available, have the students observe the surface of the moon. Make drawings of the bright areas and the dark spots. A continuing study of the moon and the areas where the astronauts have explored may be appropriate for individual research for those who are interested.
3. Have the class predict the amount of time from new moon to full moon, from first quarter to third quarter, from crescent to crescent, and from gibbous to gibbous.

ACTIVITY **15.8**

........................................................................

## Lunar Learning

........................................................................

## Introduction

A lunar eclipse occurs when the moon moves into the earth's shadow. Because of the alignment of the sun, earth, and moon, one may expect a lunar eclipse to occur each month; however, an eclipse does not occur this often because the plane of the moon's orbit is inclined about 5 degrees from the plane of the earth's orbit. Since eclipses do not occur frequently, a demonstration is the most advantageous way to help students understand this phenomenon.

## Organization and Materials

Use an adequate light source (flashlight or lamp) to represent the sun, a globe to represent earth, and a smaller object (perhaps a softball) to represent the moon. Explain the concept of planes to the class and demonstrate how the earth is moving in one plane and the moon in another. Show the class how these planes may intersect without colliding. Explain that a lunar eclipse can occur only when the earth's plane and the moon's plane intersect and when the moon, earth, and sun are aligned in that order.

Moon phases

## Procedure

1. Begin with a discussion of shadows. Take the class outside if the sun is shining, or use artificial light to create shadows indoors.

    "What causes a shadow?" (Inferring, observing)

2. Discuss the intensity of shadows.

    "Where is the shadow the darkest? Least dark?" (Observing, measuring)
    "Could we avoid the shadow of a tree, book, or table and yet continue to circle the object? How?" (Move in a plane above the object.) (Inferring, predicting, observing)

3. Have one student move the globe around the light source and have another move the softball around the globe. Show how the softball can be kept away from the shadow. Then intersect the planes with the objects aligned as above.

    "What happens?"
    "Why doesn't the eclipse last all night?"
    (Inferring, observing)

4. Ask the class how often they think lunar eclipses occur and if they are more frequent or less frequent than solar eclipses? (Predicting) Refer them to science books or encyclopedias to find answers to these and other questions that may arise. (Research, predicting)

## Conclusion

A lunar eclipse occurs when the plane of the earth's orbit intersects that of the moon's orbit. This does not occur every month because the planes are 5 degrees apart. When the planes do intersect, the moon, earth, and sun must be aligned in that order. The eclipse occurs because the moon moves into the earth's shadow, and it only happens during a full moon.

## Follow-up Activity

Have students research and report on how primitive societies reacted to lunar eclipses.

ACTIVITY **15.9**

......................................................................................................

## The Prodigal Sun

......................................................................................................

## Introduction

A total solar eclipse can result in complete darkness and a sudden drop in temperature. An eclipse of the sun occurs when the plane of the moon's orbit intersects with that of the earth's orbit and the moon moves between the sun and the earth. This phenomenon occurs during a new moon, and a total eclipse will last for approximately seven minutes.

## Organization and Materials

A total eclipse is not a common occurrence, and since it could be injurious to the eyes of the individual observing it, a simulation for students at the elementary school level is the most appropriate procedure for demonstrating the phenomenon. The materials needed are a light source to represent the sun, a globe for the earth, and a softball for the moon. Point out that the models are not to scale, nor are the distances to scale.

## Procedure

1. A review of the source of light for both the earth and the moon is a good place to begin. After the review ask the students how a light source may be removed or lessened. Ask them to demonstrate their answer. (Inferring, predicting, observing)

2. Demonstrate how the moon revolves around the earth. Explain that their respective planes are separated by about 5 degrees and, therefore, the moon's shadow passes above or below the earth and the earth's shadow passes above or below the moon, except when their planes intersect at critical times—for a solar eclipse, during a new moon phase.

3. The stage is now set for a solar eclipse. The bodies are in the appropriate sequence—sun, moon, and earth—and the planes of the moon and earth intersect. Have the students notice where the moon's conical shadow (the umbra) appears on earth. Also notice where a less dark region (the penumbra) appears. Ask where they think a total eclipse is occurring. (Inferring, observing)

4. Have the students note the length of the shadow cast by the moon.

   "What would happen if the distance between the two bodies were greater?" (Observing, inferring)

5. Discuss the concept of an elliptical orbit. Both the earth's and the moon's orbits are elliptical. The moon's shadow is only 375,000 kilometers (232,500 miles) long, and the moon is beyond this distance at apogee, since the average distance between the earth and moon is approximately 239,000 miles.

"What are the three conditions that must be met for a solar eclipse to occur?" (Observing, measuring, inference)

## Conclusion

A solar eclipse occurs when the moon blocks out the light from the sun. A complete eclipse occurs in the umbra area of the shadow cast by the moon. A partial eclipse is observed in the penumbra area. There are three conditions for an eclipse to occur: (1) The moon must be close enough to the earth for the moon's shadow to reach the earth. (2) The sun, moon, and Earth must be aligned in that order. (3) The planes of the earth's and moon's orbits must intersect.

## Follow-up Activities

1. Have students make a bulletin board demonstrating the eclipse of the sun. Indicate what would happen in each case where only two of the three criteria are met.

2. An excellent filmstrip to show students is "What Makes Day, Night, and the Seasons" (catalog no. 04591) from the National Geographic Society (Washington, DC 20036). Students will learn about the changing seasons, the spinning of the earth, and its movement around the sun.

ACTIVITY **15.10**

## Sky Watch

## Introduction

The night sky offers a wide variety of interesting sights for scientific study. Stars seem to change their positions, shadows are cast upon the surface of the moon, and the earth continues to move through the heavens. These factors set the stage for the study of stars.

## Organization and Materials

This activity should be done by each student individually. Give each student thread, a metal washer, posterboard, a pencil, a marker, clear acetate, drawing paper, tape, a protractor, and scissors. (*Note:* An overhead projector will be needed for class use.)

## Procedure

1. Have students construct a "moon tracker" as follows: Draw a 6-inch circle on posterboard, cut it out, and then cut it in half. Mark the curved part in equal increments of 10, beginning at 10 and ending with 180. Tie the washer to the thread and tape the thread to the middle of the straight edge of the half-circle.

2. Tell students to use the moon tracker by positioning the straight edge between one's eye and the top of the moon and reading the number under the thread. Direct students to take readings of the moon at the same time each night (weather permitting) for one month.

"How does the position (height) of the moon change as the month progresses?" (Observing)

3. Have students draw a picture of the moon each night, noting the changes that take place as the month progresses.

"What happens to the shape of the moon as the month progresses?" (Observing)

4. Direct students to tape a piece of acetate to the inside of a house window. Have them use a marker to indicate the positions of notable groups of stars.

5. Using the overhead projector and the acetate sheets, observe the placement of the plotted stars. Have students attempt to name as many constellations as possible.

"Would these groups of stars be at the same location throughout the year? Why?" (Inferring)

## Conclusion

As the moon revolves around the earth, its shape changes according to the shadow cast on it by the earth.

Stars also change their positions relative to the earth as the earth orbits the sun.

## Follow-up Activities

1. Have students locate several constellations. Direct them to draw the primary stars associated with each constellation and sketch the objects identified with each constellation. Resource books such as *Star Guide* by Franklyn Branley (New York: Crowell, 1987) and *Night Sky* by Martyn Hamer (New York: Watts, 1983) may be consulted.

2. Have students construct a working model of a planetarium, focusing on the moon's phases and several constellations. Punch holes for the moon and stars in one end of a shoe box and make a larger peephole in the other end. Shine a flashlight at the "stars" end and look through the peephole.

---

## Project 15.1: The Shadow Knows

### Materials

Index cards, masonry nails (nails with large flat heads), clay, pencils

### Initiating Questions

What are some of the ways people use to tell time?

Why do people want to know what time it is?

What is the difference between morning, afternoon, and evening?

Is time constant; that is, is an hour always the same length?

What are some ways we use to measure time?

How would you know what time it was if you didn't have a watch?

### Activity

Provide each child with an index card, a nail, and a small bit of clay. Have each student stand the nail on their card and affix it with a small bit of clay around the head. Early one sunny morning, take the students out to an area of the school grounds and have each one place the index card on the ground. Tell them the time (it may be advisable to start at the top of the hour—9:00 A.M., for example) and ask them to make a mark on the index card indicating the shadow of the nail. Next to the mark they should record the actual time. At one-hour intervals have the students record other marks on their cards. Continue this process throughout

the day (be sure the cards are left undisturbed throughout the day).

### Extending Questions

What did you notice about the shadow markings throughout the day?

Would the markings be the same if we repeated this activity tomorrow? Would they be the same if the activity were repeated next month? How could we find out?

How accurate is the shadow clock? Are you able to predict where the next mark will be on your clock? Why do you think the lengths of the markings and the distances between them changed?

### Curricular Extensions

*Social studies:* Encourage small groups of students to assemble a scrapbook on the history of recording time. Can they find photographs of ancient time-measuring devices? How accurate were they?

*Reading:* Students will enjoy reading *Earth: Our Planet in Space* by Seymour Simon (New York: Four Winds, 1984).

## Project 15.2: Northern Exposure

### Materials

Watch (with hour and minute hands), piece of paper, sharpened pencil

## Initiating Questions

Which way is north? How can you tell?

Why might it be important to know which way is north?

How could direction finding be useful to people in the city? In the country? Deep in a forest?

Why do people use compasses?

How does a compass work?

Are there ways to locate directions without using a compass?

## Activity

Take students outside on a sunny day. Stick the pencil upright into the ground and place the piece of paper beside it. Lay the watch on the paper so that the hour hand is in the pencil's shadow (the hour hand should be pointing away from the pencil). On the paper mark the point that is exactly halfway between the hour hand and the numeral 12 on the watch. That point is north.

## Extending Questions

Why is this a good way of locating directions?

What problems might you experience with this method of direction finding?

Is there another way we could duplicate our results?

How could this technique be useful to hunters? To deep sea fishermen? To the average person?

## Curricular Extensions

*Social studies:* Using this procedure, students may be interested in drawing a compass rose on the school playground (get administrative permission first). Colored chalk can be used to divide the rose into increments of 15 degrees around its perimeter. Have students plot the direction of various landmarks in the community or county.

*Music:* Work with the school's music teacher and have the students identify and sing songs with one or more of the cardinal directions in their titles or lyrics (for example, "North to Alaska" and "South of the Border, Down Mexico Way").

## Project 15.3: Eclipse Joint

### Materials

Softball, basketball, large flashlight (or other powerful light source, e.g., overhead projector)

### Initiating Questions

Have you ever experienced a lunar or solar eclipse? What causes eclipses?

When would you expect a solar eclipse to take place?

When would you expect a lunar eclipse to take place?

Why don't eclipses take place all the time?

What principles are at work during an eclipse?

### Activity

Have one child stand in the center of the classroom holding the basketball. Have another child hold the softball near the basketball. Project the light source (the sun) onto the basketball (the earth). Have the child with the softball (the moon) move around the basketball in a circular motion (a revolution) until he or she reaches a position in which the basketball prevents any light from falling on the softball (a lunar eclipse). Have the student holding the softball continue moving in a circle around the basketball until he or she is positioned between the light source and basketball so that no light falls on a section of the basketball (solar eclipse).

### Extending Questions

What prevents us from seeing the moon during a lunar eclipse?

What prevents the sun's rays from striking a portion of the earth during a solar eclipse?

Why are only some regions of the earth affected during a lunar or solar eclipse?

How would the sun appear to someone standing on the moon during a lunar eclipse?

### Curricular Extensions

*Reading:* Students may enjoy reading some poetry about the moon. Some well-known poems are "Winter Moon" by Langston Hughes and "The Moon's the North Wind's Cooky" by Vachel Lindsay.

*Social studies:* Many primitive people (as well as some civilized ones) had superstitions about lunar and solar eclipses. Small groups of students may wish to conduct library research to gather data on these various beliefs and present their findings to the class.

## Project 15.4: Flipping Through the Moon

### Materials

16 index cards, stapler, magic marker

### Initiating Questions

Why does the moon seem to change its shape during the course of a month?

How many different shapes (phases) does the moon have in a month?

Why does it take the moon one month to go through all those shapes (phases) and then back again to the first shape?

Does the moon always change its shape (phases)?

### Activity

On one end of each of 16 different index cards draw one of the phases of the moon (from full moon through first quarter through new moon through third quarter and back to full moon). Arrange the cards in sequential order and staple them together at the ends opposite the illustrations. Have students flip through the cards to watch (in very rapid sequence) how the moon goes through its phases.

### Extending Questions

What happened to the moon as you flipped through the flip book?

How is our flip book similar to what you've observed with the moon?

Does the sequence seem realistic to you? Why?

Why does the moon appear to have more light during some phases than it does in other phases?

Is there another way we could duplicate this demonstration?

### Curricular Extensions

*Reading:* A valuable book you and your students will thoroughly enjoy is *The Moon* by Seymour Simon (New York: Four Winds, 1984).

*Math/science:* Have your students make nightly observations (weather permitting) on the phases of the moon. Ask them to record and chart the number of days between moon phases. Based on their data, ask them to make predictions on the span of time between the four major moon phases for the following month.

### Project 15.5: Now You See It, Now You Don't

### Materials

Globe, flashlight or other light source, tennis ball, strong thread or string, knife or hole starter, low table.

### Initiating Questions

What are some of the things we notice about the moon?

Why do we see the moon in different sizes or shapes?

On a clear night, do we ever see the moon with a shadow slowly appearing on it—sometimes resulting in the moon going away completely? What causes this to happen?

### Activity

Place the light source at one end of a low table—about 1 or 2 feet off the floor. Place a globe in the center of the table. Turn off all the lights and make the room as dark as possible. Take the tennis ball, punch two holes in it, and string thread through it, making a loop of approximately 2 feet. Move the ball around the globe to demonstrate the phases of the moon. After each "phase" have small groups of students make a drawing of that phase. These illustrations can be posted on a bulletin board.

### Extending Questions

What did you notice about the different positions of the moon in the sky?

Where was the sun during the moon's phases?

Was it dark or light on the earth during a particular moon phase? Why?

### Curricular Extensions

*Language arts:* Invite students to design a short skit on the phases of the moon. Each of four students can represent one of the major moon phases, and a narrator can describe what the moon does during each phase. Students may wish to videotape their production.

*Music:* Work with the school's music teacher to put together a collection of songs with the word "moon" in their titles or lyrics (for example, "Moon River" and "Fly Me to the Moon"). Obtain recordings of these songs and play them for your students.

## RECOMMENDED CHILDREN'S LITERATURE ON SPACE SCIENCE

Distant planets, space travel, and the other "occupants" of our universe have always intrigued youngsters. That natural interest can be promoted and extended when children are provided with opportunities to make their own discoveries via some of the following books. A note of caution is in order, however. Our knowledge of space is constantly changing. The books suggested here are accurate and up to date as of this writing, but they may not be so when you begin your first year of teaching. You are encouraged to share with your students current information from your daily newspaper

or a news magazine. In this way, you will ensure that youngsters receive topical and factual data. In addition, you will be able to demonstrate the constantly evolving nature of science as a process of discovery and learning.

Anderson, Norman D., & Brown, Walter R. (1981). *Halley's Comet.* New York: Dodd. How comets are discovered and tracked through the years is the focus of this book. Although the emphasis is on Halley's Comet, readers will find a great deal of data on other comets, too.

Apfel, Necia. (1988). *Nebulae: The birth and death of stars.* New York: Lothrop. How are stars born? How do they cease to exist? These questions are wonderfully explained in this intriguing text filled with colorful photographs.

Asimov, Isaac. (1983). *How did we find out about the universe?* New York: Walker. From the invention of the telescope to the "big bang" theory, the author provides a thorough look at what we know and how we found out about the universe.

Asimov, Isaac. (1990). *How did we find out about neptune?* New York: Walker. This book examines the marvelous way this planet was discovered, in addition to covering the scientist's two basic tools: observation and prediction.

Barton, Byron. (1988). *I want to be an astronaut.* New York: Crowell. Everything a young reader would want to know about becoming an astronaut as well as the usual duties of a "typical" astronaut.

Berger, Melvin. (1988). *UFO's, ET's, and visitors from space.* New York: Putnam. Is there intelligent life somewhere out in the vast reaches of space? This book explores that possibility and offers a few answers.

Branley, Franklyn. (1982). *Space colony: Frontier of the 21st century.* New York: Lodestar. What will it be like living in space? What conditions will space colonists face in the twenty-first century? This book seeks to provide answers to these and many other questions about staying alive on other planets.

Branley, Franklyn. (1983). *Saturn: The spectacular planet.* New York: Crowell. A complete description of the rings and moons of Saturn as well as of the physical characteristics of the planet itself.

Branley, Franklyn. (1984). *Comets.* New York: Crowell. The formation and behavior of comets is detailed in this book (one of several in the Let's-Read-and-Find-Out science book series.)

Branley, Franklyn. (1986). *From Sputnik to space shuttles: Into the new space age.* New York: Crowell. The history of space exploration from the 1950s to the present day (and beyond) is the subject of this book.

Branley, Franklyn. (1986). *What the moon is like.* New York: Crowell. A vivid and accurate description of the moon from the perspective of earth observers and Apollo astronauts.

Branley, Franklyn. (1987). *Star guide.* New York: Crowell. The location of common constellations throughout the seasons is the topic of this intriguing book.

Butterfield, Moira. (1985). *Satellites and space stations.* Tulsa, OK: Usborne. A delightfully illustrated description of American and Soviet space stations and science labs.

Dwiggins, Don. (1985). *Flying the space shuttles.* New York: Dodd. All the questions children have about space shuttles and what they do are answered in the pages of this book.

Dwiggins, Don. (1987). *Hello? Who's out there? The search for extraterrestrial life.* New York: Dodd. This book examines the possibility of intelligent life elsewhere in the universe and our efforts to locate it.

Fields, Alice. (1980). *The sun.* New York: Watts. This guide to the dimensions, composition, and effects of the sun is highlighted be several simple experiments.

Fields, Alice. (1981). *Satellites.* New York: Watts. A descriptive text on the functions, construction, appearance, and discoveries of human-made satellites.

Ford, Adam. (1981). *Spaceship earth.* New York: Lothrop. A thorough book that discusses meteors, planets, and asteroids as well as gravity and light.

Gallant, Roy. (1984). *101 questions and answers about the universe.* New York: Macmillan. Children are filled with questions about the universe. This book provides fascinating answers to the questions most asked by youngsters.

Gallant, Roy A. (1986). *The Macmillan book of astronomy.* New York: Macmillan. A complete guide to all the planets, stars, asteroids, comets, and meteors of our solar system, filled with many photographs and illustrations.

Harris, Alan, & Weissman, Paul. *The great voyager adventure: A guided tour through the solar system.* New York: Messner, 1990. A wonderful journey to the solar system's four largest planets—Jupiter, Saturn, Uranus, and Neptune—via *Voyager 1* and *Voyager 2.*

Hatchett, Clint. (1988). *The glow-in-the-dark night sky book.* New York: Random House. The location and description of constellations is presented in eight night sky maps that do exactly what the title says.

Kelch, Joseph. (1990). *Small worlds: Exploring the 60 moons of our solar system.* New York: Messner. An inviting look at the 60 moons spread throughout our solar system, including data on their origin, characteristics, and discovery.

Krupp, E. C. (1985). *The comet and you.* New York: Macmillan. What is a comet? What is it like? How does it travel? Using a delightful approach, the author and illustrator have created a book worthy of any child's attention.

Krupp, E. C. (1989). *The big dipper and you.* New York: Morrow. The focus is on the Big Dipper, but the author also provides detailed information on other constellations, the North Star, and distances in space.

Lampton, Christopher. (1988). *Stars and planets.* New York: Doubleday. Everything a young reader would want to know about the solar system can be found in the pages of this book, which also includes a discussion of extraterrestrial life.

Lauber, Patricia. (1987). *Journey to the planets.* New York: Crown. Filled with NASA photographs, this book offers the reader a complete journey through the planets of the solar system.

Lauber, Patricia. (1989). *Voyagers from space: Meteors and meteorites.* New York: Crowell. The formation and journey of some of the solar system's constant travelers—comets, asteroids, and meteorites—are vividly portrayed.

Maurer, Richard. (1985). *The Nova space explorer's guide: Where to go and what to see.* New York: Potter. Any youngster planning to "travel" to any place in the solar system will want this book as a "road map." Photos, diagrams, and drawings provide exciting supplements to the text.

Maurer, Richard. (1989). *Junk in space.* New York: Simon & Schuster. Tons and tons of space litter are scattered throughout the universe. How it got there, its effects, and what can be done about it are the subjects of this revealing book.

Moche, Dinah. (1982). *Astronomy today: Planets, stars, space exploration.* New York: Random House. This book offers the young reader an inviting and interesting introduction to space exploration and discovery.

Simon, Seymour. (1982). *How to be a space scientist in your own home*. New York: Lippincott. Young readers are offered a variety of experiments to measure acceleration, demonstrate gravity, and even attempt to contact other intelligent life in space.

Simon, Seymour. (1982). *The long journey from space*. New York: Crown. What are comets, meteors, and asteroids? How are they different? How are they similar? This photo essay provides answers and will stimulate discussion in any classroom.

Simon, Seymour. (1984). *The moon*. New York: Four Winds. The moon's environment, its composition, and the discoveries made on its surface by Apollo explorers are covered in this colorfully photographed book.

Simon, Seymour. (1985). *Saturn*. New York: Morrow. All the information a young scientist would want to know about the ringed planet can be found in the pages of this engrossing and delightfully photographed book.

Simon, Seymour. (1986). *Stars*. New York: Morrow. A descriptive and engaging text, bright and colorful photographs, and a journey through the galaxy highlight this distinctive view of the stars.

Simon, Seymour. (1986). *The sun*. New York: Morrow. What the sun is, the energy it produces, its unusual "habits," and its origin are all detailed in this rich and colorful exploration of our star.

Simon, Seymour. (1987). *Mars*. New York: Morrow. The "red planet" is explored in wonderful detail and colorful photographs in Mr. Simon's engaging style.

Simon, Seymour. (1988). *Galaxies*. New York: Morrow. The formation and location of galaxies is highlighted by marvelous photographs that capture the majesty of these creations.

Smith, Howard E. (1987). *Daring the unknown: A history of NASA*. San Diego: HBJ/Gulliver. This book presents a complete history of the U.S. space program from the first rockets to the space shuttle program.

Snowden, Sheila. (1983). *The young astronomer*. Tulsa, OK: Usborne. What one sees with a telescope is featured in the pages of this book, which is filled with lots of facts and tips on becoming an astronomer.

Weiss, Malcolm. (1984). *Far out factories: Manufacturing in space*. New York: Lodestar. How can we use space technology for commercial gain? This book provides some intriguing answers.

# 16

# TEACHING SPECIAL
# STUDENTS

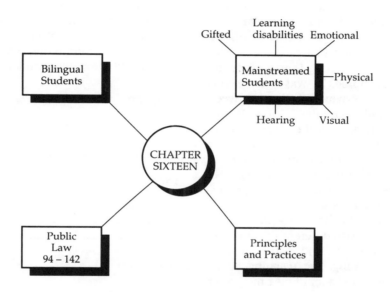

## Chapter Objectives

After reading this chapter you should be able to:

1.  Outline a philosophy of teaching "nonstandard" students.

2.  Define "mainstreaming" and its implications for the regular classroom teacher.

3.  Identify various types of handicaps that affect learning performance.

4.  Explain some strategies for teaching learning-disabled youngsters.

5.  Elaborate on the nature of and teaching strategies for gifted students.

6.  Discuss some of the principles of bilingual education.

For as long as he could remember, Marc O'Brien had wanted to be a teacher. Although nobody else in his family had ever taught, Marc had always been drawn toward education. In high school, he did some volunteer work with the local Boy's Club and a schoolwide tutoring club. In college, he was a counselor at a camp in Arizona for three summers, and he worked with a campus group that provided weekend outings and field trips for underprivileged children. Quite naturally, by his sophomore year, Marc had made the decision to become an elementary teacher.

He found his college classes exciting and stimulating, and when his student-teaching semester rolled around, he was eager to begin working in the classroom. It soon became apparent to his cooperating teacher and his college supervisor that Marc had a way with children. Students naturally gravitated toward Marc; he was a positive role model, he was enthusiastic about everything he taught, and he took time to reinforce the feelings of each child in the room. At the end of his student-teaching experience, the students put together a "surprise" going-away party for Marc, with balloons, cake, soda, and an avalanche of cards and letters ("You won't forget me, will you, Mr. O'Brien? You'll write me, won't you?").

Marc quickly got a job teaching fourth grade in a school district close to his home. He was eager, excited and, of course, just a little nervous. His first few weeks of teaching were exhilarating and demanding. He was finally able to put into practice all the ideas, theories, and strategies of his college courses. Yet he also discovered that there were aspects of teaching for which he felt underprepared. He knew these were normal feelings, yet he still wanted to provide the best possible learning environment for all his students.

Marc quickly realized that he had a diverse and eclectic group of students—with different personalities, learning styles, emotional needs, and instructional requirements. Marc was learning that teaching all the students in his room demanded a lot of his time, expertise, and commitment. It was, as his student-teaching supervisor had explained to him, a "magnificent and glorious juggling act."

In looking over his classroom, Marc recognized that four students were presenting him with his greatest challenges. How could he provide for their instructional needs without compromising the needs of other students in the room? He thought about the students for a moment:

Clayton was a small boy who had spina bifida. Confined to a wheelchair, he often found it difficult to get around the classroom. Clayton also suffered from a poor self-concept, feeling "left out" of many of the activities of the other boys and girls.

Inez was a bilingual student whose family had emigrated to the United States from Honduras two years ago. She was still learning to speak English and found it difficult to handle some of the reading assignments in the textbooks. Marc knew that Inez spoke Spanish with her family at home and used English only when she was in the classroom.

Jonathan had been diagnosed as a learning-disabled student. He had difficulty learning new ma-

terial, and Marc frequently had to explain concepts to Jonathan several times before he understood them. Jonathan always did poorly on written tests, although he could verbalize answers quite readily.

Bonnie was the top student in the class. She was gifted in every way. Often the first one to complete an assignment, she constantly asked for permission to visit the library and check out books. It wasn't uncommon for Bonnie to become bored with the classroom assignments designed for the "average" students.

Marc pondered how he could tailor a science curriculum to the needs of all his students, including Clayton, Inez, Jonathan, and Bonnie. Given what you have learned so far in this course, what would you propose as appropriate instructional strategies for each of these four youngsters? What practices would you include in your science program that would enhance the learning opportunities for these students?

## Clayton

1. _____
2. _____
3. _____

## Inez

1. _____
2. _____
3. _____

## Jonathan

1. _____
2. _____
3. _____

## Bonnie

1. _____
2. _____
3. _____

Unquestionably, your future classroom will be similar to Marc's. You will have a wide diversity of children, who will exhibit various talents, skills, emotions, physical and mental attributes, languages, and perceptions. You may feel as though you have to create 25 or 30 different curricula in five different subject areas just to begin teaching all your pupils.

Although this diversity may seem overwhelming, it needn't be. It offers some unique opportunities for every class you teach. For example, consider these principles:

1. Children will grow up and live in a pluralistic society. The attitudes and experiences they have in your

classroom and those of your colleagues will help determine their interactions with their fellow human beings.

2. All children, no matter what their physical, emotional, or educational limitations, bring unique talents to the classroom setting. A learning-disabled student can also be one who skindives for a hobby or collects butterflies. The astute teacher will take advantage of those skills and talents so that they can be appreciated by all students in the classroom.

3. It is particularly important to note that children are more alike than they are different. Although we may tend to focus on children's singular disabilities or handicaps, these youngsters watch the TV programs that other members of their peer group watch, they enjoy observing the same sporting events as their classmates, and they eat pizza, ice cream, and peanut butter sandwiches just like everyone else in the class. Indeed, one of your greatest challenges will be to see past the identified "limitations" of a particular student and focus on all the commonalities between that student and his or her classmates.

**DID YOU KNOW?** _____

Humans are capable of sneezing at a speed of approximately 200 mph.

**Classroom Activity** Children are delighted to learn all sorts of things about their bodies. Here are some trade books to help them out: *Blood and Guts: A Working Guide to Your Own Insides* by Linda Allison (Boston: Little, 1976); *Your Wonderful Body* by Donald J. Crump (Washington, DC: National Geographic Society, 1982); *The Body Victorious* by Kjell Lindqvist and Stig Nordfeldt (New York: Delacorte, 1987); *Why Does My Nose Run? And Other Questions Kids Ask About Their Bodies* by Joanne Settel and Nancy Baggett (New York: Atheneum, 1985); and *The Human Body* by Jonathan Miller (New York: Viking, 1983). ■

4. Keep in mind that you are teaching children more than you are teaching science. In other words, you need to be cognizant of every student in your classroom and how you can provide for his or her instructional needs in an encouraging and stimulating environment. Science becomes one of the tools at your disposal to help you to individualize instruction.

5 In working with special-needs students, you are not alone. There may be specialists, clinicians, and other experts in the school who are part of a "team approach" to the education of special children. Included on the team may be special education teachers, diagnosticians, parents, social workers, representatives from community agencies, administrators, and other teachers. By working in concert and shar-

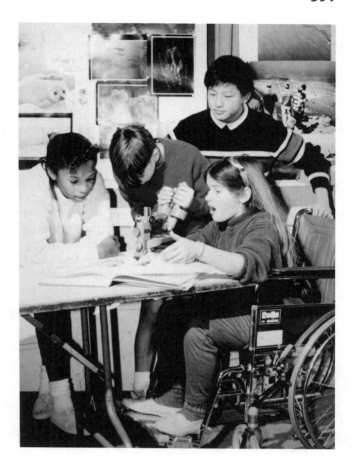

ing ideas, such a team can ensure that a purposeful and practical education plan is provided for each child.

6. Categories of learners are not independent of each other (Borich, 1988). For example, a gifted student can also be physically handicapped, a learning-disabled student can also be gifted, and a physically handicapped child can also be a non-English-speaking student. Each of us has a unique set of limitations and complementary strengths. So, too, do our students. Capitalizing on the strengths each individual student brings to your classroom is a teaching talent worth developing.

Isolating students solely because of a limitation or disability does more harm than good. Assigning a label of "learning-disabled" or "visually impaired" is sometimes necessary to structure an appropriate learning environment; but it is detrimental when it is done solely for the convenience of the educator, and it isolates the student from the mainstream of the class. Although individuals my be grouped according to one common characteristic, they will differ in many other characteristics that also affect their behavior. Sometimes the variation in behavior occurring *within* a group of learners may be greater than the variation *between* groups of learners (Borich, 1988). In other words, integrating students (and taking advantage of that combined pool of talents) is far more advantageous than isolating students.

## TEACHING MAINSTREAMED STUDENTS

For many years teachers and administrators tried to provide for special-needs children by putting them in isolated classrooms staffed by one or more specialists. Learning- and physically disabled children were grouped together and provided with instructional procedures and materials that could be completely different from those used in the regular classrooms. This "pull-out" or tutorial approach to education was deemed educationally sound because the special needs of the students could be met on an individual basis. Wang, Reynolds, and Walberg (1986, p. 26) commented on the implications of this approach:

> The widely used "pull-out" approach—removing students with special learning needs from regular classes—has been the predominant strategy for structuring programs to improve the educational attainment of students with special learning needs. Although well intentioned, the pull-out approach neglects the larger problem: regular classroom learning environments have failed to accommodate the educational needs of many students. The pull-out approach is driven by the fallacy that poor school adjustment and performance are attributable solely to characteristics of the student rather than to the quality of the learning environment.

Although pull-out programs may not be the best (and they are certainly not the only) recourse for the education of special-needs students, all children need to be involved in the science program to the fullest extent possible. To deny one child the opportunity to engage in sciencing (because of a perceived or diagnosed "limitation") is to deny that individual an opportunity to learn more about the magic and mysteries of the world.

### Public Law 94-142

One of the landmark pieces of legislation passed in recent years was Public Law 94-142, enacted in 1975 (and reauthorized in 1986 as P.L. 99-457). This legislation mandates that handicapped children be placed in "the least restrictive environment." Although it is up to each state as to how those four words are to be interpreted, they are usually taken to mean that handicapped students (those with physical, emotional, social, or learning disabilities) will be educated in the same classrooms and with the same curriculum as their nonhandicapped peers, except when special aids, devices, or services are required that are not available in the regular classroom.

Another provision of P.L. 94-142 is that an individualized education plan (often referred to as an IEP) be developed for every handicapped youngster. This plan is written in consultation with the necessary administrators, teachers, special education specialists, school counselors, and parents. It outlines the specific learning objectives for a child and how they will be carried out over the course of the school year. IEPs are reviewed and updated (as needed) on an annual basis.

An IEP must have the following features:

> (A) a statement of the present levels of educational performance of such child, (B) a statement of annual goals, including short-term instructional objectives, (C) a statement of the specific educational services to be provided to each child, and the extent to which such child will be able to participate in regular educational programs, (D) the projected date for initiation and anticipated duration of such services, and appropriate objective criteria and evaluation procedures and schedules for determining, on at least an annual basis, whether instructional objectives are being met. (Public Law 94-142, 1975, Sec. 4.a.19)

It is quite common, therefore, to find classrooms with children of all ability levels working and learning together. To assist classroom teachers in providing the best possible environment for all students, consultants or special education specialists frequently work with teachers in providing materials, ideas, and techniques useful in teaching special-needs students. Some schools have special education rooms in which handicapped students can receive individual learning programs tailored to their particular disabilities for part of the day, with the rest of the day spent in the regular classroom. Children who exhibit severe handicaps that preclude their performance in a normal classroom environment may be placed in resource rooms on a full-time basis—although this is the exception.

Special-needs children, whenever and wherever possible, should be included in all activities and functions of the regular classroom. To do so is to offer students of all abilities, talents, and skills learning opportunities that can accrue only among diverse individuals and that would not be possible in a truly *homogeneous* classroom.

Consider this: Some experts estimate that approximately 10 percent of all students have some sort of learning disability. If that is true, then it is likely that two or three students in your current science methods class have a form of learning disability. Can you identify them? Do you know who they are? Are you one?

## TO INVESTIGATE

Visit a local elementary school and ask to see one or more IEPs (you will need to obtain permission from the principal or guidance counselor, and some schools will be very reluctant to have you look at actual IEPs). If you cannot look at an actual IEP, try to get a sample (these are sometimes sent out by state departments of education as a guide for teachers in writing their own). What are some of the components of an IEP? Would you feel comfortable in following an IEP for one of your students? What do you like or dislike about an IEP? ■

## Some Principles and Practices

Your classroom will probably not be all that dissimilar from Marc O'Brien's. You will undoubtedly have a diversity of children in your room, representing a variety of talents and abilities. With that in mind, consider the following generalized strategies as you work with mainstreamed students throughout the science curriculum.

1. Mainstreamed students may not wish to be "singled out" for special treatment. To do so may identify their disability for other students and cause them to receive some form of attention they may not be able to handle. It's not necessary to "highlight" mainstreamed students in the classroom, and it may even be counterproductive to do so. Try not to emphasize a child's particular handicap. Homework assignments, classroom behavior, participation in activities, and academic achievement should be based on a child's capability; teachers should not grant privileges to students solely because of their disabilities (Pasch, Sparks-Langer, Gardner, Starko, & Moody, 1991).
2. Ensure that your attitude toward mainstreamed students is identical to that for "regular" students. If you value the diversity of students in your classroom, you will likely achieve success in mainstreaming. All students should be viewed as contributing students. Teachers who have success with mainstreaming are those who see *all* children as individuals, get to know their strengths and weak-

nesses, and attempt to meet their individual needs (Jacobson & Bergman, 1991).

## DID YOU KNOW?

Most mammals live for about 1 ½ billion heartbeats.

**Classroom Activity** Have students attempt to measure the heartbeats of their pets or other animals. (A simple stethoscope can be constructed with a small funnel and a length of rubber tubing). Have students measure and record the heartbeats of as many different animals as they can. Have them measure their own heartbeats (at rest, after recess, after lunch, after a strenuous physical activity). Students can construct charts on the different heartbeats of all the animals (themselves included) for display in the classroom. ■

3. Consider learning over a long period of time. Mainstreamed students may require extended periods of time to master a concept or learn a specific skill. Information may need to be repeated several times and reinforced in many ways.
4. As indicated previously (see Chapter 8), it is vital for all students to tap their background knowledge and prior experiences. That information forms the foundation from which new learning can emanate. This is even more important with mainstreamed students, who often require concrete experiences on which to base new concepts in science. Helping students relate what they are going to learn to what they already know can be one of the most significant determinants of a successful science lesson.
5. It is quite easy to fall in the trap of focusing on the weaknesses of mainstreamed youngsters. Yet you must seek to identify the individual strengths of every mainstreamed student in your room. For example, how can Carlos, who has cerebral palsy, share his shell collection with the other students? How can Imogene, who must wear hearing aids in both her ears, explain the living habits of the two lizards she recently brought to class? How can Vladimir, who speaks little English, show off his talent for constructing makeshift door bells?
6. It is the teacher's role to be fair and consistent in praising, punishing, assigning work, and granting privileges (Pasch et al., 1991). This will help students understand that grading, evaluation, and assessment is based on identifiable objectives in accordance with individual potential. In short, evaluation is not capricious and haphazard, and it is coupled not to the limitations of students but to their expectations.
7. Provide significant opportunities for students of all abilities to learn from each other. Structure a variety of learning activities in which students can teach other students in cooperative learning groups or other informal situations. Expand on the plethora of talents each student brings to your classroom.

8. Do not make inappropriate assumptions based on students' disabilities. Don't assume that a student who is confined to a wheelchair is an unhappy child. Don't assume that children with disabilities are disabled in *all* areas or are less mature than those without disabilities (Biklen & Bogdan, 1977). For example, it would be inappropriate to treat a hearing-impaired child as though he or she were mentally incompetent. The physical disability may have nothing to do with mental capacity.

## Strategies for Mainstreamed Students

It is inevitable that you will have the opportunity (*and pleasure*) to work with mainstreamed youngsters in your classroom. Providing for their needs will certainly be one of your greatest challenges as a professional educator, and it is not a responsibility to be taken lightly. A comment, a particular activity, or a certain word of encouragement may be all that is needed to make children (of all abilities) shine in science. Following are some tips and strategies for you to keep in mind as you plan for all your students.

### Students with Hearing Impairments

A hearing deficit may range from mild impairment to total deafness. Although it is unlikely that you will have any deaf students in your classroom, you may have one or more who will need to wear one or two hearing aids. Here are some potential strategies to utilize within the science program:

1. Provide written or pictorial directions for any experiments or activities.
2. Physically act out the steps for a science activity. This can be done by you or a student.
3. Other students can be responsible for taking notes (on a rotating basis) for a hearing-impaired student.
4. A hearing-impaired child should be seated in the front of the classroom, in a place where he or she has a good field of vision of both you and the chalkboard or demonstration table.
5. Many hearing-impaired youngsters have been taught to read lips. When addressing the class, be sure to enunciate your words (don't overdo it) and look directly at the hearing-impaired student or in his or her general direction.
6. Provide a variety of multisensory experiences for children within any science activity. Allow students to capitalize on their other learning modalities.
7. There are a variety of computer programs in science that make excellent supplements to any aspect of your curriculum and positive learning tools for hearing-impaired students.

8. It may be necessary to wait longer than usual for a response from a hearing-impaired student. Be patient.
9. Whenever possible, use lots of concrete objects such as models, diagrams, realia, and samples. Try to demonstrate what you are saying with touchable items.
10. When feasible, obtain captioned films and filmstrips, which allow hearing-impaired students to read about what they are seeing on the screen.

**IDEA BOX** _____

In your preview of AV materials, jot down some of the important points or relevant information on clear acetate sheets. When showing a filmstrip or film to the class, project each of these "note sheets" on the same screen (using an overhead projector). That way, a hearing-impaired student will be able to read the same information as classmates are hearing. Label each of these note sheets and keep them on hand for use with other hearing-impaired youngsters in succeeding years.

**DID YOU KNOW?** _____

Deaf people don't get seasick.

**Classroom Activity**  An excellent set of two sound filmstrips is available from the National Geographic Society (Washington, DC). Entitled "Your Senses and How They Help You" (catalog no. 03238), it includes a filmstrip on "Seeing and Hearing" and another on "Tasting, Touching, Smelling, and Other Senses." Try to get these and share them with your students. ■

### Students with Visual Impairments

All students exhibit different levels of visual acuity. However, it is quite likely that you will have students whose vision is severely hampered or restricted. These students may need to wear special glasses and require the use of special equipment. Although it is unlikely that you will have a blind student in your classroom, it is conceivable that you will need a modified instructional plan for visually limited students. Here are some tips:

1. Tape-record portions of textbooks, trade books, and other printed materials so that students can listen (with earphones) to an oral presentation of necessary material. You may wish to have students (with good oral reading skills) record necessary materials on a rotating basis.
2. Visually impaired children can also dictate (into a tape recorder) their reactions and comments to science demonstrations. These tapes provide students with an opportunity to take advantage of oral lan-

guage skills and offer a "refresher" for a topic or activity.

3. When using the chalkboard, use white chalk and bold lines. Also, be sure to say out loud whatever you write on the chalkboard.

4. As with the hearing-impaired student, it is important to have the visually impaired student seated close to the front of the room.

5. Allow the student to touch and feel any objects you use in a demonstration. Allow the student sufficient time to examine, explore, and handle any materials or objects.(Be sure to keep proper safety procedures in mind.)

6. Allow students to handle scientific apparatus a number of times. This gives them a sense of familiarity with the materials so that they will be comfortable for the student when used in a later demonstration or activity.

7. Be careful with any dangerous or potentially dangerous materials (glass, knives, pointed objects, open flame, etc.). When in doubt, it is always better to handle the materials yourself or pair the visually impaired student with a sighted student.

8. Be aware of any terminology you may use that demands visual acuity that the student is not capable of. For example, phrases such as "over there" and "like that one" would be inappropriate (Gega, 1990).

## IDEA BOX

An excellent program for visually impaired and blind students is called *SAVI/SELPH* (Science Activities for the Visually Impaired/Science Enrichment for Learners with Physical Handicaps). Developed at the Lawrence Hall of Science, University of California, Berkeley, it is a science program for students in grades 4 through 7. Specialized equipment and procedures allow students with varying disabilities to take an active role in the science curriculum. The multisensory, interdisciplinary science enrichment program has been a positive factor in helping visually impaired students (as well as students with other disabilities) take an active role in science. Some of the SAVI/SELPH modules include:

| | |
|---|---|
| Communication | Scientific Reasoning |
| Measurement | Magnetism and Electricity |
| Mixtures and Solutions | Kitchen Interactions |
| Environments | Environmental Energy |

Further information can be obtained by writing to:

SAVI/SELPH
Center for Multisensory Learning
Lawrence Hall of Science
University of California
Berkeley, CA 94720

## Students with Physical Impairments

Physically handicapped youngsters include those who require the aid of a wheelchair, cane, walker, brace, crutches or other physical aid for getting around. As with other impairments, these youngsters' disabilities may range from severe to mild and may be the result of one or more factors. What is of primary importance is the fact that these students are no different intellectually than the more mobile students in your classroom. Although it is quite easy to focus on what these children cannot do, it is vital that we look beyond any surface disabilities and encourage these students to become intellectually involved as much as possible. Here are some techniques to consider:

1. Be sure there is adequate access to all parts of the classroom. Aisles between desks should be kept clear, and there should be sufficient space around demonstration tables and science apparatus for physically disabled student to maneuver.

2. Students should be encouraged to participate in all activities to the fullest extent possible. Although it may be easy to accept excuses for nonparticipation, each youngster needs to have sufficient opportunities to become actively engaged in as many dimensions of the science program as is feasible.

3. Establish a rotating series of helpers to assist any physically disabled students in moving about the room. Young children enjoy this responsibility and the opportunity to assist whenever necessary.

4. Focus on the intellectual investment in an activity. That is, help the child use problem-solving abilities and thinking skills to complete an assignment without regard to his or her ability to get to an area that requires object manipulation.

5. When designing an activity or constructing necessary equipment, be on the lookout for alternative methods of display, manipulation, or presentation.

## IDEA BOX

To provide physically impaired students with an abundance of learning opportunities, some very simple modifications can be made to the usual modes of presentation. These can then stimulate the participation of all students, no matter what their handicap. Here are some examples:

- Set up a desert terrarium on a short table next to a wheelchair-bound student so that he or she can be put in charge of its maintenance.
- Set up a learning center on a higher-than-usual table (by putting blocks of wood under each leg) so that a student using a walker can stand up and complete an activity on the construction of an electrical circuit.
- Have the school's custodian install a metal bar in the wall next to a display table to allow a physically disabled student to keep his or her balance while standing.

6. Physically impaired students will, quite naturally, be frustrated at not being able to do everything the

other students can accomplish. Be sure to take some time periodically to talk with those students and help them get their feelings and frustrations out in the open. Help the child understand that those feelings are natural, but also that they need to be discussed periodically.

**DID YOU KNOW?** ————————————

Female giraffes cannot bend their knees when giving birth, so they always give birth standing up. It's a 5-foot drop for the baby.

**Classroom Activity**  Children are, quite naturally, fascinated by the miracle of birth. Here are some books to help them appreciate this natural phenomenon even more: *How You Were Born* by Joanna Cole (New York: Morrow, 1984), *The Facts of Life* by Jonathan Miller (New York: Viking, 1984), and *Hatch!* by Karyn Henley (Minneapolis: Carolrhoda, 1980).  ■

## Students with Emotional Problems

Students with emotional problems are those who demonstrate an inability to build or maintain satisfactory interpersonal relationships, who develop physical symptoms or fears associated with personal or school problems, who exhibit a pervasive mood of unhappiness under normal circumstances, or who show inappropriate types of behavior under normal circumstances (Borich, 1988). These conditions may seem insurmountable, but they can be "conditioned" by the classroom atmosphere and the academic climate you provide for all of your students. Although you will certainly not be expected to remedy all the emotional difficulties of your students, you can have a positive impact on a student's ability to seek solutions and can work in concert with those trying to help him or her. Here are some guidelines for your classroom.

1. Whenever possible, give the student a sense of responsibility. Put the student in charge of something (e.g., operating a motor, cleaning the classroom aquarium, repotting a plant) and be sure to recognize the effort the student put into the assigned task.
2. Provide opportunities for the student to personally select an activity or two that he or she would like to pursue. Invite the student to share any findings with the rest of the class.
3. Get the child involved in activities with other children, particularly children who can serve as good role models for the child. It is important that the emotionally disturbed child have opportunities to interact with fellow students who can provide appropriate behavioral guidelines through their actions.

4. Discuss appropriate classroom behavior at frequent intervals. Don't expect children to remember in May all the classroom rules established in September. Provide "refresher courses" on expected behavior throughout the year.
5. Emotionally handicapped students benefit from a highly structured program, one in which the sequence of activities and procedures is constant. Although you will certainly want to consider a varied science program for all your students, you should also think about an internal structure that provides the support emotionally impaired youngsters need.
6. Be sure an emotionally disturbed child is seated away from any distractions (highly verbal students, equipment, tools, etc.).
7. Keep the activities brief whenever possible. Provide immediate feedback, reinforcement, and a sufficient amount of praise.

## Students with Learning Disabilities

Learning-disabled (LD) students are those who demonstrate a significant discrepancy, which is not the result of some other handicap, between academic achievement and intellectual ability in one or more areas of oral expression, listening comprehension, written expression, basic reading skills, reading comprehension, mathematical calculation, mathematical reasoning, or spelling (Borich, 1988). Teachers may expect to deal with learning disabilities more frequently than any of the other impairments (Jacobson & Bergman, 1991). The manifestations of learning disabilities are many, and these problems are not easily detected or "cured." They are, however, a fact of life for most teachers, and your attention to the learning-disabled students in your room can mean the difference between a highly successful science program, one that meets the needs of all students, and one that is merely adequate.

Table 16.1 is a list of some of the common indicators of learning-disabled students. Keep in mind that these traits are usually not isolated but rather appear in combination in varying degrees. In fact, it is quite rare to find any two learning-disabled youngsters who exhibit the same traits in the same degrees.

Here are some appropriate strategies to use with learning-disabled students:

1. For students with reading disabilities, provide instruction orally. Tests and reading materials may be presented in an oral format so that the assessment is not unduly influenced by lack of reading ability.
2. Provide these students with frequent progress checks. Let them know how well they are doing, how they are progressing toward an individual or class goal, and what they can do to quickly correct any deficits.

## TABLE 16.1

### LEARNING DISABLED BEHAVIORS

1. Poor auditory memory, both short-term and long-term
2. Overreliance on adults for assistance
3. A low tolerance level and a high frustration level
4. Low self-esteem
5. A tendency to trip or stumble
6. Easily distracted
7. Finds it difficult, if not impossible, to stay on task for extended periods of time
8. Spontaneous in expression, often cannot control emotions
9. Easily confused
10. Verbally demanding
11. Has some difficulty working with others in small or large groups
12. Has difficulty following complicated directions or remembering directions for an extended period of time
13. Coordination problems with both large and small muscle groups
14. Inflexibility of thought, "stands by guns," difficult to persuade
15. Poor handwriting skills
16. Poor concept of time

3. Learning-disabled students need immediate feedback. It's important that they quickly see the relationship between what was taught and what was learned. Handing a test back several days after it was completed may be counterproductive for a learning-disabled student.
4. Whenever possible, activities should be concise and kept short. Long, drawn out projects are particularly frustrating for the LD child.
5. Offer the LD students a multisensory approach to science. Take advantage of all the senses in helping these students appreciate and learn science. If you tend to be a verbal learner, you will tend to be a verbal teacher. Be aware of your own learning and teaching styles and compensate for them when necessary in dealing with LD children.
6. Learning-disabled youngsters have difficulty learning abstract terms and concepts. Whenever possible, provide them with concrete objects and events—items they can touch, hear, and smell and that make learning science a true hands-on experience.
7. Learning-disabled students need lots of sincere praise. Instead of just saying, "You did well" or "I like your work," make sure to provide specific comments that link the activity directly with

the recognition—for example, "I was particularly pleased with the way in which you organized the rock collection for Bonnie and Max."
8. As necessary, repeat instructions or offer information in both written and verbal formats. Again, it is vital that LD children utilize as many of their sensory modalities as possible.

Following is a sequence of some activities designed for a third-grade science chapter entitled "Living Things Need Each Other" from *Discover Science* (Glenview, IL: Scott, Foresman, 1989). Note the variety of activities (which are in addition to the regular activities for the chapter) that are specifically geared for learning-disabled students.

1. Instruct students to divide a piece of posterboard in half vertically. Have students with learning disabilities make a collage of magazine pictures showing living things on one side and nonliving things on the other.
2. Allow students with learning disabilities to each choose a type of community, such as a forest, ocean, or desert. Have them make a collage of magazine pictures showing the various populations found in each community.
3. Glue pictures of plants and animals to index cards. Have students with learning disabilities sort the cards into producers and consumers. Then ask the students to select predator-prey pairs from the stack of consumer pictures.

Teaching mainstreamed students will be one of your greatest professional challenges. However, helping these students, as well as all other students in your classroom, achieve a measure of success in science is an adventure that can lead to a bounty of discoveries for all pupils, regardless of their abilities or disabilities.

## IDEA BOX

Here are some organizations you can write to for additional materials and ideas on teaching exceptional students:

Science for the Handicapped
Department of Elementary Education
University of Wisconsin,
Eau Claire, WI 54701

Foundation for Science and the Handicapped
West Virginia University
Morgantown, WV 26506

Adapting Science Materials for the Blind
Lawrence Hall of Science
University of California
Berkeley, CA 94720

In addition, the following two publications are useful in teaching exceptional children:

Council for Exceptional Children. (1970, November). *Science: A guide for teaching the handicapped* (EC 003 1252, ED 046 168). Iowa City: Iowa University, Special Education Curriculum.

Egbert, Marie, & Ricker, Ken. (1981). *Science for the handicapped: An annotated bibliography.* Columbus, OH: Educational Resources Information Center.

You should also be aware that children in the classroom who are not considered handicapped may have an experience during the school year in which they are recuperating from an illness, injury, or emotional trauma that will require you to provide special consideration for them.

# TEACHING GIFTED STUDENTS

"The time has come," the Walrus said,
  "To talk of many things:
Of shoes—and ships—and sealing-wax—
  Of cabbages—and kings—
And why the sea is boiling hot—
  And whether pigs have wings."

Lewis Carroll

Gifted students present a unique challenge to elementary teachers. They may be the first ones done with an assignment or those who continually ask for more creative and interesting work. These students frequently demand ideas and materials that are not only challenging, but relevant as well. They need exciting activities and energizing projects that offer a creative curriculum within the framework of the regular science program.

It has been estimated that 3 to 5 percent of the students in this country are gifted. If that figure is accurate, then it is quite likely that you will have one or more gifted youngsters in your classroom every year. Like special-needs students, gifted pupils will present you with unique challenges that may be unimaginable at this time. They are not easier to teach than the learning-disabled or "average" students; rather, they demand not only more stimulation, but more of your time and energy.

Gifted students take many forms. Let's take a look at one specific definition:

> Children capable of high performance, including those with demonstrated achievements or ability in any one of more of these areas—general intellectual ability, specific academic aptitude, creative or productive thinking, leadership ability, visual or performing arts, or psychomotor ability. (Sisk, n.d.)

Table 16.2 lists several other characteristics of gifted students. As in the case of LD students, giftedness usually means a combination of factors in varying degrees. No two gifted youngsters are exactly alike.

Table 16.3 is an observational checklist that teachers can use to help identify gifted students, particularly those students who may require a differentiated science curriculum.

TABLE **16.2**

## CHARACTERISTICS OF GIFTED STUDENTS

1. A high level of curiosity. Gifted children will examine, probe, poke, and look at everything in their path (and a few things off the beaten path).

2. A well-developed imagination. These students are prone to daydream and think of things that have never been thought of before.

3. Often give uncommon responses to common queries.

4. Can remember and retain a great deal of information. Can also retrieve that information easily and readily.

5. Pose not only original solutions to common problems, but also original problems. (Instead of asking, "Why is the sky blue?" a gifted child might ask, "What are the long-range effects of a depleted ozone layer on the agricultural production of third-world countries?")

6. Ability to concentrate on a problem or issue for an extended period of time.

7. Can see the various relationships between seemingly dissimilar things (for example, when asked to state the similarity between a dictionary and a rubber band, a gifted student might reply, "The rubber band stretches and the dictionary stretches a person's mind.").

8. Gifted students are capable of comprehending complex concepts. They can deal with abstract relatonships at high levels of cognition.

9. They can organize themselves and devise a sequential plan for tackling almost any problem. They can understand where to start as well as how to proceed toward a potential solution.

10. Gifted students are academically energized. That is, they are excited about learning new facts and concepts and pursue learning tasks with a vengeance.

11. They are often independent learners, needing only a task (usually in the form of a problem) and a place to pursue that task to begin working. They tend to be self-directed and exhibit an internal locus of control.

TABLE 16.3

## OBSERVATION CHECKLIST FOR GIFTED STUDENTS

Name:_____     Grade: _____ Date: _____

| | Seldom | Sometimes | Consistently |
|---|---|---|---|
| 1. Works well independently; requires little direction | | | |
| 2. Observes, explores, and investigates; asks thoughtful, searching questions | | | |
| 3. Analyzes a situation or problem in great depth and offers a variety of solutions and ideas | | | |
| 4. Masters and recalls factual information quickly | | | |
| 5. Concentrates for a long period of time when challenged and interested | | | |
| 6. Thinks logically; applies understanding in new situations | | | |
| 7. Generates unusual, unique, or clever responses; demonstrates creative thinking | | | |
| 8. Gives evidence of abstract, critical, and creative thinking; probes beyond the literal interpretation | | | |
| 9. Utilizes an advanced or extensive vocabulary for age/grade level | | | |
| 10. Attempts to understand difficult material by separating it into its component parts | | | |
| 11. Strives to improve and refine efforts by seeking suggestions; is self-evaluative | | | |
| 12. Develops new ideas or solutions when needed; is able to organize and bring structure to situations and ideas | | | |
| 13. Demonstrates special expertise in science or shows special interest in the subject | | | |
| 14. Is an avid reader | | | |

**DID YOU KNOW?** _____

The electricity used by one 100-watt light bulb during its lifetime requires an electric power plant to burn 400 pounds of coal.

**Classroom Activity** Help students organize themselves into an "Energy Awareness Patrol." Share with them some of the ideas and strategies in *50 Simple Things Kids Can Do to Save the Earth* by the Earthworks Group (Kansas City, MO: Andrews and McMeel, 1990). Have students inspect their homes for the various ways in which electricity is used as well as ways in which it can be conserved. Have students report their findings to the rest of the class for discussion. ■

## Models for Gifted Programs

Just as gifted students come in all shapes and sizes, so do programs for gifted students. Here is just a sampling of the instructional options:

1. *The self-contained classroom.* One teacher of the gifted (often assisted by an aide) provides all the instruction. Students are removed from their regular classrooms and scheduled for the "gifted" room for various periods of time throughout the school day. Course work may be devoted to single subjects (e.g., science) or may be cross-curricular. Assignment is usually for the entire school year. Often referred to as a "pull-out" program, this model is used by about 70 percent of the school districts in the country.

2. *"Enrichment" model.* Special projects and activities are provided for gifted students in the regular classroom. About two-thirds of the school districts in the country use this model.

3. *Combination model.* Nearly 25 percent of the school districts use a combination approach, in which students are pulled out for part of the day and are also provided with special projects in the regular classroom.

4. *Team teaching.* Two teachers, one classroom teacher and one teacher of the gifted, pool their resources and teaching strengths. Such a program provides for flexibility, individualization, and opportunities for large-group instruction.

5. *The integrated full-day program.* Pupils from different classrooms are pulled out for the whole day and given special or accelerated instruction by a teacher of gifted students.

6. *The departmental model.* In this model, which is popular at the junior high school level, students receive instruction in subjects from different teachers in different rooms.

7. *A regular classroom teacher assisted by a "gifted" aide.* The classroom teacher provides instruction to all the youngsters in the class. An aide supplements the instruction for gifted students with additional projects and activities.

8. *A districtwide center for gifted students.* Often referred to as a "magnet school," this model is usually offered in larger school districts. Students from various schools in the district are bused in to a special school building to receive specialized instruction.

9. *Revolving-door identification and programming model.* Renzulli, Reis, and Smith (1981) have identified a new concept for the education of gifted students. In this model, special programs are made available to a relatively large percentage of the student population (usually 15 to 25 percent), known as a "talent pool," for short periods of time. Different levels of enrichment programs are then proposed for students. The first level is designed to capitalize on the existing interests in the talent pool and to promote new ones (type I enrichment), the next level is designed to develop a wide variety of thinking processes and research skills (type II enrichment), and eventually the most successful students in type I and type II programs go on to more creative work (type III enrichment).

## TO INVESTIGATE

Visit several elementary schools in your local area. Ask the principals and teachers about some of the provisions for gifted youngsters. What special programs are in place for science? How much time do gifted students get to spend in long-term science projects? Who is responsible for teaching or monitoring the gifted program? How does the gifted program in science differ from the regular classroom program? What implications are there for your future classroom or school? ■

## Instruction for Gifted Students

"Hey, Mr. Lewis, did you know you made a parallel circuit instead of a series one?"
"Since most desert animals are nocturnal, are most desert plants nocturnal, too?"
"How do underground springs begin?"
"How are scientists able to predict when the next solar eclipse will occur?"
"Hey, when are we going to start doing some real science?"

If there's one constant about gifted students, it's that they're full of questions (and full of answers). They're imbued with a sense of inquisitiveness rivaling the best thinkers and scientists of the world. Providing for their instructional needs will extend you to the full limits of your own creativity. Nevertheless, here are some instructional strategies for you to keep in mind:

1. Allow gifted students to design and follow through on self-initiated projects. Have them pursue questions of their own choosing.

2. Provide gifted students with lots of open-ended activities, for which there are no right or wrong answers or preconceived notions. These can be initiated through open-ended questions ("How does acid rain affect different species of plants?" "Why do so many birds gather at the edge of our playground?").

3. Keep the emphasis on divergent thinking (see Chapters 3 and 4), helping gifted students focus on many possibilities rather than a set of predetermined answers.

4. Provide opportunities for gifted youngsters to engage in active problem solving. Be sure the problems assigned are not ones for which you have already established appropriate answers, but rather those that will allow gifted students to arrive at their own conclusions.

5. Encourage gifted students to take on leadership roles that enhance portions of the science program. Developing a slide program illustrating the life cycle of insects, making a videotape of the variety of plant life in a neighbor's garden, and sharing a collection of clocks are examples of appropriate activities.

6. Gifted students will enjoy talking with scientists, other science teachers, and people in the community who deal with scientific phenomena (hardware store personnel, electrician, mechanic, plumber, etc.) on a regular basis.

7. Put gifted students in charge of portions of the science program that require regular attention—for example, organizing science equipment so that it is readily available, caring for classroom flora and fauna, or working on the details associated with field trips.

8. Provide numerous opportunities for gifted youngsters to read extensively about subjects that interest them. Work closely with the school librarian and public librarian to select and provide trade books in keeping with students' interests.

9. Provide numerous long-term activities that allow gifted students the opportunity to engage in a learning project over an extended period of time.

Table 16.4 outlines the five "golden rules" for working with and designing activities for gifted young-

## TABLE 16.4

### FIVE "GOLDEN RULES" FOR GIFTED STUDENTS IN SCIENCE

1. Gifted students should be involved in a facilitative learning process. They should be encouraged to plan and select assignments that meet their individual needs and interests. In turn, these self-directed explorations will lead to greater personal involvement and participation.
2. Gifted students should learn to assume more responsibility for their own learning. In so doing, they gain a greater awareness of their own abilities, develop a sense of self-direction, and improve their self-esteem.
3. Students must be exposed to a wide range of materials, assignments, and experiences—all designed to stimulate scientific explorations above and beyond the textbook.
4. Divergent thinking skills need to be emphasized in concert with creative endeavors. Pupils should be encouraged to both process and interpret information. As a result, they will come to appreciate science as a multifaceted subject.
5. Students must be able to explore science beyond the walls of the classroom. By using their skills in practical and meaningful pursuits, they will gain a heightened awareness of their own competencies.

---

sters within the science program. Keep them in mind as you prepare projects for the gifted and talented students in your classroom.

Gifted youngsters need to be intellectually stimulated to engage in learning activities that promote and extend the science curriculum. These goals can be achieved through inclusion of the following four creative extensions into any science lesson or unit.

1. *Fluency* is the ability to create a potpourri of ideas. It involves the generation of many thoughts without regard to their quality. Brainstorming is a good way to enhance fluency. For example:
   a. Make a list of foods carnivorous animals would eat.
   b. Make a list of places in your town or city where steam is used.
2. *Flexibility* involves drawing relationships between seemingly unrelated ideas. Locating common elements between items helps students look for many possible answers to a problem. For example:
   a. Cut out several pictures from magazines. Create a scene that might be found on the surface of Mars.

b. Choose a favorite portion of the chapter on reptiles. Rewrite it from the perspective of one of the creatures.
3. *Originality* refers to the creation of ideas that are unique. It is the creative process we most often associate with gifted youngsters. For example:
   a. Create original book jackets for each of these five trade books on earthquakes.
   b. Create an electric light switch that could be used by your cat, a toddler, or a paraplegic.
4. *Elaboration* is the process individuals go through to expand an idea, to enlarge it until it is workable or feasible. It is a process of addition or multiplication that builds ideas into their final form. For example:
   a. Write a letter to a scientist explaining some of your solutions for acid rain.
   b. Develop a travel brochure on each of three major rain forest areas in the world.

Table 16.5 is a brief unit on bicycles that would be appropriate for use with gifted youngsters as part of a study on simple machines. Note that there is a lot of leeway in the design of these activities; this allows you to tailor these suggestions to the specific needs and interests of the gifted students in your classroom.

### IDEA BOX

Most children are naturally interested in bicycles. To extend their enjoyment of bicycles, you may wish to provide them with one or more of the following books: *Bike Factory* by Harold Roth (New York: Pantheon, 1985), *BMX* by Charles Coombs (New York: Morrow, 1983), *Bicycle Motocross Is for Me* by Tom Moran (New York: Lerner, 1982), and *Two Hundred Years of Bicycles* by Jim Murphy (New York: Lippincott, 1983).

### IDEA BOX

Here are three organizations you may contact to obtain materials and resources on teaching gifted students:

Office of Talented and Gifted
U.S. Office of Education
Seventh and D Streets, SW
Washington, DC 20202

National Association for Gifted Children
R.R. 5
Box 630-A
Hot Springs, AR 71901

Association for the Gifted
The Council for Exceptional Children
1920 Association Drive
Reston, VA 22091

TABLE **16.5**

......................................................................................................................

## BICYCLE BONANZA

......................................................................................................................

### Thinking Skills

1. Make a list of the major parts and components of a typical bicycle. Draw a bicycle and label all the parts.
2. There are many different types of bicycles: road bikes, racing bikes, mountain bikes, tandem bikes, and so on. Choose any two and prepare a written/oral report that compares their various features.
3. Set up a special exhibit in the classroom on both the history and the future of bicycles. What information do you think should be featured in your exhibit?
4. How does the bicycle rank as an efficient form of transportation? How does it compare with other modes of transportation in terms of cost, maintenance, speed, durability, and design? Survey several people in school to get their reactions and write a report on your findings.
5. Select one model of a particular brand of bicycle. Talk to people who own one as well as to salespeople in a bicycle store. Write to the manufacturer for a brochure on your chosen model. Afterward, put together a complete review of the bike similar to one that might appear in a biking magazine (you may want to look at reviews of other bikes first).
6. Analyze the various ways bicycles are used today. Investigate the bicycle's use in exercise, transportation, communication, and sports. Look into its uses for business as well as for pleasure. Prepare a formal report to share with others in the class.

### Creative Extensions

1. If you could put together a bicycle that had everything you ever wanted on it, what would it look like? What would be its most improtant features? How much would it cost? How would it be used? Set up a bulletin board display to illustrate your perfect bike.
2. Obtain some old bike parts from a junkyard or bicycle dealer. How can those parts be reassembled to create a new labor-saving device?
3. Look at several issues of a bicycling magazine and analyze the different features, articles, columns, and advertisements that regularly appear within its pages. Then develop your own bike magazine to include reviews of friends' bikes, advertisements for necessary equipment, an editorial on bike safety, or other pertinent features. Assemble your "magazine" in the form of a three-ring binder to share with others.

......................................................................................................................

# TEACHING BILINGUAL STUDENTS

......................................................................................................................

"Con mucho gusto, señorita."

"No hablo Ingles."

"Mi madre y padre no es aqui."

If you teach in the West, the Southwest, the South, or the Northeast, you will probably have one or more bilingual students in your classroom. Some estimates indicate that approximately 10 percent of the school-age population in this country speak a primary language other than English (Baca and Cervantes, 1984). Given the wave of immigrants coming to the shores of this country in recent years, that percentage is likely to increase.

"Bilingual" refers to an individual's ability to speak his or her native language as well as English. Obviously, not all the children in our classrooms are able to speak English. They may be recent arrivals to this country, they may use their native language exclusively at home, or they may not understand some of the patterns and grammar of English sufficiently to speak it with any degree of competence. In reality, many of these students are limited-English-proficient (LEP), which may range from being unable to express oneself at all in English, either orally or in writing, to being marginally proficient in English (Borich, 1988).

When we talk of bilingual education, we refer to the need to provide youngsters with instruction in two different languages. Borich (1988, p. 281) provides an excellent definition:

The term *bilingual education* refers to a mix of instruction through the medium of two languages. This means teaching skills and words in English as well as in another language, which in the United States is predominately Spanish. The primary goal of bilingual education is not to teach English as a second language, but to teach concepts, knowledge, and skills through the language the learner knows best and then to reinforce this information through the second language, in which the learner is less proficient.

## Bilingual Programs

There are several different types of bilingual programs available in schools around the country. The United States General Accounting Office (1987) has categorized bilingual programs as follows:

- *English as a second language:* Programs of bilingual education in which instruction is based on a special curriculum that typically involves little or no use of the native language and is usually taught only during certain periods of the school day.
- *Immersion:* A general term for an approach to bilingual instruction that does not involve the child's native language. Two variations are *structured immersion* and *submersion*.
- *Structured immersion:* Programs of bilingual education in which teaching is in English but with special features: The teacher understands the native language, and knowledge of English is not assumed.
- *Submersion:* Students whose proficiency in English is limited are placed in ordinary classrooms in which English is the language of instruction. They are given no special program to help them overcome their language problems.
- *Sheltered English:* Programs that use a simplified vocabulary and sentence structure to teach subjects to students who lack sufficient English-language skills.

- *Transitional bilingual:* Programs of bilingual education with emphasis on the development of English-language skills in order to enable students whose English proficiency is limited to shift to an all-English program of instruction.

### DID YOU KNOW?

Rain contains vitamin B-12.

**Classroom Activity** Obtain a mayonnaise jar and fill it halfway with very hot water. Place the lid on top of the jar, but upside down. Place several ice cubes in the lid and wait for about five minutes. Ask the students to observe what is happening on the bottom of the lid. Ask students to explain why water formed and dripped from the bottom of the lid. Have them speculate on how that might happen outdoors to create rain. (Warm, moist air rises and strikes cool air.) ∎

## Instruction for Bilingual Students

Teaching students whose native language is not English will be a challenge for you—not only in terms of the science program but also in terms of promoting their self-concept and acculturation into the mainstream of American society. You can help facilitate this process for bilingual students with some of the suggestions presented in Table 16.6.

### TEACHER TO TEACHER

As a teacher, curriculum specialist, science supervisor, and parent I have strived to further the learning of children. I have investigated most every learning theory, often jumping quickly on the bandwagon of what I thought would be the ultimate panacea. What I have come to learn is not very profound, but it is frequently neglected when we examine learning. No matter whether you know every child's learning style, have the perfect heterogeneous mix, or have the ultimate curriculum, **the single most important learning variable is the teacher**. And you know, it is one of only a few variables we can assuredly affect. You, the **teacher**, are the single most important element that affects learning.

Steve Fields
Rockdale County Public Schools
Conyers, GA

TABLE **16.6**

......................................................................................................

## INSTRUCTIONAL STRATEGIES FOR BILINGUAL STUDENTS

......................................................................................................

1. Be aware of as much of the culture and traditions of bilingual students as possible. Know something about their native land(s) and the customs they embrace. Use those cultural differences as a positive teaching tool.
2. Employ peer tutors to help LEP students. Older students or students who are proficient in English can act as models and "guides" through the science program.
3. Utilize all the visual resources at your disposal. Films, filmstrips, videos, and other presentations can be useful tools for helping the bilingual student.
4. Use lots of pictorial aids throughout your lessons. Graphs, charts, pictures, photographs, and other illustrations help reinforce what you are trying to communicate.

TABLE **16.6** (*Continued*)

.....................................................................

# INSTRUCTIONAL STRATEGIES FOR BILINGUAL STUDENTS

.....................................................................

5.  Establish a close working relationship with the parents of bilingual students. Letters, notes, and telephone calls can go a long way toward establishing positive home-school bonds and enlisting the aid of parents as co-workers in students' education.

6.  Focus on cooperative learning strategies, group work, and shared instruction. Reduce or eliminate the competitiveness of grades, tests, and the like. Allow children to work together and share ideas in a spirit of cooperation.

7.  You will certainly need a great deal of patience, particularly if you do not speak the native language of the student(s). It is far better to go slow than it is to try and "force-feed" them the same information you present to your native English-speaking students.

8.  Although it is in opposition to almost every guideline in this text, you may need to focus on a factual, literal-based instructional program for bilingual students. That is, offer them concrete data in an easily memorized format.

9.  Obtain information and resources from a regional bilingual education support center. There are several around the country (check your college or local public library for the addresses). Here are a few:

> Bilingual Education Training and Technical Assistance
> Network (BETTA)
> University of Texas
> College of Education
> El Paso, TX 79968
>
> Georgetown University Bilingual Education Service Center
> (GUBESC)
> Georgetown University
> 2139 Wisconsin Ave. NW
> Suite 100
> Washington, DC 20007
>
> Bilingual Education South Eastern Support Center (BS)
> Florida International Unviersity
> Tamiami Campus, TRM-03
> Miami, FL 33199
>
> Bilingual Education Multifunctional Support Center
> School of Education
> California State University
> 5151 State University Drive
> Los Angeles, CA 90032

.....................................................................

# POINTS OF DISCUSSION

.....................................................................

1.  Work with a classmate and list all the benefits that learning-disabled students should derive from a science program. How should they be involved, and what should they get out of the program?

2.  Interview a local teacher and ask how gifted students are taught within the science curriculum. Are they expected to do everything everyone else does? Are they expected to do more? Do they have a completely different science program?

3.  Select a lesson from a science textbook series. How would you alter that lesson so that it could be taught to one or more bilingual students? What modifications or extensions could you make to the lesson so that it would be beneficial to someone who speaks no English at all?

4.  Interview a novice teacher (one with less than two years of experience). What kinds of modifications to the science program does that individual make to

accommodate physical, visual, or hearing-impaired students? How do they compare with an experienced teacher's modifications? What might be the implications for your classroom?

5. Design a space science lesson for a student with limited vision. What types of activities or projects would be appropriate?

6. Design a physical science lesson for a student with limited hearing. What types of activities of projects would be appropriate?

7. If possible, interview several college students for whom English was not the native language when they were in elementary school. How did they feel? Were any modifications made to the instructional program that benefited them? If they could go back and tell their former teacher something, what would they say?

8. What kind of impact will P.L. 94-142 have on your classroom science program? Are you ready for it?

9. How will you be able to provide for the wide diversity of students and student abilities in your classroom science program? Are you comfortable in teaching students with a variety of talents and disabilities? In other words, how will you be able to create a science program that is stimulating and appealing to every child in your classroom?

**TEACHER TO TEACHER**

*If I Remember Everything*

If I remember everything
I've been taught, then,
perhaps, you'll think
me wise, but does
true wisdom come
from seeing the world
through another's eyes?
Will there ever come
a time when I can learn
with all the rest of me,
and touch and taste
and smell and feel
my own reality?
Please let there be,
for unless I can relate
your knowledge to the seeking,
wondering child in me,
it shall flash beauty
for a moment like a
transparent
fish in a crystal sea,
then be gone forever
from my reality.

Arden G. Thompson
Wiscasset Schools
Wiscasset, ME

# REFERENCES

Baca, L. M., & Cervantes, H. T. (1984). *The bilingual special education interface*. Santa Clara, CA: Times Mirror/Mosby.

Baltimore County Public Schools. (n.d.). *Summary Sheet for the Identification of Talented Students in Reading/Mathematics*. Towson, MD: Author.

Biklen, D., & Bogdan, R. (1977). Handicappism in America. In B. Blatt, D. Biklen, and R. Bogdan (Eds.), *An alternative textbook in special education*. New York: Love.

Borich, Gary D. (1988). *Effective teaching methods*. Columbus, OH: Merrill.

Fredericks, Anthony D. (1988). *The gifted reader handbook*. Glenview, IL: Scott, Foresman.

Gega, Peter C. (1990). *Science in elementary education*. New York: Macmillan.

Jacobson, Willard J., & Bergman, Abby Barry. (1991). *Science for children: A book for teachers*. Englewood Cliffs, NJ: Prentice Hall.

Pasch, Marvin, Sparks-Langer, Georgea, Gardner, Trevor G., Starko, Alane J., & Moody, Christella D. (1991). *Teaching as decision making*. White Plains, NY: Longman.

*The Education for All Handicapped Children Act*. P.L. 94-142, 20 U.S.C., §1401, 89 Stat. 773 (November 29, 1975).

Renzulli, Joseph, Reis, S. M., & Smith, L. H. (1981). *The revolving door identification model*. Mansfield Center, CT: Creative Learning Press.

Sisk, Dorothy. (n.d.) *What if your child is gifted?* Washington, DC: Office of the Gifted and Talented.

United States General Accounting Office. (1987). *Bilingual education: A new look at the research evidence.* (GAO/PEMD-87-12BR). Gaithersburg, MD: Author.

Wang, Margaret C., Reynolds, Maynard C., & Walberg, Herbert J. (1986, September). Rethinking special education. *Educational Leadership*, 44(1), 26.

# A

# SCIENCE LITERACY: ATTRIBUTES

The following attributes help to describe a scientifically literate person. Each attribute should be thought of as a continuum along which the individual may progress. The progress of the individual's science education should be equated with progress along this continuum.

The scientifically and technologically literate person:

- Uses science concepts, process skills, and values in making responsible everyday decisions
- Understands how society influences science and technology as well as how science and technology influence society
- Understands that society controls science and technology through the allocation of resources
- Recognizes the limitations as well as the usefulness of science and technology in advancing human welfare
- Knows the major concepts, hypotheses, and theories of science and is able to use them

- Appreciates science and technology for the intellectual stimulus they provide
- Understands that the generation of scientific knowledge depends upon the inquiry process and upon conceptual theories
- Distinguishes between scientific evidence and personal opinion
- Recognizes the origin of science and understands that scientific knowledge is tentative and subject to change as evidence accumulates
- Understands the applications of technology and the decisions entailed in the use of technology
- Has sufficient knowledge and experience to appreciate the worthiness of research and technological development
- Has a richer and more exciting view of the world as the result of science education
- Knows reliable sources of scientific and technological information and uses those sources in the process of decision making

# B

# ACTIVITIES FOR USE WITH SCIENCE TRADE BOOKS

The use of trade books throughout your science program can be a very positive element of the science curriculum. Trade books can provide youngsters with a host of learning possibilities that would not be available from the basal text alone. What follows is a compendium of activities that your students can use with trade books. Keep in mind that activities should be matched with students' interests and abilities and should be incorporated as a natural part of the entire science program, not simply as an "add-on" feature. These suggestions will allow you to energize students' engagement in science and motivate them to pursue information.

Look over these possibilities and modify them according to the needs of your students. No single activity is appropriate for all students in your classroom. Children should be allowed to select activities in keeping with their needs and interests.

1. Encourage students to read a new book (or part of a book) each day.
2. Have students write a letter to a friend about what he or she is learning from a science trade book.
3. Have students read both fiction and nonfiction books on the same topic.
4. Students can read several books by the same author.
5. Individual students can keep a journal or diary about what is being learned about a topic.
6. Have a small group of students make up a mock newspaper about a selected book topic.
7. Set up a reading corner in your classroom filled with periodicals, books, and other printed materials on a particular topic.
8. You or your students may wish to record part of a book on cassette tape.
9. Have students design a wordless picture book on a trade book topic.
10. Students will enjoy creating and producing an original book on an identified topic.
11. Have students frequently share a book with a classmate or partner.
12. Invite individual students to design and write a newspaper article about information learned in a special trade book.
13. Have students locate and read a relevant magazine article on a specific topic.
14. Encourage students to write a sequel or prequel to a selected book.
15. Have students convert a book into a news report or TV program.
16. Students can write a description of a book in 25 words or less, in 50 words or less, and 75 words or less.
17. Ask students to create interview questions for the author of a book.
18. Have students rewrite a portion of a book from the perspective of a student.
19. Have a small group of students create a glossary or dictionary of important words in the book.
20. One or more students may wish to create word puzzles or crossword puzzles on book information.
21. Have students make up a rebus story for younger students.
22. Students can write riddles about events in a book.
23. Encourage students to design a "question box" containing questions and answers about specific books.
24. Direct each student to keep a card file of all the books read.
25. Ask the class to develop a rating system for books read (terrific, good, OK, so-so, rotten).
26. Have individual students print important book phrases or quotations on construction paper and post them throughout the room.

27. Invite students to set up a message center to send reports to classmates and the teacher about information learned.
28. Students may enjoy creating a calendar of important facts.
29. Have students put together a scrapbook about important information or facts.
30. Ask each students to write a 10-question quiz for a book read.
31. Students may wish to play a game of "20 Questions" on the subject of a particular book.
32. Have students set up a debate or panel discussion.
33. Encourage students to interview outside "experts" in the local community.
34. Ask each student to create several new titles for a book.
35. Have students each make up a list of information they still want to learn about a topic.
36. Some students may wish to make a story map about a book they read.
37. Ask students to design a trivia game on a book or singular topic.
38. Have students create a time line about the events in a book.
39. Ask one or more students to create flash cards based on facts from a book.
40. Have students design pictographs on a particular book.
41. Ask a small group of students to create a graph or chart to record book data.
42. Some students may wish to trace the lives of certain scientists.
43. Have the class chart the environmental changes that have taken place over a period of years.
44. A small group of students may want to work together and turn part of a book into a series of cartoons.
45. Invite a student to illustrate portions of a book.
46. Have students make an advertisement for a book.
47. Encourage students to establish a science "museum" in one corner of the classroom detailing data from a book or series of books. [An excellent resource is *Classroom Museums: Touchable Tables for Kids!* by Pamela Marx (Glenview, IL: Scott, Foresman, 1992).]
48. Students may try to create a pop-up book about one or more facts.
49. Have students put together an original slide show of information related to particular books.
50. Some students can make a flip book about selected facts.
51. Ask a student to create a collage on a particular topic from old magazines.
52. Have a student design an original flannel board story to present to a younger grade.

53. A small group of students may enjoy creating a commercial to encourage others to read the book.
54. Have students paint a large wall poster about the topic of a book.
55. A few students may want to design and create a diorama pertaining to a significant fact.
56. Invite a group of students to create a three-dimensional display of artifacts associated with a book.
57. Have one or more students give a chalk talk about a specific book.
58. Have groups of students take photographs showing similar events/facts/principles from the local community and arrange them into an attractive display.
59. One or more students can make "movie rolls" using shoeboxes, adding-machine tape, and pencils (as the rollers).
60. Ask a student to assemble a collage of pictures on a specified topic.
61. Ask several students to plan a bulletin board of pictures cut out of old magazines.
62. Students can design clay models illustrating important facts.
63. Ask individual students to design transparencies about an important principle and show them to the class.
64. Ask groups of students to create a "question-and-answer relay" using specific science facts.
65. One or more groups of students can create a radio show about a book.
66. Ask student groups to each create a commercial for a science discovery.
67. Encourage a group of students to create an original song about a principle or event.
68. Students will enjoy designing a filmstrip for a book (special filmstrip kits can be obtained from education dealers).
69. Ask students to give dramatic readings of a book.
70. Student groups may wish to create cassette recordings of selected books.
71. Ask a small group of students to dramatize a section of the book for another class.
72. Have some students produce a puppet show about part of a book.

Following is an example of how a single science trade book can be extended across the curriculum. As you can see, the number of possible activities is limited only by your imagination. You will discover that trade books provide your students with many rich and exciting extensions of the science program. They allow your students to investigate areas of interest in greater detail and help them to view science as a universal subject.

## The Birds' Woodland: What Lives There?

by Richard Farrar

(New York: Coward, McCann & Geoghegan, 1976)

1. Have students make a mural. Direct students to draw a woodland scene with various birds placed in their correct habitats.
2. Take a picture of the canopy from the book, assign a scale to it, and have the students measure and graph the heights at which the various birds nest.
3. List the items in the food chain of a hawk. Then direct the students to put them in the correct order on the chain.
4. Discuss with students the various kinds of beaks. Have students identify tools humans use (e.g., pliers, tweezers, nutcracker) that are similar to different beak types. A classroom chart can be created to illustrate the comparisons.
5. Invite students to go on a nature walk and imitate various bird movements, including the hopping of the red-eyed vireo, the walking of the ovenbird, and the pecking of a woodpecker.
6. Have the students make a class collage using pictures cut from old magazines that depict several different varieties of birds and several different locations of bird nests.
7. As a long-term project, invite the class to keep a feather collection. Students can bring in various types of bird feathers, which can be glued to individual sheets of construction paper and mounted in a special scrapbook.
8. Invite students to create a new and original bird. Students can illustrate their new bird, name it, describe its habits and habitat, and make up its natural history. A summary of each new bird should be posted in the classroom.
9. Have students learn some songs about birds. These can include "Red, Red Robin" and "Mr. Bluebird," for example.
10. Some students may wish to make bird puppets using paper bags. Feathers can be cut from construction paper and glued to each puppet. Invite students to create puppets of some of the birds in the book.
11. Invite students to set up a feeding station within sight of the classroom. (Inexpensive ones can be purchased at hardware stores, or you can create your own from a used milk carton with portions of the sides cut out.) Have students keep a log of how many birds visit the station, what kinds of birds visit, and the times that the birds feed.
12. Ask students to bring in clean eggshells. Color the shells with different watercolors. Gently break the shells apart and have students create a mosaic (gluing the shell fragments to a piece of posterboard) of a favorite bird.
13. Invite students to begin a bird scrapbook containing newspaper and magazines articles about birds collected over a period of time.
14. Have students write and perform a play about birds.

# SOURCES FOR CHILDREN'S LITERATURE

Locating appropriate trade books for your classroom science program may seem like an overwhelming task, but it need not be. There are many resources at your disposal to assist you in identifying relevant literature. The following sources can be found at most college libraries and many public libraries. They offer a wealth of information, annotated bibliographies, and pertinent data on how books can be used—not just in science but across the curriculum. Use these as well as the knowledge of your school and public librarians to help you find the best books for every part of your science program.

## Publications

Arbuthnot, May Hill. (1989). *Children's books too good to miss*, 8th ed. Cleveland: Press of Case Western Reserve University.

Barstow, Barbara. (1989). *Beyond picture books: A guide to first readers*. New York: Bowker.

Children's Book Council. (1981). *Children's books: Awards and prizes*. New York: Author.

*The children's catalog*. New York: H. W. Wilson.

*Children's choices*. (Annual). Newark, DE: International Reading Association.

Cranciolo, Patricia. (1990). *Picture books for children*. Chicago: American Library Association.

Dreyer, Sharon. (1985). *The bookfinder: When kids need books*. Circle Pines, MN: American Guidance Service.

Eakin, Mary. (1967). *Subject index to books for primary grades*, 3rd ed. Chicago: American Library Association.

*The elementary school library collection*, 15th ed. (1986). Williamsport, PA: Brodart.

Ettlinger, John. (1987). *Choosing books for young people, volume 2: A guide to criticism and bibliography, 1976–1984*. Phoenix, AZ: Oryx.

Gillespie, John. (1985). *Elementary school paperback collection*. Chicago: American Library Association.

Gillespie, John. (1990). *Best books for children: Preschool through grade six*, 4th ed. New York: Bowker.

Hearne, Betsy. (1990). *Choosing books for children*. New York: Delacorte Press.

Jett-Simpson, Mary. (1989). *Adventuring with books: A booklist for pre-K–grade 6*. Urbana, IL: National Council of Teachers of English.

Kimmel, Margaret M., & Segel, Elizabeth. (1988). *For reading out loud!* New York: Delacorte Press.

Kobrin, Beverly. (1988). *Eyeopeners! How to choose and use children's books about real people, places, and things*. New York: Viking.

Lima, Carol, & Lima, John A. (1989). *A to zoo: Subject access to children's picture books*, 3rd ed. New York: Bowker.

Lukens, Rebecca. (1986). *A critical handbook of children's literature*. Glenview, IL: Scott, Foresman.

Lynn, Ruth N. (1983). *Fantasy for children: An annotated checklist and reference guide*, 2nd ed. New York: Bowker.

Monson, Dianne. (1985). *Adventuring with books: A booklist for pre-K–grade 6*. Urbana, IL: National Council of Teachers of English.

Norton, Donna E. (1991). *Through the eyes of a child: An introduction to children's literature*. New York: Merrill.

Pilla, Marianne L. (1990). *The best: High/low books for reluctant readers*. Englewood, CO: Libraries Unlimited.

*The New York Times parent's guide to the best books for children*. (1988). New York: Times Books.

Rollock, Barbara. (1984). *The Black experience in children's books*. New York: New York Public Library.

Schon, Isabel. (1980). *A Hispanic heritage: A guide to juvenile books about Hispanic peoples and cultures*. Metuchen, NJ: Scarecrow Press.

Taylor, Barbara M., & Monson, Dianne L. (1991). *Reading together: Helping children get a good start in reading*. Glenview, IL: Scott, Foresman.

Trelease, Jim. (1985). *The read aloud handbook*. New York: Penguin.

Vandergrift, Kay. (1980). *Child and story: The literary connection*. New York: Neal-Schuman.

## Review Sources

*The ALAN Review*. National Council of Teachers of English, 1111 Kenyon Road, Urbana, IL 61801.

*Bookbird,* International Periodical on Literature for Children and Young Adults. ARNIS, Bergensvej 5, DK-6230 Roderko, Denmark.

*Booklist.* American Library Association, 50 E. Huron St., Chicago, IL 60611.

*Booklures, Inc.* P.O. Box 9450, O'Fallon, MO 63366.

*Book Review Digest.* Wilson, New York, NY 10452.

*The Bulletin of the Center for Children's Books.* Graduate Library School, University of Chicago, Chicago, IL 60637.

*Children's Literature Association Quarterly.* Children's Literature Association, Purdue University Press, West Lafayette, IN 47907.

*The Five Owls.* 2004 Sheridan Avenue South, Minneapolis, MN 55405.

*The Horn Book.* Horn Book Inc., 14 Beacon St., Boston, MA 02108.

*Instructor.* Scholastic, Inc., P.O. Box 2039, Mahopac, NJ 10541.

*The Kobrin Letter: Concerning Children's Books about Real People, Places and Things.* 732 Greer Road, Palo Alto, CA 94303.

*Language Arts.* National Council of Teachers of English, Urbana, IL 61801.

*Learning.* P.O. Box 51593, Boulder, CO 80321-1593.

*The Lion and the Unicorn.* Journals Publishing Division, Johns Hopkins University Press, 701 West 40th St., Suite 275, Baltimore, MD 21211.

*The New Advocate.* P.O. Box 809, Needham Heights, MA 02194.

*The Reading Teacher.* International Reading Association, Newark, DE 19714.

*School Library Journal (Star Track).* P.O. Box 1978, Marion, OH 43306.

*Teacher.* P.O. Box 2091, Marion, OH 43305-2091.

*Teaching K–8.* P.O. Box 54808, Boulder, CO 80322-4808.

*Top of the News.* American Library Association, 50 E. Huron St., Chicago, IL 60611.

*VOYA: Voice of Youth Advocates.* Scarecrow Press, Dept. VOYA, 52 Liberty St., P.O. Box 4167, Metuchen, NJ 09884.

*The Web.* Center for Language, Literature, and Reading, Ohio State University, Columbus, OH 43210.

## Book Wholesalers

Baker and Taylor, 652 East Main St., P.O. Box 6920, Bridgewater, NJ 08807.

Book Wholesalers, Inc., 2025 Leestown Road, Lexington, KY 40511.

Bound to Stay Bound, West Morton Road, Jacksonville, IL 62560.

Brodart, 500 Arch Street, Williamsport, PA 17705.

# PROFESSIONAL ORGANIZATIONS AND ASSOCIATIONS

Your membership in one or more of the following professional organizations offers you a wealth of opportunities to expand your science teaching competence. In addition to the publications and conferences these organizations offer, they also serve as resources for materials and information that can enhance your classroom program. You are strongly urged to consider joining one or more of these associations at some time during your professional teaching career.

American Association for the Advancement of
  Science (AAAS)
1333 H Street, NW
Washington, DC 20005
(202) 326-6620

American Association of Physics Teachers
5112 Berwyn Road
College Park, MD 20740
(301) 345-4200

American Astronautical Society
Department of Mechanical Engineering
Howard University
Washington, DC 20059
(202) 636-6612

American Astronomical Society
Box 3818, University Station
Charlottesville, VA 22903
(804) 924-7955

American Chemical Society
1155 16th St., NW
Washington, DC 20036
(202) 872-6179

American Geological Institute
National Center for Earth Science Education
4220 King St.

Alexandria, VA 22302
(703) 379-2480

American Geophysical Union
2000 Florida Ave., NW
Washington, DC 20009
(202) 462-6903

American Institute of Aeronautics and Astro-
  nautics
370 L'Enfant Promenade, SW
Washington, DC 20024
(202) 646-7400

American Institute of Biological Sciences
College of Natural Sciences
University of Northern Iowa
Cedar Falls, IA 50614
(319) 273-2585

American Institute of Chemists
Northeast Missouri State University
Kirksville, MO 63501
(816) 785-4620

American Institute of Physics
335 East 45th St.
New York, NY 10017
(212) 661-9404

American Meteorological Society
Department of Meteorology
University of Wisconsin
Madison, WI 53706
(608) 262-0776

American Nature Study Society
Pocono Environmental Education Center
R.D. 1, Box 268
Dingman's Ferry, PA 18328
(717) 828-2319

American Physical Society
335 East 45th St.
New York, NY 10017
(212) 682-7341

American Society for Microbiology
1913 Eye Street, NW
Washington, DC 20006
(202) 833-9680

Association for Supervision and Curriculum
  Development (ASCD)
125 North West St.
Alexandria, VA 22314
(703) 549-9110

Association for Women in Science
2401 Virginia Ave., NW, No. 303
Washington, DC 20037
(202) 833-2998

Association of Science-Technology Centers
1413 K Street, Tenth Floor
Washington, DC 20005
(202) 371-1171

Astronomical Society of the Pacific
390 Ashton Ave.
San Francisco, CA 94112
(415) 337-1100

Biological Sciences Curriculum Study (BSCS)
830 N. Tejom St.
Suite 405
Colorado Springs, CO 80903
(719) 578-1136

Center for American Archaeology
P.O. Box 366
Kampsville, IL 62053
(618) 653-4316

Center for Excellence in Education
7710 Old Springhouse Road, Suite 100
McLean, VA 22102
(703) 448-9062

Council for Elementary Science International
  (CESI)
Department of Curriculum and Instruction
212 Townsend Hall
University of Missouri
Columbia, MO 65211
(314) 882-7247

Council of State Science Supervisors (CSSS)
Department of Public Instruction
Science Department
Old Capital Building
Mail Stop FG-11
Olympia, WA 98504
(206) 753-6738

Educational Products Information Exchange
  (EPIE)
EPIE Institute
P.O. Box 839
Water Mill, NY 11976
(516) 283-4922

Educational Resources Information Center
  (ERIC)
Ohio State University
1200 Chambers Road, Third Floor
Columbus, OH 43212
(614) 292-6717

Equals
Lawrence Hall of Science
University of California
Berkeley, CA 94720
(415) 642-1823

Foundation for Science and the Handicapped
West Virginia University
Morgantown, WV 26506
(304) 293-5201

Harvard-Smithsonian Center for Astrophysics
60 Garden St.
Cambridge, MA 02138
(617) 495-9798

National Academy of Sciences (NAS)
2101 Constitution Ave., NW
Washington, DC 20148
(202) 334-2300

National Aeronautics and Space Administra-
  tion (NASA)
NASA Headquarters
Code XEE
Washington, DC 20546
(202) 453-8396

National Association for Research in Science
  Teaching
College of Education
University of Cincinnati
Cincinnati, OH 45221
(513) 475-2335

The National Association for Science, Technology, and Society
Pennsylvania State University
128 Willard Bldg.
University Park, PA 16802
(814) 865-9951

National Audubon Society
613 Riversville Road
Greenwich, CT 06830
(203) 869-5272

National Center for the Improvement of Science Teaching and Learning
The NETWORK, Inc.
290 South Main St.
Andover, MA 01810
(617) 470-1080

National Science Foundation
1800 G Street, NW, Room 516
Washington, DC 20550
(202) 357-7078

National Science Resources Center
Arts and Industries Bldg. Room 1201
Smithsonian Institution
Washington, DC 20560
(202) 357-2555

National Science Teachers Association (NSTA)
1742 Connecticut Ave., NW
Washington, DC 20009
(202) 328-5800

National Wildlife Federation
1412 16th St., NW
Washington, DC 20036
(202) 790-4360

Native American Science Education Association
1333 H Street, NW, Room 750
Washington, DC 20005
(202) 371-8100

Sigma XI, The Scientific Research Society
345 Whitney Ave.
New Haven, CT 06511
(203) 624-9883

Smithsonian Institution
Office of Elementary and Secondary Education
Arts and Industries Bldg., Room 1163
Smithsonian Institution
Washington, DC 20560
(202) 357-2425

The Society for the Advancement of Chicanos and Native Americans in Science
Thimann Laboratories
University of California
Santa Cruz, CA 95064
(408) 429-2295

Soil and Water Conservation Society
7515 Northeast Ankeny Road
Ankeny, IA 50021
(515) 289-2331

The Wildlife Society
5410 Grosvenor Lane
Bethesda, MD 20814
(301) 897-9770

Young Astronaut Council
Box 65432
1211 Connecticut Ave., NW, #800
Washington, DC 20036
(202) 682-1986

# SCIENCE ACTIVITY BOOKS

The following books provide a wonderful collection of experiments, discoveries, and explorations into all dimensions of the elementary science curriculum. Available in most libraries, bookstores, and teacher supply stores, they offer you a host of exciting ways to energize your science program and make it dynamic and purposeful for all your students.

Of course, these aren't all the resource books available. You are encouraged to read publisher's catalogs, visit regional and national science conferences, keep up to date on new publications reviewed in journals such as *Science and Children*, and talk with teachers and colleagues in other schools about some of their recommendations. You will discover that these and other activity books will be most valuable additions to your professional library.

Abruscato, Joe, & Hassard, Jack. (1976). *Loving and beyond: Science teaching for the humanistic classroom.* Glenview, IL: Scott, Foresman. Although this book is out of print, it remains a valuable resource for a humanistic approach to science teaching. It is worth the effort to locate a copy.

Abruscato, Joe, & Hassard, Jack. (1991). *The whole cosmos catalog of science activities.* (2nd ed.). Glenview, IL: Scott, Foresman. Every teacher of science should have this book. Not only does it contain a wealth of science investigations for kids of all ages, but it is a delight to read. A resource you'll turn to again and again.

Alison, Linda. (1976). *Blood and guts: A working guide to your own insides.* Boston: Little, Brown. Seventy experiments allow students to examine, poke, push, and prod their own anatomies to discover the wonderful "laboratory" they carry with them every day.

Alison, Linda, & Katz, David. (1983). *Gee Wiz!* Boston: Little, Brown. This book takes advantage of children's imagination to present science as a thinking process. Students are allowed to explore their own interests and self-initiated discoveries as they learn about basic science concepts.

Butzow, Carol M., & Butzow, John. (1989). *Science through children's literature.* Englewood, CO: Teacher Ideas Press. An exciting and valuable resource for the teacher seeking to integrate more children's literature (principally fiction) into the science program. A detailed look at the whole-language approach to science education, this book should be on every teacher's desk!

Caney, Stanley. (1985). *Invention book.* New York: Workman. A wonderful introduction to the inventive process and how children can use the processes of famous (and not so famous) inventors to discover their own natural creativity. A wonderful supplement to any science program.

Cobb, Vicki. (1972). *Science experiments you can eat.* New York: Harper & Row. Children's natural fascination with food and cooking are the subject of this book, which wonderfully presents science in easy-to-understand and relevant terms. Be sure to check out Cobb's follow-up book, *More Science Experiments You Can Eat.*

DeVito, Alfred, & Krockover, Gerald H. (1976). *Creative sciencing: A practical approach.* Boston: Little, Brown. A great introduction to the process approach or discovery-oriented science program. Not only is this book easy to read, but the ideas are grounded in a humanistic and comfortable approach to science teaching. A wonderful addition to any science library.

Fredericks, Anthony D. (1987). *Think about it! Science problems of the day.* Sunnyvale, CA: Creative Publications. A host of problem-solving activities—one for each day of the school year—emphasizing critical thinking in all the sciences. An interesting way to make science a relevant and daily activity in any classroom.

Fredericks, Anthony D. (1991). *Science brainstretchers.* Glenview, IL: Scott, Foresman. More than 70 critical thinking and problem-solving exercises designed to help students use and extend their knowledge of the life, physical, and earth and space sciences. An interesting addition to the science program in grades 4, 5, and 6.

Fredericks, Anthony D., & Asimov, Isaac. (1990). *The complete science fair handbook.* Glenview, IL: Scott, Foresman. A handbook for teachers and parents, with timetables, project ideas, research sources, and information emphasizing a process approach to the creation of science fair projects. The emphasis is on learning and discovery for all students, not on winning the grand prize or a slew of blue ribbons.

Fredericks, Anthony D., Cressman, Brad, & Hassler, Robert. (1987). *The science discovery book.* Glenview, IL: Scott, Foresman. A selection of 42 hands-on science discovery activities that reinforce the processes of science and take advantage of students' natural curiosity. A nonthreatening approach to science teaching and learning that can be part of any science curriculum.

Gega, Peter. (1991). *Concepts and experiences in elementary school science.* New York: Macmillan. Although this book is designed for a college science methods course, it is brimming with all sorts of experiments, investigations, and demonstrations that can be easily incorporated into any classroom science program.

Graf, Rudolph F. (1973). *Safe and simple electrical experiments.* New York: Dover. More than 100 electrical experiments that use simple and inexpensive materials and rely on hands-on demonstrations for students of all ages.

Lowery, Lawrence. (1985). *The everyday science sourcebook.* Palo Alto, CA: Dale Seymour. More than 1,000 activities and investigations highlight this volume, which can be used across the science curriculum. Complete background data, directions, and materials are provided for each procedure.

McCormack, Alan J. (1981). *Inventor's workshop.* Belmont, CA: David S. Lake. This sourcebook offers a variety of activities and strategies designed to take advantage of students' natural inventive spirit. Classroom strategies and detailed projects highlight this book.

Milford, Susan. (1989). *The kid's nature book.* Charlotte, VT: Williamson. If you're looking for an activity a day to help students discover and enjoy the wonders of nature, this is the book! Filled with fascinating facts and a host of investigative activities, this book is an exciting addition to any teacher's professional library.

Nicklesburg, Janet. (1976). *Nature activities for early childhood.* Menlo Park, CA: Addison-Wesley. A collection of 44 projects that allow young children to observe nature and investigate the wonders of the world around them. This hands-on approach to science discovery will lead to more activities initiated by the students themselves.

Ontario Science Centre. (1987). *Foodworks.* Reading, MA: Addison-Wesley. Over 100 science activities and fascinating facts that explore the magic of food. Kids will love this assortment of hands-on activities about a subject they too often take for granted.

Ontario Science Centre. (1984). *Scienceworks.* Toronto: Kids Can Press. One of the "Top Ten" science resource guides. This book takes an open-ended and relaxed approach to science, one that treats students with dignity and allows them to take the initiative in a host of scientific inves-

tigations. There is a wealth of science excitement in these pages.

Rights, Mollie. (1981). *Beastly neighbors: All about wild things in the city, or why earwigs make good mothers.* Boston, MA: Little, Brown. Students are given opportunities to examine the plant and animal life in their immediate environments. For children who don't believe there is nature in the city, this book is a must.

Saul, Wendy, & Newman, Alan R. (1986). *Science fare.* New York: Harper & Row. You can't go wrong with this book! It is filled with a plethora of sources and resources for teaching and learning about science. A "Top Ten" book!

Smith, Ellyn, Blackmer, Marilyn, & Schlichting, Sandi. (1987). *Idea Factory's super science sourcebook.* Riverview, FL: Idea Factory. More than 100 activities in every dimension of elementary science help youngsters feel comfortable about learning and teachers feel at ease about guiding student discoveries.

Stein, Sara. (1980). *The science book.* New York: Workman. One of the best books around, this volume includes a variety of science experiments and demonstrations that will excite children and stimulate teachers to examine science in all its dimensions—in school, at home, and in the community.

Strongin, Herb. (1991). *Science on a shoestring.* (2nd ed.). Menlo Park, CA: Addison-Wesley. This book continues to be a staple in many science classrooms. Filled with easy-to-do science investigations, it demonstrates that a lot of expensive equipment is not necessary to help children experience the joy and wonder of science discoveries.

Ticotsky, Alan. (1985). *Who says you can't teach science.* Glenview, IL: Scott, Foresman. Provides more than 100 hands-on science activities across the sciences. The activities are well-designed, easy to do, and can be incorporated into any science curriculum.

Zubrowski, Bernie. (1985). *Raceways: Having fun with balls and tracks.* New York: Morrow. The principles of momentum, acceleration, energy, and gravity are all presented in this little book. Lots of ideas and demonstrations help children pursue answers about natural physical forces.

# SCIENCE EDUCATION PERIODICALS FOR TEACHERS

The following list contains a variety of science magazines and periodicals that can help you stay abreast of the latest in science discoveries and science education. These periodicals will help you design up-to-date science lessons.

*The American Journal of Physics*
American Association of Physics Teachers
57 E. 55th St.
New York, NY 10022
(Monthly)

*American Forests*
The American Forestry Association
919 17th St., NW
Washington, DC 20036
(Monthly)

*American Biology Teacher*
The National Association of Biology Teachers
19 S. Jackson St.
Danville, IL 61832
(Monthly)

*The Aquarium*
Innes Publishing Co.
Philadelphia, PA 19107
(Monthly)

*Art to Zoo*
Office of Elementary and Secondary Education
Smithsonian Institution
Arts and Industries Building
Washington, DC 20560
(Quarterly)

*Astronomy*
Kalmbach Publishing Co.
1027 North Seventh St.
Milwaukee, WI 53233
(Monthly)

*Audubon Magazine*
The National Audubon Society
1130 Fifth Ave.
New York, NY 10028
(Monthly)

*Biology and General Science Digest*
W. M. Welch Co.
1515 Sedgwick St.
Chicago, IL 60610
(Free)

*Chem Matters*
American Chemical Society
Room 805L
P.O. Box 57136
West End Station
Washington, DC 20037
(Quarterly)

*Chemistry*
Science Service
1719 16 St., NW
Washington, DC 20009
(Monthly)

*Connect*
Teacher's Laboratory
P.O. Box 6480
Brattleboro, VT 05301
(10 per year)

*Cornell Rural School Leaflets*
New York State College of Agriculture
Ithaca, NY 14850
(Quarterly)

*Current Science and Aviation*
American Education Publications
Education Center
Columbus, OH 43216
(Weekly during the school year)

*Geotimes*
American Geological Institute
1515 Massachusetts Ave., NW
Washington, DC 20005
(Monthly)

*International Wildlife*
National Wildlife Federation
1412 16th Street, NW
Washington, DC 20036
(Bimonthly)

*Journal of Chemical Education*
Business and Publication Office
20th and Northampton St.
Easton, PA 18042
(Monthly)

*Journal of Research in Science Teaching*
John Wiley & Sons
605 Third Ave.
New York, NY 10016

*Monthly Evening Sky Map*
Box 213
Clayton, MO 63105
(Monthly)

*National Wildlife*
National Wildlife Federation
1412 16th St., NW
Washington, DC 20036
(Bimonthly)

*National Geographic*
National Geographic Society
1146 16th St., NW
Washington, DC 20036
(Monthly)

*Natural History*
American Museum of Natural History
79th St. and Central Park West
New York, NY 10024
(Monthly)

*Nature Magazine*
American Nature Association
1214 15th St., NW
Washington, DC 20005
(Monthly, Oct. to May, and bimonthly, June to
  Sept.)

*Oceanus*
The Allen Press
104 New Hampshire St.
Box 368
Lawrence, KS 66044

*Our Dumb Animals*
Massachusetts Society for the Prevention of
  Cruelty to Animals
Boston, MA 02115
(Monthly)

*Outdoors Illustrated*
National Audobon Society
1000 Fifth Ave.
New York, NY 10028
(Monthly)

*Physics Today*
American Institute of Physics
335 E. 45th St.
New York, NY 10017
(Monthly)

*Physics and Chemistry Digest*
W. M. Welch Co.
1515 Sedgewick St.
Chicago, IL 60610

*Popular Science Monthly*
Popular Science Publishing Co.
335 Lexington Ave.
New York, NY 10016
(Monthly)

*Readers Guide to Oceanography*
Woods Hole Oceanographic Institute
Woods Hole, MA 02543
(Monthly)

*School Science and Mathematics*
Central Association Science and Mathematics
  Teachers
P.O. Box 48
Oak Park, IL 60305
(9 per year)

*Science Newsletter*
Science Service, Inc.
1719 N Street, NW
Washington, DC 20036
(Weekly)

*Science Teacher*
National Science Teachers Association
1742 Connecticut Ave., NW
Washington, DC 20036
(Monthly)

*Science*
American Association for the Advancement of
  Science
1515 Massachusetts Ave., NW
Washington, DC 20025

*Science Education*
Science Education Inc.
C. M. Pruitt
University of Tampa
Tampa, FL 33606
(5 per year)

*Science and Children*
National Science Teachers Association
1742 Connecticut Ave., NW
Washington, DC 20009
(8 per year)

*Science Scope*
National Science Teachers Association
1742 Connecticut Ave., NW
Washington, DC 20009
(6 per year)

*Scientific Monthly*
American Association for the Advancement of
  Science
1515 Massachusetts Ave.
Washington, DC 20005
(Monthly)

*Scientific American*
415 Madison Ave.
New York, NY 10017
(Monthly)

*Sky and Telescope*
Sky Publishing Corp.
Harvard College Observatory
Cambridge, MA 02138
(Monthly)

*Tomorrow's Scientists*
National Science Teachers Association
1742 Connecticut Ave., NW
Washington, DC 20036
(8 per year)

*UNESCO Courier*
The UNESCO Publications Center
801 3rd Ave.
New York, NY 10022
(Monthly)

*The Universe in the Classroom*
Teacher's Newsletter Department
Astronomical Society of the Pacific
1290 24th St.
San Francisco, CA 94122
(Quarterly)

*Weatherwise*
American Meteorological Society
3 Joy St.
Boston, MA 02108
(Monthly)

# APPENDIX
# G

## PERIODICALS FOR STUDENTS

The following list contains the names of some of the more popular magazines for children. Make sure your school library subscribes to several of these and recommend them to parents as gifts for holidays and birthdays.

*Audubon Adventure*
National Audubon Society
613 Riversville Rd.
Greenwich, CT 06830
(6 per year)

*Chickadee*
Young Naturalist Foundation
P.O. Box 11314
Des Moines, IA 50340
(10 per year)

*The Curious Naturalist*
Massachusetts Audubon Society
Lincoln, MA 01773
(4 per year)

*Dolphin Log*
Cousteau Society
8430 Santa Monica Blvd.
Los Angeles, CA 90069
(4 per year)

*Electric Company*
Children's Television Workshop
One Lincoln Plaza
New York, NY 10023
(10 per year)

*Exploratorium Magazine*
3601 Lyon St.
San Francisco, CA 94123
(4 per year)

*Faces*
Cobblestone Publishing, Inc.
20 Grove St.
Peterborough, NH 03458
(10 per year)

*Junior Astronomer*
Benjamin Adelman
4211 Colie Dr.
Silver Springs, MD 20906

*Junior Natural History*
American Museum of Natural History
New York, NY 10024
(Monthly)

*Kind News*
The Humane Society of the U.S.
2100 L St., NW
Washington, DC 20037
(5 per year)

*My Weekly Reader*
American Education Publications
Education Center
Columbus, OH 43216
(Weekly during the school year)

*National Geographic World*
National Geographic Society
17th and M St., NW
Washington, DC 20036
(Monthly)

*Naturescope*
National Wildlife Federation
1912 16th St., NW
Washington, DC 20036
(5 per year)

*Odyssey*
Kalmbach Publishing Co.
1027 North Seventh St.
Milwaukee, WI 53233
(Monthly)

*Owl*
Young Naturalist Foundation
P.O. Box 11314
Des Moines, IA 50304
(10 per year)

*Ranger Rick*
National Wildlife Federation
1412 16th St., NW
Washington, DC 20036
(Monthly)

*Science World*
Scholastic Magazines, Inc.
50 W. 44th St.
New York, NY 10036

*Science Weekly*
P.O. Box 70154
Washington, DC 20088
(18 per year)

*Science News*
Science Service, Inc.
1719 N Street, NW
Washington, DC 20036
(Weekly)

*Science Activities*
4000 Albemarle St., NW
Washington, DC 20016
(4 per year)

*Scienceland*
Scienceland, Inc.
501 Fifth Ave.
New York, NY 10017
(8 per year)

*Space Science*
Benjamin Adelman
4211 Colie Dr.
Silver Springs, MD 20906
(Monthly during the school year)

*3-2-1 Contact*
Children's Television Workshop
P.O. Box 2933
Boulder, CO 80322
(10 per year)

*Wonderscience*
American Chemical Society
P.O. Box 57136, West End Station
Washington, DC 20037
(4 per year)

*Your Big Backyard*
National Wildlife Federation
1412 16th St., NW
Washington, DC 20036
(Monthly)

*Zoobooks*
Wildlife Education, Ltd.
930 West Washington St.
San Diego, CA 92103

# COMMERCIAL SUPPLIERS
# OF SCIENCE EQUIPMENT
# AND MATERIALS

Write for the latest catalogs and enjoy!

Accent! Science
301 Cass St.
Saginaw, MI 48602
(517) 799-8103

Activity Resources Company, Inc.
P.O. Box 4875
Hayward, CA 94540
(415) 782-1300

AIMS Education Foundation
P.O. Box 7766
Fresno, CA 93747
(209) 291-1766

Albion Import Export, Inc.
Coolidge Bank Bldg.
65 Main St.
Watertown, MA 02172
(617) 926-7222

American Science Center/Jerryco
601 Linden Pl.
Evanston, IL 60202
(312) 475-8440

American Optical Instrument Division
P.O. Box 123
Buffalo, NY 14240
(716) 891-3000

American Nuclear Products, Inc.
1232 E. Commercial
Springfield, MO 65803
(417) 869-4432

Analytical Products, Inc.
P.O. Box 845
Belmont, CA 94002
(415) 592-1400

Bausch and Lomb Optical Systems Division
1400 North Goodman St.
P.O. Box 450
Rochester, NY 14692-0450
(716) 338-6005

Bel-Art Products
6 Industrial Road
Pequannock, NJ 07440
(201) 694-0500

Burt Harrison and Co.
P.O. Box 732
Weston, MA 02193
(617) 647-0647

Carolina Biological Supply Company
2700 York Road
Burlington, NC 27216
(800) 334-5551

Central Scientific Co.
11222 Melrose Ave.
Franklin Park, IL 60131
(312) 451-0150

Chem Scientific, Inc.
67 Chapel St.
Newton, MA 02158
(617) 527-6626

Connecticut Valley Biological Supply Co.
Valley Road
P.O. Box 326
Southhampton, MA 01073
(800) 282-7757

Creative Learning Systems, Inc.
9889 Hilbert St., Suite E
San Diego, CA 92131
(619) 566-2880

Creative Learning Press
P.O. Box 320
Mansfield Center, CT 06350
(203) 423-8120

Cuisenaire Company of America, Inc.
12 Church St.
New Rochelle, NY 10802
(800) 237-3142

Delta Education, Inc.
P.O. Box M
Nashua, NH 03061
(800) 258-1302

Denoyer-Geppert Science Company
5711 North Ravenswood Ave.
Chicago, IL 60646
(312) 561-9200

Edmund Scientific
101 E. Gloucester Pike
Barrington, NJ 08007
(800) 222-0224

Education Development Center
55 Chapel St.
Newton, MA 02160
(617) 969-7100

Educational Activities, Inc.
P.O. Box 392
Freeport, NY 11520
(800) 645-3739

Energy Learning Center
Edison Electric Institute
1111 19th St., NW
Washington, DC 20036
(202) 778-6400

Energy Sciences, Inc.
16728 Oakmont Ave.
Gaithersburg, MD 20877
(301) 770-2550

Estes Industries/Hi-Flier
1295 H Street
Penrose, CO 81240
(303) 372-6565

Fisher Scientific Co.
4901 W. Le Moyne St.
Chicago, IL 60651
(312) 378-7770

Forestry Suppliers, Inc.
205 West Rankin St.
Jackson, MS 39204
(601) 354-3565

Frey Scientific
905 Hickory Lane
Mansfield, OH 44905
(419) 589-9905

Hubbard Scientific Co.
P.O. Box 104
Northbrook, IL 60065
(800) 323-8368

Ideal School Supply Co.
11000 S. Lavergne Ave.
Oak Lawn, IL 60453
(312) 425-0800

Lab-Aids, Inc.
P.O. Box 158
130 Wilbur Pl.
Bohemia, NY 11716
(516) 567-6120

LaPine Scientific Co.
6001 South Knox Ave.
Chicago, IL 60629
(312) 735-4700

Lawrence Hall of Science
University of California
Berkeley, CA 94720
(415) 642-7771

Learning Things, Inc.
68A Broadway
P.O. Box 436
Arlington, MA 02174
(617) 646-0093

LEGO Systems, Inc.
555 Taylor Road
Enfield, CT 06082
(203) 749-2291

Let's Get Growing
General Seed and Feed Company
1900-B Commercial Way
Santa Cruz, CA 95065
(408) 476-5344

McKilligan Supply Corporation
435 Main St.
Johnson City, NY 13790
(607) 729-6511

Metrologic Instruments
143 Harding Ave.
Bellmawr, NJ 08031
(609) 933-0100

NASCO
901 Janesville Ave.
Fort Atkinson, WI 53538
(414) 563-2446

National Wildlife Federation
8925 Leesburg Pike
Vienna, VA 22180
(703) 790-4000

National Science Teachers Association
1742 Connecticut Ave., NW
Washington, DC 20009
(202) 328-5800

National Geographic Society
17th and M Streets, NW
Washington, DC. 20036
(202) 857-7000

Nova Scientific Corp.
P.O. Box 500
Burlington, NC 27215
(919) 229-0395

Nystrom/Eye Gate Media
3333 N. Elston Ave.
Chicago, IL 463-1144
(312) 463-1144

Play-Jour, Inc.
200 Fifth Ave., Suite 1024
New York, NY 10010
(212) 243-5200

Right Before Your Eyes
136 Ellis Hollow Creek Road
Ithaca, NY 14850
(607) 277-0384

Sargent-Welsh Scientific Co.
7300 N. Linder Ave.
Skokie, IL 60077
(312) 677-0600

SAVI/SELPH Center for Multidisciplinary
  Learning
Lawrence Hall of Science
University of California
Berkeley, CA 94720
(415) 642-8941

Science Kit, Inc.
777 E. Park Drive
Tonowanda, NY 14150
(716) 874-6020

Soil Conservation Service
U.S. Department of Agriculture
P.O. Box 2890
Washington, DC 20013
(202) 217-2290

Southern Precision Intrument Co.
3419 East Commerce
San Antonio, TX 78220
(512) 224-5801

The Teacher's Laboratory
214 Main St.
P.O. Box 6480
Brattleboro, VT 05301
(802) 254-3457

The Science Man
P.O. Box 56036
Harwood Heights, IL 60656
(312) 867-4441

Tops Learning Systems
10978 South Mulino Road
Canby, OR 97013
(503) 266-8550

Turtox
5000 W. 128th Place
Chicago, IL 60658
(312) 371-5500

Ward's Natural Science Establishment, Inc.
5100 West Henrietta Road
P.O. Box 92912
Rochester, NY 14692
(716) 359-2502

Wilkens-Anderson Co.
4525 W. Division St.
Chicago, IL 60651
(312) 384-4433

# APPENDIX

# I

## SAFETY IN THE CLASSROOM

The following suggestions are offered as guidelines for teachers to follow in using science materials and equipment. The safety, health, and well-being of students should be paramount in any scientific investigation or experiment. It is far better to err on the side of caution than it is to place students in situations that put them at risk. You should feel free to add to these guidelines according to the dynamics of your science program and setup.

1. Do not permit students to handle science supplies, chemicals, or equipment in the classroom until they have been given specific instruction in their use.

2. Instruct students to report immediately to the teacher:

    Any equipment in the classroom that appears to be in an unusual or improper condition

    Any chemical reactions that appear to be proceeding in an abnormal fashion

    Any personal injury or damage to clothing caused by a science activity, no matter how trivial it may appear

3. Prevent loose clothing and hair from coming into contact with any science supplies, chemicals, equipment, or sources of heat or flame.

4. Do not allow science materials, such as chemicals, to be transported through hallways by unsupervised students or during a time when there is traffic in the hallways.

5. Instruct students in the proper use of sharp instruments such as pins, knives, and scissors.

6. Instruct students never to touch, taste, or inhale unknown chemicals directly.

7. Instruct students never to pour chemicals (reagents) back into stock bottles and never to exchange stoppers or caps on bottles.

8. Warn students of dangers in handling hot glassware or other equipment. Be sure proper devices for handling hot objects are available.

9. Check electrical wiring on science equipment for frayed insulation, exposed wires, and loose connections.

10. Instruct students in the proper use of eye protection devices before they do activities in which there is a potential risk to the eyes.

11. Give appropriate, specific safety instructions prior to conducting any activity in which there is a potential threat to student safety and provide appropriate reminders during the activity.

12. Instruct students in the location and use of specialized safety equipment such as fire extinguishers, fire blankets, or eye baths when that equipment might be required by the science activity.

13. Instruct students in the proper care and handling of classroom pets, fish, plants, and other live organisms used as part of science activities.

14. Have sufficient lighting to ensure that activities can be conducted safely.

15. Ensure safe access to facilities, equipment, and materials for students with handicapping conditions. Consider:

    Access to laboratories and equipment, placement of chemicals, distances required for reaching, and height and arrangement of tables

    Physical accessibility to equipment needed in case of emergency

16. Provide practice sessions for safety procedures.

# AUTHOR INDEX

# SUBJECT INDEX

## A

# CREDITS

## Text, Figure, and Table Acknowledgments

*Page 19:* Adapted from Anthony D. Fredericks, Brad Cressman, and Robert Hassler. *The Science Discovery Book.* Glenview, IL: Scott, Foresman, 1987. Used by permission.

*Page 21:* Table 2.1. Joe Abruscato and Jack Hassard. *Loving and Beyond.* Glenview, IL: Scott, Foresman, 1976. Used by permission.

*Pages 29–32:* Figure 2.1. Robert G. Guy, Robert J. Miller, Mary Jane Roscoe, Anita Snell, and Sheri L. Thomas. *Discover Science—Teachers Annotated Edition: 3.* Glenview, IL: Scott, Foresman, 1989. Used by permission.

*Page 45:* Idea Box. Robert G. Guy, Robert J. Miller, Mary Jane Roscoe, Anita Snell, and Sheri L. Thomas. *Discover Science—Teachers Annotated Edition: 3.* Glenview, IL: Scott, Foresman, 1989. Used by permission.

*Page 59:* "Recipe for a Hippopotamus Sandwich." *Where the Sidewalk Ends* by Shel Silverstein © 1974 by Evil Eye Music, Inc. Reprinted by permission of HarperCollins Publishers.

*Page 72:* Table 4.2. Adapted from "Teacher Self Evaluation for Encouraging Creative Production" in *Strategies for Differentiating Curricula.* Towson, MD: Baltimore County Public Schools, 1985. Used by permission.

*Page 89:* Table 5.7. Adapted from Pat Shier and George O'Brien, *The Activity Based Primary Science Project.* Unpublished document, NSTA Convention, Atlanta, GA, 1990. Used by permission.

*Pages 107–112:* Figure 6.1. Robert Guy, Robert Miller, Mary Jane Roscoe, Anita Snell, and Sheri Thomas. *Discover Science—Grade Four.* Glenview, IL: Scott, Foresman, 1989, pp. 142–147. Used by permission.

*Page 120:* Table 7.7. Reprinted from Cohen, H. G., Staley, F. A., and Horak, W. J. *Teaching Science as a Decision Making Process.* © 1989 Kendall/Hunt Publishing Company. Used with permission.

*Pages 134–136:* Bill Smith, Susan Sprague, and Becky Smith. *Teacher's Edition AR-THRO-POOS Activity 10: Insects—Up Close and Personal.* Mesa, AZ: Mesa Public Schools, June 1989, pp. 24–25. Used by permission.

*Page 178:* Figure 9.1. Margaret Hopkins. "Students Take Crack at Embryology," *York Daily Record*, March 11, 1991. Used by permission of Margaret Hopkins and the *York Daily Record.*

*Page 185:* Figure 9.2. Reprinted with permission of the publisher, Early Years, Inc. Norwalk, CT 06854, from the February 1991 issue of *Teaching K–8.*

*Pages 188–189:* Table 9.3. Anthony D. Fredericks. *The Integrated Curriculum: Books for Reluctant Readers, Grades 2–5.* Englewood, CO: Teacher Ideas Press, 1992. Used by permission.

*Page 190:* Figure 9.3. Anthony D. Fredericks, Brad K. Cressman, Robert D. Hassler. *The Science Discovery Book.* Glenview, IL: Scott, Foresman, 1987. Used by permission.

*Pages 197–198:* Table 9.5. Anthony D. Fredericks and Isaac Asimov. *The Complete Science Fair Handbook.* Glenview, IL: Scott, Foresman, 1990. Used by permission.

*Page 210:* Table 10.1. Table from *Teacher Made Tests 2,* ed. by John A. Green. Copyright © 1975 by Harper & Row, Publishers, Inc. Reprinted by permission of HarperCollins Publishers.

*Pages 212–213:* Idea Box. Modified from an updated handout obtained from NSTA Test-Preparation Subcommittee at the 1990 NSTA Convention, Atlanta, GA, April 6, 1990.

*Pages 226–227:* Table 11.1 and Table 11.2. Reprinted by permission from the *Science Framework for California Public Schools, Kindergarten through Grade Twelve.* Copyright 1990, California Department of Education, P.O. Box 271, Sacramento, CA 95812-0271.

*Page 229:* Table 11.3. Scott, Foresman. Discover Science—Teachers Annotated Edition. Glenview, IL: Scott, Foresman, 1989. Used by permission.

*Pages 237–238:* NSTA Position Statement.

*Page 367:* Table 16.3. Adapted from "Teacher Self-Evaluation for Encouraging Creative Production," in *Strategies* for *Differentiating Curricula*. Towson, MD: Baltimore County Public Schools, 1985. Used by permission.

*Page 373:* "If I Remember Everything." From *Watching Ants*. Ventura, CA: National State Leadership Training Institute on the Gifted and Talented, 1990.

*Pages 374–375:* Appendix A. National Science Teachers Association. *Position Statement on Science–Technology–Society: Science Education for the 1980's*. 1982. Adopted unanimously by the Board of Directors, NSTA.

## Photo Acknowledgments

Unless otherwise acknowledged, all photographs are the property of Scott, Foresman and Company.

*Page 8:* Phil Borden/Photo Edit. *Page 9:* AP/Wide World. *Page 10:* Christopher S. Johnson. *Page 12:* AP/Wide World.

*Page 17:* David Young-Wolff/Photo Edit. *Page 33:* David Young-Wolff/Photo Edit.

*Page 73:* Elena Rooraid/Photo Edit.

*Page 77:* Richard Hutchings/Photo Edit. *Page 78:* Stephen McBrady/Photo Edit. *Page 79:* James L. Shaffer/Photo Edit. *Page 82:* David Schaefer/Photo Edit. *Page 86:* Rhoda Sidney/Photo Edit.

*Page 92:* Ulrike Welsch/Photo Edit. *Page 94:* David Young-Wolff/Photo Edit. *Page 96:* Tony Freeman/Photo Edit. *Page 99:* Tony Freeman/Photo Edit. *Page 100:* Mary Kate Denny/Photo Edit.

*Page 122:* Mike Penney/David R. Frazier Photolibrary. *Page 133:* Ulrike Welsch/Photo Edit.

*Page 156 (top left):* © SCRIPTA MATHEMATICA, Yeshiva University. *Page 156 (top right):* U.S. Department of the Interior, National Park Service, Edison Historic Site. *Page 156 (bottom left):* Ewing Galloway. *Page 156 (bottom right):* AP/Wide World. *Page 157:* The National Foundation for Infantile Paralysis. *Page 165:* Neg. No. 324202, Photo Logan & Rota, Courtesy Department of Library Services, American Museum of Natural History.

*Page 176:* NASA. *Page 179:* Elrike Welsch/Photo Edit. *Page 180 (top):* David R. Frazier Photolibrary. *Page 180 (bottom):* Tony Freeman/Photo Edit. *Page 186:* David Young-Wolff/Photo Edit. *Page 194:* Richard Hutchings/Photo Edit. *Page 200:* Rhoda Sidney/Photo Edit.

*Page 207:* Tony Freeman/Photo Edit.

*Page 224 (left):* Tony Freeman/Photo Edit. *Page 224 (right):* Mark Richards/Photo Edit. *Page 236:* Ulrike Welsch/Photo Edit.

*Page 244:* Tony Freeman/Photo Edit. *Page 245 (top):* David R. Frazier Photolibrary. *Page 245 (bottom):* Richard Frear/Photo Edit. *Page 249:* ANIMALS ANIMALS. *Page 254 (top left):* Darek Karp/ANIMALS ANIMALS. *Page 254 (top right):* Alan Oddie/Photo Edit. *Page 254 (center):* Alan Oddie/Photo Edit. *Page 254 (bottom left):* Leonard Lee Rue III/ANIMALS ANIMALS. *Page 254 (bottom right):* ANIMALS ANIMALS. *Page 274:* Francis Lepine/ANIMALS ANIMALS.

*Page 314:* Tony Freeman/Photo Edit. *Page 318 (top left):* Official U.S. Navy Photograph. *Page 318 (bottom):* NOAA/NESDIS/NCDC. *Page 322:* Courtesy The American Red Cross.

*Page 339:* NASA.

*Page 359:* Tony Freeman/Photo Edit. *Page 371:* Ulrike Welsch/Photo Edit.